Engine Performance Diagnosis and Tune-up

Second Edition

By Chek-Chart Publications, a Division of H. M. Gousha

Roger Fennema, *Editor*
Richard DuPuy, *Managing Editor*
Christine A. Boldt, *Contributing Editor*

 HarperCollins*Publishers*

Acknowledgments

In producing this series of textbooks for automobile mechanics and technicians, Chek-Chart has drawn extensively on the technical and editorial knowledge of the nation's carmakers and suppliers. Automotive design is a technical, fast-changing field, and we gratefully acknowledge the help of the following companies in allowing us to present the most up-to-date information and illustrations possible:

Allen Testproducts
American Motors Corporation
Borg-Warner Corporation
Caldo Automotive Supply
Champion Spark Plug Company
Chrysler Motors Corporation
Coats Diagnostic (Hennessy Industries)
Ford Motor Company
Fram Corporation, A Bendix Company
General Motors Corporation
    AC-Delco Division
    Delco-Remy Division
    Rochester Products Division
    Saginaw Steering Gear Division
    Buick Motor Division
    Cadillac Motor Car Division
    Chevrolet Motor Division
    Oldsmobile Division
    Pontiac Division
Jaguar Cars, Inc.
Marquette Mfg. Co. (Bear Mfg. Co.)
Mazda Motor Corporation
Nissan Motors
The Prestolite Company, An Eltra Company
Robert Bosch Corporation
Sun Electric Corporation
Toyota Motor Company
Volkswagen of America

95 9 8 7 6

The authors have made every effort to ensure that the material in this book is as accurate and up-to-date as possible. However, neither Chek-Chart nor Harper & Row nor any related companies can be held responsible for mistakes or omissions, or for changes in procedures or specifications made by the carmakers or suppliers.

The comments, suggestions, and assistance of the following contributors were invaluable:
    Les Clark, Russ Suzuki, Angel Santiago, Al Bauer, and Bryan Wilson; General Motors Training Center, Burbank, Calif.
    Pete Egus; AC-Delco, Los Angeles, Calif.
    Robert Baier, Dan Rupp, Nick Backer, and Bill Takayama; Chrysler Training Center, Ontario, Calif.
    Robert Van Antwerp, Jim Milum, and Ed Moreland; Ford Training Center, La Mirada, Calif.
    Bob Kruze; Merry Oldsmobile, San Jose, Calif.

At Chek-Chart, Ray Lyons managed the production of this book. Original art and photographs were produced by Gordon Agur, John Badenhop, Jim Gedes, C. J. Hepworth, Janet Jamieson, Kalton C. Lahue, and F. J. Zienty. The project is under the direction of Roger L. Fennema.

ENGINE PERFORMANCE DIAGNOSIS AND TUNE-UP, Second Edition, Classroom Manual and Shop Manual Copyright © 1989 by Chek-Chart, Simon & Schuster Inc.

Library of Congress Cataloging and Publication Data:

Chek-Chart, 1989
    Engine Performance Diagnosis and Tune-up
    (HarperCollins /Chek-Chart Automotive Series)
v. 1. Classroom Manual.   v. 2. Shop Manual.

ISBN: 0-06-454018-9
Library of Congress Catalog Card No.: 89-2142

Contents

On the Cover:
Front — Performing a diagnostic check with the Sun Modular Computer Analyzer, courtesy of Sun Electric Corporation.
Rear — The Monitor 2000 courtesy of OTC Tool & Equipment Division, SPX Corporation; and the Maxitune® MT2000, courtesy of Snap-on Tools Corporation.

Contents

Introduction to Engine Performance Diagnosis and Tune-up

Engine Performance Diagnosis and Tune-up is part of the Harper & Row/Chek-Chart Automotive Series. The package for each course has two volumes, a *Classroom Manual* and a *Shop Manual*.

Other titles in this series include:
- Automatic Transmissions and Transaxles
- Automotive Brake Systems
- Automotive Electrical and Electronic Systems
- Automotive Engine Repair and Rebuilding
- Fuel Systems and Emission Controls.

Each book is written to help the instructor teach students to become excellent professional automotive technicians. The 2-manual texts are the core of a complete learning system that leads a student from basic theories to actual hands-on experience.

The entire series is job-oriented, especially designed for students who intend to work in the car service profession. A student will be able to use the knowledge gained from these books and from the instructor to get and keep a job. Learning the material and techniques in these volumes is a giant leap toward a satisfying, rewarding career.

The books are divided into *Classroom Manuals* and *Shop Manuals* for an improved presentation of the descriptive information and study lessons, along with the practical testing, repair, and overhaul procedures. The manuals are to be used together: the descriptive chapters in the *Classroom Manual* correspond to the application chapters in the *Shop Manual*.

Each book is divided into several parts, and each of these parts is complete by itself. Instructors will find the chapters to be complete, readable, and well thought-out. Students will benefit from the many learning aids included, as well as from the thoroughness of the presentation.

The series was researched and written by the editorial staff of Chek-Chart, and was produced by Harper & Row Publishers. For over 60 years, Chek-Chart has provided car and equipment manufacturer's service specifications to the automotive service field. Chek-Chart's complete, up-to-date automotive data bank was used extensively to prepare this textbook series.

Because of the comprehensive material, the hundreds of high-quality illustrations, and the inclusion of the latest automotive technology, instructors and students alike will find that these books will keep their value over the years. In fact, they will form the core of the master mechanic's professional library.

How To Use This Book

Why Are There Two Manuals?

This two-volume text — **Engine Performance Diagnosis and Tune-up** — is not like any other textbook you've ever used before. It is actually two books, the *Classroom Manual* and the *Shop Manual*. They should be used together.

The *Classroom Manual* will teach you what you need to know about basic electricity and the electrical systems in a car. The *Shop Manual* will show you how to fix and adjust those systems, and how to repair the electrical parts of a car.

The *Classroom Manual* will be valuable in class and at home, for study and for reference. It has text and pictures that you can use for years to refresh your memory about the basics of automotive electrical systems.

In the *Shop Manual*, you will learn about test procedures, troubleshooting, and overhauling the systems and parts you are studying in the *Classroom Manual*. Use the two manuals together to fully understand how the parts work, and how to fix them when they don't work.

What's In These Manuals?

There are several aids in the *Classroom Manual* that will help you learn more:
1. The text is broken into short bits for easier understanding and review.
2. Each chapter is fully illustrated with drawings and photographs.
3. Key words in the text are printed in **boldface type** and are defined on the same page and in a glossary at the end of the manual.
4. Review questions are included for most chapters. Use these to test your knowledge.
5. A brief summary at the end of most chapters will help you to review for exams.
6. Every few pages you will find short blocks of ''nice to know'' information, in addition to the main text.
7. At the back of the *Classroom Manual* there is a sample test, similar to those given for National Institute for Automotive Service Excellence (NIASE) certification. Use it to help you study and to prepare yourself when you are ready to be certified as an expert in one of several areas of automobile mechanics.

The *Shop Manual* has detailed instructions on overhaul, test, and service procedures. These are easy to understand, and may have step-by-step, photo-illustrated explanations that guide you through the procedures. This is what you'll find in the *Shop Manual*:
1. Helpful information tells you how to use and maintain shop tools and test equipment.
2. Safety precautions are detailed.
3. System diagrams help you locate trouble-spots while you learn to read the diagrams.
4. Tips the professionals use are presented clearly and accurately.
5. A full index will help you quickly find what you need.
6. Test procedures and troubleshooting hints will help you work better and faster.

Where Should I Begin?

If you already know something about a car's basic electrical system and how to repair it, you may find that parts of this book are a helpful review. If you are just starting in car repair, then the subjects covered in these manuals may be all new to you.

Your instructor will design a course to take advantage of what you already know, and what facilities and equipment are available to work with. You may be asked to take certain chapters of these manuals out of order. That's fine. The important thing is to really understand each subject before you move on to the next.

Study the vocabulary words in boldface type. Use the review questions to help you understand the material. While reading in the *Classroom Manual*, refer to your *Shop Manual* to relate the descriptive text to the service procedures. And when you are working on actual car systems and electrical parts, look back to the *Classroom Manual* to keep the basic information fresh in your mind. Working on such a complicated piece of equipment as a modern car isn't always easy. Use the information in the *Classroom Manual*, the procedures of the *Shop Manual*, and the knowledge of your instructor to help you.

The *Shop Manual* is a good book for work, not just a good workbook. Keep it on hand while you're working on equipment. It folds flat on the workbench and under the car, and can withstand quite a bit of rough handling.

When you do test procedures and overhaul equipment, you will also need an accurate source of manufacturers' specifications. Most auto shops have either the carmaker's annual shop service manuals, which lists these specifications, or an independent guide, such as the **Chek-Chart Car Care Guide**. This unique book, which is updated every year, gives you the complete service instructions, electronic ignition troubleshooting tips, and tune-up information that you need to work on specific cars.

PART ONE

Engine Operation and Tune-Up Requirements

1

Engine Operating Principles

The modern automobile engine has many systems and parts that must work together efficiently for the best operating performance, economy, and emission control. The systems that work to meet these requirements are:

- The engine mechanical parts
- The ignition system
- The fuel system
- The engine lubrication system
- The cooling system
- The emission control systems
- The starting system
- The charging system.

Poor performance or a breakdown in any one of these areas can affect total engine operation. Automotive technicians must make sure that the systems are operating correctly and, if any problems are found, either correct the problems or warn the car owner of their findings. This process of diagnosis, preventive maintenance, and corrective maintenance is commonly called an engine tune-up.

Before you can test these areas of engine operation, you must understand how all of the engine systems work and how they relate to each other. Only then will you be able to test the systems quickly and accurately and spot faults before they become major problems.

The first five chapters of this *Classroom Manual* examine the various engine systems as they relate to proper operation and to the engine tune-up. Some of this material is a preview of subjects that are covered in detail in Parts Two, Three, Four, and Five of this book. You may already have studied some of the subjects covered by the first five chapters. If so, these chapters will be a quick review to refresh your basic understanding. If this material is new to you, study it thoroughly. In any case, the information in the first five chapters is a necessary foundation for the conclusions reached in Chapter 6.

Chapter 6, ''What Is A Tune-Up?'', introduces the concept of a *complete* tune-up and diagnosis. This chapter examines the trends and requirements that affect today's tune-up technician. In a way, Chapter 6 is the heart of this *Classroom Manual*. To get the most out of it, though, you need a thorough understanding of all the systems involved in tune-up, beginning with engine operating principles.

ENGINE OPERATION

Modern automotive engines are called internal combustion engines because fuel burns inside the engine. The engine converts the burning fuel's thermal energy to mechanical energy.

TOP OF BLOCK

WATERJACKET HOLE FOR CIRCULATING WATER AROUND CYLINDERS

CYLINDERS

BOTTOM OF BLOCK

CRANKSHAFT BEARING SUPPORTS

Figure 1-1. The engine block contains the cylinders and water jackets for cooling. The crankshaft rotates in main bearings at the bottom of the block.

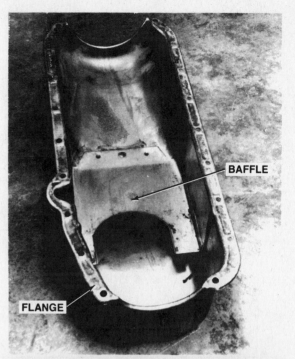

BAFFLE

FLANGE

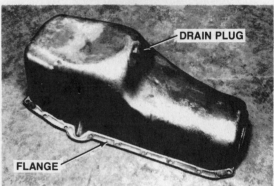

DRAIN PLUG

FLANGE

Figure 1-2. The oil pan is fastened to the bottom of the block.

Reciprocating Engine Components

Except for the Wankel rotary engine, all production automotive engines are the reciprocating, or piston, design. Reciprocating means ''up and down'' or ''back and forth''. It is this up-and-down action of a piston in a cylinder that gives the **reciprocating engine** its name. Almost all engines of this type are built upon a cylinder block, or engine block, figure 1-1. The block is an iron or aluminum casting that contains the engine cylinders. The top of the block is covered with the cylinder head, which forms the combustion chambers. The bottom of the block is covered with an oil pan, or oil sump, figure 1-2. A major exception to this type of engine construction is the air-cooled Volkswagen engine, figure 1-3. It is representative of the

horizontally opposed air-cooled engines used by Porsche, Chevrolet (Corvair), and some other automobile manufacturers in years past.

The diameter of the cylinder is called the engine's **bore**. The distance that the piston travels from its top position to its bottom position in the cylinder is called the engine's **stroke**.

Reciprocating Engine: Also called a piston engine. An engine in which the pistons move up and down or back and forth, as a result of combustion of an air-fuel mixture in the top of the piston cylinder.

Bore: The diameter of an engine cylinder.

Stroke: One complete top-to-bottom or bottom-to-top movement of an engine piston.

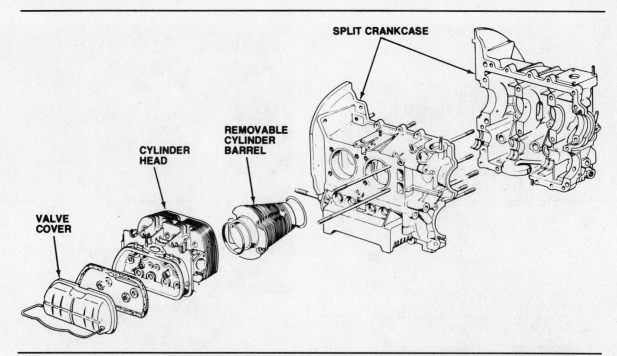

Figure 1-3. The Volkswagen horizontally opposed engine is built with a split crankcase. Individual cylinder castings bolt to the split crankcase, and cylinder heads attach to each pair of cylinders.

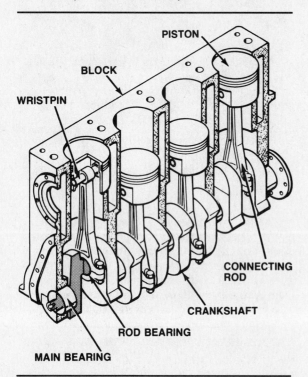

Figure 1-4. The crankshaft changes the reciprocating motion of the pistons to rotating motion.

Power is produced by the inline motion of a piston in a cylinder. However, this *linear* motion must be changed to rotating motion to turn the wheels of a car or truck. The piston is attached to the top of a connecting rod by a pin, called a piston pin or wristpin, figure 1-4. The bottom of the connecting rod is attached to the crankshaft. The connecting rod transmits the up-and-down motion of the piston to the crankshaft, which changes it to rotating motion. The connecting rod is mounted on the crankshaft with large bearings called rod bearings. Similar bearings, called main bearings, are used to mount the crankshaft in the block, figure 1-4.

The combustible mixture of gasoline and air enters the cylinders through valves. Automotive engines use **poppet valves**, figure 1-5. The valves can be in the cylinder head or in the block. The opening and closing of the valves is controlled by a camshaft. **Lobes** on the camshaft push the valves open as the camshaft rotates. A spring closes each valve when the lobe is not holding it open. The most common arrangements of engine cylinders and valves are discussed later.

In addition to being called internal combustion, reciprocating engines, most automotive engines are classified as:
• 4-stroke or 2-stroke engines
• Spark-ignition (gasoline) or compression-ignition (diesel) engines.
Because there are no 2-stroke automotive engines we will not concern ourselves with that design in this book. The most common automotive engine is the 4-stroke gasoline engine, so

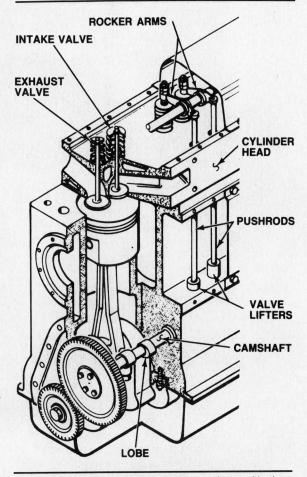

Figure 1-5. The valves in this engine are located in the cylinder head. They are operated by the camshaft lobes, valve lifters, pushrods, and rocker arms.

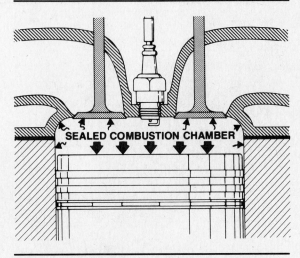

Figure 1-6. For combustion to produce power in an engine, the combustion chamber must be sealed.

we will begin our study of operating cycles with that design.

THE FOUR-STROKE CYCLE

Gasoline by itself will not burn; it must be mixed with oxygen (air). This burning is called combustion and is a way of releasing the energy stored in the air-fuel mixture. To do any useful work in an engine, the air-fuel mixture must be compressed and burned in a sealed chamber, figure 1-6. Here the combustion energy can work on the movable piston to produce mechanical energy. The combustion chamber must be sealed as tightly as possible for efficient engine operation. Any leakage from the combustion chamber allows part of the combustion energy to dissipate without adding to the mechanical energy developed by the piston movement.

The **4-stroke engine** is also called the Otto cycle engine, in honor of the German engineer, Dr. Nikolaus Otto, who first applied the princi-

ple in 1876. In the 4-stroke engine, four strokes of the piston in the cylinder are required to complete one full operating cycle: two strokes up and two strokes down. Each stroke is named after the action it performs — intake, compression, power, and exhaust — in that order, figure 1-7.

1. *Intake stroke* — as the piston moves down, the vaporized mixture of fuel and air enters the cylinder past the open intake valve.

2. *Compression stroke* — The piston returns up, the intake valve closes, the mixture is compressed within the combustion chamber, and ignited by a spark.

3. *Power Stroke* — The expanding gases of combustion force the piston down in the cylinder. The exhaust valve opens near the bottom of the stroke.

4. *Exhaust stroke* — The piston moves back up with the exhaust valve open, and the burned gases are pushed out to prepare for the next intake stroke. The intake valve usually opens just before the top of the exhaust stroke.

Poppet Valve: A valve that plugs and unplugs its opening by axial motion.

Lobes: The rounded protrusions on a camshaft that force, and govern, the opening of the intake and exhaust valves.

Four-Stroke Engine: The Otto cycle engine. An engine in which a piston must complete four strokes to make up one operating cycle. The strokes are: intake, compression, power, and exhaust.

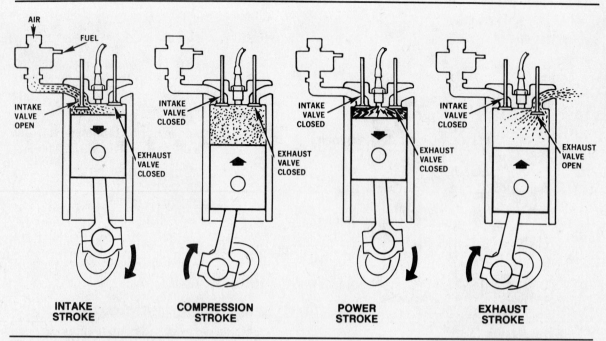

Figure 1-7. The downward movement of the piston draws the air-fuel mixture into the cylinder through the intake valve on the intake stroke. On the compression stroke, the mixture is compressed by the upward movement of the piston with both valves closed. Ignition occurs at the beginning of the power stroke, and combustion drives the piston downward to produce power. On the exhaust stroke, the upward-moving piston forces the burned gases out the open exhaust valve.

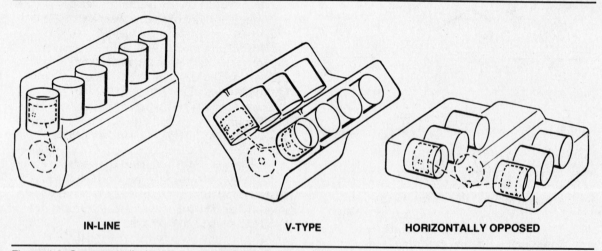

Figure 1-8. Common cylinder arrangements for automotive engines.

This 4-stroke cycle is continuously repeated in every cylinder as long as the engine remains running.

CYLINDER AND PISTON ARRANGEMENT

Up to this point, we have been talking about a single piston in a single cylinder. While single-cylinder engines are common in motorcycles, outboard motors, and small agricultural implements, automotive engines have more than one cylinder. Most car engines have 4, 6, or 8 cylinders, although engines with 5 and 12 cylinders are being built, and we are beginning to see a new generation of 3-cylinder engines in commuter cars.

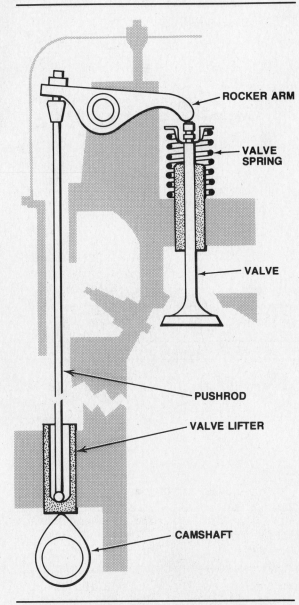

Figure 1-9. Valve mechanism for an overhead-valve engine.

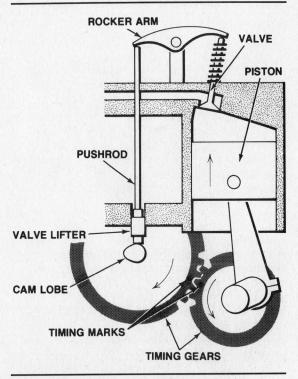

Figure 1-10. Timing marks on the timing gears synchronize valve action with piston movement.

In automobile engines, all pistons are attached to a single crankshaft. The more cylinders an engine has, the more power strokes are produced for each revolution. This means that an 8-cylinder engine produces a power stroke twice as often as a 4-cylinder engine. The 8-cylinder engine runs more smoothly because the power strokes are closer together in time and in degrees of engine rotation.

The cylinders of multi-cylinder automotive engines are arranged in one of three ways, figure 1-8.

1. Inline engines use a single back of cylinders. Most 4-cylinder and many 6-cylinder engines are of this design. The cylinders do not have to be vertical, as shown in figure 1-8. They can be inclined to either side.

2. V-type engines use two equal banks of cylinders, usually inclined 60 degrees or 90 degrees from each other. Most V-type engines have 6- or 8-cylinders, although V-4 and V-12 engines have been built.

3. Horizontally opposed, "flat", or "boxer" engines have two equal banks of cylinders 180 degrees apart. These space-saving engine designs are often air-cooled, and are found in the Chevrolet Corvair and some Ferrari, Porsche, Subaru, and Volkswagen models. Ferrari's and Subaru's designs are liquid cooled. Late-model Volkswagen vans use a liquid-cooled version of the air-cooled VW horizontally opposed engine.

As described earlier, each cylinder contains intake and exhaust poppet valves which are opened by lobes on the camshaft and closed by valve springs, figure 1-9. To coordinate this opening and closing action with piston movement, the camshaft rotation must be synchronized, or timed, with that of the crankshaft. This synchronization is accomplished in one of three ways: by gears, by a chain and sprockets, or by a timing belt and sprockets. Timing marks on the gears or sprockets are used to synchronize the two shafts with each other, figure 1-10.

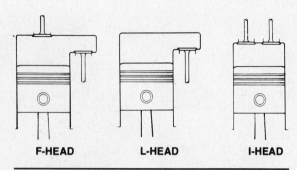

Figure 1-11. Common valve arrangements for 4-stroke automotive engines.

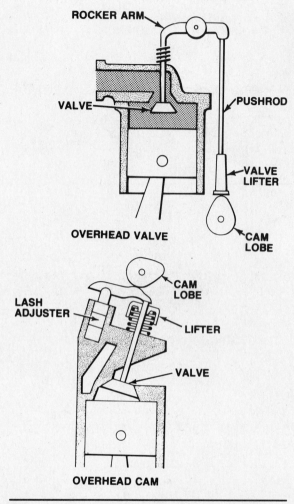

Figure 1-12. In an I-head engine, the valves may be operated by a camshaft in the block or in the head.

On most engines, a camshaft gear meshes with a driven gear on the ignition distributor to synchronize or "time" spark plug firing with piston and valve positions at the beginning of the piston stroke. The order in which the air-fuel mixture is ignited within the cylinders is called the **firing order**, and varies with different engine designs. Only one power stroke takes place at any instant, regardless of the number of cylinders in the engine. These power strokes follow each other in a rapid sequence to produce a smooth flow of power.

VALVE ARRANGEMENT

Intake and exhaust valves on modern engines are located in the cylinder head. Because the valves are "in the head", this basic arrangement is called an I-head design. In the past, valves have been arranged in three different ways, figure 1-11.
1. The L-head design locates both valves side-by-side in the engine block. Because the cylinder head is rather flat and contains only the combustion chamber, water jacket, and spark plugs, L-head engines also are called "flat-heads". Once very common, this valve arrangement has not been used in a domestic automotive engine since the early 1960s.
2. The F-head design locates the intake valve in the cylinder head and the exhaust valve in the engine block. A compromise between the L-head and I-head designs, the F-head was last used in the 1971 Jeep.
3. The I-head design, in both overhead valve or overhead cam form, locates both the intake and the exhaust valves in the cylinder head. All modern automotive engines use this design.

In the overhead valve engine, the camshaft is in the engine block and the valves are opened by valve lifters, pushrods, and rocker arms, figure 1-12. In the overhead cam engine, the cam-

shaft is mounted in the head, either above or to one side of the valves, figure 1-12. This improves valve action at higher engine speeds. The valves may open directly by means of valve lifters or cam followers, or through rocker arms. The double overhead cam engine has two camshafts, one on each side of the valves. One camshaft operates the intake valves; the other operates the exhaust valves.

Valve lifters can be mechanical or hydraulic. Mechanical valve lifters are solid metal, as shown in figure 1-12. A hydraulic lifter is a metal cylinder containing a plunger that rides

Firing Order: The order in which combustion occurs in the cylinders of an engine.

■ Plus-One Performance (If Two Valves Are Good, More Must Be Better)

Four-valve heads have been around a long time in motorcycles and automobile racing engines. Every Miller, Offenhauser, Cosworth, and Chevrolet Indy (Ilmor) engine that ever won the Indianapolis 500 had four valves per cylinder. Although the 4-valve design was refined in racing applications, it has appeared in production engines in only the past decade.

The ideal combustion chamber configuration would be a 2-valve head with a high compression ratio and valves large enough to allow enough air to flow through to produce power at high rpm — if the combustion chamber could be a perfect sphere, with the spark plug in the center. Unfortunately, while it sounds easy, designing the perfect combustion chamber isn't that simple.

The 4-valve head, with two intake valves on one side and two exhaust valves on the other, allows the designer to use a flatter piston and a centrally located spark plug. Four small valves have greater total circumference than two valves of equal area, which means greater air flow. The smaller valves are also lighter and allow the valve train to run faster and last longer.

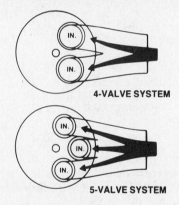

4-VALVE SYSTEM

5-VALVE SYSTEM

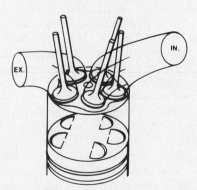

INNOVATIVE 5-VALVE CONFIGURATION

Yamaha's 5-valve motorcycle engine uses individual intake and exhaust cam lobes to operate each valve through inverted bucket-type cam followers.

Yamaha has built and extensively tested a 7-valve head with three intake and three exhaust valves around the outside of the chamber, with a fourth intake valve in the center between two spark plugs. While it ran like a lion, it was too complex and expensive to manufacture and sell, so the design was downgraded to six valves and one spark plug. Power output and fuel consumption were still good, but valve train complexity remained, and cooling the center exhaust valve proved difficult.

Dropping the center exhaust valve solved the cooling problem, and opening each valve with its own cam lobe and bucket-type tappet let the cam make greater surface contact with the lifter resulting in higher lift. While the total valve area of the 5-valve head is less than that of four valves, the effective intake area around the three intake valves is about 14 percent greater. This increased air intake means higher power output.

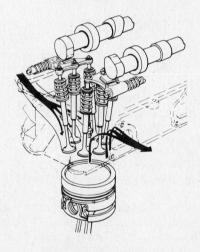

Maserati's 6-valve head uses a single intake and exhaust cam lobe to operate each set of three valves through a finger-type cam follower, or rocker arm. (Maserati)

Maserati has applied multiple valve technology to its 2.0-liter Biturbo V-6 for an amazing 43 percent gain in power — increased from 180 horsepower (134 kW) at 6,000 rpm to 243 horsepower (181 kW) at 7,200 rpm. This high-performance powerplant was a bit unusual to begin with, because it used one large exhaust and two different-sized intake valves. The redesigned version, designated the 6.36 (for 6 cylinders and 36 valves), is equally unusual because it contains three intake and three exhaust valves arranged concentrically around the bore and inclined at different angles for greater mixture swirl. Each valve trio is operated by the same cam lobe through a wide follower.

The 6.36 is also a complex and expensive engine to manufacture, but Maserati says the performance makes it ideal for limited production use in a 2-seat sports car.

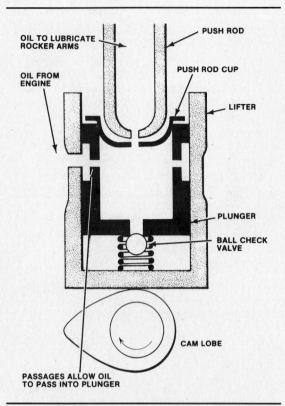

Figure 1-13. The hydraulic lifter uses engine oil to transmit motion.

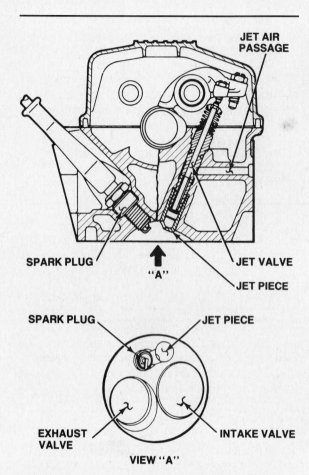

Figure 1-14. The Mitsubishi MCA engine uses a small auxiliary valve to admit a high-speed jet of air on the intake stroke. (Mitsubishi)

on oil, figure 1-13. A chamber below the plunger fills with engine oil and, as the camshaft lobe lifts the lifter, the chamber is sealed by a check valve. The trapped oil transmits the lifting motion of the camshaft lobe to the valve pushrod. Hydraulic lifters are generally quieter than mechanical lifters and do not need to be adjusted as often, because the amount of oil in the chamber varies to keep the valve adjustment correct.

Number of Valves

As you saw in figure 1-7, most automobile engines have one intake and one exhaust valve per cylinder. This means that a 4-cylinder engine has 8 valves; a 6-cylinder engine has 12 valves; and a V-8 has 16 valves.

Many engines have been built, however, with more than two valves per cylinder. Engines with four valves per cylinder have been used in race cars since the earliest days of motoring. Racing motorcycle engines with five and even six valves per cylinder have been built in recent years. In spite of performance advantages, the higher costs and greater complexity of engines with more than two valves per cylinder have kept these designs from being used in production engines until recently.

To understand the principles of 3-valve, 4-valve, and other similar designs, it is best to distinguish between auxiliary valves and main intake and exhaust valves. Honda's Compound Vortex Controlled Combustion (CVCC) engine is a type of stratified charge engine that has a small precombustion chamber above the main chamber. The precombustion chamber has its own small intake valve that admits a rich air-fuel mixture to begin combustion.

Mitsubishi engines with the Mitsubishi Clean Air (MCA) combustion chamber design have a third small valve in each chamber, figure 1-14. Mitsubishi calls this a "jet" valve because it admits a high-speed jet of air to create a swirl effect that promotes complete combustion. This MCA jet valve design has been used in the engines of many Mitsubishi and Chrysler imports since the mid-1970s. In the mid-1980s Mitsubishi redesigned the head and renamed it the "cyclone" combustion chamber.

Toyota builds a 3-valve engine with a smaller, secondary intake valve that opens later

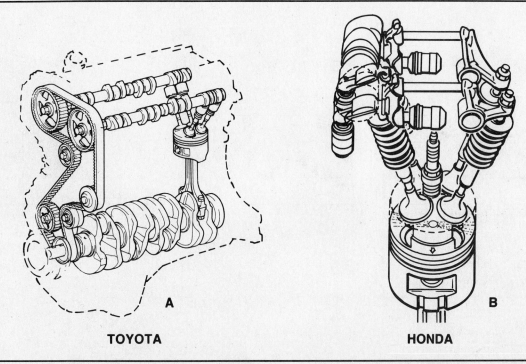

TOYOTA   **HONDA**

Figure 1-15. All 4-valve production engines use overhead cams. The engine may have separate intake and exhaust camshafts as in the Toyota example (A), or a single cam, such as the Honda Acura V-6 design (B) that operates the exhaust valves through short pushrods. (Toyota; Honda)

than the primary intake valve. The two intake valves, combined with a unique port design, promote mixture turbulence and complete combustion of lean mixtures. The Honda, Mitsubishi, and Toyota 3-valve designs are examples of auxiliary-valve engines.

Since the mid-1980s several Japanese and European carmakers have been building engines with four main valves per cylinder, figure 1-15. The triple goals of obtaining best economy, emission control, and performance, plus the competitive nature of the auto market in the 1980s, led manufacturers to adopt these designs for production vehicles. The benefits of 4-valve engines involve a lot of complex engineering considerations that are beyond the scope of this text. The following points, however, summarize the advantages of multiple valves:
• Two small valves in place of one large one can provide a larger total inlet or exhaust area, which improves volumetric efficiency.
• Smaller individual valves, springs, and retainers reduce the weight of each valve assembly. This reduces valve train inertia and allows higher maximum engine speeds.
• Smaller valves allow the engineer more flexibility in combustion chamber design. Valve angles and ports can be designed for improved air-fuel turbulence and combustion. Also, valve

installations can be designed for lower overall engine height under the hoods of late-model cars.
• Separated intake and exhaust ports can be designed, or "tuned", for optimum intake and exhaust velocity. Individual, smaller diameter ports of larger *total* area can provide increased intake and exhaust volume at higher speed.
• Electronically controlled fuel injection combined with two intake valves allows engineers to design induction systems with separate air-fuel flow for different engine speeds and loads. On some engines, the two intake valves open and close at different times to fine-tune the air-fuel metering for different operating conditions.

Modern Combustion Chamber Design

Engineers have worked with combustion chamber design since the automobile was first invented. In the years before exhaust emission controls, much of the experimentation and design work was done with racing engines in an effort to make them go ever faster. The need to reduce exhaust emissions, however, refocused attention on the combustion chamber. Efforts were made to promote rapid, uniform burning of the air-fuel charge to control emissions and improve fuel economy.

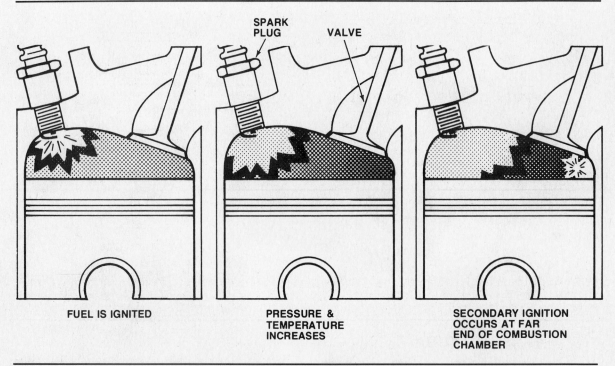

Figure 1-16. Detonation is a secondary ignition of the air-fuel mixture caused by high cylinder temperatures. It is commonly called "pinging" or "knocking".

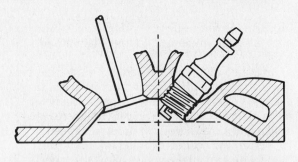

Figure 1-17. Central location of the spark plug in the combustion chamber reduces the distance the flame front must travel to reach the cylinder walls. (Ford)

Combustion of the air-fuel charge in a cylinder is not an instantaneous explosion, but rather, a controlled burning of the charge by the spark from the spark plug. When the spark ignites the air-fuel mixture, a flame front spreads out across the combustion chamber to consume the mixture. Movement of the flame front is called burn time and requires about 3 milliseconds.

However, combustion chamber design, high engine temperature, pressure, or poor gasoline quality can cause an unwanted, violent explosion of the air-fuel charge. A single one of these factors or a combination of them may cause this abnormal combustion, which takes two forms: **detonation** or **pre-ignition**. Detonation occurs if the air-fuel charge ignites before the flame front reaches it, this secondary explosion, figure 1-16, is popularly known as "knocking" or "pinging". The distinctive sound is caused by the two flame fronts colliding. Detonation causes a loss of power and overheating of valves, pistons, and spark plugs. The overheating in turn causes more detonation and may eventually damage the engine. Pre-ignition occurs when the air-fuel charge is ignited *before* the spark plug fires. During pre-ignition, combustion usually comes from excessive combustion chamber temperatures, heat caused by extended detonation, or a single "hot-spot" in the combustion chamber.

In the ideal combustion chamber design, the entire air-fuel charge would burn completely, leaving no unburned areas to be exhausted and eliminating the possibility of detonation. In actual practice, however, there is always some part of the mixture that does not completely burn.

Current combustion chamber design favors the **fast-burn** or **high-swirl combustion chamber** in which the combustion process is completed in a shorter period of time. This design usually incorporates the following features:
• *Compact combustion chamber* — By providing a smaller amount of surface area for a given

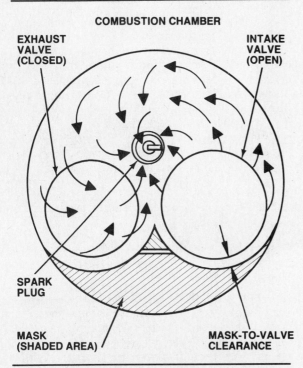

Figure 1-18. By masking (shrouding) the area around the intake valve with additional metal, the air-fuel charge is directed into the combustion chamber with a swirling motion to promote more even distribution. (Ford)

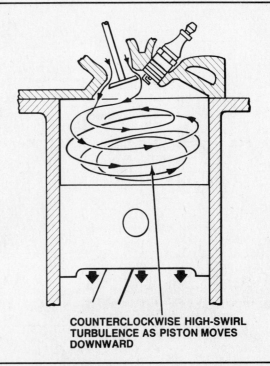

Figure 1-19. Downward piston movement in cylinders with shrouded valves causes a high-swirl turbulence of the air-fuel charge. (Ford)

chamber volume, the flame front is reduced and the time required for combustion is shortened.

• *Centralized spark plug location* — Positioning the spark plug electrode closer to the center of the combustion chamber, figure 1-17, reduces the distance the flame must travel to the edges of the chamber. This also shortens the combustion period.

• *Masked or shrouded intake port* — By masking or shrouding the intake valve area in the combustion chamber, figure 1-18, the air-fuel mixture is directed in a concentrated stream as it is drawn in through the valve and subjected to turbulence or swirl as the piston moves downward, figure 1-19.

• *Higher compression ratio* — Positioning the spark plug deeper in the combustion chamber reduces the chamber volume and increases the compression ratio. In some designs, this is advantageous. In other designs, the piston crown is dished to offset plug positioning and maintain the compression ratio at a point where no decrease in spark advance is required. The desired end result of using a higher compression ratio is to obtain a more densely compressed

and fully atomized air-fuel charge for more complete combustion in less time. Fast-burn combustion chambers with four valves per cylinder have become common in late-model engine design.

Detonation: Also called knocking or pinging. An unwanted explosion of an air-fuel mixture caused by high heat and compression.

Pre-ignition: A premature ignition of the air-fuel mixture before the spark plug fires. It is caused by excessive heat or pressure in the combustion chamber.

Fast-Burn Combustion Chamber: A compact combustion chamber with a centrally located spark plug. The chamber is designed to shorten the combustion period by reducing the distance of flame front travel.

High-Swirl Combustion Chamber: A combustion chamber in which the intake valve is shrouded or masked to direct the incoming air-fuel charge and create turbulence that will circulate the mixture more evenly and rapidly.

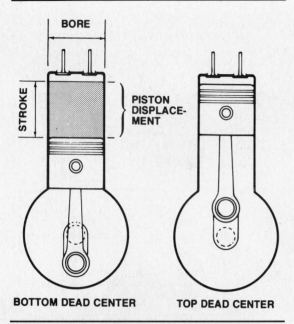

Figure 1-20. Basic engine dimensions.

ENGINE DISPLACEMENT AND COMPRESSION RATIO

Two frequently used engine specifications are **engine displacement** and **compression ratio**. Displacement and compression ratio are related to each other, as we will learn in the following paragraphs.

Engine Displacement

Commonly used to indicate engine size, this specification is really a measurement of cylinder volume. The number of cylinders is a factor in determining displacement, but the arrangement of the cylinders or valves is not. Engine displacement is calculated by multiplying the number of cylinders in the engine by the piston displacement of one cylinder. The total engine displacement is the volume displaced by all the pistons.

The displacement of one cylinder is the space through which the piston's top surface moves as it travels from the bottom of its stroke (**bottom dead center**) to the top of its stroke (**top dead center**), figure 1-20. It is the volume displaced by the cylinder by one piston stroke. Piston displacement can be calculated as follows:
1. Divide the bore (cylinder diameter) by two. This gives you the radius of the bore.
2. Square the radius (multiply it by itself).
3. Multiply the square of the radius by 3.1416 (pi or π) to find the area of the cylinder cross section.

4. Multiply the area of the cylinder cross section by the length of the stroke.

You now know the piston displacement for one cylinder. Multiply this by the number of cylinders to determine the total engine displacement. The formula for the complete procedure reads:

$R^2 \times \pi \times$ stroke $\times$ No. of cylinders = displacement

For example, to find the displacement of a V-6 engine with a 3.80-inch bore and a 3.40-inch stroke:

radius $= \dfrac{3.80}{2} = 1.9$ in.

radius squared $= 1.9$ in. $\times 1.9$ in. $= 3.61$ in.^{2}

cross section $= 3.61$ in.$^2 \times 3.1416 = 11.3412$ in.^{2}

displacement of one cylinder $= 11.3412$ in.^{2} $\times 3.40$ in. $= 38.56$ in.^{3}

total displacement $= 6 \times 38.56$ in.$^3 = 231.36$ in.^{3}

The engine displacement is 231 cubic inches. Fractions of an inch are usually not included.

This procedure can be greatly simplified by using a cubic inch displacement chart. You simply locate that point on the chart where the bore and stroke specifications for a given engine intersect, then multiply that figure by the total number of cylinders in the engine to find its displacement.

The greater the engine displacement, the more air-fuel mixture the cylinders can accept, and so the greater the power output (assuming all other factors remain equal).

Metric displacement specifications

When stated in English values, displacement is given in cubic inches; the engine's cubic inch displacement is abbreviated as "cu. in." or "cid". When stated in metric values, displacement is given in cubic centimeters (cc) or in liters (one liter equals approximately 1,000 cc). To convert engine displacement specifications from one value to another, use the following formulas:
• To change cubic centimeters to cubic inches, multiply by 0.061 (cc $\times$ 0.061 = cid).
• To change cubic inches to cubic centimeters, multiply by 16.39 (cid $\times$ 16.39 = cc).
• To change liters to cubic inches, multiply by 61.02 (liters $\times$ 61.02 = cid).

Our 231-cid engine from the previous example is also a 3,792-cc engine (231.36 $\times$ 16.39 = 3,792). When expressed in liters, this figure would be rounded off to 3.8 liters. Metric displacement can also be calculated directly with the displacement formula, using centimeter measurements instead of inches.

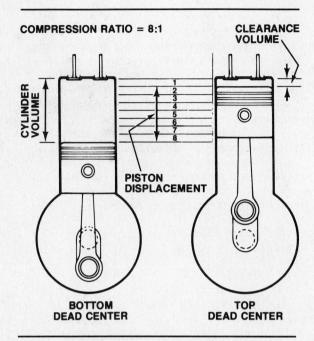

Figure 1-21. Compression ratio is the ratio of the total cylinder volume to the clearance volume.

Compression Ratio

This specification compares the total cylinder volume to the volume of only the combustion chamber, figure 1-21. Total cylinder volume may seem to be the same as piston displacement, but it is not. Total cylinder volume is the piston displacement plus the combustion chamber volume. The combustion chamber volume with the piston at top dead center is often called the **clearance volume**.

Compression ratio is the total volume of a cylinder divided by its clearance volume. If the clearance volume is one-eighth of the total cylinder volume, the compression ratio is 8 (8 to 1). The formula is as follows:

$$\frac{\text{Total volume}}{\text{Clearance volume}} = \text{Compression ratio}$$

To determine the compression ratio of an engine in which each piston displaces 31.12 cu. in. and which has a clearance volume of 4.15 cu. in.:
31.12 + 4.15 = 35.27 (total cylinder volume)

$$\frac{35.27}{4.15} = 8.498$$

The compression ratio is 8.498; this would be rounded and expressed as a compression ratio of 8.5. This can also be written 8.5:1.

In theory, the higher the compression ratio, the greater the efficiency of the engine, and the more power an engine will develop from a given quantity of fuel. The reason for this is that combustion takes place faster because the fuel molecules are more tightly packed and the flame of combustion travels more rapidly.

Engine Displacement: A measurement of the volume of air displaced by a piston as it moves from bottom to top of its stroke. Engine displacement is the piston displacement multiplied by the number of pistons in an engine.

Compression Ratio: The total volume of an engine cylinder divided by its clearance volume.

Bottom Dead Center: The exact bottom of a piston stroke. Abbreviated: bdc.

Top Dead Center: The exact top of a piston's stroke. Also a specification used when tuning an engine. Abbreviated: tdc.

Clearance Volume: The volume of a combustion chamber when the piston is at top dead center.

■ "I Wouldn't Touch Metric Conversion with a 3.049-Meter Pole"

The attempt to convert the United States system to metrics has taken many years, cost enormous amounts of money, and has not yet been completely successful, although many measurements are now in metric units.

For instance, cameras and film generally use millimeters (mm) for measuring the focal length of lenses or the size of the film. In electronics, we use the metric system of seconds, volts, watts, amperes, and hertz (cycles per second). The drug industry changed over to metrics more than two decades ago. Domestic automakers are not only using some imported engines with metric designations (such as the 2.3-liter engine), but have built many of their own engines and cars with metric measurements.

Despite the fact that metric measurement is still not universally used, technicians need to know and understand the metric system. Domestic tire manufacturers use kilopascals (kPa) as well as pounds per square inch (psi) to indicate inflation pressure. The fasteners used on many automotive components may be either U.S. or metric, which means that you need two sets of some tools. And tightening torque values given in metric units are useless if you only have a foot-pound torque wrench and can't convert the specification.

Yes, the grand dream of completely converting the automotive industry to metrics is still alive; it's just taking longer than anyone thought.

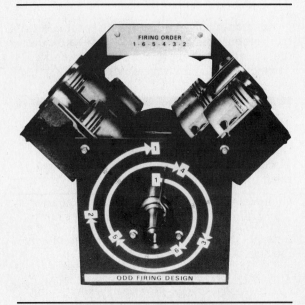

Figure 1-22. The uneven firing intervals of Buick's early V-6 engine. (Buick)

But there are practical limits to how high a compression ratio can be. Because of the unavailability of high octane fuel, most gasoline-burning engines are restricted to a compression ratio no greater than 11.5 to 1. Ratios this high, however, create high combustion chamber temperatures. This in turn creates oxides of nitrogen (NO_x), a primary air pollutant. In the early 1970s, compression ratios were lowered to around 8 to permit the use of lower octane, low-lead or unleaded fuel, and to reduce NO_x formation. Advances in electronic engine controls in the 1980s have allowed engineers to raise compression ratios to the 9 and 10 to 1 range for optimum performance and economy.

IGNITION INTERVAL

Every two strokes of a piston cause the crankshaft to rotate 360 degrees, as we have seen. Therefore, every four strokes of a piston causes the crankshaft to rotate 720 degrees (360 + 360 = 720). Because four strokes of a piston equal one engine operating cycle, one engine operating cycle equals 720 degrees of crankshaft rotation.

During the four strokes of the operating cycle, the spark plug fires only once, at the beginning of the power stroke. In a 1-cylinder engine, there would be only one ignition spark every 720 degrees of crankshaft rotation. These 720 degrees are called the **ignition interval**, or **firing interval**, of the engine. It is the number of degrees of crankshaft rotation that occur between ignition sparks.

The more cylinders an engine has, the more power strokes are produced per engine revolution. A 4-cylinder engine produces a power stroke four times as often as a 1-cylinder engine. The 4-cylinder engine has power strokes that are closer together in terms of degrees of crankshaft rotation.

A 1-cylinder engine has one power stroke during each engine operation cycle, that is, one power stroke for every two crankshaft revolutions. In a 4-cylinder engine, the operating cycles of each cylinder mean that there are four power strokes for every two crankshaft revolutions.

Common Ignition Intervals

Since a 4-cylinder engine has four power strokes during 720 degrees of crankshaft rotation, one power stroke must occur every 180 degrees (720 ÷ 4 = 180). The ignition system must produce a spark for every power stroke, so it produces a spark every 180 degrees of crankshaft rotation. This means that a 4-cylinder engine has an ignition interval of 180 degrees.

An inline 6-cylinder engine has six power strokes during every 720 degrees of crankshaft rotation, for an ignition interval of 120 degrees (720 ÷ 6 = 120). An 8-cylinder engine has an ignition interval of 90 degrees (720 ÷ 8 = 90).

Unusual Ignition Intervals

Most automotive engines have 4, 6, or 8 cylinders, but other engines are in use today. Some companies, such as Jaguar, Ferrari, and BMW, produce 12-cylinder engines, with a 60-degree firing interval. Audi and Mercedes have 5-cylinder engines with a 144-degree firing interval; Suzuki produces a 3-cylinder engine with a 240-degree firing interval used in Chevrolet's Sprint, as does Subaru.

Other unusual firing intervals result from other engine designs. General Motors has produced two different 6-cylinder engines from 8-cylinder engine blocks. The Buick engine developed in the 1960s has alternating 90- and 150-degree firing intervals, figure 1-22. The uneven firing intervals resulted from building a V-6 with a 90-degree crankshaft and block. This engine was modified in mid-1977 by redesigning the crankshaft to provide uniform 120-degree firing intervals, as in an inline six. (The Honda Acura V-6 uses the same block and crankshaft arrangement.) In 1978, Chevrolet introduced a 90-degree V-6 engine that fires at alternating 108- and 132-degree intervals.

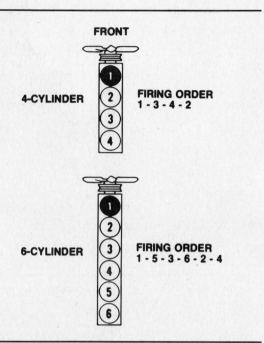

Figure 1-23. Cylinder numbering of an inline engine.

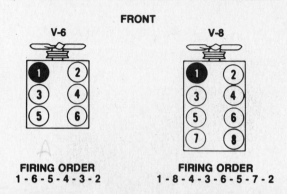

Figure 1-24. American Motors, Chrysler Motors, and most General Motors V-type engines are numbered in this way.

Chrysler's 3.9-liter V-6, derived from its 90-degree 318-cid (5.2-liter) V-8, has split crank pins offset by 22 degrees instead of the 30 degrees necessary to produce uniform firing. This gives it an alternating firing interval of 112 and 128 degrees.

Spark Frequency

In a spark-ignition engine, each power stroke is caused by a spark igniting the air-fuel mixture. Each power stroke needs an individual spark. An 8-cylinder engine, for example, requires four sparks per engine revolution (remember that there are two 360-degree engine revolutions in each 720-degree operating cycle). When the engine is running at about 1,000 rpm, the ignition system must deliver 4,000 sparks per minute. At high speed (about 4,000 rpm), the ignition system must deliver 16,000 sparks per minute. Precise ignition system performance is needed to meet these demands.

FIRING ORDER

To cause each cylinder in an engine to fire once within 720 degrees of crankshaft rotation and at regular intervals, the pistons and connecting rods are arranged on the crankshaft in a specific order. This is called the firing order, and it varies with different engine designs. Firing orders are designed to reduce the vibration and imbalance created by the power strokes of the pistons.

Engine cylinders are numbered for easy identification. However, the cylinders do not fire in the order in which they are numbered. Straight or inline engines are numbered from front to rear, figure 1-23. A typical 4-cylinder engine firing order is 1-3-4-2. That is, the number 1 cylinder power stroke is followed by the number 3 cylinder power stroke, then the number 4 power stroke, and finally the number 2 power stroke. The cycle then repeats itself. A few 4-cylinder engines have different firing orders. For example, the English Ford and Pinto 1,600-cc engines fire 1-2-4-3.

The cylinders of an inline 6-cylinder engine also are numbered from front to rear, but do not fire in that order. The firing order for all inline 6-cylinder engines is 1-5-3-6-2-4, figure 1-23.

Except for Ford vehicles and a few GM engines, the cylinders of all domestic V-type engines are numbered the same, figure 1-24. The front cylinder on the left (driver's) side is number 1. The front cylinder on the right (passenger's) side is number 2. Behind number 1 is number 3; behind number 2 is number 4, and so on. The firing order for a V-6 numbered this way is 1-6-5-4-3-2. For a V-8, the firing order is 1-8-4-3-6-5-7-2.

Besides Fords, the exceptions to this rule for V-type engine cylinder numbering are:
1. Vertical-valve Buick V-8s built before 1967
2. Older Cadillac V-8s
3. The Chevrolet 173-cid (2.8-liter) 60-degree V-6.

Ignition Interval (Firing Interval): The number of degrees of crankshaft rotation between ignition sparks.

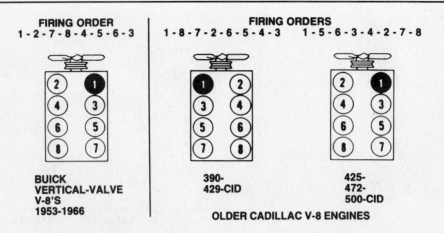

Figure 1-25. Cadillac V-8's and older Buick V-8's have unusual firing orders.

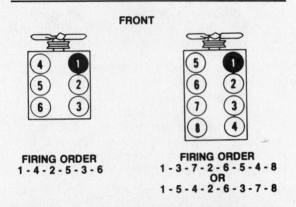

Figure 1-26. Ford numbers its V-type engines in this way.

The older Buick V-8s have the number 1 cylinder at the front of the right side, figure 1-25, rather than the left side. The firing order is 1-2-7-8-4-5-6-3.

Cadillac 425-, 472-, and 500-cid engines are numbered like the older Buicks, figure 1-25, but the firing order is 1-5-6-3-4-2-7-8. Cadillac 390- and 429-cid engines are numbered in the more conventional manner, with the number 1 cylinder at the front left, figure 1-25. However, the firing order for these engines is 1-8-7-2-6-5-4-3.

The Chevrolet 60-degree 173-cid (2.8-liter) V-6 engine has the cylinder banks reversed, that is, the number 1, 3, and 5 cylinders are on the right (passenger's) side and the number 2, 4, and 6 cylinders are on the left (driver's) side. The firing order is 1-2-3-4-5-6.

Ford V-type engines have the number 1 cylinder at the right front, figure 1-26. The numbering continues down the right side, then goes to the left side from front to rear. A Ford V-6 firing order is 1-4-2-5-3-6. Ford V-8 firing orders

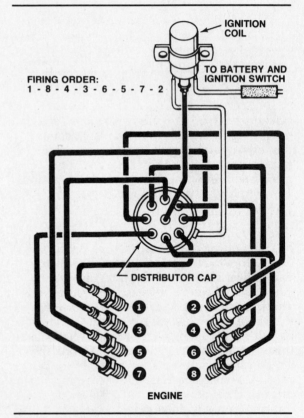

Figure 1-27. The spark plug cables must be connected to the distributor in the proper firing order.

are 1-3-7-2-6-5-4-8 or 1-5-4-2-6-3-7-8, depending on engine size.

The ignition system must deliver ignition voltage to the correct cylinder at the correct time. To maintain the firing order, the spark plug cables must be attached to the distributor cap in the proper order, figure 1-27.

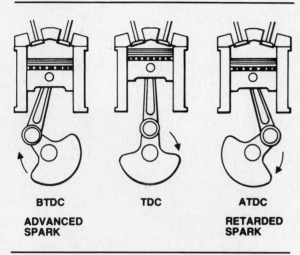

BTDC — **ADVANCED SPARK**

TDC

ATDC — **RETARDED SPARK**

Figure 1-28. Piston position is identified in terms of crankshaft rotation.

ENGINE-IGNITION SYNCHRONIZATION

During the engine operating cycle, the intake and exhaust valves open and close at specific times. The ignition system delivers a spark when the piston is near the top of the compression stroke and both valves are closed. These actions must all be coordinated or engine damage can occur.

Distributor Drive

The distributor must supply one spark to each cylinder during each cylinder's operating cycle. The distributor cam has as many lobes as the engine has cylinders. In a solid-state system, the trigger wheel has as many teeth as the engine has cylinders. One revolution of the distributor shaft will deliver one spark to each cylinder. Since each cylinder needs only one spark for each *two* crankshaft revolutions, the distributor shaft must turn at one-half engine crankshaft speed. Therefore, the distributor is driven by the camshaft, which also turns at one-half crankshaft speed.

CRANKSHAFT POSITION

The bottom of the piston stroke is called bottom dead center (bdc). The top of the piston stroke is called top dead center (tdc), figure 1-28. The ignition spark occurs near top dead center, as the compression stroke is ending. As the piston approaches the top of its stroke, it is said to be **before top dead center** (btdc). A spark that occurs before top dead center is called an advanced spark. As the piston passes top dead

center and starts down, it is said to be **after top dead center** (atdc). A spark that occurs after top dead center is called a retarded spark.

Burn Time

Approximately 3 milliseconds (0.003 second) elapse from the instant the air-fuel mixture ignites until its combustion is complete. Remember that this burn time is a function of *time* and not of piston travel or crankshaft degrees. The ignition spark must occur early enough so that the combustion pressure reaches its maximum just after top dead center, when the piston is beginning its downward power stroke. Combustion should be completed by about 10° atdc. If the spark occurs too soon before top dead center, the rising piston will be opposed by combustion pressure. If the spark occurs too late, the force on the piston will be reduced. In both cases, power will be lost. In extreme cases, the engine could be damaged. Ignition must start at the proper instant for maximum power and efficiency.

Engine Speed

As engine speed increases, piston speed increases. If the air-fuel ratio remains relatively constant, the fuel burning time will remain constant. However, at greater engine speed, the piston will travel farther during this burning time. Ignition timing must be changed to ensure that maximum combustion pressure occurs at the proper piston position.

For example, consider an engine, figure 1-29, that requires 0.003 second for the fuel charge to burn and that achieves maximum power if the burning is completed at 10° atdc.
• At an idle speed of 625 rpm, position A, the crankshaft rotates about 11 degrees in 0.003 second. Therefore, timing must be set at 1° btdc to allow ample burning time.
• At 1,000 rpm, position B, the crankshaft rotates 18 degrees in 0.003 second. Ignition should begin at 8° btdc.

Before Top Dead Center: The position of a piston as it nears top dead center. Abbreviated: btdc. Usually expressed in degrees, such as 5° btdc.

After Top Dead Center: The position of a piston after it has passed top dead center. Abbreviated: atdc. Usually expressed in degrees, such as 5° atdc.

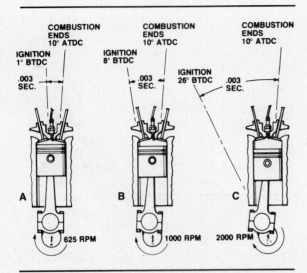

Figure 1-29. As engine speed increases, ignition timing must be advanced.

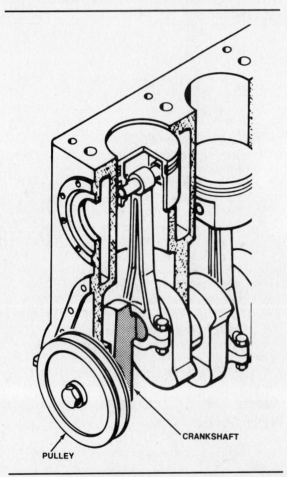

Figure 1-30. Most engines have a pulley bolted to the front end of the crankshaft.

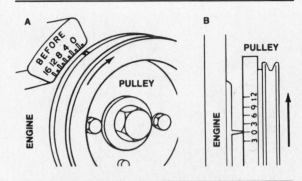

Figure 1-31. Common timing marks.

• At 2,000 rpm, position C, the crankshaft rotates 36 degrees in 0.003 second. Spark timing must be advanced to 26° btdc.

Change in timing is called spark advance, or ignition advance, and is explained in greater detail in Chapter 9.

INITIAL TIMING

As we have seen, ignition timing must be set correctly for the engine to run at all. This is called the engine's initial, or basic, timing. Initial timing is the correct setting at a specified engine speed. In figure 1-29, initial timing was 1° btdc. Initial timing is normally within a few degrees of top dead center. For many years, most engines were timed at the specified slow idle speed for the engine. However, since about 1974, a number of engines have required timing at speeds either above or below the slow idle speed. Initial timing can be adjusted to compensate for mechanical wear, slippage, and other factors. We will learn more about setting the ignition timing in the *Shop Manual*.

Timing Marks

We have seen that initial timing is related to crankshaft position. To properly time the engine, we must be able to determine crankshaft position. The crankshaft is completely enclosed in the engine block, but most engines have a pulley and vibration damper or harmonic balancer bolted to the front of the crankshaft, figure 1-30. This pulley rotates with the crankshaft and can be considered an extension of the shaft.

Marks on the pulley show crankshaft position. For example, when a mark on the pulley is aligned with a mark on the engine block, the number 1 piston is at top dead center.

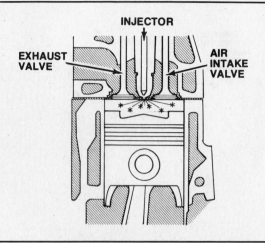

Figure 1-32. Diesel combustion occurs when fuel is injected into the hot, highly compressed air in the cylinder. (Cummins)

Timing marks vary widely, even within a manufacturer's product line. There are two common types of timing marks, figure 1-31:
• A mark on the crankshaft pulley and marks representing degrees of crankshaft position on the engine block, position A.
• Marks on the pulley representing degrees of crankshaft position and a pointer on the engine block, position B.

Some engines have timing marks on their flywheel, or a notch on the engine flywheel and a scale on the transmission cover or bellhousing. The flywheel is attached to the end of the crankshaft opposite the pulley. Most front-wheel-drive imported cars have these types of timing marks. Some older domestic engines also have a flywheel timing mark.

Most late-model engines have a special socket used for electromagnetic timing, in addition to traditional timing marks. These can be timed with a timing light or, for greater accuracy, with a special test probe that fits into the socket. The electromagnetic probe works like the pickup coil in an electronic ignition. It produces a signal voltage pulse each time a magnetic particle or notch on the crankshaft passes the probe socket. The signal voltage operates a timing meter that displays the ignition timing.

OTHER ENGINE TYPES

Other engine types besides the 4-stroke engine have been installed in automobiles over the years, but only three have been used with any real success — the diesel, the rotary, and the stratified charge engines.

The Diesel Engine

In 1892, a German engineer named Rudolf Diesel perfected the compression-ignition engine that bears his name. The diesel engine uses heat created by compression to ignite the fuel, so it requires no spark ignition system.

The diesel engine requires compression ratios of 16:1 and higher. Incoming air is compressed until its temperature reaches about 1,000°F (538°C). As the piston reaches the top of its compression stroke, fuel is injected into the cylinder, where it is ignited by the hot air, figure 1-32. As the fuel burns, it expands and produces power.

■ Plastic Engines Are on the Way

Automotive engines have traditionally been manufactured of cast iron — an alloy of iron, carbon, and silicon which is hard but, unlike most metals, non-malleable. Since cast iron cannot be stretched or extended by the high pressures and temperatures inherent in engine operation, it can withstand considerable overheating without permanent damage.

So what's wrong with cast iron? Not much, except its weight. Cast iron engines are heavy and, in an era when vehicle weight is directly related to fuel economy, engineers take every possible opportunity to reduce weight.

Enter aluminum. This malleable metal has the advantage of light weight. It's been around for many years now, and engineers are finally beginning to overcome its inherent weaknesses as a substitute for cast iron. Pure aluminum cannot be used, but aluminum alloyed with other metals has the qualities that make it a contender in today's automotive engine designs for smaller 4-cylinder powerplants.

The use of composite materials is in the not-too-distant future. Various fiber-reinforced plastics are capable of withstanding the high temperatures and stress factors of an automotive engine. And in the same way that engineers once alloyed one metal with others, they are now combining fiber types to obtain a composite material with all the specific qualities desired. Ford's Special Vehicles Operation (SVO) has been deeply involved in testing nonmetallic composite components in high-performance racing engines for several years.

A company called Polimotor has produced a working prototype of the Ford 2.3-liter 4-cylinder engine manufactured primarily of composite materials. It weighs only 152 pounds (69 kilograms), compared to the 415-pound (188-kilogram) engine from which it was derived. The twin-cam Polimotor composite engine can deliver over 300 horsepower (224 kW) at 9,200 rpm without redlining the engine under 14,000 rpm. Cost is the present drawback, but by the time the technical bugs are all worked out, it should be within reason.

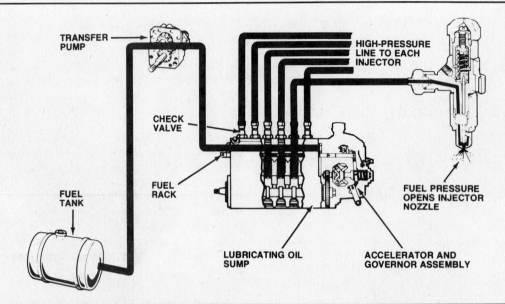

Figure 1-33. Typical automotive diesel fuel injection system.

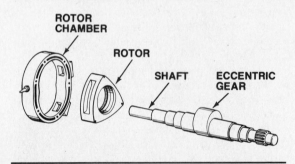

Figure 1-34. The main parts of a Wankel rotary engine are the rotor chamber, the three-sided rotor, and the shaft with an eccentric gear.

Diesel engines differ from gasoline-burning engines in other ways. Instead of a carburetor to mix the fuel with air, a diesel uses a precision **injection pump** and individual fuel injectors. The pump delivers fuel to the injectors at a high pressure and at timed intervals. Each injector measures the fuel exactly, spraying it into the combustion chamber at the precise moment required for efficient combustion, figure 1-33. The injection pump and injector system thus perform the fuel delivery job of the carburetor and the ignition timing job of the distributor in a gasoline engine.

The air-fuel mixture of a gasoline engine remains nearly constant — changing only within a narrow range — regardless of engine load or speed. But in a diesel engine, *air* remains constant and the amount of *fuel* injected is varied to control power and speed. The air-fuel mixture of a diesel can vary from as little as 85:1 at idle, to as rich as 20:1 at full load. This higher air-fuel ratio and the increased compression pressures make the diesel more efficient in terms of fuel consumption than a gasoline engine.

Like gasoline engines, diesel engines are built in both 2-stroke and 4-stroke versions. The most common 2-stroke diesels are the truck and industrial engines made by the Detroit Diesel Allison Division of General Motors. In these engines, air intake is through ports in the cylinder walls, aided by supercharging. Exhaust is through valves in the head. Crankcase fuel induction cannot be used in a 2-stroke diesel.

For many years, diesel engines were used primarily in trucks and heavy equipment. Mercedes-Benz, however, has built diesel cars since 1936, and the energy crises of 1973 and 1979 focused attention on the diesel as a substitute for gasoline engines in automobiles.

In the late 1970s, General Motors and Volkswagen developed diesel engines for cars. They were followed quickly by most major automakers in offering optional diesel engines for their vehicles. By the early 1980s many carmakers were predicting diesel power for more than 30 percent of the domestic auto population. These predictions did not come true, however.

Increasing gasoline supplies and lower prices in the mid-1980s combined with the diesel disadvantages of noise and higher manufacturing costs to reduce the incentives for customers to buy diesel automobiles. Stringent diesel emission regulations added to manufacturing costs and made the engines harder to

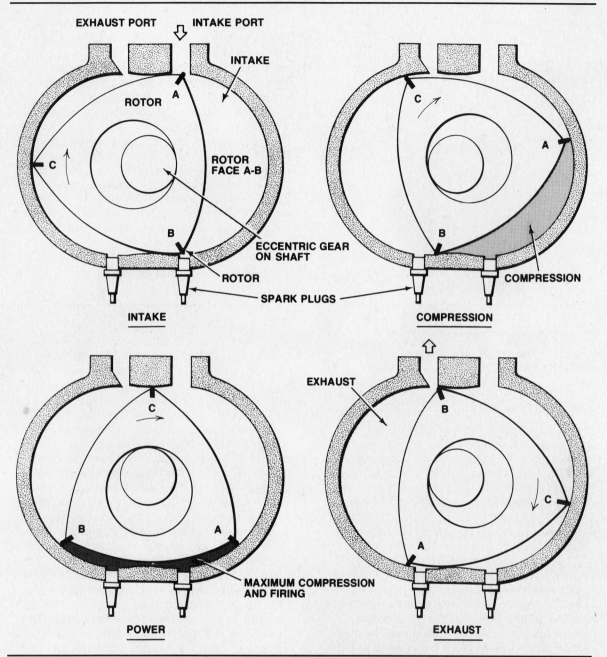

Figure 1-35. This shows the four stages of rotary engine operation. They correspond to the intake, compression, power, and exhaust strokes of a four-stroke reciprocating engine. The sequence is shown for only one rotor face, but each face of the rotor goes through all four stages during each rotor revolution.

certify for sale. A few automobile diesel engines, such as the Oldsmobile V-8, were derived from gasoline powerplants and suffered reliability problems. In the late 1980s diesel engine use is mostly limited to truck and industrial applications in the U.S. and Canada, although diesel automobiles continue to sell well in Europe where gasoline costs remain high.

Injection Pump: A pump used on diesel engines to deliver fuel under high pressure at precisely timed intervals to the fuel injectors.

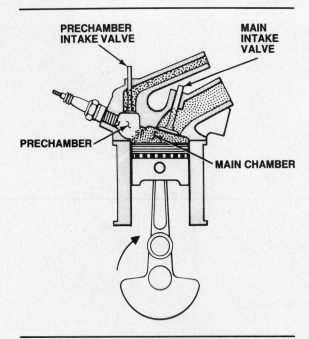

PRECHAMBER
INTAKE VALVE

MAIN
INTAKE
VALVE

PRECHAMBER

MAIN CHAMBER

Figure 1-36. Honda CVCC cylinder head, showing main combustion chamber and precombustion chamber (prechamber) with extra intake valve.

The Rotary (Wankel) Engine

The reciprocating motion of a piston engine is both complicated and inefficient. For these reasons, engine designers have spent decades attempting to devise engines in which the working parts would all rotate on an axis. The major problem with this rotary concept has been the sealing of the combustion chamber. Of the various solutions proposed, only the rotary design of Felix Wankel — as later adapted by NSU, Curtiss-Wright and Toyo Kogyo (Mazda) — has proven practical.

Although the same sequence of events occur in both a rotary and a reciprocating engine, the rotary is quite different in design and operation. A curved triangular rotor moves on an **eccentric**, or off-center, geared portion of a shaft within a long chamber, figure 1-34. As it turns, the rotor's corners follow the housing shape. The rotor thus forms separate chambers whose size and shape change constantly during rotation. The intake, compression, power, and exhaust functions occur within these chambers as shown in figure 1-35. Wankel engines can be built with more than one rotor. Mazda production engines, for example, are 2-rotor engines.

One revolution of the rotor produces three power strokes or pulses, one for each face of the rotor. In fact, each rotor face can be considered the same as one piston. Each pulse lasts

for about three-quarters of a rotor revolution. The combination of rotary motion and longer power pulses which overlap results in a smooth-running engine. While the rotary overcomes many of the disadvantages of the piston engine, it has its own disadvantages.

About equivalent in power output to that of a 6-cylinder piston engine, a 2-rotor engine is only one-third to one-half the size and weight. With no pistons, rods, valves, lifters, and other reciprocating parts, the rotary engine has 40 percent fewer parts than a piston engine. But it is also basically a very "dirty" engine. In other words, it gives off a high level of emissions and so it requires additional external devices to clean up the exhaust.

The Stratified Charge Engine

Like the rotary design, the concept of a **stratified charge** engine has been around in many forms for many years. Honda, however, was the first carmaker to produce and use one successfully. Honda's Compound Vortex Controlled Combustion (CVCC) design was the first stratified charge gasoline engine used in a mass-produced car.

The CVCC engine has a separate small precombustion chamber located above the main combustion chamber and contains a tiny additional valve, figure 1-36. Except for this feature, the CVCC is a conventional 4-stroke piston engine. However, it uses a 2-stage combustion process. Figure 1-37 shows the stages in the operating cycle.

The first stage is one of precombustion, in which the air-fuel mixture is ignited in the precombustion chamber. In the second stage, the flame front created moves down into the main combustion chamber to ignite a mixture with less fuel in it. The stratified charge engine takes its name from this layering or stratification of the air-fuel mixture just before combustion. At that time, there is a rich mixture (with lots of fuel) near the spark plug, a moderate mixture in the auxiliary combustion chamber, and a lean mixture (with little fuel) in the main chamber. The result is a more complete combustion of the air-fuel mixture, which keeps unburned fuel and emissions to a minimum.

The stratified charge principle is a *method* of controlling the combustion process. It does not represent a *type* of engine construction, such as the reciprocating or rotary engine types. In fact, charge stratification has been applied both to

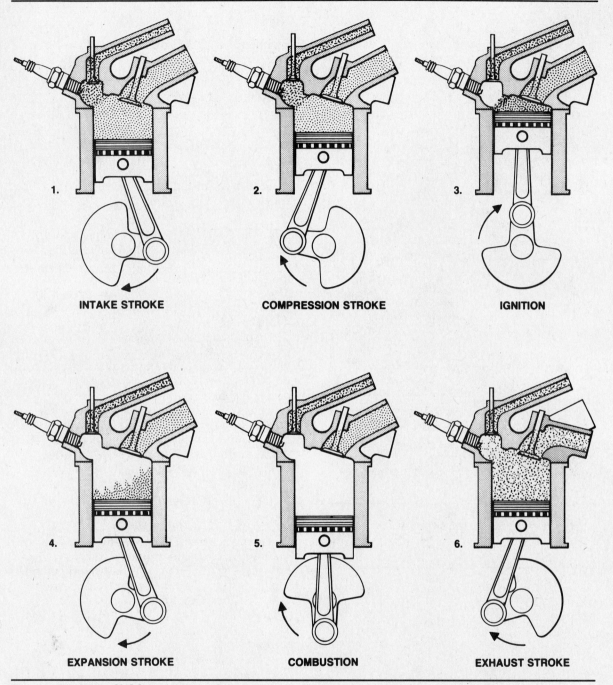

1. INTAKE STROKE
2. COMPRESSION STROKE
3. IGNITION
4. EXPANSION STROKE
5. COMBUSTION
6. EXHAUST STROKE

Figure 1-37. Honda CVCC engine operating cycle.

reciprocating diesel engines and to rotary gasoline engines. Most diesel engines used in cars have a precombustion chamber into which the fuel is injected, figure 1-38. This allows the combustion to occur in two stages: in the precombustion chamber and in the main chamber. This improves cold starting and combustion efficiency and reduces engine noise and vibration.

Eccentric: Off center. A shaft lobe which has a center different from that of the shaft.

Stratified Charge Engine: An engine that uses 2-stage combustion: first is combustion of a rich air-fuel mixture in a precombustion chamber, then combustion of a lean air-fuel mixture in the main combustion chamber.

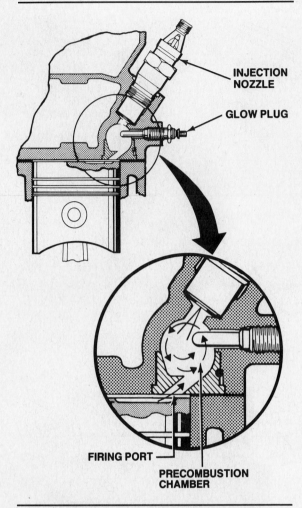

INJECTION
NOZZLE

GLOW PLUG

FIRING PORT

PRECOMBUSTION
CHAMBER

Figure 1-38. Volkswagen's passenger car diesel engine uses a precombustion swirl chamber.

SUMMARY

Engine tune-up is a combination of preventive and corrective maintenance. Before you can tune an engine, you must understand how it works.

Most automobile engines are internal combustion, reciprocating 4-stroke engines. An air-fuel mixture is drawn into sealed combustion chambers by a vacuum created by the downward stroke of a piston. The mixture is ignited by a spark.

Valves at the top of the cylinder open and close to admit the air-fuel mixture and release the exhaust. These valves are driven by a camshaft and synchronized with engine speed. The sequence in which the cylinders fire is the firing order. Several valve designs have been used, including I-head, F-head, and L-head designs. Most engine cylinders have two valves, but some engines have three, four, or five valves per cylinder.

Displacement and compression ratio are two frequently used engine specifications. Displacement indicates engine size, and compression ratio compares total cylinder volume to compression chamber volume.

The ignition interval is the number of degrees between ignition sparks. A 4-cylinder engine commonly has an ignition interval of 180 degrees, although many intervals have been used over the years. Still, each cylinder fires once every 720 degrees of crankshaft rotation. The ignition spark is provided by the distributor or electronic ignition, and is synchronized with the crankshaft rotation.

Timing is essential for the engine to operate. Timing marks on the front of the engine block or the pulley indicate crankshaft position, and can be used to alter the timing from the engine's basic initial timing.

Review Questions

Choose the single most correct answer.
Compare your answers with the correct answers on page 451.

1. The combustion chamber is usually contained in the:
   a. Engine block
   b. Piston
   c. Cylinder head
   d. Water jacket

2. The bore is the diameter of the:
   a. Connecting rod
   b. Cylinder
   c. Crankshaft
   d. Combustion chamber

3. The four-stroke engine is also called the:
   a. Otto cycle engine
   b. Diesel engine
   c. Rotary engine
   d. None of the above

4. The four-stroke cycle operates in which order?
   a. Intake, exhaust, power, compression
   b. Intake, power, exhaust, compression
   c. Compression, power, intake, exhaust
   d. Intake, compression, power, exhaust

5. Which of these engines is most often air cooled?
   a. Rotary
   b. Horizontally opposed
   c. V-type
   d. Incline

6. Valves are opened by:
   a. Camshaft lobes
   b. Connecting rods
   c. The crankshaft
   d. Valve springs

7. Synchronization of camshaft and crankshaft rotations is accomplished by:
   a. Gears
   b. A chain and sprockets
   c. A timing belt and sprockets
   d. Any of the above

8. In an eight-cylinder engine, the number of power strokes at a given instant is:
   a. 8
   b. 2
   c. 4
   d. 1

9. In an I-head engine:
   a. The intake valves are in the block; the exhaust valves are in the head
   b. All the valves are in the block
   c. All the valves are in the head
   d. None of the above

10. Which of the following is *not* used in calculating engine displacement?
    a. Stroke
    b. Bore
    c. Number of cylinders
    d. Valve arrangement

11. To change cubic centimeters to cubic inches, multiply by:
    a. 0.061
    b. 16.39
    c. 61.02
    d. 1000

12. Compression ratio is:
    a. Piston displacement plus clearance volume
    b. Total volume times number of cylinders
    c. Total volume divided by clearance volume
    d. Stroke divided by bore

13. Diesel engines:
    a. Have no valves
    b. Produce ignition by heat of compression
    c. Have low compression
    d. Use special carburetors

14. Because of its fuel injection system, a diesel engine:
    a. Needs no carburetor or distributor
    b. Has a constant fuel mixture
    c. Is inefficient
    d. Operates only in a two-stroke configuration

15. How many strokes of a piston are required to turn the crankshaft through 360 degrees?
    a. One
    b. Two
    c. Three
    d. Four

16. A "retarded spark" is one that occurs:
    a. At top dead center
    b. Before top dead center
    c. After top dead center
    d. At bottom dead center

17. The firing interval of an engine is the number of degrees of crankshaft rotation that:
    a. Take place in a 4-stroke engine
    b. Are required to complete one full stroke
    c. Occur between ignition sparks
    d. All of the above

18. Which of the following is *not* a necessary characteristic of a "fast burn" combustion chamber?
    a. Centrally located spark plug
    b. High compression
    c. Compact design
    d. 4 valves

2

Engine Air-Fuel Requirements

Automobile engines run on a mixture of gasoline and air. Gasoline has several advantages as a fuel:

1. Vaporization, or evaporation, occurs easily.
2. It burns quickly, but under control, when mixed with air and ignited.
3. It has a high heat value and produces a large amount of heat energy.
4. It is easy to store, handle, and transport.

Gasoline also has certain disadvantages. The chief disadvantage is that combustion produces air pollutants that are given off into the atmosphere through the engine's exhaust.

As a fuel, however, there is no better substitute for gasoline currently available. To understand how the fuel system works in an engine, we must understand:

- How internal combustion engines use air pressure
- The engine's air-fuel requirements.

AIR PRESSURE — HIGH AND LOW

You can think of an internal combustion engine as a big air pump. As the pistons move up and down in the cylinders, they pump in air and fuel for combustion and pump out exhaust gases. They do this by creating a difference in air pressure. The air outside an engine has weight and exerts pressure. So does the air inside an engine.

As a piston moves down on an intake stroke with the intake valve open, it creates a larger area inside the cylinder for the air to fill. This lowers the air pressure within the engine. Because the pressure inside the engine is lower than the pressure outside, air flows into the engine to fill the low-pressure area and equalize the pressure.

The low pressure within the engine is called **vacuum**. You can think of the vacuum as sucking air into the engine, but it is really the higher pressure on the outside that forces air into the low-pressure area inside. The difference in pressure between the two areas is called a **pressure differential**. The pressure differential principle has many applications in automotive fuel and emission systems.

An engine pumps exhaust out of its cylinders by creating pressure as a piston moves upward on the exhaust stroke. This creates high pressure in the cylinder, which forces the exhaust toward the lower pressure area outside the engine.

Pressure differential can be applied to liquids as well as to air. Fuel pumps work on this same principle. The pump creates a low-pressure area in the fuel system that allows the higher pressure of the air and fuel in the tank to force the fuel through the lines to the carburetor or the injection system.

AIRFLOW REQUIREMENTS

All gasoline automobile engines share certain air-fuel requirements. For example, a 4-stroke engine can take in only so much air and fuel at any one time. How much fuel it consumes depends upon how much air the engine can take in. This in turn depends upon four major factors:
1. Engine displacement
2. Maximum engine revolutions per minute (rpm)
3. Carburetor airflow capacity
4. Volumetric efficiency.

The first two factors can be used to figure the engine's airflow requirement. The carburetor airflow capacity must match the engine's requirement. This requirement is measured in cubic feet per minute (cfm). To do this, we assume that the engine has 100-percent **volumetric efficiency**, or what is often called "perfect breathing". The following paragraphs describe volumetric efficiency and how it is related to engine airflow.

Volumetric Efficiency

Volumetric efficiency is a term used to describe the airflow volume *actually* entering an engine, compared to the engine displacement, which is the maximum volume that it *could* take in. Volumetric efficiency is expressed as a percentage, and it changes with engine speed. For example, an engine might have 75 percent volumetric efficiency at 2,000 rpm. The same engine might be rated at 85 percent at 1,000 rpm and 60 percent at 3,000 rpm.

To find volumetric efficiency, the airflow volume must be measured at a specified temperature and pressure. This is because the airflow volume will increase as pressure increases and as temperature decreases. Standard pressure for measuring volumetric efficiency is **atmospheric pressure** at sea level, which is 14.7 pounds per square inch (psi), 101 kiloPascals (kPa), or 760 millimeters of mercury (mm Hg). Standard temperature is 0°C or 32°F.

Although we calculated an engine's cubic feet per minute of airflow at a volumetric efficiency of 100 percent, this figure is seldom if ever reached by a stock engine. With a stock engine, you can expect a volumetric efficiency of about 75 percent at maximum speed, or 80 percent at the highest torque, or turning force.

A high-performance engine will be about 5 percent more efficient, and a racing engine will add another 10 percent to that.

AIR-FUEL RATIOS

Because liquid fuel will not burn, it must first be changed into a vapor and mixed with air before it is ignited in the cylinders. For most engines, this is done by the carburetor. For fuel-injected engines, the fuel vaporization and mixing with air is done in the intake manifold or in the combustion chamber before ignition.

In both cases, there is a direct relationship between an engine's airflow and its fuel requirements. This relationship is called the **air-fuel ratio**.

The air-fuel ratio is the proportion by weight of air and gasoline mixed by the carburetor or injection system as required for combustion by the engine. This ratio is important, since there are limits to how rich (with more fuel) or how lean (with less fuel) it can be, and still remain fully combustible for efficient firing. The mixtures with which an engine can operate efficiently range from 8 to 18.5 to 1, figure 2-1. These ratios are usually stated this way: 8 parts of air by weight combined with 1 part of gasoline by weight (8:1) is the richest mixture which an engine can tolerate and still fire regularly; 18.5 parts of air mixed with 1 part of gasoline (18.5:1) is the leanest. Richer or leaner air-fuel ratios will cause the engine to misfire or not run at all.

To get the best engine efficiency and economy, about 9,000 gallons or liters of air are needed to burn 1 gallon or liter of gasoline, respectively. When expressing this in terms of volume, we find the air-fuel ratio to be 9,000:1.

Vacuum: A pressure less than atmospheric pressure.

Pressure Differential: A difference in pressure between two points.

Volumetric Efficiency: The comparison of the *actual* volume of air-fuel mixture drawn into an engine to the *theoretical maximum* volume that could be drawn in. Written as a percentage.

Atmospheric Pressure: The pressure caused by the weight of the earth's atmosphere. At sea level, this pressure is 14.7 psi (101 kPa) at 32°F (0°C).

Air-Fuel Ratio: The ratio of air to gasoline in the air-fuel mixture which enters an engine.

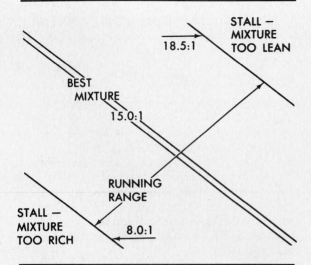

Figure 2-1. Air-fuel ratio limits for a 4-stroke gasoline engine. (Chevrolet)

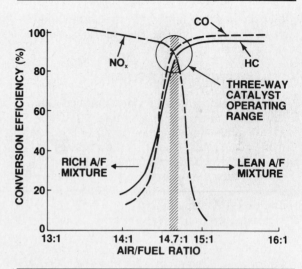

Figure 2-3. All three pollutants are controlled best with an air-fuel ratio of 14.7. A leaner mixture increases NO_x; a richer mixture increase HC and CO. (AC-Delco)

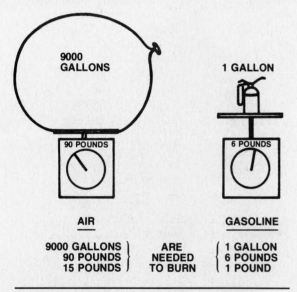

Figure 2-2. The most efficient air-fuel ratio is 15 parts (pounds) of air to 1 part (pound) of gasoline (15:1). (Chevrolet)

Not only are ratios of this size hard to understand, they are also difficult for engineers to use in their designs and experiments. Therefore, *weight* rather than *volume* is used to calculate air-fuel ratios, since it is easier to work with pounds and kilograms than with gallons and liters.

For example, to convert a volume ratio of 9,000:1 into a more useful weight ratio:
1. 100 gallons of air = 1 pound
2. 9,000 gallons of air = 9,000 ÷ 100 = 90 pounds
3. 1 gallon of gasoline = 6 pounds (approximate).

This means that it requires approximately 15 pounds or kilograms of air to burn one pound or kilogram of gasoline, so our air-fuel ratio is 15:1, figure 2-2.

This relationship between the amounts of air and fuel flow in an engine is sometimes called the fuel-air ratio. Because an engine uses far more air than fuel, the fuel-air ratio is always a number less than one, such as 0.0625. The fuel-air ratio is just a different way of expressing the more familiar air-fuel ratio.

Stoichiometric Air-Fuel Ratio

The ideal mixture or ratio at which all the fuel will blend with all of the oxygen in the air and be *completely burned* is called the **stoichiometric ratio** — a chemically perfect combination. In theory, an air-fuel mixture of about 14.7:1 will produce this ratio, but the exact ratio at which perfect mixture and combustion occurs depends upon the molecular structure of gasoline, which varies somewhat. The stoichiometric ratio is somewhat of a compromise between maximum power and maximum economy, but both are good at 14.7 to 1.

Emission control is also optimum at this ratio, if a 3-way oxidation-reduction catalytic converter is used. As the mixture richens, HC and CO conversion efficiency falls off. With leaner mixtures, NO_x conversion efficiency also falls off. As figure 2-3 shows, the conversion efficiency range is very narrow — between 14.65 and 14.75 to 1. A fuel system without feedback control cannot maintain this narrow range.

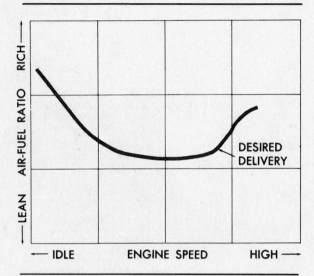

Figure 2-4. The desired air-fuel ratio changes as engine operating conditions change. (Chevrolet)

Engine Air-Fuel Requirements

An automobile engine will work with the air-fuel mixture ranging from 8 to 18.5 to 1. But the ideal ratio would be one that provides both the most power *and* the most economy, while producing the least emissions. But such a ratio does not exist because the fuel requirements of an engine vary widely depending upon temperature, load, and speed conditions.

Research has proved that the best fuel economy is obtained with a 15 to 16:1 ratio, while maximum power output is achieved with a 12.5 to 13.5:1 ratio. A rich mixture is required for idle, heavy load, and high speed conditions; a leaner mixture is required for normal cruising and light load conditions. As you can see, no single air-fuel ratio provides the best fuel economy *and* the maximum power output at the same time, figure 2-4.

Just as outside conditions such as speed, load, temperature, and atmospheric pressure change the engine's fuel requirements, other forces at work inside the engine cause additional variations. Here are three examples:
1. Exhaust gases remain inside the cylinders and dilute the incoming air-fuel mixture, especially during idle.
2. The mixture is imperfect because complete vaporization of the fuel may not occur.
3. Mixture distribution from a carburetor through the intake manifold to each cylinder is not exactly equal; some cylinders get a richer or leaner mixture than others.

If an engine is to run well under such a wide variety of outside and inside conditions, the carburetor or the injection system must be able to vary the air-fuel ratio quickly, and to give the best mixture possible for the engine's requirements at a given moment.

The best air-fuel ratio for one engine may not be the best ratio for another, even when the two engines are of the same size and design. Engines are mass-produced but will have slight variations in manifolding, combustion chambers, valve timing, and ignition timing. To accurately determine the best mixture, the engine should be run on a **dynamometer** to measure speed, load, and power requirements for all types of driving conditions.

Power Versus Economy

If the goal is to get the most power from an engine, all of the oxygen in the mixture must be burned, because the power output of any engine is limited by the amount of air it can pull in. To be sure that the oxygen combines properly with the available fuel, extra fuel must be provided. This increases the air-fuel ratio (makes it richer in fuel), resulting in some fuel which remains unburned.

This is also true at idle because of exhaust gases remaining in the cylinders. These tend to dilute the incoming mixture since some of the fuel combines with the exhaust. To make certain that the mixture is properly combustible during idle, more fuel must be delivered to make up for the fuel that combines with the exhaust gases. This makes it more difficult to equally distribute the mixture to the cylinders and creates waste material in the form of carbon monoxide, which is emitted into the atmosphere as a pollutant. To get the best fuel economy and the lowest emissions, the gasoline must be burned as completely as possible in the combustion chamber. This means that the greatest amount of energy (economy) will be produced with the least amount of leftover waste material (emissions). If enough oxygen is to be available to combine with the gasoline, then more air must be provided. This results in a leaner air-fuel mixture (less gasoline) than the ideal ratio.

Stoichiometric Ratio: An ideal air-fuel mixture for combustion in which all oxygen and all fuel will be completely burned.

Dynamometer: A device used to measure mechanical power, such as the power of an engine.

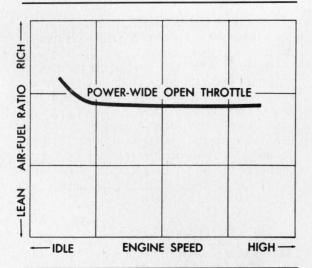

Figure 2-5. The air-fuel ratio needed for maximum power is relatively constant, except at low speed, where it must be slightly richer. (Chevrolet)

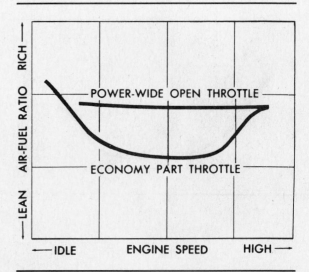

Figure 2-7. The engine must receive lean air-fuel ratios for best economy or rich ratios for maximum power at any given speed. (Chevrolet)

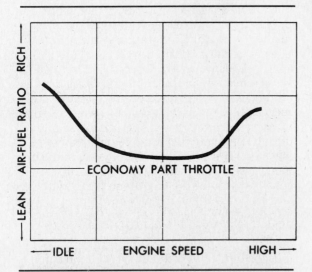

Figure 2-6. The air-fuel ratio for best economy is lean in the middle of the speed range but requires enrichment at high and low speeds. (Chevrolet)

The air-fuel ratio required to provide maximum power will change very little, except at low speeds, figure 2-5. Reducing speed reduces the airflow into the engine. The result is a poorer mixing of the air and fuel, and less efficiency in its distribution to the cylinders. Thus, at low speeds, a slight enrichment of the mixture is required to make up for this.

The same is true for maximum fuel economy — the leaner air-fuel ratio used will remain virtually the same throughout most of the operating range, figure 2-6. But enrichment will be required during idle and low speeds, as well as during higher speeds and under load — two conditions which require more power.

Enrichment also can occur when it is not required or wanted, as in the case of high-altitude driving. As altitude increases, atmospheric pressure drops and the air becomes thinner than it is at sea level. The same amount of air actually weighs less and contains less oxygen at higher altitudes. This means that an engine will take in fewer pounds or kilograms of air and less oxygen. The result is a richer air-fuel ratio, which must be corrected for efficient high-altitude engine operation. Altitude-compensating carburetors and fuel-injection air sensors solve this problem.

For these reasons, the carburetor or injection system must deliver fuel so that the best mileage is provided during normal cruising, with maximum power available whenever the engine is under load, acceleration, or high-speed, figure 2-7.

INTRODUCTION TO ELECTRONIC ENGINE CONTROLS

Electronic engine controls appeared on the automotive scene with some 1977 models. The early control systems regulated only a single function, either ignition timing or fuel metering. However, they were rapidly expanded to incorporate control over both systems, as well as numerous other engine functions.

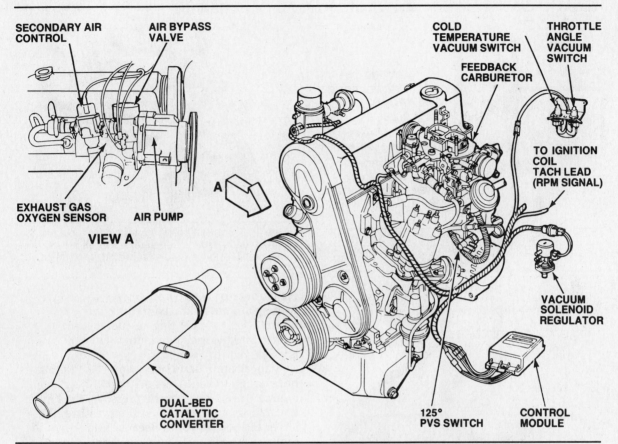

SECONDARY AIR CONTROL

AIR BYPASS VALVE

COLD TEMPERATURE VACUUM SWITCH

THROTTLE ANGLE VACUUM SWITCH

FEEDBACK CARBURETOR

TO IGNITION COIL TACH LEAD (RPM SIGNAL)

A

EXHAUST GAS OXYGEN SENSOR

AIR PUMP

VIEW A

VACUUM SOLENOID REGULATOR

DUAL-BED CATALYTIC CONVERTER

125° PVS SWITCH

CONTROL MODULE

Figure 2-8. Ford's Feedback Carburetor Electronic Control System was one of the first electronically controlled fuel management systems. (Ford)

The basic parts of the first electronically controlled fuel management systems were a feedback carburetor, an electronic control module or microprocessor, an exhaust gas oxygen (EGO) sensor mounted in the exhaust manifold, and a catalytic converter, figure 2-8.

Two types of fuel control actuators are used with carburetors:
• A solenoid or stepper motor mounted on or in the carburetor to directly control the fuel-metering rods or air bleeds, or both.
• A remote-mounted, solenoid-actuated vacuum valve to regulate carburetor vacuum diaphragms that control the fuel-metering rods and air bleeds.

The fuel management microprocessor constantly monitors the oxygen content of the exhaust gas through signals received from the EGO sensor. The microprocessor sends a pulsed voltage signal to the control device, varying the ratio of on-time to off-time according to the signals received from the EGO sensor. As the percentage of on-time is increased or decreased, the mixture is leaned or richened.

With fuel injection systems, the microprocessor exercises ratio control by switching one or more fuel injectors on and off. The switching rate is determined by engine speed. The microprocessor varies the length of time the injectors remain open to establish the air-fuel ratio. As the microprocessor receives data from its sensor inputs, it lengthens or shortens the pulse width (on-time) according to engine operating and load conditions.

FUEL DISTRIBUTION

Before gasoline can do its job as a fuel, it must be metered, atomized, and distributed to each cylinder in the form of a burnable mixture. To do this, a metering device — a carburetor, figure 2-9 — mixes the gasoline with air in the correct ratio and distributes the mixture as required by engine load, speed, throttle plate position, and operating temperature. On most late-model engines, a fuel injection system does the jobs of air-fuel mixing done by a carburetor on older engines. We will begin the study of fuel distribution, however, by concentrating on a basic carbureted engine.

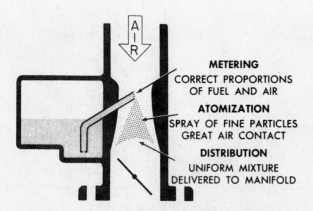

Figure 2-9. The carburetor does the basic job of fuel metering, atomization, and distribution. (Chevrolet)

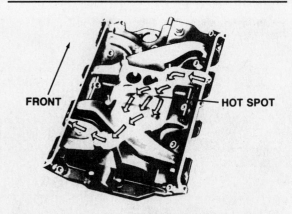

Figure 2-11. Exhaust gases are routed from ports in the cylinder heads through separate passages in the intake manifold to form the manifold hot spot. (Ford)

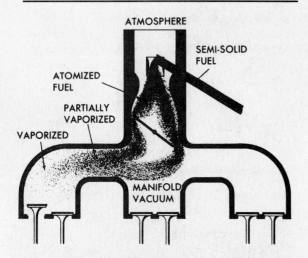

Figure 2-10. Changing liquid fuel to a combustible material is a two-stage process. First, it is atomized to a mist and mixed with air. The air-fuel mixture then must be vaporized. (Chevrolet)

Proper fuel distribution depends on six factors:
1. Correct fuel **volatility**
2. Proper fuel **atomization**
3. Complete fuel **vaporization**
4. Intake manifold passage design
5. Intake throttle plate angle
6. Carburetor or throttle-body location on the intake manifold.
    We will discuss volatility later in this chapter.

Fuel Atomization and Vaporization

Several factors are involved in changing gasoline from a liquid into a combustible vapor. In a carbureted engine, the liquid fuel first enters

the carburetor where it is sprayed into the incoming air and atomized (reduced to a mist), figure 2-10. The resulting air-fuel mixture then moves into the intake manifold where the mist is changed into a vapor.

Vaporization occurs only when the fuel is hot enough to boil. The boiling point is related to pressure; the higher the pressure, the higher the boiling point; the lower the pressure, the lower the boiling point. Because intake manifold pressure is quite a bit less than atmospheric pressure, the boiling point of gasoline drops when it enters the manifold.

Heat from the intake manifold floor combines with heat absorbed from air particles surrounding the fuel particles to begin vaporization. It is helped by raising the temperature of the intake manifold, since the higher the temperature, the more complete the vaporization will be. This heated area in the intake manifold is called a "hot spot".

Poor vaporization can be caused by several things:
- A mixture velocity that is too low
- A cold manifold or low manifold vacuum
- Cold incoming air
- Insufficient fuel volatility
- Poor manifold design
- Low carburetor flow capacity.

When poor vaporization occurs, too much liquid reaches the cylinders. Some of this additional fuel is given off as unburned hydrocarbons, and some will wash oil from the cylinder walls, causing engine wear. The rest will be carried past the piston rings as blowby gases.

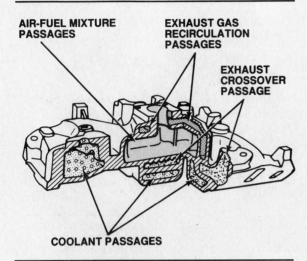

Figure 2-12. A fuel-vaporizing hot spot is created by engine coolant flowing through the intake manifold shown here, or through a spacer between the manifold and carburetor. (Chrysler)

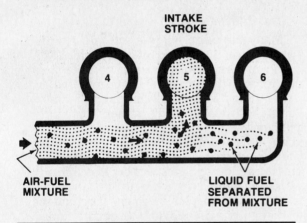

Figure 2-13. An intake manifold with large passages and sharp angles will cause liquid fuel to separate out of the air-fuel mixture. (Chevrolet)

Intake Manifold Design

The design of an intake manifold has a direct bearing on mixture distribution and volumetric efficiency over the speed range of an engine. The location, size, and surface area of the hot spot on the manifold floor affects vaporization. The hot spot is normally just beneath the carburetor, figure 2-11. Although the hot spot is usually heated by exhaust, engine coolant is sometimes circulated through passages between the carburetor base and the manifold, figure 2-12.

Older engines usually had cast iron manifolds, but the intake manifolds on modern engines are often made of aluminum because of its superior heat conductivity and light weight.

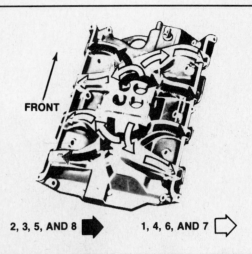

Figure 2-14. Typical V-8 intake manifold fuel passages. (Ford)

Aluminum's heat conductivity helps transfer heat to the air-fuel mixture faster and more uniformly.

Both velocity and heating are also affected by the size of the manifold passages through which the mixture must travel. If the passages are large, the mixture will travel slowly, allowing fuel particles to cling to the manifold wall and thus avoid vaporization. Small passages create a higher velocity, but restrict the travel and distribution of the mixture. The angles at which internal manifold passages turn also can be critical, figure 2-13. When they are too sharp, fuel tends to separate out of the mixture.

The air-fuel mixture should be distributed as evenly as possible among the cylinders. Figure 2-14 shows a typical V-8 intake manifold designed for good distribution to all cylinders. If one or more cylinders receives an overly lean mixture, an increase in the overall mixture will be necessary for that cylinder to fire properly. This will cause the other cylinders to receive a mixture that is too rich. Overly lean combustion produces oxides of nitrogen (NO_x), while overly rich combustion produces unburned hydrocarbons (HC) and carbon monoxide (CO). Neither condition is desirable, since they raise emissions and lower fuel economy.

Volatility: The ease with which a liquid changes from a liquid to a gas or vapor.

Atomization: Breaking down into small particles or a fine mist.

Vaporization: Changing a liquid, such as gasoline, into a gas (vapor).

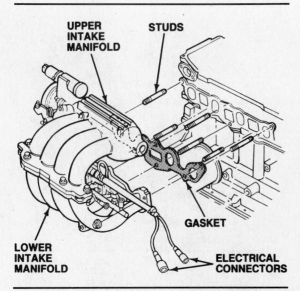

Figure 2-15. One style of intake manifold with tuned runners from the plenum to the intake ports, this Ford EFI manifold is a 2-piece assembly. (Ford)

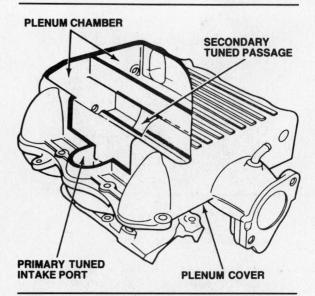

Figure 2-16. This Chrysler intake manifold is manufactured in two pieces that are permanently bonded together. It also has tuned runners. (Chrysler)

Ford 200- and 250-cid (3.3- and 4.1-liter) car engines had the intake manifold cast into the head to reduce cost and simplify overall engine manufacturing. The last of the inline Chevrolet 6-cylinder engines in the late 1970s had intake manifolds that were integral with the heads. This design was an attempt to improve mixture temperature and distribution, which are hard to control uniformly for an inline 6-cylinder engine.

The trend toward using engines with four valves per cylinder often involves a "split-level" manifold with variable induction and differences in intake valve timing. The manifold usually has an induction **plenum** that stabilizes the incoming air charge and actually allows it to rise slightly in pressure. This provides a uniform air charge that can be distributed equally to each cylinder, unaffected by momentary variations in throttle position and intake turbulence. The plenum feeds air into collector boxes, which, in turn, feed separate intake runners for each intake valve.

The engine computer controls separate throttle valves for intake runners to one of the two intake valves for each cylinder. At low- and mid-range speeds, one set of long runners feeds the intake air to one valve for each cylinder. At high speed, the computer opens the high-speed set of intake throttles to admit air through shorter runners. The principle is that long intake runners increase airflow speed at low engine speed, and short runners accelerate the intake charge at high engine speed.

Many late-model engines with fuel injection have 2-piece, dual-tuned intake manifolds. The design of these manifolds varies considerably according to the type of fuel injection used, figures 2-15 and 2-16, but all share similar features. Individual "tuned" runners connect the plenum chamber to each intake port. These runners are specifically designed for the intake ports to which they connect and provide increased airflow at high speed for maximum power. In figure 2-16, a large-diameter passage located inside the plenum chamber behind the airflow entry point provides secondary tuning. This increases airflow at low speeds for better torque.

Carburetor Size and Placement

Carburetor airflow must be matched to the airflow requirements of the engine. A carburetor that will provide more air and fuel than the engine requires will produce a rich mixture. This can reduce *both* fuel economy *and* power. A carburetor that provides less fuel and air than the engine needs will cause the engine to work harder to provide the power for any speed and load condition. Again, this means that the engine will not be providing the best combination of economy and power.

The location of the carburetor on the intake manifold is important. Incorrect placement in relation to the manifold passages can interfere with proper fuel distribution. If the carburetor

Figure 2-17. A single-bore TBI unit, the Rochester Model 700 uses one Multec fuel injector.

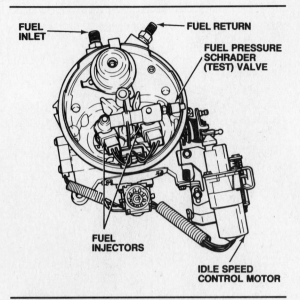

Figure 2-19. A two-bore TBI unit contains one fuel injector in each bore. (Ford)

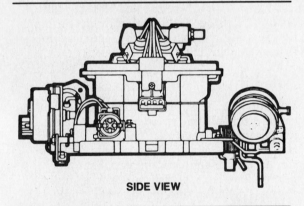

Figure 2-18. Ford's fuel charging assembly looks similar to the Motorcraft 2150 carburetor. (Ford)

is located closer to one cylinder than to the others, improper vaporization and distribution to the cylinders may result.

Fuel Injector Location

A carburetor mixes air with fuel and delivers the mixture to the intake manifold. In a fuel injection system, the injectors deliver the fuel to the manifold where it is mixed with the air. Although the role of the injector and carburetor differ somewhat, proper positioning of fuel injectors is as important as the location of the carburetor.

Throttle body injectors

A throttle body injection (TBI) system uses a throttle body, figure 2-17, or fuel charging assembly, figure 2-18, similar in design to a carburetor. In fact, the design of Ford's 2-barrel, 2-injector fuel charging assembly, figure 2-18, bears a strong resemblance to the Motorcraft 2150 carburetor. The TBI unit is positioned on the intake manifold and contains one or two solenoid-operated injectors, figure 2-19, which deliver fuel intermittently to the intake air charge.

Since TBI units deliver fuel for all the cylinders from one or two injectors, their operating cycles and injection duration are calculated to coincide with airflow requirements and engine operation. With a 2-injector TBI unit, the injectors can be calibrated differently according to the cylinders they feed. In this way, injector flow can be coordinated with manifold design to improve distribution.

Port injectors

A port, or multipoint, fuel injection system uses a series of individual solenoid-operated

Plenum: A chamber that stabilizes the air-fuel mixture and allows it to rise to a pressure slightly above atmospheric pressure.

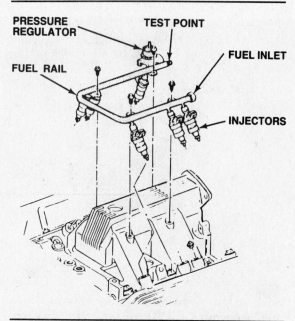

Figure 2-20. Injectors installed at individual ports are connected by a fuel rail. (AC-Delco)

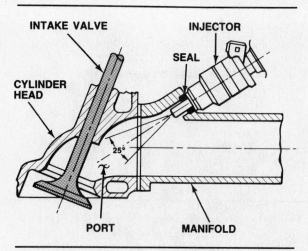

Figure 2-21. A port fuel injector is installed in the intake manifold at each cylinder port. (AC-Delco)

injectors connected to a fuel rail, figure 2-20, which supplies fuel under pressure. One injector is positioned in the intake manifold at each cylinder, figure 2-21, and sealed with an O-ring to prevent air leakage that would cause a lean cylinder.

Depending upon system design, the injectors may be energized as one or more groups, or individually. When they are energized as groups, half the fuel required by each cylinder is injected every crankshaft revolution and the fuel waits at the intake port for the incoming charge of air. When energized individually, the fuel is delivered with the incoming air charge in time for combustion.

FUEL COMPOSITION

Gasoline is a clear, colorless liquid — a complex blend of various basic hydrocarbons (hydrogen and carbon). As a fuel, it has good vaporization qualities and is capable of producing tremendous power when combined with oxygen and ignited. However, it is impossible to accurately predict how a certain blend of gasoline will perform in a particular engine, since no two engines are identical. Remember, mass-produced engines are subject to individual variations in production, which can affect fuel efficiency.

In laboratory tests, oil refiners calculate and measure the characteristics most important to produce gasolines suitable for specific jobs. Fuels are blended to meet particular temperature and altitude conditions. The gasoline you use

during the summer is not the same blend available in the winter, nor is the gasoline sold in Denver the same as that sold in Death Valley. In addition to temperature and altitude, refiners must consider several other things during the blending process: volatility, chemical impurities, octane rating, and additives.

Volatility

Volatility is a measure of gasoline's ability to change from a liquid to a vapor and is related to temperature and altitude. The more volatile it is, the more efficiently the gasoline will vaporize. As we've seen, efficient vaporization is needed for even fuel distribution to all of the engine's cylinders and for complete combustion.

Volatility is controlled by blending different hydrocarbons that have different boiling points. In this way, it is possible to produce a fuel with a high boiling point for use in warm weather, and one with a lower boiling point for cold-weather driving. Such blending involves some guesswork about weather conditions, so severe and unexpected temperature changes can cause a number of temperature-related problems ranging from hard starting to **vapor lock**, a condition in which gasoline passing through an overheated area of a fuel line vaporizes more rapidly than the fuel pump can create suction. When this happens, the fuel pump will pump only vapor, which passes into the carburetor and out through the bowl vent without the engine receiving any gasoline.

Chemical Impurities

Gasoline is refined from crude oil and contains a number of impurities which can harm engines and fuel systems. For example, if the sulfur content is too high, some of it may reach the engine crankcase, where it will combine with water to form sulfuric acid. This substance will corrode engine parts, although proper crankcase ventilation helps to avoid damage. Another impurity, gum, tends to form sticky deposits that will eventually clog carburetor and injector passages and cause piston rings and valves to stick.

To a large extent, the amount of chemical impurities present in gasoline depends upon the type of crude oil used, the refining process, and the oil refiner's desire to keep his production costs low. The more expensive process of **catalytic cracking** usually produces a gasoline with a lower sulfur content than the **thermal cracking** method, which is less expensive and therefore more common.

Vapor Lock: A condition in which bubbles are formed in a car's fuel system when the fuel gets hot enough to boil. Flow is stopped or restricted as a result.

Catalytic Cracking: An oil refining process which uses a catalyst to break down (crack) the larger components of the crude oil. The gasoline produced usually has a lower sulfur content than gasoline produced by thermal cracking.

Thermal Cracking: A common oil refining process which uses heat to break down (crack) the larger components of the crude oil. The gasoline which is produced usually has a higher sulfur content than gasoline produced by catalytic cracking.

■ The Brief History Of Propane As An Alternative Fuel

As a result of the two energy crises during the 1970s, intense effort was devoted to developing a replacement fuel for gasoline. Ford Motor Company led the way in translating this effort into vehicles that would use such fuels. One result was the propane-fueled 2.3-liter inline 4-cylinder engine that briefly graced 1982 Ford Granada/Mercury Cougar and 1983 Ford LTD/Mercury Marquis cars.

Propane, or liquified natural gas (LNG), is a liquid form of the same clean-burning natural gas used in the home. Liquified by chilling to –258°F (–161°C), it is stored in thermos-type containers. Extensive testing of propane in automobiles showed that exhaust pollutants were practically eliminated. Since many drivers of motor homes were accustomed to using propane gas, it was felt that cars could operate on the same fuel.

The Ford system included a unique air cleaner, a propane carburetor, a fuel lock, and a converter/regulator assembly — all in the engine compartment. Twin propane tanks mounted beneath the trunk floor provided the necessary fuel. The only external sign of the vehicle's power source was a small "PROPANE" emblem on each front fender.

Propane is a flammable substance like gasoline but is a vapor at normal temperatures and barometric pressures. The Ford system had two relief valves to vent excessive pressure resulting from high ambient temperatures. If a leak developed or the system vented through the relief valves, the propane immediately vaporized and expanded to about 270 times its liquid volume. Since it is heavier than air, propane settles in low spots and gradually dissipates. This created the possibility of a dangerous fire hazard.

For this reason, there were many prohibitions for propane-fueled vehicles:
- Do not vent fuel unnecessarily.
- Do not drain the fuel tanks.
- Do not use a drying oven when refinishing the paint.
- Do not weld near the fuel system tanks or components.
- Do not service the vehicle near electrical equipment such as motors or switches that may discharge sparks.
- Do not store or service the vehicle over a confined area, such as a lube pit, where vapors might accumulate.

Mechanics were not thrilled with such prohibitions, since the numerous safety precautions involved with propane vehicles interfered with their normal shop operation. Furthermore, these vehicles did not prove popular with the driving public either, and the majority of these Ford cars ended up as fleet sales to companies that were interested in fuel conservation.

The lack of consumer response to Ford's effort was attributed to the difficulty in refueling the propane tanks and a general unavailability of the fuel in many areas. The cars required a greater-than-normal amount of care on the part of drivers and died a quick death in the marketplace.

Gasoline prices started to stabilize at about the same time as the propane-fueled Fords were made available to the public. Most drivers were not willing to cope with the particular problems presented by this alternative fuel source. Thus, the propane Fords passed into the pages of automotive history much as the Chrysler turbine-powered vehicles had a decade earlier.

Octane Rating

When engine compression pressure reaches a certain level, a great deal of heat is generated as the air-fuel mixture is compressed. Unless gasoline is formulated to hold up under such high pressures and temperatures, detonation or pre-ignition can result.

To prevent these violent forms of combustion, gasoline must have a certain **antiknock value**. This characteristic derives from the type of crude oil and the refining processes used to extract the gasoline. It is measured by an **octane rating**. Gasoline with a high octane rating resists detonation during combustion, while one with a low octane value does not.

Another cause of knocking is called preignition. This condition occurs when deposits which build up on the combustion chamber surfaces get hot enough to ignite the air-fuel mixture before the spark plug can. Knocking or pinging also can be caused by ignition timing that is advanced more than it should be for a particular engine and fuel combination.

Additives

Certain chemicals not normally present in gasoline are added during refining to improve its performance:
• Anti-icers are specially treated alcohols which act as antifreeze in the gasoline to prevent moisture in the air from causing carburetor or throttle body icing at low temperatures.
• **Antioxidant inhibitors** are used to prevent the formation of gum.
• Phosphorus compounds prevent spark plug misfiring and preignition.
• Metal deactivators prevent gasoline from reacting chemically with metal storage containers in which it is stored and transported.
• Cleaners and detergents are added to prevent the formation or accumulation of compounds that could clog the many small passages or orifices in a carburetor or fuel injector. Major gasoline refiners use different proprietary chemicals for this task. The use of aftermarket cleaners and detergents is especially desirable when the quality of fuel used is otherwise below standard.
• **Tetraethyl lead** (TEL) is used to prevent detonation and provide lubrication for valve seats and many other moving parts. TEL is a highly toxic substance that is emitted as a particulate in the engine's exhaust. Studies have shown that lead particulate emissions can be a health problem if a large quantity collects in a small geographic area. Lead also destroys the capability of a catalytic converter to work properly.

For these reasons, the Environmental Protection Agency instituted a phaseout of lead content in gasoline. Beginning July 1, 1983, the use of lead was restricted to 1.1 grams per gallon. On July 1, 1985, the standard dropped to 0.5 gram, and then to 0.1 gram on January 1, 1986. The EPA further proposed that no more leaded gasoline be produced after January 1, 1988.
• Octane boosters and lead substitutes sold in the automotive aftermarket may provide some octane increase. Some care is required in selecting an appropriate additive, since many are only alcohol solutions, a common but not so desirable octane booster. All are both expensive and impractical for everyday use. Also because of EPA and health regulations, no aftermarket fuel additive contains actual tetraethyl lead.

Alcohol Additives and Fuel Quality

Gasoline blended with alcohol is widely available, although it is not legally required to be labeled as such in many states. A mixture of 10 percent ethanol (ethyl alcohol) and 90 percent unleaded gasoline is called "gasohol". **Gasohol** is a generic term, however, and there are no set standards for the type and amount of alcohol it contains. Several companies now sell premium fuels that use ethanol as the octane booster.

Alcohol improperly blended with gasoline can cause numerous and serious problems with an automotive fuel system, including:
• Corrosion formation on the inside of fuel tanks, steel fuel lines, fuel pumps, carburetors, and fuel injectors.
• Deterioration of the plastic liner used in some fuel tanks, resulting in eventual plugging of the in-tank filter.

Antiknock Value: The characteristic of gasoline that helps prevent detonation or "knocking".

Octane Rating: The measurement of the antiknock value of a gasoline.

Antioxidant Inhibitor: A gasoline additive used to prevent oxidation and the formation of gum.

Tetraethyl Lead: A gasoline additive used to help prevent detonation.

Gasohol: A blend of ethanol and unleaded gasoline, usually at a one to nine ratio.

Ethanol: Ethyl alcohol distilled from grain or sugar cane.

Methanol: Methyl alcohol distilled from wood or made from natural gas.

• Deterioration and premature failure of fuel line hoses and synthetic rubber or plastic materials such as O-ring seals, diaphragms, inlet needle tips, accelerator pump cups, and gaskets.

• Driveability problems such as hard starting, poor fuel economy, lean surge, or vapor lock.

Fuels with an alcohol content tend to absorb moisture from the air. Once the moisture content of the fuel reaches approximately one percent, it combines with the alcohol and separates from the fuel. This water-alcohol mixture then settles at the bottom of the fuel tank where the fuel pickup carries it into the fuel line to the carburetor or fuel injectors, creating a lean surge condition.

All alcohols are solvents. While **ethanol** is relatively mild, **methanol** (methyl alcohol) is highly corrosive. It attacks fuel system components unless properly mixed with corrosion inhibitors and appropriate suspension agents or cosolvents to prevent separation of the water-alcohol combination from the gasoline.

Gasohol has a cleaning effect on service station storage tanks, as well as the vehicle's fuel tank. As a result of this cleaning action, a combination of rust, a jelly-like sludge, and metallic particles passes into the automotive fuel system. These substances cause reduced fuel flow through the filter and will eventually plug the carburetor or injector passageways.

Fuel economy and driveability are other areas of concern with alcohol-gasoline blends. Alcohols contain fewer BTU's of energy per gallon or liter than gasoline, which can result in reduced fuel mileage. In addition to their lower energy content, alcohols are less volatile than gasoline; they require higher temperatures before they will ignite and burn. Since the stoichiometric ratio for alcohol is 6.5 rather the 14.7 of gasoline, an alcohol-gasoline blend creates a lean mixture. In turn, this creates or worsens lean surge in some driving conditions and increases the probability of vapor lock.

The problem of alcohol improperly blended with gasoline has become so common around the United States that automotive tool manufacturers offer alcohol detection kits so that you can determine the quality of fuel being used.

The detection procedure is performed with water as a reacting agent. However, if cosolvents have been used as a suspension agent in alcohol blending, the test will not show the presence of alcohol unless ethylene glycol (automotive antifreeze) is used instead of water as a reacting agent. It is suggested that a gasoline sample be tested twice using the detection kit: first with water and then with ethylene glycol.

The procedure cannot differentiate between types of alcohol (ethanol or methanol), nor is it considered to be absolutely accurate from a scientific standpoint. These tests are accurate enough, however, to determine whether or not there is enough alcohol in the fuel to cause the user to take precautions.

SUMMARY

Piston movement creates a pressure differential between the air inside the engine and the air outside the engine. This causes airflow into and out of the engine.

The engine air-fuel ratio is commonly measured in terms of the weight of the air taken in versus the weight of the gasoline taken in. Because an engine must operate with the best possible combination of power, economy, and clean exhaust, the desired air-fuel ratio changes as operating conditions change.

The carburetor varies the air-fuel ratio and atomizes the fuel in the airflow to ease vaporization. Manifolds must be designed to provide the best possible combination of vaporization, mixture distribution, and volumetric efficiency. Carburetors and manifolds are carefully matched to each other and to the engine.

Fuel composition also affects engine efficiency. Fuel volatility, purity, octane rating, and additives are considered during fuel blending, as well as the geographical region in which the fuel will be sold.

Gasoline must be properly refined to remove chemical impurities and blended with additives to prevent preignition, detonation, carburetor icing, gum and varnish formation, and misfiring. Tetraethyl lead was once the major octane booster, but its use was severely limited and eventually prohibited by the EPA.

Alcohol and gasoline blends are called gasohol. Gasohol has a number of disadvantages, particularly when it is misblended, and can permanently damage a fuel system. Alcohol detection kits allow you to determine the alcohol content, if any, of gasoline.

Review Questions

Choose the single most correct answer.
Compare your answers with the correct answers on page 451.

1. A disadvantage of gasoline is that it:
   a. Vaporizes easily
   b. Burns quickly
   c. Produces pollutants upon combustion
   d. Has a high heat value

2. Which is *not* a factor in determining airflow requirement?
   a. Engine displacement
   b. Maximum rpm
   c. Carburetor size
   d. Volumetric efficiency

3. Volumetric efficiency:
   a. Is the ratio of air entering the engine to engine displacement
   b. Decreases as engine speed increases
   c. Is expressed as a percentage
   d. All of the above

4. At maximum speed, the volumetric efficiency of a stock engine is approximately:
   a. 75%
   b. 50%
   c. 10%
   d. None of the above

5. The richest air-fuel ratio that an internal combustion engine can tolerate is about:
   a. 4:1
   b. 2.5:1
   c. 8:1
   d. 18.5:1

6. To burn one pound of gasoline with maximum efficiency requires about:
   a. 8 pounds of air
   b. 15 pounds of air
   c. 18.5 pounds of air
   d. 17.9 pounds of air

7. A rich air-fuel mixture is needed for:
   a. Idle
   b. Heavy load
   c. Acceleration
   d. All of the above

8. An internal engine condition affecting fuel requirements is:
   a. Engine load
   b. Mixture distribution
   c. Atmospheric pressure
   d. Engine speed

9. Obtaining maximum power results in:
   a. No change in air-fuel ratios
   b. Leather mixtures
   c. Unburned oxygen
   d. Excess unburned fuel

10. Maximum fuel economy requires:
    a. Less air
    b. Leaner air-fuel mixtures
    c. Richer air-fuel mixtures
    d. Higher temperatures

11. For maximum power, the air-fuel ratio:
    a. Becomes leaner at low speeds
    b. Becomes richer at low speeds
    c. Becomes richer at high speeds
    d. None of the above

12. For maximum fuel economy, the air-fuel ratio:
    a. Is lean for middle speeds
    b. Becomes richer at high speeds
    c. Becomes richer at low speeds
    d. All of the above

13. Different fuel blending techniques are used by refiners to:
    a. Obtain the desired volatility and increase the octane rating
    b. Replace impurities with additives
    c. Both a and b
    d. Neither a nor b

14. Mechanic A says that an engine fuel management system is electronically controlled.
    Mechanic B says that an engine fuel management system uses an EGO sensor.
    Who is right?
    a. A only
    b. B only
    c. Both A and B
    d. Neither A nor B

15. Mechanic A says that a TBI injection system uses one injector at each cylinder port.
    Mechanic B says that the TBI unit is installed on the intake manifold where a carburetor would be.
    Who is right?
    a. A only
    b. B only
    c. Both A and B
    d. Neither A nor B

16. Which of the following is *not* a quality of tetraethyl lead?
    a. Prevents detonation
    b. Lubricates valve seats
    c. Can destroy a catalytic converter
    d. Is a non-toxic substance

17. Gasohol is generally regarded as a blend of:
    a. 10 percent ethanol and 90 percent gasoline
    b. 90 percent ethanol and 10 percent gasoline
    c. 50 percent ethanol and 50 percent gasoline
    d. None of the above

3

Engine Lubrication

The lubrication system circulates motor oil throughout the engine to do a number of jobs. This chapter will tell you:
• The purpose of motor oil
• How it is rated
• What additives do to help motor oil
• How the lubrication system works
• The relationship between lubrication and performance, economy, and emission control.

PURPOSES OF MOTOR OIL

Motor oil in a car engine does five major jobs:
1. It reduces friction between moving parts, which lessens both wear and heat.
2. It acts as a coolant, removing heat from the metal of the engine.
3. It carries dirt particles away from moving surfaces, cleaning the engine.
4. It helps seal the combustion chamber by forming a film around the valve guides and between the piston rings and the cylinder wall.
5. It acts as a shock absorber, cushioning engine parts to protect them from the force of combustion.

   All of these jobs help keep the engine running smoothly and efficiently. If the motor oil fails to do any one of these, engine performance may be reduced and the engine might be damaged.

MOTOR OIL COMPOSITION AND ADDITIVES

Motor oil is a byproduct of petroleum, as are gasoline and kerosine. To change or improve the performance of a motor oil, manufacturers blend in chemical additives.

Motor Oil Composition

Petroleum-based motor oils contain mostly hydrogen and carbon. They are complex hydrocarbon compounds, as is gasoline.

Motor Oil Additives

The purpose of a motor oil additive can be to:
• Replace a property of the oil that was lost during refinement.
• Strengthen a natural quality already in the oil.
• Add a property that the oil did not naturally have.

   A few of the common motor oil additives and their jobs are described in the following paragraphs.

   Oxygen tends to combine chemically with hot motor oil. This process of oxidation can

ACCEPTABLE   **BORDERLINE**

Figure 3-1. Sludge deposits in an engine.

leave hard carbon and **varnish** deposits in the engine. **Antioxidants** reduce this high-temperature problem.

In any engine, some of the combustion chamber gases get past the piston rings and enter the crankcase. This is called **blowby**. Blowby gases contain water vapor and acids that will rust or corrode engine parts. Rust and corrosion preventives are added to motor oil to neutralize acids and reduce the bad effects of blowby gases.

The oil in an engine is constantly being churned by moving parts. This can mix air with the oil and cause it to foam. Oil foam does not protect moving parts as well as liquid oil. Foam inhibitors in a motor oil will reduce foaming. Both the water vapor and the fuel in blowby gases tend to mix with cold oil and cause **sludge**, figure 3-1. This thick black deposit clogs oil passages and increases engine friction. **Dispersants** reduce sludge formation by keeping sludge particles suspended in the oil, to be removed when the oil and filter are changed. **Detergents** clean piston ring grooves and keep the rings free to seal with maximum effectiveness, which maintains peak engine performance.

Viscosity is the tendency of a liquid to keep from flowing. Some additives help an oil to flow under wide temperature ranges. These are called "viscosity index (VI) improvers" and pour-point depressants.

Additive precautions
Because different manufacturers use different additives, it is good practice not to mix oil brands within an engine. The chemicals could oppose each other and decrease the cleaning and lubricating abilities of the oil. For the same reason, many oil manufacturers advise against

the use of other oil additives that are sold separately. Under most circumstances the extra additives are not needed.

MOTOR OIL DESIGNATIONS

Because engines and operating conditions vary greatly, oil refiners blend and sell different types of motor oil. For example, the oil used in a diesel truck is different from that used in a high-performance car engine. Both engines need lubrication, and as we shall see, an oil may or may not meet all the requirements of both engines.

Engine oil is commonly identified in two ways: by American Petroleum Institute (API) service classification and by Society of Automotive Engineers (SAE) viscosity number.

Another method for identifying oils is by military specification numbers or "MIL-specs". While they are rarely used to specify engine oils for cars and trucks, they often appear on oil containers.

API Service Classification

The **API service classification** rates engine oils on their ability to lubricate, resist oxidation, prevent high- and low-temperature engine deposits, and protect the engine from rust and corrosion. API has organized a system of letter classifications with two categories, the S-series and the C-series. The S-series service classification emphasizes oil properties critical to gasoline engines, while the C-series emphasizes oil properties for diesel engines. In order for an oil formulation to be given a particular classification, the oil is run through a series of tests in specific engines. If the oil's performance meets the minimum standard, the oil can be sold bearing that API service classification.

The S-Series Oils

The S-series oils come under the following classifications: SA, SB, SC, SD, SE, SF, and SG. No performance tests are required to meet the SA classification.

• The SB classification requires that the oil provide some anti-scuff capability and resistance to oil oxidation. This type of protection dates back to the 1930s.

• The SC classification requires the oil to provide control of high- and low-temperature deposits, wear, rust, and corrosion in gasoline engines. This level of protection was required by new car warranties from 1964 through 1967.

• The SD classification requires an increased level control of high- and low-temperature deposits, wear, rust, and corrosion in gasoline engines over SC oils. This classification meets new car warranties from 1968 through 1970, and some in 1971.

•The SE classification requires still higher levels of control of high- and low-temperature deposits, wear, rust, and corrosion in gasoline engines over SC and SD oils, plus some anti-wear performance. This level of protection was required for some cars and some trucks beginning in 1971, and continued through 1979.

• The SF classification requires increased oxidational stability and anti-wear performance relative to SE oils. This classification was required to meet new-car warranties from 1980 through 1988.

• The SG classification requires increased control of engine deposits, oil oxidation and engine wear relative to the other oils in this series. SG oils exceed the performance of SF and also CC oils, to be discussed below. This classification meets new-car warranty requirements from 1989 on.

It is readily apparent that as these designations progress alphabetically they increase in levels of protection. For this reason, each classification replaces the one before it, with SG offering the most protection. The SF and SG classifications are also the only ones for which the various tests can be performed, because the engines used in the other tests are no longer available.

The C-Series Oils

The C-series oils are: CA, CB, CC, CD, CD-II and CE. The CA classification requires that the oil protect against bearing corrosion and ring-belt deposits in naturally aspirated (non-supercharged) diesel engines running on fuel with a minimum sulfur content of 0.35 percent.

The requirements of this classification date back to the late 1940s. These oils meet military specification MIL-L-2104A.

• The CB designation requires the same protection as CA, but the engine is run on fuel with a minimum of 0.95 percent sulfur. These oils meet the obsolete "Supplement 1" specification added to MIL-L-2104A, and were used in gasoline engines as well.

• The CC designation requires that the oil provide protection from high temperature deposits in lightly supercharged diesel engines running on low-sulfur-content fuel, and also protection from rust, corrosion and low-temperature deposits in gasoline engines. This designation was introduced in 1961, and meets the MIL-L-2104B specification.

• The CD classification requires oils to provide protection from bearing corrosion and high-temperature deposits in supercharged diesel engines running on fuels of various qualities. Oils meeting the CD classification meet the Caterpillar Series-3 specification introduced in 1955, and also MIL-L-45199.

• The CD-II classification requires the same performance as CD oils, and is designated for

Varnish: An undesirable deposit, usually on the engine pistons, formed by oxidation of fuel and of motor oil.

Antioxidants: Chemicals or compounds added to motor oil to reduce oil oxidation, which leaves carbon and varnish in the engine.

Blowby: Combustion gases that get past the piston rings into the crankcase; these include water vapor, acids, and unburned fuel.

Sludge: A thick, black deposit caused by the mixing of blowby gases and oil.

Dispersant: A chemical added to motor oil that keeps sludge and other undesirable particles picked up by the oil from gathering and forming deposits in the engine.

Detergent: A chemical compound added to motor oil that removes dirt or soot particles from surfaces, especially piston rings and grooves.

Viscosity: The tendency of a liquid such as oil to resist flowing.

API Service Classification: A system of letters signifying an oil's performance; assigned by the American Petroleum Institute.

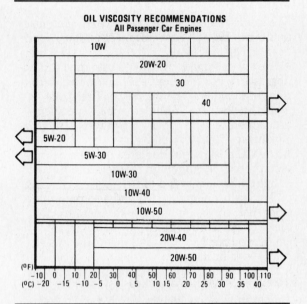

OIL VISCOSITY RECOMMENDATIONS
All Passenger Car Engines

10W
20W-20
30
40
5W-20
5W-30
10W-30
10W-40
10W-50
20W-40
20W-50

(°F) -10 0 10 20 30 40 50 60 70 80 90 100 110
(°C) -20 -15 -10 -5 0 5 10 15 20 25 30 35 40

Figure 3-2. Engine oil viscosity recommendations based on ambient temperature.

two-stroke cycle diesel engines where deposit and wear control are critical. Two-stroke diesels are most commonly used in intercity and highway buses. This classification came into being in 1988.

• The CE classification also requires the same performance as CD oils, plus passing the engine oil performance tests for the Mack EO-K/2 specification, and the Cummins NTC-400 test for piston deposits and oil consumption. This classification was introduced in 1987, although oils meeting its individual requirements were already available for some time. CE oils are intended for heavy-duty diesel engines, such as those used in large on- and off-highway trucks, and construction equipment.

It is noteworthy that while each S-series classification exceeds the one before it, this is not necessarily the case in the C-series. For instance, the CB tests are run on higher-sulfur fuel than the CC tests. As a result, a CC oil may not offer equivalent protection from the effects of sulfur on the engine. On the other hand, CD and CE oils must pass tests running on high-sulfur-content fuels, and thus would offer the similar protection in this area.

Some oils are identified with dual service classifications separated by a virgule (slash), for example, SE/CC, SE/CD, SF/CC, or SF/CD. These oils meet the requirements of both service classifications shown, and can be used in any engine that calls for one or the other. Many manufacturers specify oils that meet both "S" and "C" service classifications; this is particularly true for heavy-duty and turbocharged en-

gines. Where an oil with a dual service classification is specified, oils that meet only a single classification should *not* be used or the engine warranty may be voided.

SAE Viscosity Grades

The **SAE viscosity grade**, expressed as a number, refers to an oil's resistance to flow. Typical oil viscosity grade numbers are 5W, 10W, 15W, 20W, 20, 30, 40, and 50. Lower viscosity grade numbers indicate thinner oils that flow more easily. Higher numbers indicate thicker oils with a greater resistance to flow.

The viscosity of an oil is greatly affected by its temperature. When an oil is cold, its viscosity increases and it does not flow as well. If an oil's viscosity is too high at low temperatures, there will be a lag between the time the engine is started and when oil actually reaches heavily loaded engine parts. When an oil is hot, it thins out and flows quite easily. If an oil's viscosity is too low at high temperatures, the oil film between critical engine parts may break down and allow them to make contact, causing damage.

To make sure oils are capable of providing adequate lubrication, they are tested for viscosity at both high and low temperatures. Viscosity numbers *without* a "W" suffix indicate that the oil meets certain viscosity requirements at 212°F (100°C) only. Grades *with* a "W" suffix meet the requirements at 212°F (100°C), and they also meet certain minimum flow rates at temperatures ranging from 23°F (–5°C) down to –22°F (–30°C).

Oils with only one SAE viscosity number (**single-grade** oils) were once widely recommended; however, they must be changed with the seasons to ensure that the oil in the crankcase strikes the proper balance between high- and low-temperature operation. Low-viscosity oils are required in winter, while high-viscosity oils are needed in summer. Today, single-grade oils are still recommended in some heavy-duty and diesel engine applications.

Most modern oils have dual viscosity grade numbers separated by a hyphen (dash) such as 5W-30, 10W-30, 15W-40, or 20W-50. These **multigrade** oils meet the low- and high-temperature specifications for both grades of oil indicated. They contain VI improver additives that allow them to flow well at low temperatures, yet still resist thinning at high temperatures. These properties allow multigrade oils to be used throughout the year with less concern about temperature fluctuations. Figure 3-2 shows general engine oil viscosity recommendations based on ambient temperature.

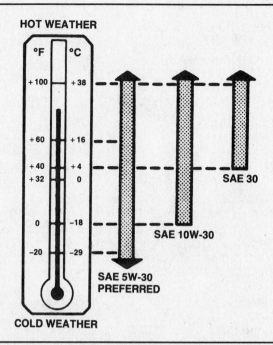

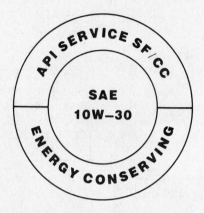

Figure 3-5. The API Engine Service Classification Symbol, or "doughnut".

Figure 3-3. Engine oil viscosity recommendations for 1988 Chevrolet car engines. (Chevrolet)

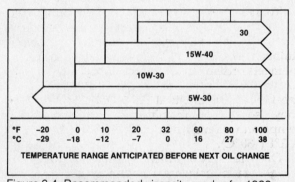

Figure 3-4. Recommended viscosity grades for 1988 Chrysler front-wheel-drive passenger cars.

Vehicle manufacturers today recommend multigrade oils for most of their engines; however, not all multigrade oils are recommended for all cars. For example, General Motors and Chrysler do not recommend 10W-40 oils. Also, most automakers warn against the use of low-viscosity multigrade (and single-grade) oils, such as 5W-20 and 10W, for sustained high-speed driving, trailer towing, or any other circumstance in which the engine is placed under constant heavy load. Carmakers specify the exact kind of oil that should be used under certain operating conditions. Figures 3-3 and 3-4 show engine oil charts prepared by two different manufacturers.

Energy-Conserving Oils

In addition to their service classification and viscosity grade, certain oils are also designated as Energy Conserving by the API. These oils are specially formulated to reduce internal engine friction, and thus improve fuel economy. These oils usually have friction-reducing additives and a lower viscosity than oils that are not Energy Conserving.

Engine Oil Identification

To allow easy identification of engine oils, the API established the Engine Service Classification Symbol, or "doughnut", figure 3-5. The upper half of the symbol displays the API service classifications of the oil, the center of the doughnut displays the SAE viscosity grade of the oil, and the lower half of the symbol contains the words "Energy Conserving" if the oil is formulated to meet those requirements. When selecting an oil, always make sure the oil quality information on the API doughnut conforms with the vehicle manufacturer's specifications.

SAE Viscosity Grade: A system of numbers signifying an oil's viscosity at a specific temperature; assigned by the Society of Automotive Engineers.

Single Grade: An oil that has been tested at only one temperature, and so has only one SAE viscosity number.

Multigrade: An oil that has been tested at more than one temperature, and so has more than one SAE viscosity number.

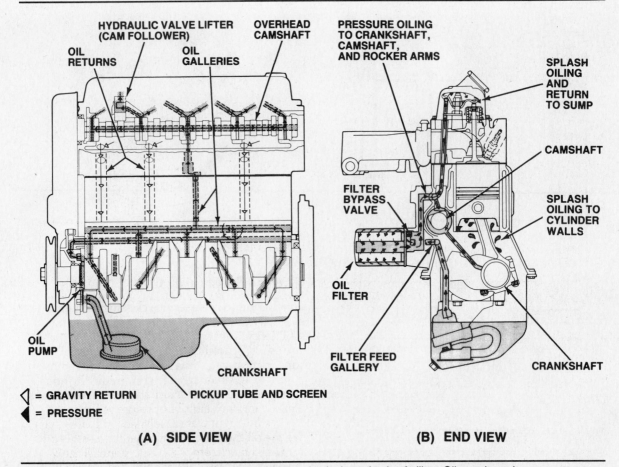

Figure 3-6. Modern engine design uses both pressure and splash methods of oiling. Oil travels under pressure through galleries to reach the top end of the engine (A); gravity flow or splash oiling lubricates many parts. A bypass valve is used to prevent oil starvation if the filter clogs (B). (Ford)

Synthetic Motor Oils

Synthetic-base lubricants have been used in aviation and special-purpose engines for decades. Since the late 1970s, **synthetic motor oils** have attracted a lot of attention and have slowly gained in popularity because they offer several advantages over petroleum-based engine oils.

Synthetic oils are created by reacting various complex molecules to form a new molecular structure. Petroleum, several types of acids and alcohols may be used in varying proportions to make synthetic base oils. The process involved is complex, consequently synthetic oils may sell for 3 to 5 times the price of their petroleum-based counterparts.

Synthetics contain less wax than petroleum oils, and so tend to remain liquid when cold. This permits faster lubrication in very cold temperatures, which is perhaps the greatest advantage of synthetic engine oils. In some cases, they cause less friction inside the engine, thus contributing to increased fuel economy. In addition to these benefits, many synthetic oils have been shown to deteriorate at a slower rate than comparable petroleum-based oils, thus they can remain in service longer between oil changes. However, the issue of extending oil drain intervals is complicated, thus you should not assume that the use of a synthetic oil alone justifies postponing scheduled oil and filter changes. While synthetic oil base stocks and additives may differ chemically from petroleum oils, they are designated by the same SAE viscosities and API service classifications, and are selected in the same manner, according to the engine or car manufacturers' specifications.

ENGINE OILING SYSTEM AND PRESSURE REQUIREMENTS

All modern car engines have a pressurized lubrication system. The parts of this system, figure 3-6, are the:
- Oil reservoir and its ventilation
- Oil pump and pickup
- Pressure relief valve
- Filter

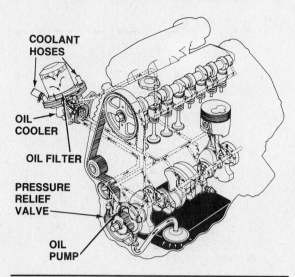

Figure 3-7. A separate coolant jacket allows engine coolant to circulate around the oil cooler of this diesel engine to help reduce oil temperatures.

- Galleries and lines
- Indicators.

These parts are described in the following paragraphs.

Reservoir and Ventilation

There must be enough oil in the engine to circulate throughout the system, plus some reserve so that the oil can cool before being recirculated. All of this oil is kept in the engine oil pan, or sump. Because the oil pan is at the bottom of the engine, the oil drains into the pan after passing through the engine. The flow of air past the pan when the car is moving helps cool the oil. If this cooling effect is not sufficient, the manufacturer may add an external oil cooler, which is common on diesel, turbocharged, or air-cooled engines, figure 3-7. Heat is removed from oil passing through the cooler by airflow or coolant circulation, depending upon the cooler design.

Engine oil pan capacities vary greatly. Four-cylinder engines can hold 3 to 5 quarts of oil. Most V-type engines hold 4 to 5 quarts. Some high-performance and diesel V-type engines require 6 or 7 quarts. Oil is put in the crankcase through a capped oil filler hole at the top of the engine.

We have seen that blowby gases enter the crankcase from the combustion changers. The gases can mix with motor oil and cause engine damage. Because the combustion chamber gases are under very high pressure, they increase

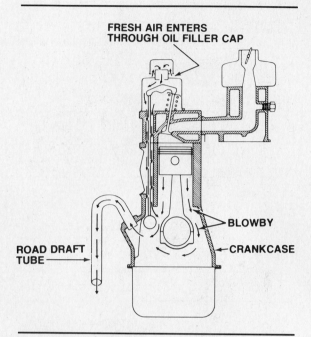

Figure 3-8. An open crankcase ventilation system using a road draft tube.

the pressure within the crankcase. If the crankcase is not vented, the pressure will force oil out of the engine at loosely sealed points such as the oil filler cap and the junction of the oil pan and block, among other points. This is messy, wasteful, and can be dangerous as a fire hazard or if the oil gets on the brake or clutch materials. To prevent this, the crankcase is ventilated.

On older cars, the oil pan was vented directly to the atmosphere through a **road draft tube**, figure 3-8. Until the 1960s, this was the most common type of crankcase ventilation.

All late-model cars have **positive crankcase ventilation** (PCV) systems, figure 3-9. In a PCV system, clean, filtered air is drawn into the crankcase, and crankcase vapors are recycled to

Synthetic Motor Oils: Lubricants formed by artificially combining molecules of petroleum and other materials.

Road Draft Tube: The earliest type of crankcase ventilation; it vented blowby gases to the atmosphere.

Positive Crankcase Ventilation (PCV): Late-model crankcase ventilation systems that return blowby gases to the combustion chambers.

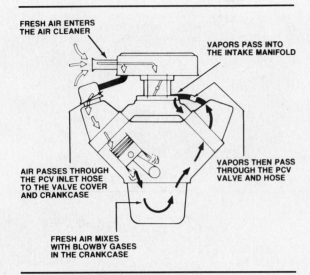

Figure 3-9. Modern PCV systems are totally closed.

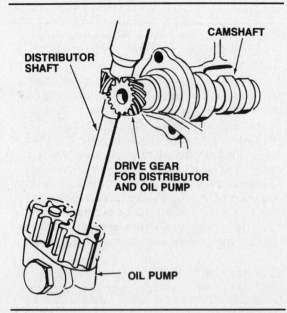

Figure 3-10. The oil pump is driven by the camshaft.

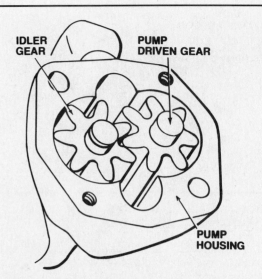

Figure 3-11. A gear-type oil pump.

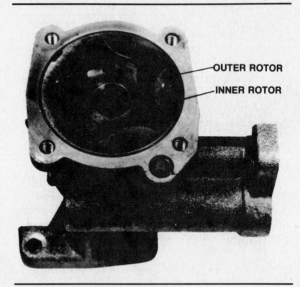

Figure 3-12. A rotor-type oil pump.

Oil Pump and Pickup

The oil pump is a mechanical device that forces motor oil to circulate through the engine. On most engines, the pump is driven by the camshaft through an extension of the distributor shaft, figure 3-10. Some engines have a crankshaft-driven oil pump, and most the intake manifold. This keeps blowby from polluting the air and provides better crankcase ventilation than the road draft tube. Crankcase ventilation and PCV systems are explained in detail in Chapter 16.

overhead-cam engines use a separate engine shaft to drive the oil pump and the distributor.

Two types of oil pumps are in use today:
• The gear type
• The rotor type.

The most common pump is the gear type, figure 3-11. One gear is driven by gears and a shaft from the camshaft and is called the drive gear. When the drive gear turns it forces the second gear, called the idler gear, to turn. As the two gears turn, the oil between the gear teeth is carried along. At the point where the two gears mesh, there is very little room for oil, so the oil is forced out of the area under pressure.

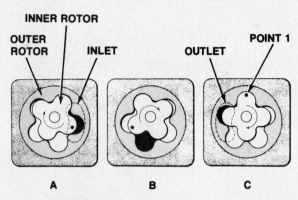

A. Oil is picked up in lobe of outer rotor.
B. Oil is moved in lobe of outer rotor to outlet.
C. Oil is forced out of outlet because the inner and outer rotors mesh too tightly at point 1 and the oil cannot pass through.

Figure 3-13. The operating principle of the rotor-type oil pump.

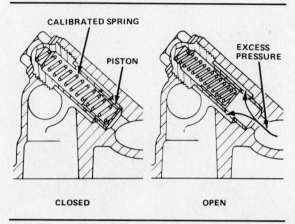

Figure 3-14. The oil pressure relief valve.

The rotor type pump works on the same principle of carrying oil from a large area into a smaller area to create pressure. An inner rotor is mounted off-center within an outer rotor, figure 3-12. The inner rotor is driven through gears by the camshaft. The outer rotor is driven by the inner rotor. As the rotors turn, they carry oil from the areas of large clearance to the areas of small clearance, figure 3-13, forcing the oil to flow from the pump under pressure.

The oil entering the pump comes from the oil pan. An oil pickup tube extends from the pump to the bottom of the pan. A screen at the bottom end of the pickup tube keeps sludge and large particles from entering the oil pump and damaging it, or clogging the oil lines and galleries.

Pressure Relief Valve

The oil leaving the pump passes through a pressure relief valve, or pressure regulating valve. The valve limits the maximum engine oil pressure. It consists of a spring-loaded ball or piston set into an opening in the valve body, figure 3-14. Oil pressure forces the ball or piston to move against spring tension and open the hole in the valve body. Some oil can escape through this hole to decrease the overall system pressure.

The pressure relief valve is usually built into the oil pump housing. The oil that escapes through the relief hole is sent back to the inlet side of the pump. This arrangement of oil flow from the relief valve reduces oil foaming and agitation so that the pump puts out a steady stream of oil.

Filter

Oil leaving the pressure relief valve flows through the oil filter before reaching the rest of the system. The filter is made of paper or cloth fibers that will pass liquid oil but trap dirt. If the filter becomes plugged with dirt, oil flow is restricted.

To prevent a clogged filter from completely stopping oil flow and damaging the engine, a bypass valve is built into the filter or the filter housing. It allows oil to flow around the filter instead of through it when the oil is too thick to go through the filter because of its low temperature, or when the filter outlet pressure drops. Oil filters must be replaced at specific intervals to prevent clogging. Older cars have replaceable oil filter elements inside permanent housings. Most modern engines use spin-on filters that are completely disposable, figure 3-15.

Galleries and Lines

A modern engine has many areas that must have a constant supply of oil under pressure. To ensure that they do, the lubrication system includes a network of passages that direct oil to

■ Splash Oiling

Some older car engines and small gasoline engines do not have an oil pump or a pressurized oiling system. Instead, they depend on the motion of engine parts to splash oil from the oil pan into the engine.

Scoops on the connecting rod big ends scoop up the oil and direct it toward critical spots. Some engines may rely on splash oiling for the lower half of the engine and use an oil pump to supply oil to the upper half of the engine.

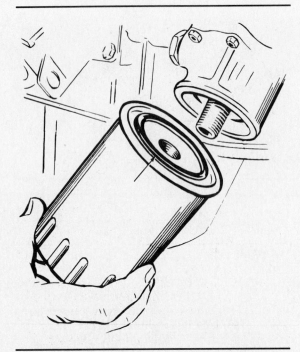

Figure 3-15. A spin-on, completely disposable oil filter.

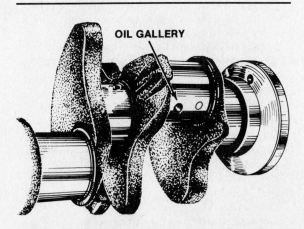

Figure 3-16. Oil galleries are drilled in the crankshaft.

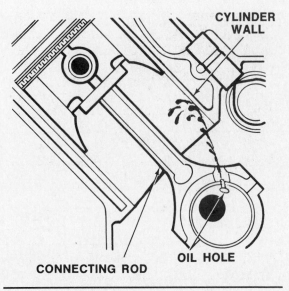

Figure 3-17. Some oil spurts through the connecting rod cap onto the cylinder walls.

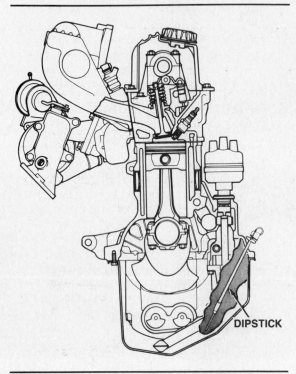

Figure 3-18. The engine dipstick.

these parts of the engine, figure 3-6. These passages, called oil galleries, can be drilled through the block, the head, and the crankshaft. They can also be separate tubes, called oil lines, connected to the engine. Not all engines have separate oil lines, but all do have oil galleries.

From the filter, oil flows to a large main gallery. Inline engines and some V-type engines have one main gallery. Other V-type engines have two main galleries, one for each bank of cylinders. From the main gallery, smaller passages direct oil to the camshaft bearings and to the crankshaft main bearings.

Oil must also reach the crankshaft connecting rod bearings. This is done by drilling holes through the crankshaft, figure 3-16, so that oil at the main bearings can also flow to the rod bearings. The caps that are bolted around the rod bearings have small holes that can line up with similar holes in the crankshaft and the rod

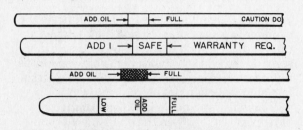

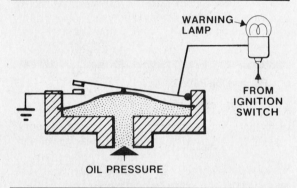

Figure 3-19. Typical dipstick markings.

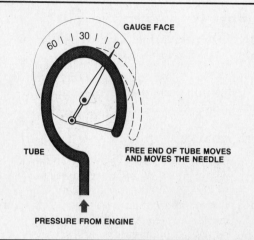

Figure 3-21. A typical mechanical oil pressure gauge.

WARNING LAMP

FROM IGNITION SWITCH

OIL PRESSURE

Figure 3-20. A diagram of a low oil pressure warning lamp.

bearings. When the holes in the cap and bearing align with the hole in the crankshaft, figure 3-17, a small stream of oil squirts through and hits the lower cylinder wall. This helps lubricate the cylinder wall and piston.

Different engine designs have different ways of getting oil from the main gallery to the head and valve assemblies. There can be galleries drilled through the block and the head, or the oil can travel through hollow valve pushrods. Also, an enlarged head-bolt hole can allow oil flow. From the valve assembly, the oil drains down through the engine into the oil pan. The oil drain holes can be placed so that the dripping oil helps lubricate the camshaft.

Indicators

To check the oil level when the engine is at rest, a dipstick is installed in the oil pan. To keep the driver informed of engine oil pressure while the engine is running, carmakers equip cars with a low oil pressure warning lamp or a gauge that indicates the pressure at all times.

Dipstick

When the engine is at rest, almost all of the oil drains into the oil pan. All engines have a measuring rod, called a dipstick, that extends from the outside of the engine into the pan, figure

3-18. The dipstick has markings on it that indicate the maximum and minimum oil levels for that engine. When you pull the dipstick out of the pan, a film of oil can be seen on the stick. The level of the film relative to the markings on the stick indicates how much oil is in the pan, figure 3-19.

Oil pressure warning lamp

The oil pressure warning lamp lights when the oil pressure is less than a set amount. This happens during cranking and when there is a problem in the lubricating system.

Warning lamps light when a set of electrical contacts close, figure 3-20. The contacts are controlled by a movable diaphragm that is exposed to engine oil pressure. The contacts close when oil pressure is low, and the lamp lights. When pressure increases, the diaphragm moves and the contacts open, turning off the lamp.

The contacts and diaphragm are contained within a sending unit. The sending unit is threaded into the engine block or into the oil filter housing.

Oil pressure gauge

Oil pressure gauges are operated electrically or mechanically. An electric gauge has a sending unit similar to the warning lamp sending unit. A movable diaphragm varies the current flow through the gauge in proportion to oil pressure. The current flow determines the position of the gauge needle.

Mechanical gauges, figure 3-21, have a tube running from the engine to the gauge. When there is engine oil pressure, oil is forced into the tube and to the gauge. The pressure at the gauge end of the tube is the same as the engine oil pressure, and determines the position of the gauge needle.

LUBRICATION EFFECTS ON PERFORMANCE, ECONOMY, AND EMISSION CONTROL

The lubrication system can have direct, measurable effects on performance, economy, and exhaust emissions.

Performance

An engine's performance is related to its mechanical condition. When an engine is new, the moving parts fit together very closely. The distance between two moving parts is called clearance. As the engine wears, the clearance increases. When an engine wears, or gets ''loose'', it does not operate as efficiently as it once did, and performance suffers.

The lubrication system helps keep engine wear to a minimum. Using the proper API rated oil will reduce engine wear because the oil is formulated to match the engine's requirements. Changing the oil and filter at or before recommended intervals will minimize engine wear by replacing used additives and by keeping harmful particles out of circulation.

The SAE oil viscosity rating will affect engine wear and performance as well. If oil with too low a viscosity is used during high-speed or high-temperature operation, the oil film between moving parts may become so thin that it breaks down, allowing metal-to-metal contact and rapid wear. If oil with too high a viscosity is used during low-temperature operation, power will be wasted in forcing engine parts to overcome the resistance of the thick oil. In some cases, a combination of cold temperature and high-viscosity oil will prevent the starting system from cranking the engine at all.

Economy

Economy is also affected by engine mechanical condition. Camshaft and valve assembly wear, for instance, will change valve timing. Other factors such as the amount of power wasted as blowby will also affect economy.

Some manufacturers of synthetic oils claim that the increased slipperiness of their oil will decrease engine friction and increase fuel economy. Although these claims have been substantiated in some cases, the savings in fuel economy must be weighed against the higher price of the oil.

Emission Control

A small amount of oil is normally present in the combustion chamber when the air-fuel mixture is ignited. The oil must be there to lubricate the cylinder walls and to help seal the chamber. Because oil does not burn as easily as gasoline, some of the oil leaves with the exhaust gases as unburned hydrocarbons (HC), one of the gasoline engine's main pollutants.

When the engine oil is old and diluted by blowby gases, or when the engine is worn and clearances have increased, more oil than normal will enter the combustion chamber. The oil can come down through the valve assembly or get past the piston rings. Once the oil is in the chamber it is a source of HC emissions.

■ Bypass Oil Filters

Before the full-flow oil filtering system was invented, engines that used oil filters had what is called a bypass system. The filter was mounted on a bracket attached to the engine or anywhere in the engine compartment. Oil lines were connected to a tapped hole in the side of the engine block, and to a drain on the pan or block. The oil was fed under pressure to the filter, and allowed to drain back into the oil pan after filtration.

Since the oil did not have to go through the engine filter before getting to the bearings, a piece of dirt could, theoretically, circulate through the oil system indefinitely until it happened to get into the filter and be trapped. This catch-as-catch-can system was discontinued in favor of the full-flow system.

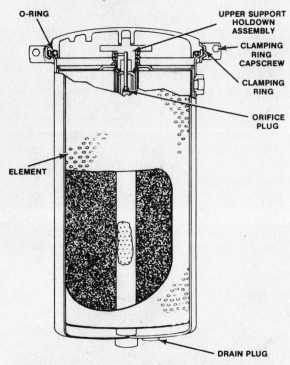

SUMMARY

Motor oil has five major jobs in an engine: reducing friction, cooling, cleaning, sealing, and absorbing shock. Additives mixed with the oil help it to do these jobs. Two oil rating systems are generally used: the API service classification and the SAE viscosity rating. The API number rates an oil's performance in a laboratory engine, and the SAE viscosity number rates the oil's thickness. An oil may have one or more API ratings. An oil's service classification and viscosity rating must be matched to an engine's requirements for best performance, economy, and emission control.

An engine lubrication system includes the pan, filter, pump, oil galleries or oil lines (or both), dipstick, and pressure warning lamp or pressure gauge. The oil is stored in the oil pan. The pump takes it from the pan, pressurizes it, and sends it through the oil galleries or oil lines to lubricate the moving parts of the engine. The filter traps dirt and other particles that the oil holds in suspension, so the oil and filter must be changed periodically. A dipstick is used to measure the oil level in the pan when the engine is not running, and a pressure warning lamp (for low oil pressure) or a pressure gauge (for continuous pressure reading) is used when the engine is running.

The main purpose of engine lubrication is control of mechanical wear. Excessive wear will hurt performance, economy, and emission control. The use of the proper oil, and regular oil and filter changes, will keep engine wear to a minimum.

Review Questions
Choose the single most correct answer.
Compare your answers with the correct answers on page 451.

1. Which of the following is *not* a primary job done by motor oil:
   a. Cooling the engine
   b. Reducing friction
   c. Reducing exhaust emissions
   d. Cleaning the engine

2. Additives in motor oil can:
   a. Replace qualities lost during refinement
   b. Strengthen natural qualities
   c. Add qualities not naturally present
   d. All of the above

3. Blowby gases come from the:
   a. Crankcase
   b. Combustion chamber
   c. Oil filter
   d. Carburetor

4. The oil used in a 1989 passenger-car gasoline engine should have an API service classification of:
   a. SD
   b. CD
   c. CC
   d. SG

5. The "W" in an SAE viscosity grade indicates that the oil:
   a. Has been tested at 0°F
   b. Is for winter use
   c. Has no additives
   d. None of the above

6. Typically, the highest viscosity number given to motor oils is:
   a. SAE 40
   b. SAE 50
   c. SAE 100
   d. SAE 70

7. The term "multigrade" means that an oil:
   a. Has been given two API service classifications
   b. Has many additives
   c. Has been tested for viscosity when hot and cold
   d. Can be used in gasoline or diesel engines

8. Most synthetic motor oils:
   a. May deteriorate at a slower rate than conventional petroleum oils
   b. Cost less than conventional oils
   c. Contain more wax than conventional petroleum oils
   d. Require more frequent drain intervals

9. If the crankcase is not ventilated:
   a. Exhaust emissions will increase
   b. The oil will foam and not protect the engine
   c. Too much oil will enter the combustion chambers
   d. Blowby gases will pressurize it and force oil out

10. The oil pump is usually driven by the:
    a. Distributor
    b. Camshaft
    c. Fuel pump
    d. Timing gears

11. The oil pressure relief valve:
    a. Is usually mounted in the oil pump housing
    b. Limits the maximum pressure in the oiling system
    c. Contains a spring-loaded ball or piston
    d. All of the above

12. When an oil filter becomes clogged:
    a. A bypass valve allows dirty oil to lubricate the engine
    b. The oil pump must slow down
    c. Engine operating temperature increases
    d. All of the above

13. To direct oil to critical points, the oiling system includes:
    a. Internal galleries
    b. Connecting rod squirt holes
    c. Holes drilled in the crankshaft
    d. All of the above

14. Most dipsticks will show you:
    a. What grade of oil to use
    b. If the oil is oxidized
    c. The maximum and minimum oil levels
    d. None of the above

15. Oil pressure warning lamps have a _____ installed in the engine:
    a. Sending unit
    b. Lamp bulb
    c. Oil tube
    d. Pressure gauge

16. Lubrication's greatest effect on performance, economy, and emission control is:
    a. Making the engine run cooler
    b. Keeping the compression ratio steady
    c. Controlling engine mechanical wear
    d. Increasing engine horsepower

4

Cooling and Exhaust Systems

When the air-fuel mixture in a combustion chamber burns, the cylinder temperature can soar to 6,000°F (3,316°C). During the complete 4-stroke cycle, the average temperature is about 1,500°F (816°C). About one-third of this heat energy is turned into mechanical energy by the engine. The remaining two-thirds must be removed from the engine so that the engine can operate efficiently. If the heat energy remains, several things will happen:
• The engine oil temperature will increase, affecting engine lubrication.
• The incoming air-fuel mixture will become too hot, making it expand and reduce engine efficiency.
• Metal engine parts will expand, eventually causing the engine to seize.

Where does the extra heat energy from combustion go? About half of it is absorbed by the metal in the engine, which is then cooled by the cooling system. The other half remains in the combustion gases, and exit through the exhaust system. This chapter describes these two systems, and their relationship to performance, economy, and emission control.

COOLING SYSTEM FUNCTION

We have said that about one-third of the total heat energy from combustion is absorbed by the engine's metal. This is both good and bad:
• It is good because an engine that is too cool will have poor fuel vaporization, poor lubrication, excessive acids in the blowby gases, and high HC emissions.
• It is bad because an engine that is too hot will have weakened metal, poor volumetric efficiency, poor lubrication, high oxides of nitrogen (NO_x) emissions, and in extreme cases may exhibit harmful detonation or pre-ignition.

Obviously, there must be a "just-right" engine operating temperature that will minimize these problems. This temperature is slightly different from engine to engine, depending on the design. Early engines ran at about 180°F (82°C). Late-model engines run as high as 230°F (110°C). These temperatures will vary depending on driving conditions.

Cooling System Operation

Most automotive engines use a liquid cooling system, figure 4-1. Liquid coolant constantly circulates through the engine, absorbing heat from the engine block and cylinder head. The coolant is then circulated outside of the engine and exposed indirectly to the air. The air absorbs heat from the coolant, so that the coolant can go back into the engine and absorb more

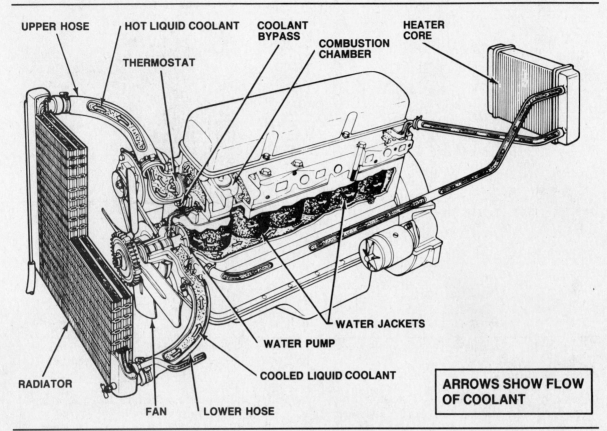

UPPER HOSE   HOT LIQUID COOLANT   COOLANT BYPASS   HEATER CORE

THERMOSTAT   COMBUSTION CHAMBER

WATER JACKETS

WATER PUMP

COOLED LIQUID COOLANT

RADIATOR

FAN   LOWER HOSE

ARROWS SHOW FLOW OF COOLANT

Figure 4-1. A typical liquid cooling system.

heat. The greater the difference in temperature between the coolant and the air, the more heat will be absorbed by the air.

Circulation Patterns

Within the engine, coolant circulates in passages called **water jackets**, figure 4-1. Outside the engine, the coolant circulates through hoses and the radiator. To keep the engine running at its ideal temperature, there are two patterns of coolant circulation. The two patterns are controlled by the thermostat, which is a temperature-sensitive valve that opens and closes a passage between the engine and the radiator.

Circulation when cold
When the engine is cold, it must be warmed quickly to its ideal temperature. With the cooling system in full operation, it would take a long time for this to happen. To speed the warm-up, the thermostat is closed when the coolant is cold, figure 4-2. This keeps the coolant in the engine from circulating through the radiator. The coolant, does however, circulate inside the engine, so the coolant warms uniformly. Because there is no heat transfer between the

Water Jackets: Passages in the head and block that allow coolant to circulate throughout the engine.

■ **Adding Temporary Antifreeze**

Permanent antifreeze was introduced in the United States by Union Carbide in 1927. Before that, car owners used alcohol, molasses, kerosene, salt, sugar, or even honey to keep their cars running in the winter. There was no problem with freezing as long as the engine was running. But if a car was parked outside, the water might freeze and crack the engine cylinder block.

The most popular antifreeze was alcohol. At the first sign of winter, it was time to drain the water and add alcohol to prevent freezing. But alcohol evaporates quickly. In cold climates, car owners made weekly or even daily hydrometer checks to be sure they still had enough alcohol in the water.

After 1927, alcohol was still sold because it was less expensive than "permanent" antifreeze. Today, alcohol, or "temporary" antifreeze, has completely disappeared from the marketplace.

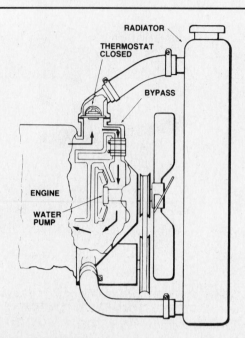

Figure 4-2. The thermostat prevents cold coolant from entering the radiator.

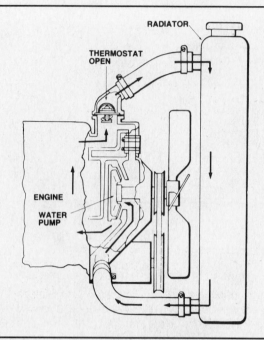

Figure 4-3. As the coolant warms, the thermostat opens and allows it to flow through the radiator.

coolant in the engine and the air passing the radiator, the heat of combustion quickly warms the engine.

Circulation when warm

As the coolant within the engine gets warm, the thermostat opens, figure 4-3. This allows full coolant circulation between the engine and the radiator. The operating temperature of the engine is determined by the thermostat, which opens between 180° and 210°F (82° and 99°C) — depending on its design. The amount of coolant in the system and the size of the radiator determine the cooling capacity of the system.

System Pressure

There are two reasons for pressurizing a cooling system: to increase water pump efficiency, and to raise the boiling point of the coolant.

Pump efficiency is affected by pressure. Without a pressure cap installed in the system, a water pump is only about 85 percent efficient. With a 14-psi (97-kPa) pressure cap, the pump becomes almost 100 percent efficient.

Coolant boiling-point control is equally important. Water boils at 212°F (100°C) under atmospheric pressure (14.7 psi or 100 kPa) at sea level. An average solution of engine coolant boils at around 223°F (106°C) under the same conditions. Even this higher figure may be dangerously close to, or even below the operating

temperature of late-model engines. Pressurizing the system raises the boiling point of the coolant. Each 1-psi (7-kPa) increase in pressure raises the boiling point about 3°F (1.7°C). Thus, coolant under 15-psi (103-kPa) pressure boils at approximately 268°F (131°C), 45° Fahrenheit degrees (or 24 Celsius degrees) higher than without the cap. Most cooling systems are pressurized at 12 to 17 psi (83 to 117 kPa). Remember that when removing the radiator pressure cap on a hot engine, as the pressure is released, the coolant will boil instantly.

ENGINE COOLANT

Although pure water transfers heat very well, it has disadvantages when used in a cooling system:
• Metal exposed to water will oxidize and corrode, and rust particles will clog water jackets.
• When the car is not running and the system is not pressurized, water will freeze at 32°F (0°C), damaging the engine block, cylinder head, or other parts.

Early cooling systems used water blended with a rust inhibitor and alcohol to lower the freezing point. Alcohol, however, boils at a lower temperature than water and escapes from the system more easily than water.

Modern cooling systems use a mixture of water and antifreeze, an ethylene-glycol based solution. Glycol does not transfer heat as well as water, but its freezing point is much lower

Ethylene Glycol Proportions By volume	Freezing Point °F	Boiling point With 15-pound Operation Pressure in Cooling system
33 percent	0 degrees	259 degrees
40 percent	—12 degrees	261 degrees
50 percent	—34 degrees	264 degrees
60 percent	—62 degrees	269 degrees
70 percent	—85 degrees	275 degrees

Figure 4-4. If you need a different freezing or boiling point, see the table.

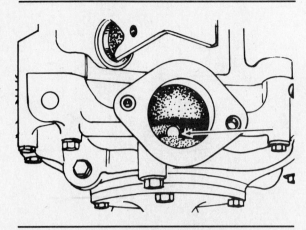

Figure 4-5. This internal passage in the thermostat housing directs cold coolant to the water pump.

and its boiling point is much higher, figure 4-4. Many modern cooling systems need the antifreeze in the coolant to activate the temperature warning lamp, which comes on at temperatures above the boiling point of water. Without antifreeze in the system, the water can boil away and cause severe damage to the engine block; yet the warning lamp will not light.

Antifreeze usually contains corrosion preventives, rust preventives, and water pump lubricants. It may also contain small particles designed to seal minor leaks in the cooling system. A coolant mixture that contains from 35- to 50-percent ethylene-glycol antifreeze will protect the engine and cooling system while improving the system's high- and low-temperature operation.

A 50-percent mixture of ethylene-glycol and water will protect against freezing to approximately –30°F (–34°C). If the car is going to be operated in colder climates, additional antifreeze should be added. A solution of 68-percent antifreeze will give protection down to –90°F (–62°C). If the percentage of ethylene-glycol is any higher than that, the freezing point will actually go back up. One hundred-percent antifreeze will freeze at slightly below zero. For this reason, never put more than 68-percent antifreeze in the system.

Although 50-percent antifreeze is the industry standard, some manufacturers recommend only a 33-percent solution or less. A less than 50-percent solution will protect from freezing but does not give the corrosion protection that a 50-percent solution does. For this reason, the industry recommends filling all coolant systems with about 50-percent ethylene-glycol.

Antifreeze also protects against boiling. A cooling system filled with only water may boil when the engine is turned off. This will open the pressure cap and force water out of the radiator.

This is avoided by using a 50-percent antifreeze mixture. Water boils at about 248°F (120°C) under 14-psi pressure. The 50-percent

solution boils at about 263°F (128°C). The 15 degrees of added protection will prevent boiling after shutdown in normal operation.

COOLING SYSTEM COMPONENTS

A typical liquid cooling system, figure 4-1, includes the:
- Water jackets
- Thermostat-controlled bypass
- Core, or freeze, plugs
- Radiator
- Water pump
- Radiator fan
- Thermostat
- Radiator pressure cap
- Coolant hoses
- Drive belt
- Coolant recovery system.

The following paragraphs describe these parts.

Water Jackets, Bypass, and Core Plugs

Water jackets and coolant passages are cast into the cylinder block and head. They are designed

■ **If a Little Is Good, a Lot Can Be Worse**

It doesn't happen too often, but it is possible. Too much antifreeze in an engine's cooling system will *raise* the freezing point. The "right" amount of antifreeze varies from one part of the country to another and from one vehicle to another. However, in almost all cases, maximum freeze protection is provided by a coolant solution with about 68-percent antifreeze by volume. When the antifreeze concentration goes above this level, the coolant may freeze or become slushy at higher temperatures, and coolant heat transfer will be reduced.

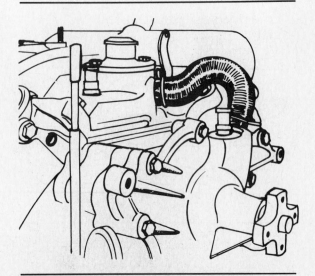

Figure 4-6. This external bypass hose connects the thermostat housing to the water pump.

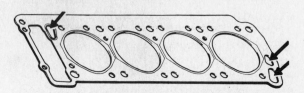

Figure 4-7. These holes in the head gasket carry coolant the full length of the cylinder head.

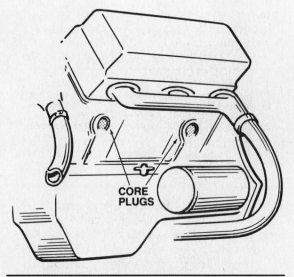

Figure 4-8. Core plugs are pressed into the cylinder block.

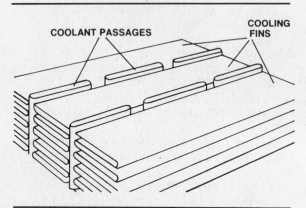

Figure 4-9. The tubes and cooling fins of the radiator core. (Chrysler)

so that the coolant will circulate freely and not remain stationary in pockets.

The thermostat-controlled bypass is a passage that can direct coolant back into the engine before it has circulated through the radiator. The bypass can be an internal passage in the block, figure 4-5, or an external hose or tube, figure 4-6.

Head gaskets also aid in water distribution. The front holes in the gasket are frequently smaller than the rear holes. This forces the coolant to flow to the rear of the block, figure 4-7. Because more coolant goes to the back of the block, it means more coolant will flow the full length of the cylinder head. This is necessary for better circulation because the coolant outlet is at or near the front of the cylinder head.

Core plugs are pressed or clamped into the sides of the cylinder block to close the holes left by the foundry where the block and heads are cast, figure 4-8. They are called core plugs because the holes are used by the foundry to remove core sand from the inside of the block. Core plugs are also called freeze plugs. Some people mistakenly believe that the plugs are there to relieve pressure in the block if the water in the engine freezes. Core plugs will frequently pop out if the water freezes, but that is not their purpose. If one does pop out, the chances are that the same freeze also cracked the block. Core plugs are definitely not insurance against freeze damage.

Radiators

The purpose of the radiator is to expose a large amount of surface area to the surrounding air. Radiators are made of thin metal tubes, usually brass or aluminum, with cooling fins attached, figure 4-9. Coolant flows through the tubes and transfers its heat to the radiator metal. The air

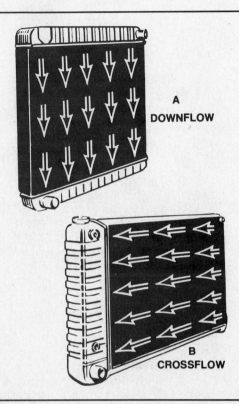

Figure 4-10. A radiator may be either a downflow type or a crossflow type.

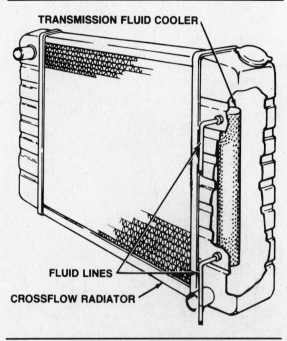

Figure 4-11. The transmission fluid cooler is installed in one of the radiator tanks. (Harrison)

flowing past the radiator tubes and fins absorbs this heat. The number of tubes and fins in a radiator determines the unit's heat-transferring capacity.

The assembly of tubes and fins is called the radiator core. To keep a steady stream of coolant flowing into and out of the core, two larger metal tanks are connected to opposite ends of the tubes. There are two types of radiator construction for cars and light trucks:
- Downflow radiators have vertical tubes and a tank at the top and bottom of the core, figure 4-10, position A.
- Crossflow radiators have horizontal tubes and a tank on both sides of the core, figure 4-10, position B.

Crossflow radiators usually allow a lower hood line on the car. Other than the flow direction, there is no difference in operation between the two types.

One of the radiator tanks, either the top tank or a side tank, has an open neck sealed with a pressure cap. On cars with automatic transmissions, one of the tanks contains a cooler for the transmission fluid, figure 4-11. The fluid and the coolant do not mix, but the extra heat of the transmission fluid adds to the work of the cooling system. For this reason systems on automatic-transmission cars are usually built with a greater capacity than those on manual-transmission cars.

Water Pumps

The water pump uses **centrifugal force** to circulate the coolant. It consists of a fan-shaped impeller, figures 4-12 and 4-13, set in a round chamber with curved inlet and outlet passages. The chamber is called a scroll because of these curved areas. The impeller is driven by a belt from the crankshaft pulley, and spins within the scroll. Coolant from the radiator or the bypass enters the inlet and is picked up by the impeller blades. Centrifugal force flings the coolant outward, and the scroll walls direct it to the outlet passage and the engine. Because the water pump is driven by the engine, it keeps coolant circulating whenever the engine is running. Centrifugal pumps must turn fast to be efficient. Worn or loose belts slip, causing the pump to turn slower and lose efficiency, and

Centrifugal Force: A force applied to a rotating object, tending to move the object toward the outer edge of the circle in rotation.

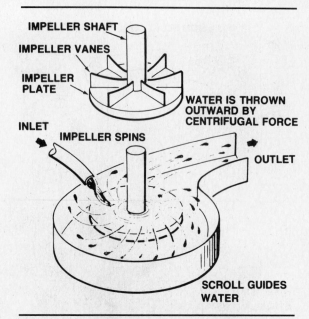

Figure 4-12. The water pump impeller is driven by the engine. Its spinning blades apply centrifugal force to the engine coolant.

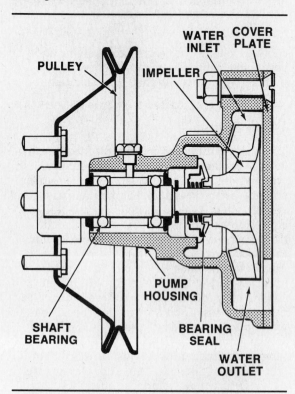

Figure 4-13. Cutaway of a typical water pump.

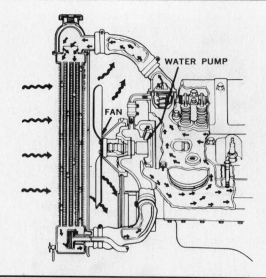

Figure 4-14. The engine-driven fan blows air into the engine compartment through the radiator core. (Harrison)

possibly result in engine overheating. Early water pumps had to be externally lubricated, but modern coolant mixtures contain a water pump lubricant. The pump bearings must be well sealed to prevent lubricant or coolant leaks.

Radiator Fan

When the car is traveling above 25 mph (40 kph), airflow through the radiator core is great enough to absorb all excess heat. However, at low speed or idle there is not enough natural airflow. To increase the amount of air passing through the radiator, a fan is mounted in the engine compartment, figure 4-14. The fan is often mounted on the same shaft as the water pump impeller. The fan blades pull extra air through the radiator. Many late-model cars have shrouds around the fan to increase the fan's cooling efficiency by channeling all airflow through the radiator.

If engine power drives the fan, this power is wasted at high speeds when natural airflow will do the job. There are three ways to avoid this waste:
- Flexible fan blades
- Clutch fans
- Electric fans.

Flexible fan blades change their angle, or pitch, with changing engine speeds. At low speed, the blades are sharply angled, figure 4-15, position A. This uses a lot of engine power. At high speeds, position B, centrifugal

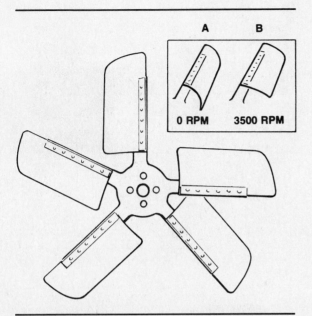

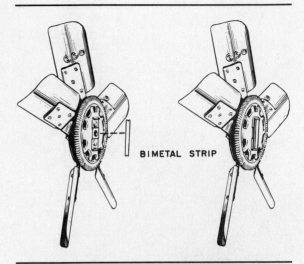

Figure 4-17. The bimetal temperature sensor spring controls the amount of silicone that is allowed into the drive and that, in turn, controls the speed of the fan.

Figure 4-15. The flexible blades of this fan change shape as engine speed changes.

the fan turns at less than drive pulley speed. When the drive is slipping, less engine power is used to drive the fan.

The amount of silicone fluid present is controlled by a **bimetal temperature sensor** spring exposed to the airflow from the radiator, figure 4-17. When the airflow is cool, the spring lets

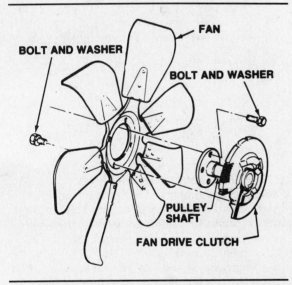

Figure 4-16. This fan has a fluid clutch controlling the speed of rotation. (Ford)

Bimetal Temperature Sensor: A sensor or switch that reacts to changes in temperature. It is made of two strips of metal welded together that expand differently when heated or cooled causing the strip to bend.

■ **The Engine Without a Water Pump**

All modern liquid-cooled engines have a pump to circulate the coolant. But there was a time when the water pump was something that only the more expensive cars had. In the early days of the automotive industry, many automotive engines had cooling systems operated by the thermo-syphon principle. This means, simply, that hot water rises and cold water sinks. As the water in the block was heated, it rose out to the top of the radiator. Once in the radiator, it started to cool, and slowly sank. This heating and cooling created enough circulation to keep the engine from overheating, as long as the weather was cool. In hot weather, or when pulling hard up a hill, the engines would sometimes overheat. Because overheating was common, motorists accepted it as just one more hazard of motoring, like flat tires or getting stuck in the mud.

force flattens the fan blades. They pull less air and require less power. This also reduces fan noise at high speeds.

Clutch fans are heavier than conventional fans, but the power saved makes them worthwhile. The drive, figure 4-16, is a clutch assembly that depends on a silicone fluid to transmit motion from the drive belt pulley to the fan itself. These are also called fluid drive fans. When there is a lot of fluid present, the drive pulley and fan rotate at the same speed. When there is little fluid present, the drive slips and

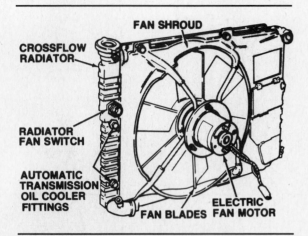

Figure 4-18. In this car, an electric motor drives the radiator fan. (Chrysler)

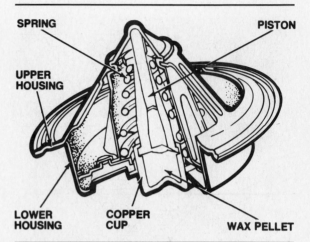

Figure 4-20. A cross section of a wax-actuated thermostat. (Stant)

Figure 4-19. Always disconnect the fan power lead before working near an electric fan.

Figure 4-21. These bellows-actuated thermostats are not used in late-model cars because the bellows operation is affected by coolant pressure.

very little silicone into the drive, and the fan turns slowly or idles. When the airflow is hot, the spring allows a lot of silicone into the drive, and the fan turns faster.

Electric fans are not driven by the engine but by an electric motor, figure 4-18. The motor is switched on and off by a temperature-sensitive switch that senses engine coolant temperature. Many late-model automobiles and light trucks use electric fans; in fact, all late-model cars with transversely-mounted engines have electric fans. When you work on a car with an electric fan, disconnect the battery ground cable or the fan power lead before getting near the fan, figure 4-19. The fan can switch on whether or not the engine is running on many cars.

Thermostats

The thermostat regulates coolant flow between the engine and the radiator. When the coolant

is cold, the thermostat is completely closed. As the coolant warms, the thermostat begins to open. The thermostat's position varies during normal operation, but it is rarely opened completely, unless the engine is working very hard or the weather is hot.

All late-model thermostats are wax-actuated, figure 4-20. A chamber in the thermostat is filled with wax that is solid when cold, but melts and expands when heated. When the wax is cold, a spring holds the thermostat closed. As the coolant temperature increases, the wax expands and forces the thermostat to open against the spring tension. This type of thermostat will work reliably under normal system pressure. Earlier types that used an **aneroid bellows**, figure 4-21, could be affected by coolant pressure and did not work reliably.

The thermostat's opening temperature is stamped on the outside. Replacement thermostats must have the correct opening temperature for the system to work properly. The

Figure 4-22. A typical thermostat location.

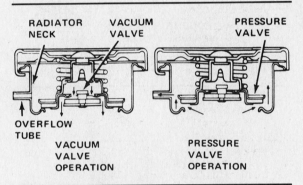

Figure 4-23. A cross-section of a typical radiator pressure cap. (AMC)

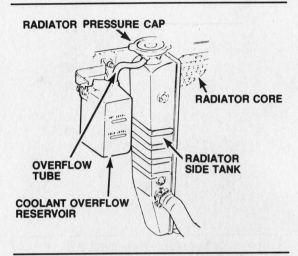

Figure 4-24. Most radiator caps are mounted on one of the radiator tanks. (Ford)

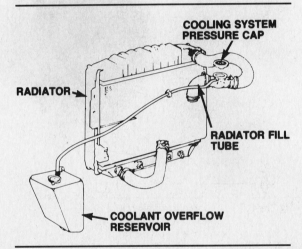

Figure 4-25. Some radiator caps are mounted away from the radiator to shorten the radiator profile. (Ford)

thermostat is mounted in a metal housing at the top front of the engine, figure 4-22.

Radiator Pressure Cap

To improve the performance of the coolant, the cooling system is sealed and pressurized. Part of the pressure comes from the water pump. The rest of the pressure comes from expansion of the coolant as it warms.

The radiator cap must keep the system pressurized, vent any excess pressure, and allow atmospheric pressure to re-enter the system as the coolant cools and contracts after the engine is shut off.

To do this, radiator caps have two valves, figure 4-23. A pressure valve relieves the excess pressure inside the system during engine operation. A vacuum valve allows outside air to enter the system when the engine is off. These pressure caps usually are on the top or side

tank, figure 4-24, but occasionally can be found in unusual locations such as on a special hose section, figure 4-25.

Radiator Hoses and Drive Belts

Radiator hoses connect the cooling system passages to the radiator tanks. The hoses are flexible and will absorb the motion between the vibrating engine and the stationary radiator. The hoses are made of synthetic rubber, and

Aneroid Bellows: An accordion-shaped bellows that responds to changes in coolant pressure or atmospheric pressure by expanding or contracting.

Figure 4-26. Various types of hose clamps.

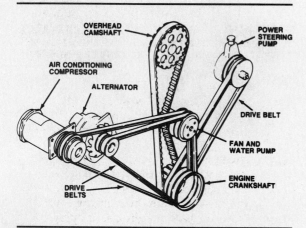

Figure 4-27. The fan and water pump drive belt also drives the alternator in many cases. (Harrison)

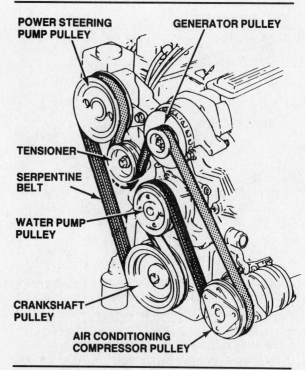

Figure 4-28. A serpentine accessory drive belt.

Figure 4-29. When adding coolant to the recovery system reservoir, be sure to take note of the "hot" and "cold" fill marks and fill accordingly.

are often reinforced with a wire coil. The hoses can be molded in a specific shape or they can be ribbed, flexible lengths that adapt to different installations.

The hose ends fit over necks on the engine and radiator and are held in place with hose clamps, figure 4-26. Hose clamps can be held in place by spring tension or by a screw.

For many years, the drive belt that operated the radiator fan and water pump was a reinforced rubber V-belt, figure 4-27. It fit tightly over the crankshaft pulley, the fan pulley, and the alternator pulley. Belt tension was usually adjusted by moving the alternator in its mounting. Today, most new domestic and many new imported automobiles use a single serpentine belt to drive all accessories, figure 4-28. The belt is made of reinforced rubber, and has several, small V-shaped grooves that run the length of the belt. These grooves fit corresponding grooves in the accessory drive pulleys. Belt tension is maintained at all times by an automatic

tensioner assembly. These belts are designed to last 100,000 miles (160,000 km) or more.

Coolant Recovery System

Most late-model cars have a closed cooling system. Instead of a pressure cap that vents to the atmosphere, the pressure cap is connected to a coolant tank or overflow reservoir, figure 4-29. When system temperature increases and the coolant expands, the extra coolant flows out of

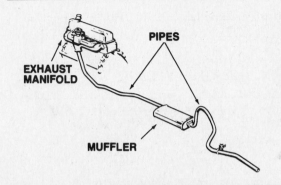

Figure 4-30. The exhaust system used with an inline engine.

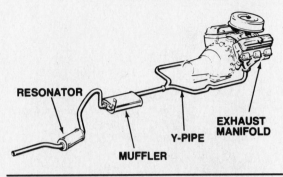

Figure 4-31. This V-type engine uses a Y-pipe to connect the two cylinder banks to a single exhaust pipe.

the radiator neck, through an overflow hose, and into a coolant overflow tank. When the system cools and a vacuum develops in the system, coolant is drawn back into the radiator through the same hose. On earlier systems, expanding coolant went out the overflow hose and onto the ground. This coolant loss made frequent coolant top-ups necessary, and the presence of air in the cooling system increased rust and corrosion.

A coolant recovery system is even more necessary in late-model cars, which tend to run hotter because of emission control equipment, automatic transmissions, air conditioning, and other power-consuming accessories. The coolant tank ensures that there will always be enough coolant to fill the system because none is lost if the radiator overflows. Coolant recovery systems are said to increase cooling system efficiency about 10 percent.

When more coolant must be added to a recovery system, it is added to the overflow tank, not directly to the radiator. The tank is marked with "hot" and "cold" fill levels, figure 4-29.

ENGINE TEMPERATURE EFFECTS ON PERFORMANCE, ECONOMY, AND EMISSIONS

When the engine is too cold, performance suffers because of poor fuel vaporization. The liquid fuel entering the cylinders also tends to wash oil off the cylinder walls, reducing lubrication. The liquid fuel runs past the piston rings and into the crankcase, where it dilutes the oil and further hinders lubrication.

A cold engine affects economy in several ways. Because the air-fuel mixture is not vaporizing and burning completely, less energy is extracted from the fuel. Cold oil mixes with moisture to form sludge, which increases engine friction, robs it of power, and increases mechanical wear.

Many emission control systems use coolant temperature to activate switches and vacuum valves. If the coolant does not reach the proper temperature, the emission control systems do not work properly. The unburned fuel in the combustion chambers also increases exhaust HC emissions.

An engine that is too hot will have lower volumetric efficiency and decreased performance. Hot oil will form carbon and varnish deposits that affect engine operation.

Excessive heat also thins the engine oil to the point that it no longer lubricates well, and increases mechanical wear results. The thin oil will also be drawn into the combustion chamber in greater amounts, fouling spark plugs and increasing both HC and CO emissions.

EXHAUST SYSTEM TYPES

The exhaust system routes engine exhaust gases to the rear of the car, quiets the exhaust noise, and, in most cases, reduces the pollutants in the exhaust. The system design varies according to engine design. The three major types are:
- Inline
- Single V-type
- Dual V-type.
These designs are described in the following paragraphs.

Inline

When an engine's cylinders are arranged in line, figure 4-30, all of the exhaust valves are on the same side of the engine. An exhaust system pipe connects to this side of the engine at the exhaust manifold. The single pipe connects to one or more units that may include a muffler, a resonator, and a catalytic converter.

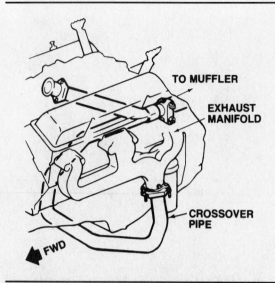

Figure 4-32. This V-type engine has a crossover pipe connecting the two banks to a single exhaust.

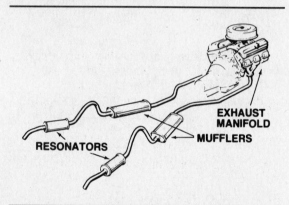

Figure 4-33. This V-type engine has two separate exhaust systems.

Single V-Type

A V-type engine has exhaust valves on both cylinder banks. There are two ways in which these valves can be connected to a single exhaust pipe:
● There can be a Y-pipe behind the engine, figure 4-31.
● There can be a crossover pipe beneath the engine, figure 4-32.

Dual V-Type

Some V-type engines have two separate exhaust systems, one for each cylinder bank, figure 4-33. The systems are similar to the single systems used on an inline engine.

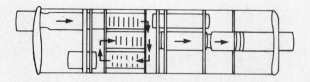

Figure 4-34. Exhaust gases must twist and turn to travel through this muffler.

EXHAUST SYSTEM COMPONENTS

Major parts of the exhaust system include:
● Manifolds
● Pipes
● Mufflers
● Resonators
● Catalytic converters.
Manifolds and manifold heat control valves will be covered in Chapter 13. We will study catalytic converters in detail in Chapter 21. The other exhaust system parts are described in the following paragraphs.

Pipes

The flow of exhaust gases from the engine should be as smooth as possible. If there are restrictions in the flow, there will be **backpressure** at the engine. Backpressure is the pressure resisting the flow of exhaust from the cylinders. Too much backpressure will not allow all the exhaust to leave the combustion chamber before the next stroke starts. This preheats and leans the incoming air-fuel mixture, hurting efficiency. It can also cause engine mechanical failures such as burned valves. Exhaust system pipes should be as straight as possible, without sharp turns and restrictions. Pipes must also be able to withstand the constant presence of hot, corrosive exhaust gases and undercar hazards such as rocks.

The exhaust pipes on many late-model cars are formed with an inner and an outer skin. Occasionally, the inner skin will collapse and form a restriction in the system. From the outside, the exhaust pipe will look normal even when the inside is partially or almost completely blocked. Close inspection is necessary to locate such a defect.

Mufflers and Resonators

The muffler is an enclosed chamber that contains baffles, small chambers, and pipes to direct exhaust gas flow. The gas route through the muffler is full of twists and turns, figure 4-34. This quiets the exhaust flow but also cre-

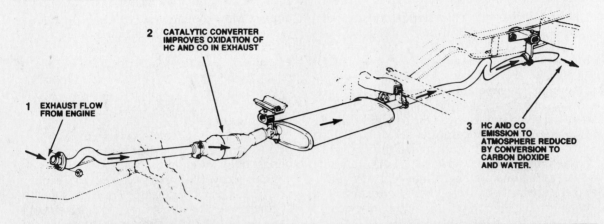

1 EXHAUST FLOW FROM ENGINE

2 CATALYTIC CONVERTER IMPROVES OXIDATION OF HC AND CO IN EXHAUST

3 HC AND CO EMISSION TO ATMOSPHERE REDUCED BY CONVERSION TO CARBON DIOXIDE AND WATER.

Figure 4-35. Typical catalytic converter installation. (Ford)

ates backpressure. For this reason mufflers must be carefully matched to the engine and exhaust system.

Some mufflers consist of a straight-through perforated pipe surrounded by sound-deadening material, usually fiberglass. These "glass-pack" mufflers, as they are often called, reduce backpressure but are not nearly as quiet as conventional mufflers.

Some engines also add resonators to the system. These are small mufflers specially designed to "fine tune" the exhaust and give it a pleasant, quiet, "resonant" tone.

Catalytic Converters

In order to meet tightening exhaust emission standards, carmakers turned to the catalytic converter in 1975. These were oxidation converters that changed HC and CO to harmless CO_2 and H_2O. Reduction converters first appeared on some 1978 cars which also help eliminate NO_x emissions.

In the simplest arrangement, one catalytic converter is installed in the exhaust system between the manifold and the muffler, figure 4-35. Many cars, however, use two converters. Some cars have converters bolted directly to the exhaust manifold.

Catalytic converters are simple. The catalyst combines with the exhaust gases, and causes a chemical reaction to take place. This amounts to a "realignment" of molecules that results in less emissions to the atmosphere. Catalytic converters have no moving parts and never need adjusting. Most converters have a guaranteed lifespan of 50,000 miles, and may outlast the car. The pellets in early General Motors converters can be removed and replaced by removing a plug in the bottom of the unit. Tetraethyl

Backpressure: A pressure that tends to slow the exit of exhaust gases from the combustion chamber; usually caused by restrictions in the exhaust system.

■ Air-Cooled Engines

All automotive engines are air-cooled. That is, even engines with liquid cooling systems rely on air to absorb the heat from the coolant. Some automotive engines, and many nonautomotive engines, do not use a liquid coolant but instead transfer engine heat directly from the cylinders' metal to the air. These types are called "air-cooled" engines to distinguish them from engines with liquid cooling systems.

Air-cooled engines can be found in everything from a fraction-of-a-horsepower model airplane to the 214-horsepower Porsche 911 Carrera. The Porsche and Volkswagen engines are the most common automotive air-cooled engines, along with the General Motors air-cooled Corvair built in the 1960s.

The Volkswagen engine is typical of air-cooled construction. It has individual cylinder castings with cooling fins. The castings are bolted to a split crankcase in an opposing pattern. A cylinder head is attached to adjacent pairs of cylinders. A large fan directs air over the engine. A radiator-like oil cooler is sometimes added to help cool the engine.

Air-cooled engines are made largely from aluminum for quick heat transfer and light weight. Tolerances within an air-cooled engine are greater than those of a liquid-cooled engine, because the aluminum expands greatly during normal hot operation.

lead, the gasoline octane booster described in Chapter 2, will coat or "poison" the catalyst and reduce its efficiency. This may make converter replacement necessary.

The link between a converter and a well-tuned engine is important. An engine that is misfiring or improperly tuned can also destroy a catalytic converter, because the converter cannot accept exhaust temperatures above 1,500°F (815°C). Neither will it work right if the air-fuel mixture is too rich. Two spark plugs misfiring in succession for a prolonged time will raise the temperature in the converter and shorten its life.

Exhaust System Effects on Performance, Economy, and Emissions

The main effect of the exhaust system on the engine is the backpressure it creates. Too much backpressure will restrict the flow of exhaust gases from the cylinders and hurt engine performance. The catalytic converter affects emissions, as we will learn in Chapter 21.

SUMMARY

The cooling and exhaust systems must remove about two-thirds of the heat produced by a car

engine. Most cooling systems use coolant to remove this heat. It circulates through the engine block where it picks up the heat, then goes through the radiator where the outside air flowing past removes heat. The coolant is a mixture of water and ethylene glycol antifreeze, which permits a greater range of engine operating temperatures.

The coolant is circulated through the system by a water pump. As the coolant heats, it expands, often overflowing the radiator. Newer systems recover this excess coolant in a separate reservoir, where it can be reused as the engine cools. An electric or engine-driven fan cools the radiator by drawing air through it at low speeds and idle. A pressure cap keeps the system pressurized, and a thermostat regulates the flow of coolant by sensing engine temperature. Engine operating temperatures that are either too hot or too cold will produce greater emissions and poor performance, and can damage the engine.

Exhaust systems carry the exhaust away from the combustion chambers through a series of pipes, mufflers, resonators, and catalytic converters. The system must be as straight as possible to reduce backpressure in the cylinders, and generally must dampen the noise from combustion.

Review Questions

Choose the single most correct answer.
Compare your answers with the correct answers on page 451.

1. Which of the following terms describes a type of radiator?
   - a. Downflow
   - b. Backflow
   - c. Thruflow
   - d. Acrossflow

2. In order to work properly, a catalytic converter must have:
   - a. Exhaust gas hotter than 1,500°F (815°C)
   - b. A rich air-fuel mixture
   - c. Gasoline without MMT in it
   - d. None of the above

3. The automobile engine converts about _____ of its total heat energy into mechanical energy.
   - a. One-fourth
   - b. One-third
   - c. One-half
   - d. Two-thirds

4. All of the following conserve power at high engine speeds except:
   - a. Flexible blade fans
   - b. Multiblade fans
   - c. Clutch fans
   - d. Electric fans

5. In extremely cold climates the cooling system should be filled with:
   - a. 100% ethylene glycol
   - b. 73% ethylene glycol and 27% water
   - c. 68% ethylene glycol and 32% water
   - d. 50% ethylene glycol and 50% water

6. Core plugs are installed in the engine block to:
   - a. Relieve pressure if the coolant should freeze
   - b. Allow the block to be flushed during engine overhaul
   - c. Provide inspection points for internal block condition
   - d. None of the above

7. An engine that is too hot will have:
   - a. Poor volumetric efficiency
   - b. Poor cooling system circulation
   - c. High oxides of carbon
   - d. High thermal inefficiency

8. A 50% water and antifreeze mixture under a pressure of 14 psi will boil at approximately:
   - a. 248°F (120°C)
   - b. 255°F (124°C)
   - c. 263°F (128°C)
   - d. 270°F (132°C)

9. The water pump uses _____ to circulate the coolant.
   - a. Positive pressure
   - b. Gravitational force
   - c. Centripetal force
   - d. Centrifugal force

10. The greater the difference in temperature between the coolant and the air, the:
    - a. Hotter the engine will run
    - b. Greater the cooling system pressure will be
    - c. More heat will be absorbed by the air
    - d. Faster the coolant will circulate through the system

11. A pressurized cooling system will:
    - a. Reduce engine temperature
    - b. Increase the coolant circulation rate
    - c. Reduce the coolant boiling point
    - d. Increase water pump efficiency

12. If the incoming fuel mixture becomes too hot, it will:
    - a. Cause the engine to backfire
    - b. Expand, which will reduce engine efficiency
    - c. Preignite and cause pinging
    - d. Wash the oil from the cylinder walls

13. A disadvantage of ethylene glycol when used as a coolant is that:
    - a. Its freezing point is much lower than water
    - b. It does not transfer heat as well as water
    - c. Its boiling point is much higher than water
    - d. None of the above

14. The thermostat regulates coolant flow between the engine and the:
    - a. Cylinder head
    - b. Heater
    - c. Radiator
    - d. Transmission cooler

15. Which of the follow is *not* a part of the water pump?
    - a. Pulley
    - b. Impeller
    - c. Stator
    - d. Scroll

16. For every one psi increase in pressure, the coolant boiling point is raised about:
    - a. 1°F (0.6°C)
    - b. 2°F (1.1°C)
    - c. 3°F (1.7°C)
    - d. 4°F (2.2°C)

17. A major type of exhaust system is the:
    - a. Inline
    - b. Single V
    - c. Dual V
    - d. All of the above

18. Catalytic converters help change:
    - a. HC and CO to H_2O and CO
    - b. HC and CO to H_2O and C
    - c. HC and CO to HC_2O
    - d. HC and CO to CO_2 and H_2O

5

Introduction to Emission Controls

The combustion process in automotive engines produces some harmful byproducts which are discharged from the engine and become air pollutants. Emission control systems are necessary to minimize the formation and discharge of these pollutants.

When emission control requirements were first introduced, automakers and car owners were able to comply by installing add-on or "hang-on" equipment, devices that were not an integral part of engine and vehicle design. As regulations became more strict, carmakers had to include emission controls in basic engine design.

The first emission control regulation was adopted in California in 1961. Today, almost three decades later, emission control regulations are still being tightened and new control systems developed. Sophisticated computer-controlled systems appear on most cars, and emission control requirements are important considerations in the design and operation of all parts of the fuel system. The ignition system, which provides the spark to begin combustion, plays an equally important role in emission control.

How did these great changes in automotive emission controls come about? What exactly *is* air pollution, and how does the automobile contribute to it? This chapter examines air pollution and automotive emissions, including the legislation controlling emissions and the ways in which carmakers have met the regulations.

AIR POLLUTION — A PERSPECTIVE

Air pollution usually is defined as the introduction of contamination into the atmosphere in an amount large enough to injure human, animal, or plant life. There are many types and causes of air pollution, but they all fall into two general groups: natural and manmade. Natural pollution is caused by such things as the organic plant life cycle, forest fires, volcanic eruptions, and dust storms. While pollution from such sources is often beyond our control, manmade pollution from industrial plants and automobiles *can* be controlled to a certain degree.

Most urban and large industrial areas around the world suffer periodic air pollution. During the late 1940s, a unique form of air pollution was identified in the Los Angeles area. This combination of smoke and fog, which forms irritating chemical compounds, is called **photochemical smog**, figure 5-1. As this phenomenon increased both in intensity and frequency, it posed more of a problem. California took the lead in combating it by becoming the first state to place emission controls on motor

Figure 5-1. Smog engulfs the Los Angeles Civic Center in the 1960s. When the base of the temperature inversion is 1,500 feet (457 meters) above ground, the inversion layer — a layer of warm air above a layer of cool air — prevents the natural dispersion of air contaminants into the upper atmosphere. (LA County)

vehicles. As smog gradually began to appear in other parts of the country, the Federal government moved into the area of regulation. To understand why, we must look at the elements produced by the automobile which form air pollution and smog.

MAJOR POLLUTANTS

An internal combustion engine emits three major gaseous pollutants into the air: **hydrocarbons (HC)**, **carbon monoxide (CO)** and **oxides of nitrogen (NO$_x$)**, figure 5-2. In addition, an automobile engine gives off many small liquid or solid particles, such as lead, carbon, sulfur and other **particulates**, which contribute to pollution. By themselves, all these emissions are not smog, but simply air pollutants.

Hydrocarbons (HC)

Gasoline is a hydrocarbon compound. Unburned hydrocarbons given off by an automobile are largely unburned portions of fuel. Over 200 different varieties of hydrocarbon pollutants come from automotive sources. While

Photochemical Smog: A combination of pollutants which, when acted upon by sunlight, forms chemical compounds that are harmful to human, animal, and plant life.

Hydrocarbon (HC): A chemical compound made up of hydrogen and carbon. A major pollutant given off by an internal combustion engine. Gasoline itself is a hydrocarbon compound.

Carbon Monoxide (CO): An odorless, colorless, tasteless poisonous gas. A major pollutant given off by an internal combustion engine.

Oxides of Nitrogen (NO$_x$): Chemical compounds of nitrogen given off by an internal combustion engine which combine with hydrocarbons to produce smog.

Particulates: Liquid or solid particles such as lead and carbon that are given off by an internal combustion engine as pollution.

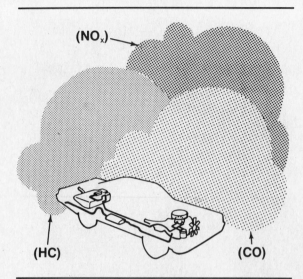

Figure 5-2. Hydrocarbons (HC), carbon monoxide (CO), and oxides of nitrogen (NOₓ) are the three major pollutants emitted by an automobile.

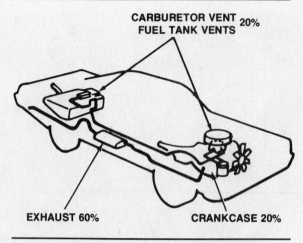

Figure 5-3. Sources of hydrocarbon emissions.

most come from the fuel system and the engine exhaust, others are oil and gasoline fumes from the crankcase. Even a car's tires, paint, and upholstery emit tiny amounts of hydrocarbons. Figure 5-3 shows the three major sources of hydrocarbon emissions from an automobile:
1. Fuel system evaporation — 20 percent
2. Crankcase vapors — 20 percent
3. Engine exhaust — 60 percent.
Hydrocarbons are the only major automotive air pollutant that come from sources *other than* the engine's exhaust.

Hydrocarbons of all types are destroyed by combustion. If an automobile engine burned gasoline completely, there would be no hydrocarbons in the exhaust, only water and carbon dioxide. But when the vaporized and compressed air-fuel mixture is ignited, combustion occurs so rapidly that gasoline near the sides of the combustion chamber may not get burned. This unburned fuel then passes out with the exhaust gases. The problem is worse with engines that misfire or are not properly tuned.

Carbon Monoxide (CO)

Although not part of photochemical smog, carbon monoxide is also found in automobile exhaust in large amounts. A deadly poison, carbon monoxide is both odorless and colorless. Carbon monoxide is absorbed by the red corpuscles in the body, displacing the oxygen. In a small quantity, it causes headaches and vision difficulties. In larger quantities, it is fatal.

Because it is a product of incomplete combustion, the amount of carbon monoxide produced depends on the way in which hydrocarbons burn. When the air-fuel mixture burns, its hydrocarbons combine with oxygen. If the air-fuel mixture contains too much fuel, there is not enough oxygen to complete this process, so carbon monoxide is formed. To make combustion more complete, an air-fuel mixture with less fuel is used. This increases the ratio of oxygen, which reduces the formation of CO by producing harmless carbon dioxide (CO_2) instead.

Oxides Of Nitrogen (NOₓ)

Air is about 78 percent nitrogen, 21 percent oxygen, and 1 percent other gases. When the combustion chamber temperature reaches 2,500°F (1,370°C) or greater, the nitrogen and oxygen in the air-fuel mixture combine to form large quantities of oxides of nitrogen (NOₓ). NOₓ also is formed at lower temperatures, but in far smaller amounts. By itself, NOₓ is of no particular concern. But when the amount of hydrocarbons in the air reaches a certain level and the ratio of NOₓ to HC is correct, the two pollutants will combine chemically to form smog.

Lowering the temperature of combustion in the engine reduces the amount of NOₓ formed. However, it also results in less efficient burning of the air-fuel mixture. This, in turn, increases hydrocarbons and carbon monoxide, both of which are formed in large quantities at lower combustion chamber temperatures. Automakers have used various emission control systems to combat this problem.

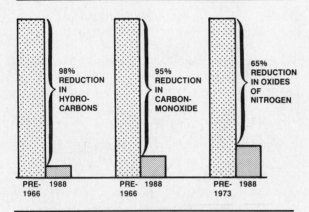

Figure 5-4. Automotive emission reductions.

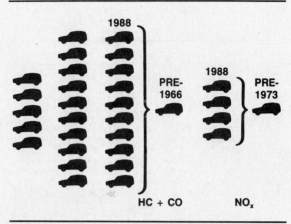

Figure 5-5. Vehicle emission comparisons.

Particulates

Particulates are microscopic solid particles, such as dust and soot. Because these fragments remain in the atmosphere for a long time, particulates are a prime cause of secondary pollution. For example, particulates such as lead and carbon tend to collect in the atmosphere. These are all harmful substances, large amounts of which can injure our health.

Particulates produced by automobiles are a small percentage of the total particulates in the atmosphere. Most come from fixed sources, such as factories. While automobiles *do* produce particulates, the amount can be reduced considerably. This is accomplished by eliminating certain additives such as lead from gasoline, and by changing other characteristics of the fuel. As a result, the amount of additives used in gasoline has been reduced and the types of additives are now carefully controlled.

Sulfur Oxides

Sulfur in gasoline and other fossil fuels (coal and oil) enters the atmosphere in the form of **sulfur oxides**. As these oxides break down, they combine with water in the air to form corrosive sulfuric acid, which is a secondary pollutant. In the past decade, there has been a great deal of publicity about this type of pollution, especially in the northeastern United States.

POLLUTION AND THE AUTOMOBILE

While it is true that a single car gives off only a microscopic amount of these pollutants, remember that there are more than 150 million automobiles in use in the United States. Multiply each car's contribution toward air pollution by that figure and you have the potential for a staggering amount of pollution. Without emission controls, automobiles would create almost as much air pollution as all other sources combined.

Great progress has been made in reducing — almost eliminating — automobile air pollution since 1966. Those HC emissions that come from the engine crankcase and fuel system (40 percent of the total) have been almost totally eliminated. The other 60 percent of HC emission, from the exhaust, has been lowered considerably. Total hydrocarbon emissions have been reduced by about 98 percent. Total carbon monoxide emissions have been reduced by a similar amount, about 95 percent, since 1966. Between 1973 and 1988, total NO_x emissions have been reduced about 65 percent. These accomplishments are shown in figure 5-4. Figure 5-5 shows us that twenty-five 1988 cars emit less HC and CO than one pre-1966 model, and four 1988 cars emit less NO_x than one pre-1973 model.

SMOG — CLIMATIC REACTION WITH AIR POLLUTANTS

Smog and air pollution are not the same thing: smog is a form of air pollution, but air pollution is not necessarily smog. Although all are byproducts of combustion, each of the three major pollutants is created in different ways. Hydrocarbons come mostly from unburned fuel; carbon monoxide results from air-fuel mixtures

Sulfur Oxides: Chemical compounds given off by processing and burning gasoline and other fossil fuels. As they decompose, they combine with water to form sulfuric acid.

YEAR	REGULATIONS	HC	CO	NOx
Before Controls		850 ppm (16.8 g/mi) *	3.4% (125.0 g/mi) *	1000 ppm (4.0 g/mi) *
1966-67	Calif.	275 ppm	1.5%	none
	U.S. Federal	none	none	none
1968-69	Calif. & U.S. Federal	275 ppm	1.5%	none
1970	Calif. & U.S. Federal	4.6 g/mi	46.0 g/mi	none
1971	Calif.	4.6 g/mi	46.0 g/mi	4.0 g/mi
	U.S. Federal	4.6 g/mi	46.0 g/mi	none
	Canadian	2.2 g/mi **	23.0 g/mi **	none
1972	Calif.	3.2 g/mi	39.0 g/mi	3.2 g/mi
	U.S. Federal	3.4 g/mi	39.0 g/mi	none
	Canadian	3.4 g/mi	39.0 g/mi	none
1973	Calif.	3.2 g/mi	39.0 g/mi	3.0 g/mi
	U.S. Federal	3.4 g/mi	39.0 g/mi	3.0 g/mi
	Canadian	3.4 g/mi	39.0 g/mi	3.0 g/mi
1974	Calif.	3.2 g/mi	39.0 g/mi	2.0 g/mi
	U.S. Federal	3.4 g/mi	39.0 g/mi	3.0 g/mi
	Canadian	3.4 g/mi	39.0 g/mi	3.0 g/mi
1975-76	Calif.	0.9 g/mi	9.0 g/mi	2.0 g/mi
	U.S. Federal	1.5 g/mi	15.0 g/mi	3.1 g/mi
	Canadian	2.0 g/mi	25.0 g/mi	3.0 g/mi
1977-78	Calif.	0.41 g/mi	9.0 g/mi	1.5 g/mi
	U.S. Federal	1.5 g/mi	15.0 g/mi	2.0 g/mi
	Canadian	2.0 g/mi	25.0 g/mi	3.0 g/mi
1979	Calif.	0.41 g/mi	9.0 g/mi	1.5 g/mi
	U.S. Federal	0.41 g/mi	15.0 g/mi	2.0 g/mi
	Canadian	2.0 g/mi	25.0 g/mi	3.0 g/mi
1980	Calif.	0.39 g/mi	9.0 g/mi	1.0 g/mi
	U.S. Federal	0.41 g/mi	7.0 g/mi	2.0 g/mi
	Canadian	2.0 g/mi	25.0 g/mi	3.0 g/mi
1981-88	Calif.	0.39 g/mi	7.0 g/mi	0.07 g/mi
	U.S. Federal	0.41 g/mi	3.4 g/mi	1.0 g/mi
	Canadian	2.0 g/mi	25.0 g/mi	3.1 g/mi

ppm = parts per million
g/mi = grams per mile
* approximate estimations of uncontrolled levels
** theoretical flow rate

Figure 5-6. Exhaust emission limits for new cars by model year.

that contain too much fuel; and oxides of nitrogen are created by high combustion chamber temperatures. HC and NOx are the two principal materials that combine in the atmosphere to form smog.

The Photochemical Reaction

Although smog can be created in a laboratory experiment, scientists still do not completely understand the nature of smog. They do know, however, that three things must be present for smog to form in the atmosphere: sunlight, relatively still air, and a high concentration of hydrocarbons and oxides of nitrogen. When these three elements exist at the same time, sunlight causes a chemical reaction between the HC and NOx, resulting in smog.

Temperature Inversion

Normally, air temperature decreases at higher altitudes. Warm air near the ground rises and becomes cooler by contact with the cooler air above it. When nature follows this normal pattern, smog and other pollutants are carried away. But some areas experience a natural weather pattern called a **temperature inversion**. When this occurs, a layer of warm air prevents the upward movement of cooler air near the ground. This inversion acts as a ''lid'' over the stagnant air. Since the air cannot rise, smog and pollution collect.

When the inversion layer is several thousand feet high, the smog will rise enough to provide reasonable visibility. But when the inversion layer is within a thousand feet (300 meters) of the ground, it traps the smog. This reduces visibility, making the distant landscape impossible to see, figure 5-1. Many people experience eye irritation, headaches and difficulty in breathing as a result. Temperature inversion was first noted in the Los Angeles area, which provides a classic example of this phenomenon. Surrounding mountains in that area form a natural basin in which temperature inversion is present to some extent for more than 300 days a year.

AIR POLLUTION LEGISLATION AND REGULATORY AGENCIES

Once the problem of air pollution was recognized, it became the subject of intense research and investigation. By the early 1950s, it was believed that smog in Los Angeles was caused by the photochemical process. California, as we noted earlier, became the first state to enact legislation designed to limit automotive emissions. Standards established by California one year often become U.S. Federal standards the next year.

Emission Control Legislation

Beginning with the 1961 new cars, California required control over crankcase emissions. This became standard for the rest of the United States with new 1963 cars. That year, domestic automakers voluntarily equipped their new models with a blowby device which virtually eliminated crankcase emissions on all cars.

California followed by requiring that 1966 and later new cars sold within its boundaries have exhaust emission controls. The use of exhaust emission control systems was extended nationwide during the 1967-1968 model years.

The first Federal air pollution research program began in 1955. In 1963, Congress passed the Clean Air Act, providing the states with money to develop air pollution control programs. This law was amended in 1965 to give

PASSENGER CAR		LIGHT DUTY TRUCKS *			
MODEL YEAR	MPG	4 × 2	4 × 4	COMBINED MPG	GVWR
1978	18	none	none	—	—
1979	19	17.2	15.8	—	0-6000
1980	20	16.0	14.0	—	0-8500
1981	22	16.7	15.0	—	0-8500
1982	24	18.0	16.0	17.5	0-8599
1983	26	19.5	17.5	19.0	0-8500
1984	27	20.3	18.5	20.0	0-8500
1985	27.5	19.7	18.9	19.5	0-8500
1986	26.0	20.5	19.5	20.0	0-8500
1987	27.5	21.0	19.5	20.5	0-8500
1988	26	21.0	19.5	20.5	0-8500
1989	27.5	21.5	19.0	20.5	0-8500
1990	27.5	20.5	19.0	20.0	0-8500
1991	27.5	20.7	19.1	20.2	0-8500

* Manufacturer can choose to meet individual or combined standard for 1983-85.

Figure 5-7. Corporate Average Fuel Economy (CAFE) standards imposed by Congress.

the Federal government authority to set emission standards for new cars, and was amended again in 1977-1978. Under this law, emission standards were first applied nationwide to 1968 models, figure 5-6.

In addition to the Clean Air Act, a new approach to air pollution was enacted in 1967. The Air Quality Act and its major amendments of 1970, 1974, and 1977 instituted changes that were designed to turn piecemeal programs into a unified attack on pollution of all kinds. Canada attacked its own smog problem with vehicle emission requirements established by the Ministry of Transport that took effect with 1971 models.

Regulatory Agencies

The Environmental Protection Agency (EPA) is the U.S. Federal agency responsible for enforcing the Air Quality Act. It was formed as part of the Department of Health, Education, and Welfare. The EPA first established standards which required that HC and CO levels for 1975 cars be reduced 90 percent from 1970 levels, with a 90-percent reduction in NO_x by 1976. These standards were later amended to those shown in figure 5-6.

In addition, the EPA has established standards in other automotive areas, such as fuel consumption and fuel additives. California established its own Air Resources Board (ARB), whose authority roughly parallels that of the Federal EPA. The California ARB operates under permission from the EPA, but its authority extends only to those vehicles sold in or

brought into California. Canadian vehicle emission standards are established by the national Ministry of Transport.

Corporate Average Fuel Economy (CAFE) Standards

Long gasoline lines and near-rationing of fuel during the energy crisis of 1973 (and again in 1979) resulted in focusing national attention on fuel economy. This resulted in the establishment of Corporate Average Fuel Economy (CAFE) standards, figure 5-7, as a part of the

Temperature Inversion: A weather pattern in which a layer or "lid" of warm air keeps the cooler air beneath it from rising.

■ Incident Number 104 and Beyond

Manmade contaminants in the air we breathe have been a problem ever since we entered the industrial revolution a century and a half ago. Not all pollution is manmade, of course. Smoke from fires, dust, methane from decaying organic matter, vapors from pine trees, volcanic ash — all of these contribute to air pollution. But under normal conditions, Nature is able to cleanse herself of these contaminants.

With the arrival of heavy industry, man began to pump more junk into the air than Nature was able to clean out. Factories spewing out tons of particulates, cars emitting many more tons of dangerous and harmful emissions, agricultural spraying adding yet more tons of highly toxic poisons to the air — all of these can combine to make the air unhealthy to breathe in some areas.

Air pollution disasters have occurred around the world for two generations or so. Donora, Pennsylvania, achieved unwanted fame when pollution killed 17 and caused another 6,000 persons to become ill. London suffered through a black smog attack in 1952 that left 4,000 dead. New York City has gone through several periods of dangerously heavy air pollution. In 1969, more than 20 Midwestern states were involved in a major air pollution attack for several days. It came close to being a fearful disaster until atmospheric conditions changed and the contaminants were cleared away. This near-disaster was officially known as Incident Number 104.

The gravity of Incident Number 104, however, pales in comparison with the catastrophe that occurred in Bhopal, India, in 1984 when toxic methyl isocyanate gas leaked from a Union Carbide India Ltd. chemical pesticide tank. Borne on the wind, the lethal cloud within hours had killed an estimated 2,000 residents of Bhopal and injured 50,000 more. That incident is one of the worst air-pollution disasters on record.

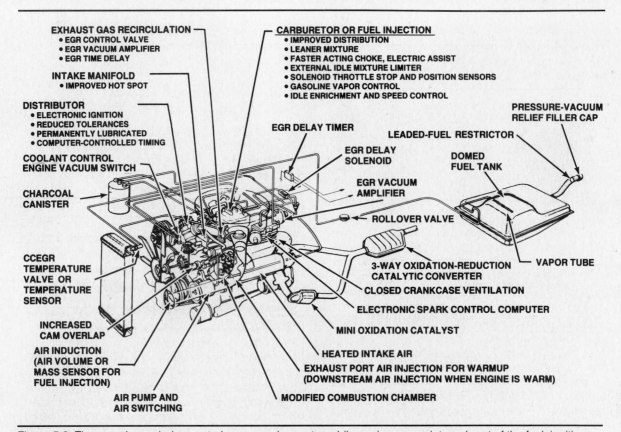

EXHAUST GAS RECIRCULATION
• EGR CONTROL VALVE
• EGR VACUUM AMPLIFIER
• EGR TIME DELAY

INTAKE MANIFOLD
• IMPROVED HOT SPOT

DISTRIBUTOR
• ELECTRONIC IGNITION
• REDUCED TOLERANCES
• PERMANENTLY LUBRICATED
• COMPUTER-CONTROLLED TIMING

COOLANT CONTROL
ENGINE VACUUM SWITCH

CHARCOAL
CANISTER

CCEGR
TEMPERATURE
VALVE OR
TEMPERATURE
SENSOR

INCREASED
CAM OVERLAP

AIR INDUCTION
(AIR VOLUME OR
MASS SENSOR FOR
FUEL INJECTION)

AIR PUMP AND
AIR SWITCHING

CARBURETOR OR FUEL INJECTION
• IMPROVED DISTRIBUTION
• LEANER MIXTURE
• FASTER ACTING CHOKE, ELECTRIC ASSIST
• EXTERNAL IDLE MIXTURE LIMITER
• SOLENOID THROTTLE STOP AND POSITION SENSORS
• GASOLINE VAPOR CONTROL
• IDLE ENRICHMENT AND SPEED CONTROL

EGR DELAY TIMER

EGR DELAY
SOLENOID

EGR VACUUM
AMPLIFIER

ROLLOVER VALVE

3-WAY OXIDATION-REDUCTION
CATALYTIC CONVERTER

CLOSED CRANKCASE VENTILATION

ELECTRONIC SPARK CONTROL COMPUTER

MINI OXIDATION CATALYST

HEATED INTAKE AIR

EXHAUST PORT AIR INJECTION FOR WARMUP
(DOWNSTREAM AIR INJECTION WHEN ENGINE IS WARM)

MODIFIED COMBUSTION CHAMBER

PRESSURE-VACUUM
RELIEF FILLER CAP

LEADED-FUEL RESTRICTOR

DOMED
FUEL TANK

VAPOR TUBE

Figure 5-8. The complex emission controls on a modern automobile engine are an integral part of the fuel, ignition, and exhaust systems. (Chrysler)

Federal Energy Act of 1975. The EPA and Department of Transportation (DOT) are responsible for administering the CAFE standards.

This gave automotive engineers two conflicting goals. They had to continue reducing emissions while improving fuel economy. If the CAFE standards were not reached each year, automakers were required by law to pay a penalty on each vehicle sold — the so-called "gas guzzler" tax. However, automakers who *exceeded* the yearly average on a corporate basis were granted a credit which could be applied to later years.

By downsizing vehicles, using smaller engines, and paying particular attention to reducing weight and improving aerodynamic efficiency, the domestic automotive industry transformed itself in the early 1980s to meet both goals. During this period, there was a concerted national effort to conserve fuel because of high prices at the pump and a desire to reduce the nation's dependence on foreign oil.

This national effort worked so well that oil prices, which had stabilized by 1983, collapsed in 1985-1986. At the same time, car owners indicated a desire to return to larger cars by ignoring the fuel-efficient small cars and purchasing

less efficient cars with bigger engines and more room. This led General Motors and Ford to petition the EPA for a "rollback" of CAFE standards to avoid massive fines resulting from meeting customer demand. Over the objections of Chrysler and other small automakers who had met the standards on time, a temporary return to the 1983 level was enacted for 1986, with the 1987 standard returning to that of 1985, figure 5-7. As of this writing, the future of CAFE standards and what will happen to them is clouded in a national debate as to whether they should be retained, modified, or abandoned.

AUTOMOTIVE EMISSION CONTROLS

Early researchers dealing with automotive pollution and smog began work with the idea that *all* pollutants were carried into the atmosphere by the car's exhaust pipe. But auto manufacturers doing their own research soon discovered that pollutants were also given off from the fuel tank and the engine crankcase. The total automotive emission system, figure 5-8, contains three different types of controls. This picture illustrates that the emission controls on a modern automobile are not a separate system, but part of an engine's fuel, ignition, and exhaust systems.

Automotive emission controls can be grouped into major families, as follows:

1. *Crankcase emission controls* — Positive crankcase ventilation (PCV) systems control HC emissions from the engine crankcase. These are described in Chapter 18.

2. *Evaporative emission controls* — Evaporative emission control (EEC or EVAP) systems control the evaporation of HC vapors from the fuel tank, pump, and carburetor or fuel injection system. These are described in Chapter 12.

3. *Exhaust emission controls* — Various systems and devices are used to control HC, CO, and NO_x emissions from the engine exhaust. These controls can be subdivided into the following general groups:

a. *Air injection systems* — These systems provide additional air to the exhaust system to help burn up HC and CO in the exhaust and to aid catalytic conversion. They are described in Chapter 19.

b. *Engine modifications* — Various changes have been made in the design of engines and in the operation of fuel and ignition system components to help eliminate all three major pollutants.

c. *Spark timing controls* — Automakers have used various systems to delay or retard ignition spark timing to control HC and NO_x emissions. Most of these systems modify the distributor vacuum advance; however, late-model cars with electronic engine control systems have eliminated the need for mechanical or vacuum timing devices. Ignition spark timing and its role in controlling emissions are discussed in Chapter 10. Electronic engine control systems are discussed in Chapter 15.

d. *Exhaust gas recirculation* — An effective way to control NO_x emissions is to recirculate a small amount of exhaust gas back to the intake manifold to dilute the incoming air-fuel mixture. Exhaust gas recirculation (EGR) systems are described in Chapter 20.

e. *Catalytic converters* — The first catalytic converters installed in the exhaust systems of 1975-76 cars helped the chemical oxidation or burning of HC and CO in the exhaust. Later catalytic converters, which began to appear on 1977-78 cars, also promoted the chemical reduction of NO_x emissions. Catalytic converters are discussed in Chapter 21.

TUNE-UPS AND EMISSION CONTROL

Although a brand-new automobile must meet emission control standards when sold, the wear and tear of everyday operation soon can change this. Settings and tolerances change, engine parts wear, and conditions in other systems indirectly affect the engine's performance.

One of the major goals of a tune-up is to bring the car back in line with the emission control standards that it met when new. Here is a

■ How New Cars Are Emission-Certified

Whether or not you can buy a new car each year depends upon the success of the automakers in completing the emission certification process. The constant volume sampling test is performed by the Federal Environmental Protection Agency (EPA), although California's Air Resources Board tests some vehicles.

As each new model year approaches, automakers build prototype or emission data cars for EPA use. The automakers are responsible for conducting a 50,000-mile (80,000- kilometer) durability test of their emission control systems. The test cars are driven for 4,000 miles (6,500 kilometers) to stabilize the emission systems before testing.

The first step is to precondition the car. Then it stands for 12 hours at an air temperature of 73°F (22°C) to simulate a cold start. The actual test is done on a chassis dynamometer, using a driving cycle which represents urban driving conditions. The car's exhaust is mixed with air to a constant volume and analyzed for harmful pollutants.

The entire test requires about 41 minutes. The first 23 minutes are a cold-start driving test. The next 10 minutes are a waiting, or hot-soak period. The final eight minutes are a hot-start test, representing a short trip in which the car is stopped and started several times while hot. If the emissions test results for all data cars are equal to, or lower than, all of the HC, CO, and NO_x standards, the manufacturer receives certification of the engine "family" and the car can be offered for sale to the public.

This explains why some engines have disappeared — they were too "dirty" and could not be "cleaned" up. It also explains why some powertrain combinations may not be available in California (which has different requirements) when they can be purchased in the other 49 states. Automakers are now facing the prospects of certifying their vehicles for 100,000 miles (160,000 km) or more, a development which may be necessary in the near future.

quick review of how changing engine conditions affect vehicle emissions, and how the corrections that can be made during a tune-up will reduce emissions.

How Air-Fuel Ratio Affects Emissions

The air-fuel ratio determines how much fuel is present in the cylinder when combustion begins. Different air-fuel ratios have different effects on exhaust emissions.

If there is too much fuel present, it will not burn completely. Unburned fuel in the exhaust is the principal source of HC emissions. The lack of oxygen in the mixture also increases the amount of CO in the exhaust.

If the air-fuel ratio is made leaner, these problems decrease. Combustion is more complete, reducing HC, and the excess oxygen allows the formation of harmless carbon dioxide (CO_2) instead of CO. These advantages of a lean air-fuel mixture disappear, however, if the mixture is made *too* lean.

A lean mixture is very hard to ignite, because the particles of fuel are far apart. If the mixture is so lean that the ignition spark does not cause combustion, a **misfire** occurs. The entire chamber full of vaporized, unburned fuel enters the exhaust system, and HC emissions skyrocket. Older engines with mechanical ignition systems use air-fuel ratios for cruising of about 12:1 to 14:1, which allows some of the lean mixture advantages while avoiding misfire. Newer computer-controlled ignition timing systems are able to run an 18:1 mixture by precise control of the ignition spark. A mixture this lean burns at a very low temperature and NO_x formation is reduced.

How Ignition Timing Affects Emissions

The timing of the ignition spark affects both the quality and the temperature of combustion. The quality of combustion, or how completely the air-fuel mixture burns, directly affects HC and CO emissions. The temperature of combustion affects NO_x formation and, indirectly, HC and CO.

We have seen in previous chapters that the ignition spark timing must be set correctly at the engine idle speed and then must vary to match other engine speeds. Older ignition systems use mechanical devices to vary ignition timing. Most late-model systems have small computers, or microprocessors, that compute ignition timing.

If the spark timing is advanced until combustion is complete and HC and CO emissions decrease, then NO_x formation is greatly increased by the high combustion chamber temperatures. If the spark timing is retarded to lower combustion chamber temperatures and NO_x formation, the mixture does not have enough time to burn completely and HC and CO increase.

The different ignition timing settings that are specified for different engines are a carefully engineered compromise between these two extremes. Generally, initial timing is slightly retarded to reduce NO_x formation. Other emission control devices are added to reduce the resulting HC and CO emissions.

How Engine Mechanical Condition Affects Emissions

Engine mechanical wear cannot be corrected during a tune-up. This requires engine service, such as valve grinding or timing chain repair, or an overhaul. The tune-up technician, though, must be able to *recognize* engine wear and inform the car owner. Otherwise, the car owner may not realize that work is needed and may be disappointed that the tune-up did not completely restore the car's performance.

The engine mechanical wear that affects exhaust emissions includes items such as valve train wear, which will change the valve timing and affect combustion. Increased clearances from mechanical wear will also allow excessive amounts of oil into the cylinders, contributing to HC emissions.

How Lubrication, Cooling, and Exhaust Systems Affect Emissions

The lubrication system helps to keep engine mechanical wear to a minimum, reducing the effects of wear on emissions. If the lubrication system is neglected, engine wear will occur faster. Also, if the wrong viscosity oil is used or if the oil becomes diluted, it will be drawn into the combustion chamber and increase HC emissions.

The cooling system keeps the engine at an ideal operating temperature. If the engine is too cold, the fuel will not vaporize well and will not

Misfire: Failure of the air-fuel mixture to ignite during the power stroke.

burn completely. Unburned gasoline can wash oil off the cylinder walls, which leads to rapid cylinder wear and increased blowby. High engine temperatures can thin the oil and lead to oil burning. The cooling system also helps to control the operation of some emission control systems. Their performance will suffer if the cooling system does not work correctly.

Exhaust backpressure prevents exhaust gases from being completely cleared from the cylinder. The incoming air-fuel mixture is diluted by these gases. This is done purposely in many cases to reduce emissions. Too much backpressure and too much dilution, however, can cause misfiring and increased emissions. The catalytic converter is a major part of many emission control systems. If it is physically damaged or if the catalyst is contaminated by gasoline additives, exhaust emissions will increase.

SUMMARY

The automobile is a major source of air pollution resulting from the gasoline burned in the engine and the vapors escaping from the crankcase, the fuel tank, and the rest of the fuel system. The major pollutants are unburned hydrocarbons (HC), carbon monoxide (CO), and oxides of nitrogen (NO_x). The most visible and irritating form of air pollution is photochemical smog, which is formed when HC and NO_x emissions combine in the presence of sunlight. The use of emission controls in the past two decades has reduced automotive pollutants by 65 to 98 percent.

Emission controls began as separate ''add-on'' components and systems, but are now completely integrated into engine and vehicle design. The major emission control systems used are PCV systems, evaporative control systems, air injection, spark timing controls, exhaust gas recirculation, catalytic converters, and electronic engine control systems.

California introduced the first emission control legislation, and the Federal government followed. The Federal Environmental Protection Agency and California's Air Resources Board establish and enforce pollution control standards for automobiles. Increasingly stringent emission standards combined with the CAFE regulations imposed during the late 1970's have reshaped the domestic automotive industry. The end result has been smaller, more fuel-efficient vehicles that produce much less pollution than those of two decades ago.

Two major goals of a tune-up are to make the car meet its original emissions standards and to recognize any problems that cannot be corrected by a tune-up.

Review Questions

Choose the single most correct answer.
Compare your answers with the correct answers on page 451.

1. Smog:
   a. Is a natural pollutant
   b. Cannot be controlled
   c. Is created by a photochemical reaction
   d. Was first identified in New York City

2. The three *major* pollutants in automobile exhaust are:
   a. Sulfates, particulates, carbon dioxide
   b. Sulfates, carbon monoxide, nitrous oxide
   c. Carbon monoxide, oxides of nitrogen, hydrocarbons
   d. Hydrocarbons, carbon dioxide, nitrous oxide

3. Fuel evaporation accounts for what percentage of total HC emissions?
   a. 10%
   b. 60%
   c. 33%
   d. 20%

4. Carbon monoxide is a result of:
   a. Incomplete combustion
   b. A lean mixture
   c. Excess oxygen
   d. Impurities in the fuel

5. Which of the following is *not* true?
   a. High temperatures increase NO_x emissions
   b. High temperatures reduce HC and CO emissions
   c. Low temperatures reduce HC and CO emissions
   d. Low temperatures reduce NO_x emissions

6. Particulates are:
   a. Microscopic particles suspended in the atmosphere
   b. Produced in emissions by additives such as lead
   c. Harmful to our lungs
   d. All of the above

7. Sulfur oxides are harmful because:
   a. They damage catalytic converters
   b. They combine with water in the air to form sulfuric acid
   c. They are primary pollutants
   d. They are visible

8. Since 1966, total HC emissions have been reduced by about:
   a. 65%
   b. 47%
   c. 82%
   d. 98%

9. Smog is created by a combination of sunlight, still air, and:
   a. High levels of CO and HC
   b. High levels of CO and NO_x
   c. High levels of HC and NO_x
   d. High levels of HC and sulfur oxides

10. A temperature inversion increases air pollution by:
    a. Pushing cool air up
    b. Forming a "lid" over stagnant air
    c. Pushing warm air down
    d. None of the above

11. U.S. Federal emission limits are established by the:
    a. Air Resources board
    b. Ministry of Transport
    c. Environmental Protection Agency
    d. Department of Transportation

12. Corporate Average Fuel Economy (CAFE) standards were first applied to vehicles for which model year?
    a. 1976
    b. 1978
    c. 1979
    d. 1981

13. Sulfur byproducts of combustion can combine with water to form:
    a. Sulfates
    b. Particulates
    c. Oxides of sulfur
    d. Sulfuric acid

14. The only major type of pollutant that comes from a vehicle source *other than the exhaust* is:
    a. HC
    b. CO
    c. CO_2
    d. NO_x

6

What Is a Tune-Up?

The previous chapters have explained why engine maintenance is necessary for the best performance, economy, and emission control. Now we can look more closely at the combination of engine maintenance services commonly called a tune-up. This chapter describes:
• The difference between traditional and modern ideas of tune-up
• Carmakers' and equipment suppliers' tune-up recommendations
• The effects of emission control regulations on tune-up services.

TUNE-UP'S CHANGING MEANING

The automobile has undergone many changes since the first emission control regulations appeared in 1961. Engine equipment has changed, and the services necessary to maintain that equipment have changed. Today, compared to 20 years ago, this means that:
• Fewer items need to be replaced
• Service intervals for replacement items have lengthened
• More testing procedures are required than replacement and adjustment procedures.
    However, the goal of today's tune-up is still the same as yesterday's — to restore a vehicle's performance, fuel economy, and emissions level by returning the engine as nearly as possible to manufacturer's specifications.

Periodic Service — The Traditional Tune-Up

Before and during the infancy of emission control regulations, an engine tune-up was done at regular intervals based on items that needed to be replaced at those intervals, figure 6-1. This was usually called preventive maintenance or periodic maintenance. The tune-up included:
• Testing the engine's general mechanical condition to find any major problems
• Replacing certain parts, such as filters and ignition system parts
• Adjusting tolerances, especially in the ignition and fuel systems.

Diagnosis and Correction — The Modern Tune-Up

As the number of serviceable items decreased and service intervals lengthened, tune-up technicians could no longer simply replace parts and make a few adjustments. They had to be aware of problems that could appear in systems where maintenance is not normally needed.

**TUNE-UP RELATED SERVICES REQUIRED DURING
4 YEARS OR 50,000 MILES OF OPERATION —
1968 Dodge**

Change crankcase oil	12 times
Replace crankcase oil filter	6 times
Lubricate manifold heat valve	12 times
Check PCV system	12 times
Replace PCV valve and clean system	4 times
Clean air cleaner filter	12 times
Replace air cleaner filter	2 times
Clean carburetor choke shaft, fast-idle cam, and pivot pin	8 times
Oil distributor shaft	8 times
Clean and oil the oil filer cap	8 times
Change engine coolant	4 times
Lubricate distributor cam	4 times
Engine tune-up (replace or adjust as needed):	
• Spark Plugs	4 times
• Ignition points	4 times
• Distributor cap and rotor	4 times
• Ignition coil	4 times
• Ignition cables	4 times
• Carburetor choke	4 times
• Idle speed and fuel mixture	4 times
Replace fuel filter	2 times

Figure 6-1. These tune-up services concentrate on replacing or adjusting items at regular intervals.

**TUNE-UP RELATED SERVICES REQUIRED DURING
4 YEARS OR 50,000 MILES OF OPERATION —
1988 Dodge**

Change crankcase oil	6 times
Replace crankase oil filter	3 times
Replace air filter	1 time
Replace PCV valve	As needed
Replace fuel filter	As needed
Inspect fuel injection system	1 time
Change engine coolant	1 time
Replace spark plugs	1 time
Inspect and adjust drive belts	3 times
Check cooling system	4 times

Figure 6-2. These tune-up requirements illustrate the reduced servicing needs of late-model cars.

The emphasis of a tune-up changed from routine services to a concentration on testing. Extensive checks of overall performance and individual system performance are now needed to pinpoint problems that could have been missed during a traditional replace-and-adjust tune-up. Testing, diagnosis, and correction, combined with those periodic services that remain, make up current tune-up procedures.

CARMAKERS' MAINTENANCE RECOMMENDATIONS

We have said that the change in tune-up procedures is caused by changing service recommendations. Carmakers have always published servicing guidelines to inform the owner and technician how the car should be maintained. Recommended service schedules allow the carmaker to place under warranty various items of

	CHEVROLET			
	1968 Service Intervals		1988 Service Intervals	
	Months	Miles	Months	Miles
REPLACE:				
Crankcase oil	4	6,000	12	7,500
Crankase oil filter	8	12,000		7,500
PCV valve	12	12,000	As needed	
Ignition Points		12,000	None	
Spark plugs		12,000		30,000
Fuel filter	12	12,000	As needed	
Coolant	24		24	30,000
Air cleaner filter:				
Rotate		12,000	Not required	
Replace		24,000	36	30,000
ADJUST:				
Valves		12,000	Not required	
Idle speed		12,000	Not required	
Rotate distributor				
cam lubricator		12,000	Not required	
Ignition timing		12,000		30,000
CHECK:				
Ignition condenser		12,000	None	
PCV system	4	6,000		30,000
Ignition cables		12,000		30,000
Carburetor choke	Not required		24	30,000
Vacuum advance		12,000		30,000
Evap. fuel control system	None			30,000
EGR system	None			30,000
Thermostatic air cleaner	None			30,000

Figure 6-3. A comparison of the tune-up services and intervals for a 1968 Chevrolet and a 1988 Chevrolet.

the car based on a specific program of maintenance. Today's maintenance schedules represent the minimum amount of service that the car will require when used in "normal" driving. The following paragraphs explain how and why carmakers' maintenance recommendations have changed.

Services

Most tune-up related services have been eliminated from late model cars. Compare the typical late-model tune-up requirements shown in figure 6-2 with those listed in figure 6-1 to see the contrast. For another example, between 1972 and 1982 ten routine maintenance items were dropped from Ford's maintenance schedule. Not all of these were tune-up related, but one item dropped was distributor cap and rotor replacement:

• The 1972 model has a 24,000-mile (38,400-km) replacement interval

• The 1982 model does not have a specified replacement interval.

Figure 6-3 shows the tune-up services recommended by Chevrolet for its 1968 and 1988 models. You can see that six services required in 1968 are not called for in 1988; some of these

service parts are not on 1988 models, while other service requirements were simply eliminated:
- Ignition points replacement
- Air cleaner filter rotation
- Valve adjustment (on some engines)
- Distributor cam lubricator rotation
- Ignition condenser testing
- Idle speed.

You will also note that there are three system checks required for 1988 that were not called for in 1968; these are driveability and emission controls not used on the older models:
- Evaporative fuel control
- Exhaust gas recirculation (EGR)
- Thermostatically controlled air cleaner.

These system checks are a good example of the changing nature of the tune-up, from replacement and adjustment to testing and diagnosis.

Intervals

The other major change in manufacturers' maintenance recommendations has been the lengthening of the time and mileage intervals between required services. For instance, the service intervals on 1988 Ford products with V-8 engines have been extended for more than 25 items, including:
- Spark plug replacement — from every 12,000 miles (19,200 km) in 1972 to every 30,000 miles (48,000 km) in 1988.
- Engine oil replacement — from every 4,000 (6,400 km) in 1972 to every 7,500 (12,000 km) in 1988.
- Engine coolant replacement — from every 24 months in 1972 to every 36 months in 1988.

The Chevrolet servicing table in figure 6-3 shows that almost every 1988 tune-up service interval has been lengthened compared with 1968 intervals.

Legal Requirements

There are two main reasons behind these changes in carmakers' tune-up services and intervals:
1. The 1970 Amendment to the Federal Clean Air Act requires that carmakers provide a 5-year, 50,000-mile (80,000-km) warranty on their products' emission control devices.
2. During the EPA's new-car certification procedures, recommended maintenance schedules *must* be followed. These schedules are then given to the new-car buyer.

The extended warranty requirement has caused carmakers to add many testing requirements to their maintenance schedules, as we saw in figure 6-3. This makes the car owner responsible for maintaining the emission control devices so that they will operate properly for 5 years or 50,000 miles (80,000 km), whichever comes first.

The rule that maintenance schedules be followed during EPA certification tests has two results. Low-maintenance electronic ignition systems are now standard because they do not require adjustment like breaker-point systems, making it easier for emissions to be controlled over a long period of operation. We will learn more about this in Chapter 11. Also, the complete maintenance schedules that must be published for consumers have become a sales issue. Manufacturers compare their schedules with those of their competition and also with the schedules recommended in earlier years. For example, Ford's 1982 sales literature pointed out that the changes in maintenance requirements meant a savings in maintenance costs. When comparisons are made between competing car models, it is obviously to a carmaker's advantage to have a cheaper maintenance schedule. This is one of the reasons that manufacturers have worked to eliminate service items and to extend intervals.

PARTS AND EQUIPMENT SUPPLIERS' RECOMMENDATIONS

Carmakers supply specific maintenance schedules for their products. More general recommendations are made by:
- Manufacturers of replacement parts
- Manufacturers of tune-up testing equipment.

Their recommendations differ from carmakers' schedules for several reasons.

Carmakers tend to base their schedules on the least demanding vehicle operating conditions in order to reduce services and lengthen intervals. Parts and equipment suppliers base their recommendations on more severe operating conditions, which are closer to what the average car encounters. This tends to shorten their recommended service intervals. Of course, they are also interested in selling as many parts and as much equipment as possible, so they recommend more frequent replacement and testing.

CALIFORNIA

HIGHWAY EMISSION STANDARDS STATE OF CALIFORNIA **AIR RESOURCES BOARD** IDLE EMISSION STANDARDS FOR LIGHT DUTY VEHICLE ROADSIDE INSPECTION		
Standard Domestic Vehicles 140 CID or Greater	HC ppm	CO%
a.　1955 - 1965	1200	8.0
b.　1966 - 1969		
Air Injection	400	4.0
Engine Modification	500	7.0
c.　1970 - 1971 (EM & AI)	350	4.0
d.　1972 - 1973		
Air Injection	275	2.5
Engine Modification	350	4.0
Imported Vehicles and Compact Domestic Vehicles Under 140 CID		
a.　1955 - 1967	1900	8.0
b.　1968 - 1969		
Air Injection	500	5.0
Engine Modification	700	7.0
c.　1970 - 1973		
Air Injection	300	3.0
Engine Modification	600	5.0

Figure 6-4. These are the inspection limits that were used by California is 1973. This particular inspection program has since been discontinued. (California Highway Patrol)

NEW JERSEY

MODEL YEAR	CO%	HC ppm
1967 and earlier	8.5	1400
1968-69	7.0	700
1970-74	5.0	500
1975-later	3.0	300

Figure 6-5. New Jersey's auto emissions inspection program adopted these standards in November, 1975.

SEVERE SERVICE EFFECTS ON TUNE-UP REQUIREMENTS

If the term "severe service" makes you think of police cars, taxicabs, and other special-duty vehicles, you may be surprised at today's severe service definition. A car is in severe service if:
• Most of its trips are less than 10 miles (16 km)
• It is used in stop-and-go driving
• Its engine is idled for long periods
• It is driven in dusty or sandy conditions
• It is driven in very hot or very cold weather
• It is used to pull a trailer.
Other severe service factors include individual driving habits such as the use of air conditioning, extended high-speed driving, and rapid acceleration.

ARIZONA

ENGINE TYPE	MODEL YEAR	CO%	HC ppm
4 cylinder	1969-71	6.5	800
	1972-74	6.0	450
	1975-80	2.5	250
	1981-86	1.5	250
	1987-88	1.2	220
6 and 8 cylinder	1969-71	6.5	750
	1972-74	5.5	400
	1975-80	2.2	250
	1981-86	1.5	250
	1987-88	1.2	220

Figure 6-6. These inspection standards are typical of recent programs required to meet EPA air quality mandates. The inspections and standards apply only to the Phoenix (Maricopa Co.) and Tucson (Pima Co.) areas.

Today's common definition of normal driving is actually an *ideal* condition: long-distance driving on relatively dust-free roads. Almost any other driving condition qualifies as severe service.

Carmakers include severe service recommendations in their maintenance schedules. These usually call for cutting certain service intervals in half. A few tune-up items are affected by severe service recommendations, including:
• Air cleaner filters (affected by dusty or sandy conditions)
• Crankcase oil and filter
• Spark plugs.
Transmission, transaxle, differential, and wheel bearing services are also affected by severe service operation.

EXHAUST EMISSION INSPECTION STANDARDS

All cars manufactured for sale in the United States have had to meet U.S. Federal exhaust emission standards since 1968. These standards apply to new cars as they come off the assembly line. Because of ongoing air quality problems, the California Air Resources Board (CARB) requires that all new vehicles sold in that state meet an even more stringent set of emission standards. Canada first imposed emission standards in 1971, and the most recent regulations for that country approximate the U.S. standards of the early- to mid-1970s. For this reason, catalytic converters are usually not necessary on Canadian vehicles, although models with catalytic converters that meet U.S. specifications may be sold in Canada as well.

As discussed earlier, vehicle manufacturers must warrant the emission performance of their cars for five years or 50,000 miles (80,000 km), whichever comes first. Beyond this point it is the responsibility of the car owner to maintain the emission control system in good condition. Because owners tend to ignore vehicle maintenance requirements, and in some cases actively disconnect or remove emission control devices with resulting increase in tailpipe pollutants, the EPA has been given the power to withhold Federal highway funds from cities and states that fail to meet certain standards of ambient air quality. This has led to Periodic Motor Vehicle Inspections (PMVI) and specific emission control system and tailpipe emission inspections in many areas. Figures 6-4, 6-5, and 6-6 illustrate some of the standards used. Once a car is in use and mechanical wear has begun, its emission control systems start to lose efficiency. For this reason, inspection standards for cars that are in use are generally not as strict as the requirements for the same car when it was new.

Depending on the city or state in which you live and work, adjusting cars to meet these or similar standards will be an important part of the tune-up process.

TUNE-UP MERCHANDISING

Few car owners consistently have their automobiles serviced according to factory recommendations. Many people bring their cars in for service when they "think" it is time, or they get an annual tune-up and lube job. Some individuals wait until there is something wrong with the car to bring it in for service. You can do your customers a favor by pointing out the factory-recommended services their cars require. For the customer it is better service — for you it is greater profit.

Many companies supply promotional items that can help a tune-up shop sell its services. These companies include carmakers, replacement parts suppliers, test equipment makers, and magazines aimed at the automotive service trade. The promotional products range from eye-catching signs and banners to ideas and suggestions for bringing tune-ups to the car owner's attention. Some ideas include:
- Displaying new and used parts side-by-side to emphasize the wear caused by everyday use
- Asking the car owners what fuel mileage their cars get, then showing them the appropriate EPA mileage estimate, to emphasize what the car *might* be getting if properly tuned
- Setting up specific appointments for the work to be done

- After the tune-up, showing the customer the parts that were replaced and explaining *why* they were replaced
- Showing the customer before-and-after test results in writing.

Our definitions of an engine tune-up do not tell you what specific services should be included. The services contained in your tune-up package should be clearly explained to the car owner. First, of course, you must decide for yourself what items will be serviced. Many shops offer a one-price service that covers an overall engine test and the replacement of a few common parts. If any unusual problems are found, they will be fixed only at additional cost. A similar tune-up package charges a fixed labor rate for engine testing, then adds the cost of any replacement items needed. These methods are often used in high-volume tune-up specialty shops. Other shops usually charge for the actual amount of time spent working on the car plus the cost of the parts replaced.

THE TOTAL TUNE-UP

According to the Ignition Manufacturers Institute (IMI), a trade association of major parts manufacturers, a quality tune-up must include these five elements:
- A trained technician with
- Dependable test equipment and
- Accurate specifications, performing a
- Specific test procedure and using
- Quality replacement parts.

This definition of an engine tune-up agrees with our earlier explanation. When tuning a late-model car, the technician must be able to understand the information obtained from the car's condition and from test equipment. The equipment must be dependable and accurate, or the test results are meaningless. A vital part of diagnosis is having accurate specifications, so that you can compare how the car *should* be operating with how it is *actually* operating. A specific test procedure ensures that all engine performance areas are thoroughly checked in the proper order. Using quality replacement parts reduces the risk of installing new parts that are already defective or might wear out in less than the recommended service interval.

The remaining chapters in this *Classroom Manual* cover the operation of the various engine systems that are involved in tune-up testing and service. The relationship of each of these systems to engine performance, economy, and emission control is also explained.

SUMMARY

The changes in the automobile caused by emission control regulations have in turn caused changes in engine tune-up ideas and procedures. The traditional tune-up's replace/adjust/test structure has shifted to the modern emphasis on comprehensive testing and fault diagnosis. In general, today's service recommendations contain fewer replacement items, longer service intervals, and more testing of engine systems.

Carmakers' recommendations are based on ideal driving conditions which very few cars actually meet. Shorter servicing intervals are often recommended by replacement parts man-

ufacturers and test equipment suppliers. Carmakers recognize this difference and include severe service recommendations in their schedules.

Many areas of the country now require Periodic Motor Vehicle Inspections (PMVI) and specific emission control system and tailpipe emission inspections to ensure that cars meet Federal emission control standards. Like any other service, however, tune-up service still has to be *sold* to consumers. Large companies supply advertising aids and tune-up procedure checklists to help the tune-up technician attract and keep business. The total tune-up is an important idea if late-model cars are to be serviced properly.

Review Questions
Choose the single most correct answer.
Compare your answers with the correct answers on page 451.

1. Emission control regulations for cars first appeared in:
   a. 1958
   b. 1961
   c. 1964
   d. 1969

2. Which of the following is generally *not true* for a modern tune-up?
   a. Fewer items need to be replaced
   b. The service intervals have gradually lengthened
   c. Tune-ups are no longer as important as they used to be
   d. More testing procedures are required now than before

3. Which of the following is *true* of the carmakers' service recommendations?
   a. They represent the minimum service under normal driving
   b. They represent the maximum service under normal driving
   c. They represent the maximum service under severe driving
   d. They represent the minimum service under severe driving

4. The 1970 Amendment to the Federal Clean Air Act requires cars to have a _____ warranty on their emission control devices.
   a. 2-year, 20,000-mile
   b. 3-year, 30,000-mile
   c. 4-year, 40,000-mile
   d. 5-year, 50,000-mile

5. Which of the following is *not* a part of severe service driving?
   a. Most of the trips are 10 miles or less
   b. The car frequently is used for trailer towing
   c. The car is driven at moderate speeds for extended periods of time on highways
   d. The car is driven in dusty or sandy conditions

6. Which of the following *are* included as normal service driving?
   a. Long distance driving
   b. Driving at cruising speeds
   c. Driving on dust-free highways
   d. All of the above

PART TWO

Electrical Systems

7

The Battery, Charging, and Starting Systems

At a glance, you may think that the ignition system is the only automotive electrical system that needs to be considered during a tune-up. If you ignore other systems, however, you may miss the causes of engine performance problems. This chapter contains a brief explanation of the battery, the charging system, and the starting system, and shows how they relate to engine performance.

To examine the car's electrical systems we should be familiar with some electrical terms and ideas. Electricity can be defined as the flow of electrical current through a **conductor**, which is a material that allows easy current flow. An **insulator** is a material that does not allow current flow. The amount of current flow through a conductor is called the **amperage**. It is measured in **amperes**, commonly called amps. The force that causes current flow is called **voltage**, and is measured in **volts**. In order for current to flow, there must be a complete path of conductors to carry the current. This path is called a **circuit**. Although there can be no current flow if the circuit is not complete, there *can* be voltage present in the incomplete circuit. All circuits contain some amount of **resistance** to current flow. This resistance ismeasured in **ohms**.

The voltage for a car's electrical circuits comes from the battery. The circuits are made up of:
● Wiring
● The engine, frame, and body of the car.
The engine, frame, and body are called the **ground**. The cable from one battery post, or terminal, is bolted to the car engine or frame, figure 7-1. This is called the **ground cable**. The cable from the other battery terminal provides current for all the car's electrical loads. This is called the **insulated**, or **hot**, **cable**. The insulated side of every circuit in the vehicle is the wiring running from the battery to the devices in the circuit. The ground side of every circuit is the vehicle chassis, figure 7-1. This is called a single-wire, or a ground-return, system.

We will be showing you pictures of circuits that are called circuit diagrams. These show the wires and devices that are in the circuit. They do not show the car engine, frame or body. Instead, the ground symbol, figure 7-1, is used to show that the wire or device is bolted to the car chassis. You can think of the ground symbol as showing a direct connection back to the battery ground cable.

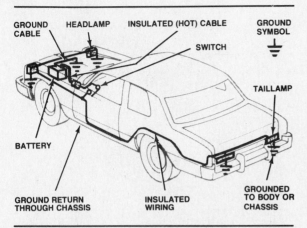

Figure 7-1. Half of the automotive electrical system is the ground path through the vehicle chassis.

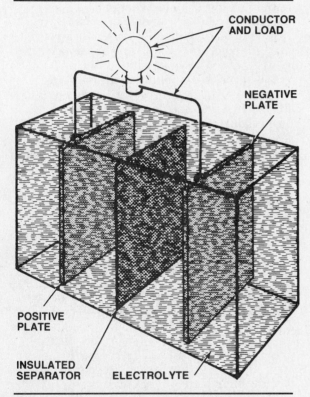

Figure 7-2. The potential difference between the two plates of a battery can cause current to flow in an outside circuit. (Chevrolet)

BATTERY OPERATION AND CONSTRUCTION

The automotive battery does not actually store electricity, as is often believed. It converts electrical energy into chemical energy, which is stored until the battery is connected to an external circuit. The stored chemical energy is then converted back to electrical energy, which flows

from one battery terminal, through the circuit, and back to the other battery terminal.

Battery Electrochemical Action

All automotive wet-cell batteries operate because of the chemical action of two dissimilar metals in the presence of a conductive and reactive solution called an **electrolyte**. Because this chemical action produces electricity, it is called electrochemical action. The chemical action of the electrolyte causes one metal plate to be positively charged and the other metal plate to be negatively charged. This difference between the charged plates is the battery's voltage.

We can see from the simple battery shown in figure 7-2 that when a positive plate and a

Conductor: A material that allows easy flow of electricity.

Insulator: A material that will not conduct electricity.

Amperage: The amount of current flow through a conductor.

Ampere: The unit for measuring the rate of electric current flow.

Voltage: The electromotive force that causes current flow. The potential difference in electrical force between two points when one is negatively charged and the other is positively charged.

Volt: The unit for measuring the amount of electrical force.

Circuit: A circle or unbroken path of conductors through which an electric current can flow.

Resistance: Opposition to electrical current flow.

Ohm: The unit for measuring electrical resistance.

Ground: The connection of an electrical circuit or unit to the engine or chassis to return electrical current to the battery.

Ground Cable: The battery cable that provides a ground connection from the vehicle chassis to the battery.

Insulated (Hot) Cable: The battery cable that conducts battery current to the automotive electrical system.

Electrolyte: The chemical solution in a battery that conducts electricity and reacts with the plate materials.

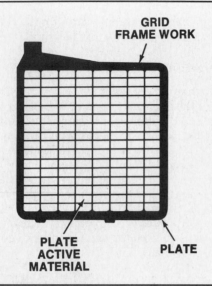

Figure 7-3. The grid provides a support for the plate active material.

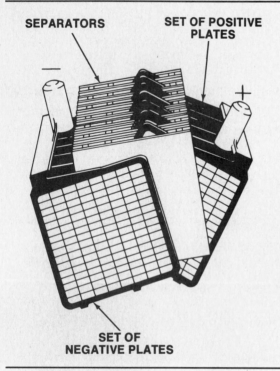

Figure 7-4. Two groups are interlaced to form a battery element.

negative plate are put in a container of electrolyte, and a conductor is connected between them, the battery's voltage will cause electrical current to flow through the conductor.

As the current flows, the chemical structure of the plates and the electrolyte changes. This is called discharging. When a battery is totally

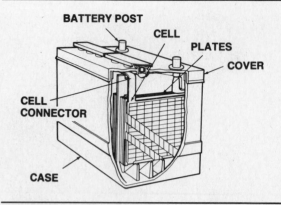

Figure 7-5. A cutaway view of an assembled battery. (Chrysler)

discharged, the chemical energy has all been converted to electrical energy and used in the outside circuit. Automotive batteries can be recharged, however, by applying an outside current to the battery terminals and forcing current to flow through the battery in the opposite direction. This current flow causes chemical action which restores the battery materials to their original condition, and the battery can again supply voltage. This is called charging the battery. The condition of the battery materials is called the battery's state of charge.

Battery Construction

There are four types of automotive batteries currently in use:
• Vent-cap (requires maintenance)
• Low-maintenance (requires limited maintenance)
• Maintenance-free (requires no maintenance)
• Recombinant (requires no maintenance).
    The basic physical construction of all types of automotive batteries is similar, but the materials used are not. We will look at traditional vent-cap construction first and then explain how the other battery types differ.

Vent-cap batteries
Battery construction begins with the positive and negative plates. The plates are built on grids of conductive materials, figure 7-3, which act as a framework for the dissimilar metals. These dissimilar metals are called the active materials of the battery. The active materials, sponge lead and lead dioxide, are pasted onto the grids. When dry, the active materials are very porous, so that the electrolyte can easily penetrate and react with them.

    A number of similar plates, all positive or all negative, are connected together into a plate group. A positive and a negative plate group

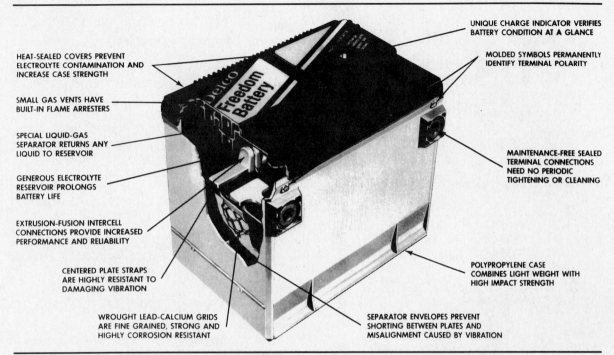

HEAT-SEALED COVERS PREVENT ELECTROLYTE CONTAMINATION AND INCREASE CASE STRENGTH

SMALL GAS VENTS HAVE BUILT-IN FLAME ARRESTERS

SPECIAL LIQUID-GAS SEPARATOR RETURNS ANY LIQUID TO RESERVOIR

GENEROUS ELECTROLYTE RESERVOIR PROLONGS BATTERY LIFE

EXTRUSION-FUSION INTERCELL CONNECTIONS PROVIDE INCREASED PERFORMANCE AND RELIABILITY

CENTERED PLATE STRAPS ARE HIGHLY RESISTANT TO DAMAGING VIBRATION

WROUGHT LEAD-CALCIUM GRIDS ARE FINE GRAINED, STRONG AND HIGHLY CORROSION RESISTANT

UNIQUE CHARGE INDICATOR VERIFIES BATTERY CONDITION AT A GLANCE

MOLDED SYMBOLS PERMANENTLY IDENTIFY TERMINAL POLARITY

MAINTENANCE-FREE SEALED TERMINAL CONNECTIONS NEED NO PERIODIC TIGHTENING OR CLEANING

POLYPROPYLENE CASE COMBINES LIGHT WEIGHT WITH HIGH IMPACT STRENGTH

SEPARATOR ENVELOPES PREVENT SHORTING BETWEEN PLATES AND MISALIGNMENT CAUSED BY VIBRATION

Figure 7-6. A cutaway view of a maintenance-free battery. Notice the internally threaded connections that form the battery terminals.

are interlaced so that their plates alternate, figure 7-4. The negative plate group normally has one more plate than the positive group. To reduce the possibility of a short between plates of the two groups, they are separated by chemically inert separators, figure 7-4. Separators are usually made of plastic or fiberglass. A complete assembly of positive plates, negative plates, and separators is called an **element**.

The element is placed in a **cell** of a battery case, figure 7-5. Because each cell provides approximately 2.1 volts, a 12-volt battery has six cells and produces approximately 12.6 volts when fully charged.

Vent caps in the battery top provide an opening for adding electrolyte and for the escape of gases that form during charging and discharging. The battery is connected to the car's electrical system by two external terminals. These terminals are either tapered posts on top of the case, as shown in figure 7-5, or internally threaded connectors on the side of the case, figure 7-6. The positive terminal, marked (+), is connected to all of the positive plates in the battery. The negative terminal, marked (–), is connected to all of the negative plates in the battery.

Low-maintenance and maintenance-free batteries

Most new batteries today are either semisealed low-maintenance or sealed maintenance-free

Element: A complete assembly of positive plates, negative plates, and separators making up one cell of a battery.

Cell: A case enclosing one element in an electrolyte. Each cell produces approximately 2.1 to 2.2 volts. Cells are connected in series.

■ Repairing Storage Batteries

Car mechanics of two generations ago found battery repairs a frequent part of their service routine. Those old batteries were usually in wooden or hard rubber cases, and the plate groups were in "jars" sealed into the case with a sealing compound. The mechanic could easily loosen this sealant to pull the plates out for inspection and repairs.

Early repair manuals give detailed instructions on how to straighten the plates, how to replace the wooden spacers between the plate groups, how to clean the sediment off the inside of the case, or how to take the elements apart.

Even though the old batteries could be easily serviced and today's batteries cannot be, they all look about the same on the outside. In fact, the biggest advance in batteries in the last generation is the development of the maintenance-free battery.

Figure 7-7. Many maintenance-free batteries have envelope separators that hold active material near the plates.

batteries, figure 7-6. Low-maintenance batteries provide some method of adding water to the cells, such as:
• Individual slotted vent caps installed flush with the top of the case
• Two vent panel covers, each of which exposes three cells when removed
• A flush-mounted strip cover which is peeled off to reveal the cell openings.

Maintenance-free batteries have only small gas vents that prevent pressure buildup in the case. A low-maintenance battery requires that water be added much less often than with a traditional vent-cap battery, while a maintenance-free battery will never need to have water added during its lifetime.

These batteries differ from vent-cap batteries primarily in the materials used for the plate grids. For decades, automotive batteries used antimony as the strengthening ingredient of the grid alloy. In low-maintenance batteries, the

amount of antimony is reduced to about 3 percent. In maintenance-free batteries, the antimony is eliminated and replaced by calcium or strontium.

Reducing the amount of antimony or replacing it with calcium or strontium alloy results in lowering the battery's internal heat and reduces the amount of gassing that occurs during charging. Since these are the principal reasons for battery water loss, these changes reduce or eliminate the need to periodically add water. Reduced water loss also minimizes terminal corrosion, since the major cause of this corrosion is condensation from normal battery gassing.

In addition, nonantimony lead alloys have better conductivity, so a maintenance-free battery has about a 20 percent higher cranking performance rating than a traditional vent-cap battery of comparable size.

Sealed maintenance-free batteries

Recently, completely sealed maintenance-free batteries have been introduced. These batteries do not require, and do not have, the small gas vents used on previous maintenance-free batteries. Although these batteries are basically the same kind of lead-acid voltage cells used in automobiles for decades, a slight change in plate and electrolyte chemistry reduces hydrogen generation to almost nothing.

During charging, a vent-cap or maintenance-free battery releases hydrogen at the negative plates and oxygen at the positive plates. Most of the hydrogen is released through electrolysis of the water in the electrolyte near the negative plates as the battery reaches full charge. In the new sealed maintenance-free design, the negative plates *never* reach a fully charged condition and therefore cause little or no release of hydrogen. Oxygen *is* released at the positive plates, but it passes through the separators and recombines with the negative plates. The overall effect is virtually no gassing from the battery. Because the oxygen released by the electrolyte recombines with the negative plates, some manufacturers call these batteries "recombination" or "**recombinant**" electrolyte batteries.

Recombinant batteries

Recombination electrolyte technology and improved grid materials allow some sealed, maintenance-free batteries to develop fully charged, open-circuit voltage of approximately 2.2 volts per cell, or a total of 13.2 volts for a 6-cell battery. Microporous fiberglass separators reduce internal resistance and contribute to higher voltage and current ratings.

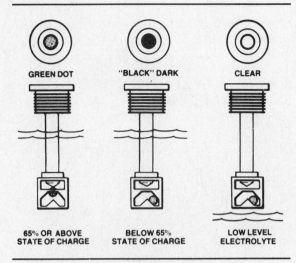

GREEN DOT   "BLACK" DARK   CLEAR

65% OR ABOVE
STATE OF CHARGE   BELOW 65%
STATE OF CHARGE   LOW LEVEL
ELECTROLYTE

Figure 7-8. Delco "Freedom" batteries have this integral hydrometer built into their tops.

In addition, the electrolyte in these new batteries is contained within plastic envelope-type separators around the plates, figure 7-7. The entire case is not flooded with electrolyte. This eliminates the possibility of damage due to sloshing or acid leaks from a cracked battery. This design feature reduces battery damage during handling and installation, and allows a more compact case design. Because the battery is not vented, terminal corrosion from battery gassing and electrolyte spills or spray is also eliminated.

The envelope design also catches active material as it flakes off the positive plates during discharge. By holding the material closer to the plates, envelope construction ensures that it will be more completely redeposited during charging.

Although recombinant batteries are examples of advanced technology, test and service requirements are basically the same as for other maintenance-free, lead-acid batteries. Some manufacturers caution, however, that fast charging at high current rates may overheat the battery and can cause damage. Always check the manufacturer's instructions for test specifications and charging rates before servicing one of these batteries.

BATTERY ELECTROLYTE

For the battery to become chemically active, it must be filled with an electrolyte solution. The electrolyte in an automotive battery is a solution of sulfuric acid and water. In a fully charged battery, the solution is approximately 35 to 39 percent acid by weight (25 percent by volume) and 61 to 65 percent water by weight.

The state of charge of a battery can be measured by checking the **specific gravity** of the electrolyte.

Specific gravity is the weight of a given volume of liquid divided by the weight of an equal volume of water. Since the acid is heavier than water, and water has a specific gravity of 1.000, the specific gravity of a fully charged battery is approximately 1.260 when weighed in a hydrometer. As the battery discharges, the specific gravity of the electrolyte decreases because the acid is changed into water. The specific gravity of the electrolyte can tell you approximately how discharged the battery has become:

1.265 specific gravity	100% charged
1.225 specific gravity	75% charged
1.190 specific gravity	50% charged
1.155 specific gravity	25% charged
1.120 specific gravity or lower	discharged

These values may vary slightly, according to the design factors of a particular battery.

Specific gravity measurements are based on a standard temperature of 80°F (26.7°C). At higher temperatures, specific gravity is lower. At lower temperatures, specific gravity is higher. For every change of 10 degrees, specific gravity changes by four points (0.004). That is:
• For every 10 degrees above 80°F, add 0.004 to the specific gravity reading.
• For every 10 degrees below 80°F, subtract 0.004 from the specific gravity reading.

STATE-OF-CHARGE INDICATORS

Many low-maintenance and maintenance-free batteries have a visual state-of-charge indicator installed in the battery top. The indicator shows whether the electrolyte has fallen below a minimum level, and it also functions as a go/no-go hydrometer.

The indicator, figure 7-8, is a plastic rod inserted in the top of the battery and extending into the electrolyte. In the design used by Delco, a green plastic ball is suspended in a cage from the bottom of the rod. Depending upon the specific gravity of the electrolyte, the

Recombinant: A nongassing battery design in which the oxygen released by the electrolyte recombines with the negative plates.

Specific Gravity: The weight of a volume of liquid divided by the weight of the same volume of water at a given temperature and pressure. Water has a specific gravity of 1.000.

ball will float or sink in the cage, changing the appearance of the indicator "eye" from green to dark. When the eye is dark, the battery should be recharged.

Other manufacturers either use the "Delco Eye" under license, or one of several variations of the design. One variation contains a red and blue ball side by side in the cage. When the specific gravity is high, only the blue ball can be seen in the "eye". As the specific gravity falls, the blue ball sinks in the cage, allowing the red ball to take its place. When the battery is recharged, the increasing specific gravity causes the blue ball to move upward, forcing the red ball back into the side of the cage.

Another variation is the use of a small red ball on top of a larger blue ball. When the specific gravity is high, the small ball is seen as a red spot surrounded by blue. As the specific gravity falls, the blue ball sinks, leaving the small ball to be seen as a red spot surrounded by a clear area. The battery then should be recharged.

If the electrolyte drops below the level of the cage in batteries using a state-of-charge indicator, the "eye" will appear clear or light yellow. This means that the battery must be replaced because it has lost too much electrolyte.

WET-CHARGED AND DRY-CHARGED BATTERIES

Batteries may be manufactured and sold as either wet-charged or dry-charged batteries. Before maintenance-free batteries became widely used, dry-charged batteries were very common. A wet-charged battery is completely filled with an electrolyte when it is built. A dry-charged battery is shipped from the factory without electrolyte. During manufacture, the positive and negative plates are charged and then completely washed and dried. The battery is then assembled and sealed to keep out moisture. It will remain charged as long as it is sealed, and it can be stored for a long time in any reasonable environment. A dry-charged battery is put into service by adding electrolyte, checking the battery's state of charge, and charging if needed.

Even when a wet-charged battery is not in use, a slow reaction occurs between the plates and the electrolyte. This is a self-discharging reaction, and will eventually discharge the battery almost completely. Because this reaction occurs faster at higher temperatures, wet-charged batteries should be stored in as cool a place as possible when not in use. A fully charged battery stored at a room temperature of 100°F (38°C) will almost completely discharge

after 90 days. If the battery is stored at a temperature of 60°F (16°C), very little discharge will take place.

BATTERY SELECTION AND RATING METHODS

Automotive batteries are 12-volt, wet-cell, lead-acid batteries which are available in a variety of sizes, shapes and current ratings. These are called starting batteries and are designed to deliver a large current output for a brief time to start an engine. After starting, the charging system takes over to supply most of the current required to operate the car. The battery acts as a system stabilizer and provides current whenever the electrical loads exceed the charging current output.

An automotive battery must provide good cranking power for the car's engine and adequate reserve power for the electrical system in which it is used. Test standards and rating methods devised by the Battery Council International (BCI) and the Society of Automotive Engineers (SAE) are designed to measure a battery's ability to meet these requirements and do its job.

The BCI publishes application charts that list the correct battery for any car. Optional heavy-duty batteries are normally used in cars with air conditioning or several major electrical accessories or in cars operated in cold climates. To ensure adequate cranking power and to meet all other electrical needs, a replacement battery may have a higher rating, but never a lower rating, than the original unit. The battery must also be the correct physical size for the car, and have the correct type of terminals. BCI standards include a coding system, called the group number.

BCI battery rating methods are explained in the following paragraphs.

Ampere-Hour Rating

The oldest battery rating method, no longer used to rate batteries, is the ampere-hour rating. This rating method was the industry standard for decades. It was replaced, however, over 10 years ago by the cranking performance and reserve capacity ratings, which provide better indications of a battery's performance.

The ampere-hour method was also called the 20-hour discharge rating method. This rating represented the steady current flow which a battery delivered at a temperature of 80°F (27°C) without cell voltage falling below 1.75 volts (a total of 10.5 volts for a 12-volt battery).

For example, a battery that continuously delivered 3 amperes for 20 hours was rated as a 60 ampere-hour battery (3 amperes × 20 hours = 60 ampere-hours).

Cranking Performance Rating

The **cranking performance rating** indicates the power a battery can supply for engine cranking at 0°F (–18°C). The rating figures for car and light truck batteries range from 165 to 1,050 cold-cranking amperes. These figures represent the current flow a battery can deliver for 30 seconds at 0°F (–18°C) while maintaining at least 1.2 volts per cell (for a minimum terminal voltage of 7.2 volts for a 12-volt battery.)

Reserve Capacity Rating

The **reserve capacity rating** indicates the long-term power available from a battery for ignition, lighting, and accessories required in emergencies. Reserve capacity (listed in minutes) is the time a fully charged battery at 80°F (27°C) can deliver 25 amperes and maintain at least 1.75 volts at every cell (10.5 volts total for a 12-volt battery). Battery reserve capacity ratings range from 30 to 175 minutes, and correspond approximately to the length of time a vehicle can be driven after the charging system has failed.

Group Number

Carmakers provide a designated amount of space in the engine compartment to accommodate the battery. Since battery companies build batteries of various current-capacity ratings in a variety of sizes and shapes, it is useful to have a guide when replacing a battery, because it must fit into the space provided. The BCI size **group number** identifies a battery in terms of its length, width, height, terminal design, and other physical features.

BATTERY CHARGING VOLTAGE AND LIFE

A battery is charged by forcing current to flow through it in the direction opposite to its discharge current. In an automobile, this charging current is supplied by the generator or alternator. The battery offers some resistance to this charging current because of the battery's chemical voltage and the resistance of the battery's internal parts. For charging current to enter the battery, the charging voltage must be great enough to overcome this resistance.

Charging Voltage Levels

When a battery is fully charged, its internal resistance is very high. Very little charging current can flow through it. When the battery is discharged, its internal resistance is very low, and charging current flows freely.

The temperature of the battery affects the charging voltage because temperature affects the resistance of the electrolyte. Cold electrolyte has higher resistance than warm electrolyte, so a colder battery is harder to charge.

Battery Life

All batteries have a limited life, but certain conditions can shorten that life. The important factors that affect battery life are discussed in the following paragraphs.

Electrolyte level

As we have seen, the design of maintenance-free batteries has minimized the loss of water from electrolyte so that battery cases can be sealed. Given normal use, the addition of water to such batteries is not required during their service life. However, even maintenance-free batteries will lose some of their water to high temperature, overcharging, deep cycling and recharging — all factors in battery gassing and resulting water loss.

With vent-cap batteries, and to some extent, low-maintenance batteries, water is lost from the electrolyte during charging in the form of hydrogen and oxygen gases. This causes the electrolyte level to drop. If the level drops below the top of the plates, active material will be exposed to the air. The material will harden and resist electrochemical reaction. Also, the remaining electrolyte will have a high concentration of acid, which can cause the plates to

---

Cranking Performance Rating: A battery rating based on the amperes of current that a battery can supply for 30 seconds at 0°F, with no battery cell falling below 1.2 volts.

Reserve Capacity Rating: A battery rating based on the number of minutes a battery at 80°F can supply 25 amperes, with no battery cell falling below 1.75 volts.

Group Number: A battery identification number that indicates battery dimensions, terminal design, holddown location, and other physical features.

COMPARISON OF CRANKING POWER AVAILABLE FROM FULLY CHARGED BATTERY AT VARIOUS TEMPERATURES.

80°F(26.7°C)	100%
32°F(0°C)	65%
0°F(−17.8°C)	40%

Figure 7-9. Battery power decreases as temperature decreases.

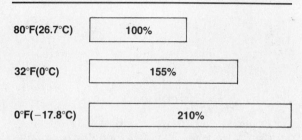

80°F(26.7°C)	100%
32°F(0°C)	155%
0°F(−17.8°C)	210%

Figure 7-10. This graph represents the increased power required to crank an engine at low temperatures.

deteriorate quickly. Even the addition of water will not restore such hardened plates to a fully active condition.

Corrosion

Battery corrosion is caused by spilled electrolyte and by electrolyte condensation from gassing. The sulfuric acid attacks and can destroy not only connectors and terminals, but metal holddowns and carriers, as well. Corroded connectors increase resistance at the battery connections. This reduces the applied voltage for the car's electrical system. Corrosion also can cause mechanical failure of the holddowns and carrier, which can damage the battery. Spilled electrolyte and corrosion on the battery top also can create a current leakage path, which can allow the battery to discharge.

Overcharging

Batteries can be overcharged either by the automotive charging system or by a separate battery charger. In either case, there is a violent chemical reaction in the battery. The water in the electrolyte is rapidly broken down into hydrogen and oxygen gases. These gas bubbles can wash active material off the plates, as well as lower the level of the electrolyte. Overcharging can also cause excessive heat, which can oxidize the positive grid material and even buckle the plates.

Undercharging and sulfation

If an automobile is not charging its battery, either because of stop-and-start driving or a fault in the charging system, the battery will be constantly discharged. When a battery plate is discharged, it is covered with lead sulfate. The amount of lead sulfate on the plate will vary according to the state of charge. As the lead sulfate builds up in a constantly undercharged battery, it can crystallize and not recombine with the electrolyte. This is called battery **sulfation**. The crystals are difficult to break down by

normal recharging and the battery becomes useless. Despite the chemical additives sold as "miracle cures" for sulfation, a completely sulfated battery cannot be effectively recharged.

Cycling

The operation of a battery from fully charged to discharged and back to charged is called **cycling**. If an automotive battery is repeatedly cycled from a fully charged condition to an almost discharged condition, the active material on the positive plates may shed and fall into the bottom of the case. If this happens, the material cannot be restored to the plates. Cycling thus reduces the capacity of the battery and shortens its useful service life.

Temperature

Temperature extremes affect battery service life and performance in a number of ways. High temperature, caused by overcharging or excessive engine heat, increases electrolyte loss and shortens battery life.

Low temperatures in winter can also harm a battery. If the electrolyte freezes, it can expand and break the case, ruining the battery. The freezing point of electrolyte depends upon its specific gravity and thus, on the battery's state of charge. A fully charged battery with a specific gravity of 1.265 to 1.280 will not freeze until its temperature drops below −60°F (−51°C). A discharged battery with an electrolyte which is mostly water can freeze at 18°F (−8°C).

As we saw earlier, cold temperatures make it harder to keep the battery fully charged, yet this is when a full charge is most important. Figure 7-9 compares the energy levels available from a fully-charged battery at various temperatures. Figure 7-10 compares the energy required to crank an engine at those temperatures. As you can see, the colder a battery is, the less energy it can supply. Yet the colder an engine gets, the more energy it requires for cranking. This is why battery care is especially important in cold weather.

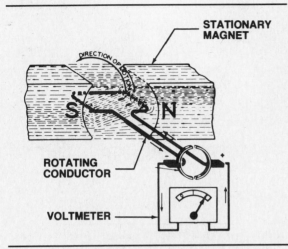

Figure 7-11. A simplified generator. (Prestolite)

Vibration

A battery must be securely mounted in its carrier to protect it from vibration. Vibration can shake the active materials off the plates and severely shorten a battery's life. Severe vibration can even crack a battery case and loosen cable connections.

CHARGING SYSTEM OPERATION

The charging system converts some of the engine's mechanical energy into electrical energy. This electrical energy is used to maintain the battery's state of charge and to operate the car's electrical system while the engine is running.

During cranking, all electrical energy for the car is supplied by the battery. Once the engine starts and runs, the charging system must produce enough electrical energy both to recharge the battery and to supply the demands of other parts of the electrical system, such as the ignition system, lighting systems, and accessories. If the starting system is in poor condition and uses too much energy, or if the charging system cannot both recharge the battery and supply the other parts, more energy must be drawn from the battery for short periods.

Voltage Sources

The two devices that convert mechanical energy to electrical energy are the generator and the alternator. Both of these units use the principle of **induction** to create an electrical voltage. When the lines of force of a magnetic field cut through a conductor (wire), a voltage will appear in the wire. The voltage will cause current flow in a complete circuit such as the automobile electrical system.

The generator is constructed with a stationary magnet, figure 7-11, and loops of wire that rotate within the magnet's field. The loops of wire are turned by a drive belt from the engine. When the loops turn, the lines of force from the magnet cut through them, and a voltage is induced within the loops. This voltage is used to recharge the battery and operate the rest of the car's electrical system.

The current that recharges the battery must be **direct current** (d.c.), that is, current that always flows in the same direction. Induction as used in generators and alternators will cause **alternating current** (a.c.), a current that flows first in one direction and then in the other. This alternating current must be **rectified**, or changed to direct current, before it can be used in the car's electrical system.

The generator is constructed so that the current is rectified mechanically. The alternator cannot use a mechanical rectifier. Until a practical way was developed to rectify alternator output, generators were used in cars. Today, alternators use **solid-state** electronic parts as rectifiers. These are called **diodes**, and they act

Sulfation: The crystallization of lead sulfate on the plates of a constantly discharged battery.

Cycling: Battery electrochemical action and operation. One complete cycle is operation from fully charged to discharged and back to fully charged.

Induction: The production of an electrical voltage in a conductor or coil by moving the conductor or coil through a magnetic field, or by moving the magnetic field past the conductor or coil.

Direct Current: A flow of electricity in one direction through a conductor.

Alternating Current: A flow of electricity through a conductor, first in one direction, then in the opposite direction.

Rectified: Electrical current changed from alternating (a.c.) to direct (d.c.).

Solid-State: A method of controlling electrical current flow, in which the parts are primarily made of semiconductor materials.

Diodes: Electronic devices made of semiconductor material that allow current flow in one direction but block it in the other.

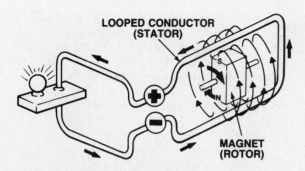

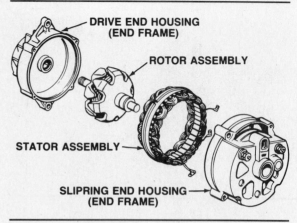

Figure 7-12. A simplified alternator.

Figure 7-14. The alternator housing encloses the rotor and stator.

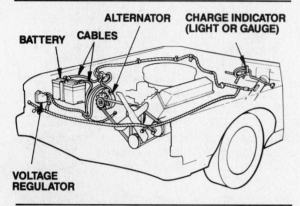

Figure 7-13. The major components of an automotive charging system. (Chrysler)

as one-way electrical check valves. Current can flow through a diode in one direction but not in the other.

The alternator, figure 7-12, works on the same principle of induction as the generator. As the lines of force from the magnet cut through the conductor, voltage is induced.

Charging Voltage

Although the automotive electrical system is called a 12-volt system, the alternator must produce more than 12 volts. We learned earlier in this chapter that each battery cell produces about 2.1 volts when fully charged. This means that the open-circuit voltage of a fully charged 12-volt battery (6 cells) is approximately 12.6 volts. If the alternator cannot produce more than 12 volts, it cannot charge the battery until system voltage drops under 12 volts. This would leave nothing extra to serve the other electrical demands put on the system by lights, air conditioning, and power accessories.

Alternating-current charging systems are generally regulated to produce a maximum output of 14.5 volts. Output of more than 16 volts will overheat the battery electrolyte and shorten

its life. High voltage also can damage components that rely heavily on solid-state electronics, such as fuel injection and engine control systems. On the other hand, low voltage output will cause the battery to become sulfated. As you can see, the charging system must be maintained within the voltage limits specified by the carmaker if the vehicle is to perform properly.

A.C. CHARGING SYSTEM COMPONENTS

The automotive charging system, figure 7-13, contains:
• A battery, which provides the initial field current required to operate the alternator and, in turn, is charged and maintained by the alternator.
• An alternator, which is belt driven by the engine and converts mechanical motion into charging voltage and current. A simple alternator, figure 7-12, consists of a magnet rotating inside a fixed-loop stator, or conductor. The alternating current produced in the conductor is rectified by diodes for use by the electrical system.
• A regulator, which limits the field current flow and thus the alternator's voltage output according to the electrical system demand. A regulator can be either an electromechanical or a solid-state device. Some late-model solid-state regulators are part of the vehicle's onboard computer.
• An ammeter, a voltmeter, or an indicator warning lamp mounted on the instrument panel to give a visual indication of charging system operation. The following paragraphs describe these units and show the designs used by major manufacturers.

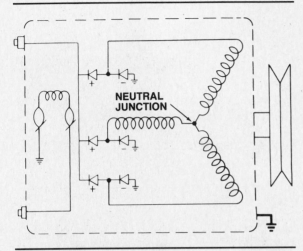

Figure 7-15. The circuit diagram of a typical automotive alternator. (Prestolite)

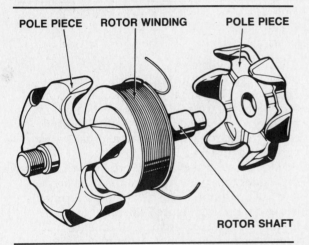

Figure 7-16. The magnetic field of the rotor is caused by current flow through the rotor winding. (Bosch)

Alternator

A disassembled alternator is shown in figure 7-14. The rotor is the magnet that is turned by the engine. The stator is the collection of three looped conductors within which voltage is induced. The two end frames enclose the rotor and stator. The end frames hold the bearings that support the rotor shaft and provide the terminals where the stator conductors and rotor winding are connected to the rest of the electrical system.

In most alternators, each of the three stator conductors is connected to two diodes, figure 7-15. This allows all of the alternator's output to be rectified and used in the car's electrical system. Some heavy-duty alternators have more than six diodes. The diodes are mounted on one alternator end housing.

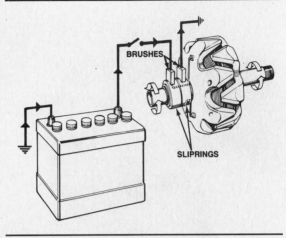

Figure 7-17. The sliprings and brushes carry current to the rotor windings.

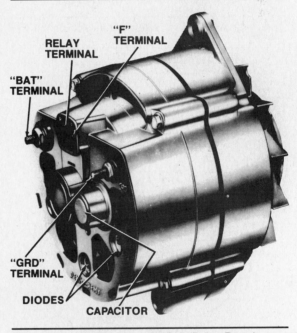

Figure 7-18. The Delcotron 10-DN. (Delco-Remy)

Whenever current flows through a conductor, a magnetic field is created around the conductor. The magnetic field of the rotor is created by the flow of electrical current through a coil of wire in the rotor assembly, figure 7-16. This coil is called the rotor winding, and the current flow is called the field current. Field current reaches the rotor through sliprings and brushes, figure 7-17. Each slipring is attached to one end of the rotor winding. The sliprings are mounted on the rotor shaft and rotate with the shaft. The brushes are held in place within the alternator end housing. Spring tension holds

Figure 7-19. A 10-SI series alternator. (Delco-Remy)

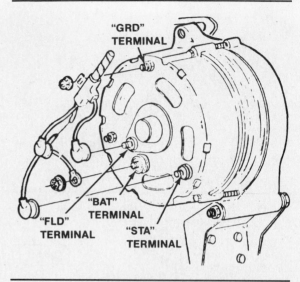

Figure 7-21. A Motorcraft rear-terminal alternator. (Ford)

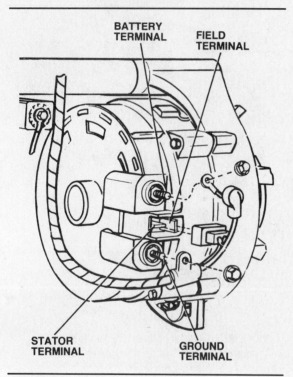

Figure 7-20. The Motorcraft side-terminal alternator. (Ford)

each brush against the surface of one of the sliprings. Field current flows through one brush and its slipring, through the rotor winding, and back out through the other slipring and brush.

Specific alternators
Delco-Remy, a division of General Motors Corporation, supplies most of the electrical devices used on GM vehicles, as well as those of some other carmakers. The trademarked name for Delco-Remy's alternators is Delcotron® generators. Until the early 1970s, the most common model was the 10-DN, figure 7-18. The most common late-model Delcotron alternators are part of the SI series, figure 7-19.

Motorcraft, a division of Ford Motor Company, makes most of the alternators used on domestic Ford automobiles. These have terminals either on the side, figure 7-20, or on the rear, figure 7-21. The Motorcraft IAR (integral alternator/regulator) model was introduced on some front-wheel-drive Ford cars in 1985. This alternator also has a solid-state regulator mounted on its rear housing, figure 7-22.

Chrysler Corporation manufactures all of the alternators for its domestic cars. Most 1972 through 1984 Chrysler models use the alternator shown in figure 7-23, which has a remotely mounted solid-state regulator. Chrysler eliminated the use of a separate voltage regulator on most 1985 and later fuel-injected and turbocharged engines by incorporating the regulator function in the engine control computer.

Regulator

The regulator used with an alternator has only one job: to limit the voltage strength of the alternator's output. The car's electrical system is designed to work on about 12 volts. If a greater voltage is applied to the battery and electrical circuits, they could be damaged. The regulator limits the alternator output to about 12 volts.

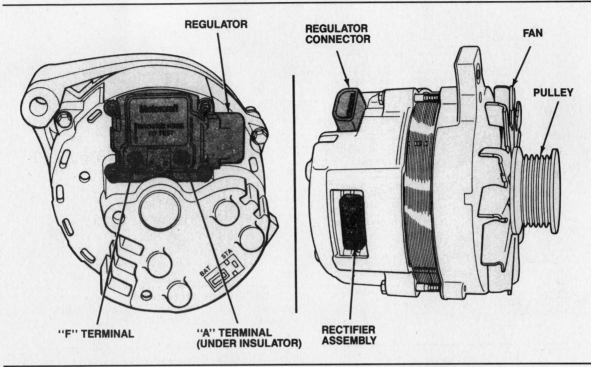

Figure 7-22. The 1985 and later Motorcraft IAR alternator also has a rear-mounted regulator.

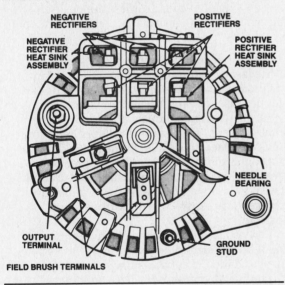

Figure 7-23. The terminals on a Chrysler standard-duty alternator. (Chrysler)

The alternator uses induction to limit its current output. When an induced voltage causes current flow in a conductor, that conductor creates its own magnetic field. As current flow increases, the magnetic field expands. This expanding magnetic field induces another voltage within the same conductor. This countervoltage will tend to oppose any change in the original current flow.

When induced voltage causes current flow in the conductors of the stator, a countervoltage also appears. The countervoltage opposes any increased current flow in the stator. The more current the alternator puts out, the greater this countervoltage becomes. The alternator reaches its maximum current output when the countervoltage is great enough to totally stop any further increase in the *current*. However, because the two *voltages* will continue to increase as alternator speed increases, a method of regulating alternator voltage is required.

Voltage regulation
Alternator output voltage is directly related to the strength of the rotor's magnetic field and the speed of rotation. An increase in either factor will increase voltage output. Similarly, a decrease in either factor will decrease voltage output. Rotor speed is controlled by engine speed, and cannot be changed simply to control the alternator. The field strength can be changed by controlling the field current in the rotor windings. This is how both alternator and generator voltage regulators work.

Figure 7-24 shows how the field current (dashed line) is lowered to keep alternator voltage output (solid line) at a constant maximum, even when the rotor speed increases. At low rotor speeds, the field current is allowed to flow at full strength for relatively long periods of time, and is reduced only for short periods. At

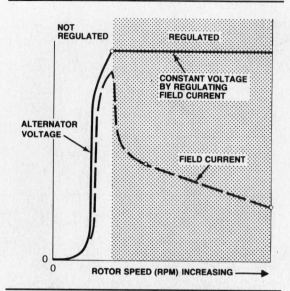

Figure 7-24. Field current is decreased as rotor speed increases to keep alternator output voltage at a constant level.

Figure 7-26. An example of the latest integrated circuit regulator design, Ford's IAR regulator and brush holder are combined.

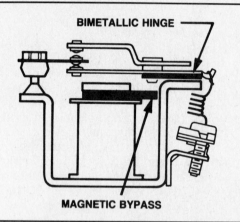

Figure 7-25. An alternator's electromagnetic voltage regulator. (Delco-Remy)

high rotor speeds, the field current is reduced for long periods of time and flows at full strength only for short periods. The regulator that controls this flow can be an electromagnetic switch or a solid-state device.

Electromagnetic regulators

An electromagnetic regulator is a mechanical switch that is opened and closed by magnetism. It has a coil, figure 7-25, and a hinged armature. Current flow through the coil creates a magnetic field that moves the armature. The current flow through the coil is caused by the alternator's voltage. As the alternator's voltage varies, the current flow through the regulator coil varies. Field current for the alternator must flow through contact points on the regulator

armature. The position of the armature determines how much field current can reach the alternator. As the alternator's voltage varies, and the coil's magnetic field varies, the position of the armature changes and the field current flow is affected.

Solid-state regulators

In the last decade, semiconductor technology has made solid-state voltage regulators possible. Because they are smaller, have no moving parts, and are not seriously affected by temperature changes, solid-state regulators have completely replaced older electromagnetic designs in a.c. charging systems on late-model cars. Because of their construction, however, all solid-state regulators are nonserviceable and must be replaced if defective. No adjustments are possible.

Early solid-state designs combined transistors with the electromagnetic field relay. The latest and most compact is the integrated-circuit (IC) regulator, figure 7-26. This combines all control circuitry and components on a single silicon chip. Attaching terminals are added, and the chip is sealed in a small plastic module that mounts inside, or on the back of, the alternator. This eliminates exposed wiring and connections that could be damaged. In the mid-1980s, many carmakers moved the regulator function into the engine control computer of fully integrated electronic engine control systems.

Specific solid-state regulator designs

A solid-state automotive regulator is integrally mounted in the alternator housing of Delco-

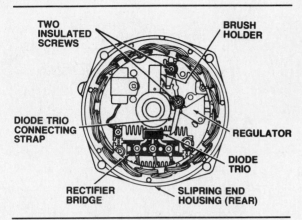

Figure 7-27. The rear end housing of the 10-SI Delcotron alternator. (Delco-Remy)

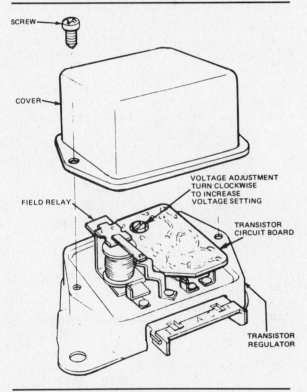

Figure 7-28. The Ford solid-state voltage regulator with electromagnetic field relay. (Ford)

Figure 7-29. The Ford remote solid-state regulator.

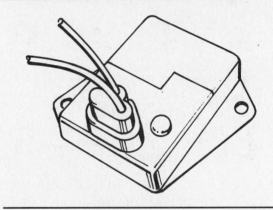

Figure 7-30. The Chrysler solid-state regulator is mounted on the firewall or shock tower.

Remy 10-, 12-, and 15-SI series alternators, see figure 7-27.

Ford Motorcraft alternators use both remote-mounted and integral solid-state regulators. An early remote-mounted unit, figure 7-28, had both a transistorized voltage regulator and an electromagnetic field relay in the same housing. In 1978, Ford began using a remote-mounted, fully solid-state regulator, figure 7-29, on its intermediate and large cars. The Motorcraft integral alternator/regulator (IAR) introduced in 1985 uses an integrated circuit regulator mounted on the outside of the alternator rear housing.

Many late-model Chrysler products use a remote-mounted solid-state regulator, figure 7-30, which has two terminals — one connected to the ignition system, the other to the alternator field. Chrysler eliminated the separate regulator by moving its function to the engine control computer on 1985 and later 4-cylinder engines. On these models, the onboard diagnostic capability of Chrysler's engine control system detects charging system problems and records fault codes in the system memory. Some of the codes will light a POWER LOSS or POWER LIMITED lamp on the instrument panel.

Figure 7-31. An automotive voltmeter for the instrument panel.

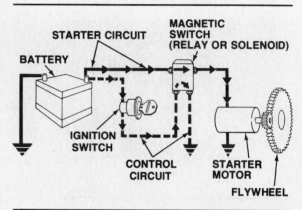

Figure 7-32. In this diagram of the starting system, the starter circuit is shown as a solid line and the control circuit is shown as a dashed line. (Delco-Remy)

Indicators

A charging system indicator lets the driver check on the charging system. It can be:
• A warning lamp that lights when the alternator is not supplying voltage greater than battery voltage
• An ammeter that shows current flow into and out of the battery
• A voltmeter that shows the battery or electrical system voltage, figure 7-31.

STARTING SYSTEM OPERATION

The automotive starting system is also called the cranking system. Its only job is to crank the engine fast enough for the engine to fire and run. The ignition and fuel systems must supply the spark and fuel for the engine to start and run, but the starting system cranks the engine to get it going. The starting system is controlled by the driver through the ignition switch.

System Circuits

The starting system draws a large amount of current from the battery to power the starter motor. To handle this current safely and with a minimum voltage loss from resistance (**voltage drop**), the cables must be the correct size, and all connections must be clean and tight. If the heavy cables that carry current to the starter were routed to the instrument panel and the switch, they would be so long that the starter would not get enough current to operate properly. To avoid such a voltage drop, the starting system has two connected circuits. One circuit, the starter circuit, consists of the large cables between the battery and the motor. The other circuit, the control circuit, includes the ignition switch and a magnetic switch that allows the driver to open and close the starter circuit.

The starter circuit, or motor circuit, shown as the solid lines of figure 7-32, consists of:
1. The battery
2. A magnetic switch coil
3. The starter motor
4. Heavy-gauge cables.
    The control circuit, shown as the dashed lines of figure 7-32, consists of:
1. The ignition switch
2. Magnetic switch contact points
3. Normal-gauge wiring.
    When the driver closes the ignition switch (turns it to the start position), a small amount of current flows through the coil of the magnetic switch. This creates a magnetic field in the switch that closes a set of contact points, which are part of the contact circuit. When the contacts are closed, current can flow directly from the battery to the starter motor. When the motor has cranked the engine and the engine is running, the driver opens (releases) the ignition switch. This stops the current flow through the magnetic switch and the magnetic field disappears. The contact points open, opening the starter circuit and stopping current flow to the motor.

Starter Motor Drive

The starter motor cranks a car's engine through a pinion gear that engages a ring gear on the engine flywheel. When current flow reaches the motor, the pinion gear spins and the engine is cranked. If the starter motor were always connected to the engine, it would be turned by the engine once the engine had started and was running. This would damage the starter motor, because it is not designed to turn at such high speeds. The pinion gear must be moved into and out of mesh with the engine flywheel gear every time the engine is cranked.

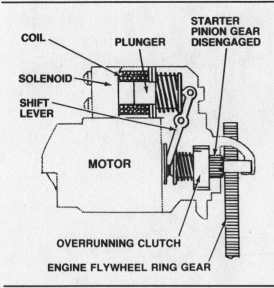

Figure 7-33. A typical solenoid-actuated drive.

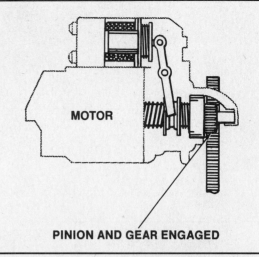

Figure 7-34. The movement of the solenoid plunger meshes the pinion gear and the flywheel ring gear.

This is the job of the starter motor drive. On most automotive starters, the drive is operated by magnetism. The most common type is a solenoid-actuated drive, figure 7-33. When current flow reaches the motor through the starter circuit, it flows through the coils of the solenoid and creates a magnetic field. The solenoid's plunger is pulled into the coils by the field force. This motion is transferred through a shift lever to the pinion gear. The gear is moved into mesh with the flywheel, figure 7-34. When the engine has started and the driver stops current flow to the starter motor, the solenoid's magnetic field disappears. A return spring forces the solenoid plunger out of the coil and the pinion gear is moved out of mesh with the engine flywheel.

To protect the motor from being turned at high speed before the driver releases the ignition switch, starter drives include an overrunning clutch, figure 7-33. This is a mechanical device, mounted on the armature shaft, that transfers the rotation of the shaft to the pinion gear so that the engine can be cranked. The clutch works through anarrangement of rollers and notches. When the motor armature is turning faster than the flywheel, the clutch transfers the motion. When the flywheel is turning faster than the motor armature, the clutch will not transfer the motion. The clutch simply spins by itself, protecting the armature.

Voltage Drop: The measurement of the loss of voltage caused by the resistance of a conductor or a circuit device.

STARTING SYSTEM COMPONENTS

We have already studied the battery, which is an important part of the starting system. The other circuit parts are the:
1. Ignition switch
2. Starting safety switch (on some systems)
3. Relays or solenoids (magnetic switches)
4. Starter motor
5. Wiring.

■ Early Starting Systems

The earliest cars generally used a hand crank to turn the engine over until the compression built up enough to ignite the air-fuel mixture and the engine began to run on its own. Much later, electric starters were used. In the meantime, several other systems saved the driver from having to crank the engine by hand.

One of these was the Prest-O-Lite gas starter, which injected a small air-fuel charge into the cylinders, instead of mechanically turning the crankshaft. The driver operated a small hand pump to charge the cylinders, then turned on the ignition switch to fire the charge in proper firing order. This would turn over the engine and generate the current necessary for continued operation.

Another system used compressed air or compressed exhaust to drive the pistons. The exhaust was stored in a tank when the engine was still running, and would presumably still be compressed when the driver needed to start the car again. The compressed air would drive a "starter motor" attached to the front of the engine where the crank used to be. This would turn over the engine until it began firing by itself.

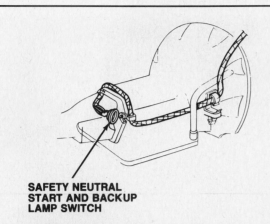

**SAFETY NEUTRAL
START AND BACKUP
LAMP SWITCH**

Figure 7-35. An electrical safety switch mounted on the transmission housing. (Chrysler)

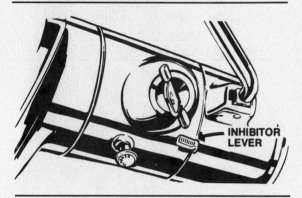

INHIBITOR LEVER

Figure 7-36. A lever on the steering wheel blocks the movement of the ignition key when the transmission is in gear.

Ignition Switch

The ignition switch has jobs other than controlling the starting system. The ignition switch normally has at least four positions:
1. Accessories
2. Off
3. On (Run)
4. Start.

Switches on late-model cars also have a lock position to lock the steering wheel. All positions except start are **detented**. That is, the switch will remain in that position until moved. When the ignition key is turned to start and released, it will return to the on (run) position. The start position is the actual starter switch part of the ignition switch. It applies battery voltage to the magnetic switch.

Starting Safety Switch

The **starting safety switch** is also called a neutral start switch. It is a normally open switch

Figure 7-37. The Ford starter relay or magnetic switch.

that prevents the starting system from operating when the automobile's transmission is in gear. If the car has no starting safety switch, it is possible to spin the engine with the transmission in gear. This will make the car lurch forward or backward which could be dangerous. Safety switches or interlock devices are used with all automatic transmissions and on many late-model cars with manual transmissions. The safety switch can be an electrical switch, figure 7-35, that opens the control circuit if the car is in gear. It can also be a mechanical interlock device, figure 7-36, that will not let the ignition switch turn to start if the car is in gear.

Magnetic Switch (Relays and Solenoids)

A magnetic switch in the starting system allows the control circuit to open and close the starter circuit. The switch can be a:
- **Relay**, which uses the electromagnetic field of a coil to attract an armature and close the contact points.
- **Solenoid**, which uses the electromagnetic field of a coil to pull a plunger into the coil and close the contact points. The plunger's movement can also be used to do a mechanical job, such as shifting the starter motor gear in a solenoid-actuated drive.

GM cars use the solenoid that is mounted on the starter as the system magnetic switch. Ford products usually have a remotely mounted solenoid, called a starter relay, figure 7-37, or they use a starter-mounted solenoid. Chrysler products have a starter relay, figure 7-38.

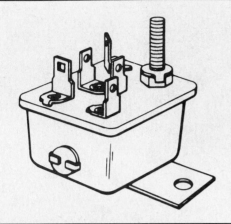

Figure 7-38. The Chrysler starter relay.

Starter Motor

The starter motor converts electrical energy from the battery into mechanical energy to turn the engine. It does this through the interaction of magnetic fields, figure 7-39. When current flows through a conductor, a magnetic field is formed around the conductor. If the conductor is placed in another magnetic field, the two fields will be weakened at one side and strengthened at the other side, position A. The conductor will tend to move from the strong field into the weak field, position B. Positions C and D show how a simple motor can use this movement to make the conductors rotate. An automotive starter motor has many conductors and uses a lot of current to create enough rotational force to crank the engine.

Figure 7-40 shows a cutaway view of a starter motor. The armature is the collection of conductors that will spin to crank the engine. The starter drive gear is mounted on the armature shaft. The pole pieces are the stationary magnetic fields. The motor housing encloses the armature and pole pieces, holds the bearings that support the armature shaft, and provides the terminals for connecting the motor to the rest of the starting system.

All GM starters are solenoid-actuated, figure 7-41. Chrysler uses two solenoid-actuated starters. One type has a reduction gear within the motor drive assembly, figure 7-42.

Ford uses both a solenoid-actuated starter and a movable pole shoe starter, figure 7-43. This has one pole piece that is hinged and held up out of the motor housings by spring tension. When the ignition switch is turned to start, a small amount of current flows to the movable pole shoe. The magnetic field that is created

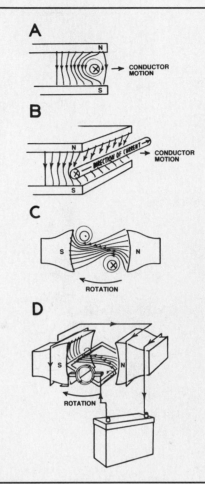

Figure 7-39. The motor principle. (Prestolite)

Detented: Positions in a switch that allow the switch to stay in that position. In an ignition switch, the On, Off, Lock, and Accessory positions are detented.

Starting Safety Switch: A neutral start switch. It keeps the starting system from operating when a car's transmission is in gear.

Relay: An electromagnetic switch. A relay uses a small amount of current flow to control the flow of a larger amount of current through a separate circuit.

Solenoid: An iron core with a wire coil surrounding it. The core moves when electrical current is applied to the coil. It is used to convert electrical energy to mechanical energy.

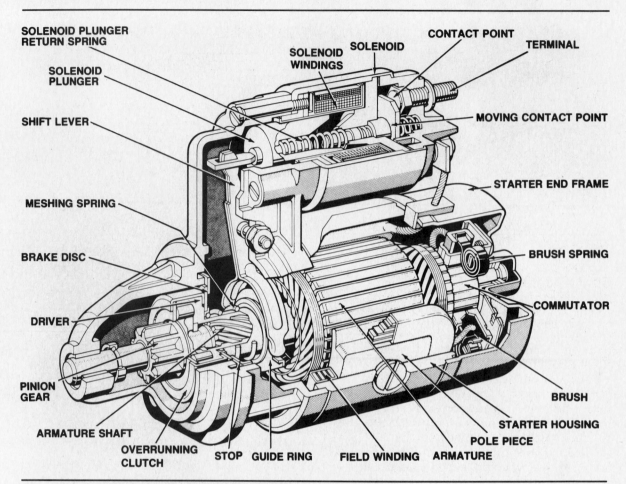

Figure 7-40. A cutaway view of a typical starter motor.

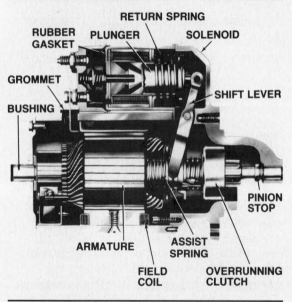

Figure 7-41. The Delco-Remy solenoid-actuated drive motor. (Delco-Remy)

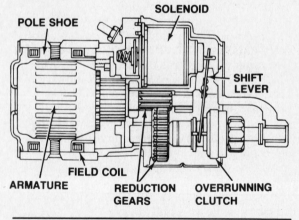

Figure 7-42. The Chrysler reduction gear starter motor. (Chrysler)

pulls the pole piece down into the starter housing. This motion does two things:
• It shifts the pinion gear into mesh with the flywheel
• It closes contact points to connect the starter motor directly to the battery.

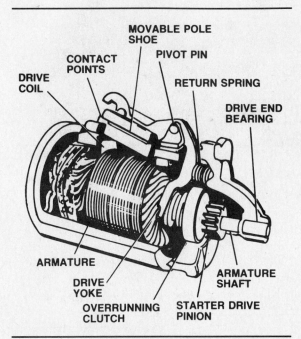

Figure 7-43. The Ford movable pole shoe starter.

When the engine has started and the driver releases the ignition switch, there is no magnetic field to hold the pole piece down. The spring pulls the pole piece back up. This disengages the pinion gear and opens the contact points to stop current flow to the motor.

SUMMARY — EFFECTS OF BATTERY, CHARGING, AND STARTING SYSTEMS ON ENGINE PERFORMANCE

The symptoms caused by defects in these systems are often very similar. To make the relationships between these systems more clear, we have organized the possible defects into groups according to the engine performance symptoms that they may cause:

- No cranking or slow cranking
- Normal cranking — no starting or hard starting
- Engine quits under electrical load.

Before using these paragraphs to identify defects, make sure all other systems have been checked out first.

No Cranking or Slow Cranking

If the engine does not turn over, or if it cranks too slowly, the starting system may be at fault. However, this could also be caused by a discharged battery, which in turn can be caused by a battery defect or a weak charging system.

Normal Cranking — No Starting or Hard Starting

When the engine is being cranked at normal speed but the engine will not start or is hard to start, the engine is probably not getting enough ignition system voltage. This can be caused by a weak battery that does not have enough energy for both the starting and the ignition systems.

■ Parasitic Losses

Parasitic losses are small current drains required to operate electrical systems, such as the clock, that continue to work when the car is parked and the ignition is off. The current demand of a clock is small and not likely to cause a problem.

The advent of computer controls, however, has made parasitic losses more serious. Many late-model cars have computers to control such diverse items as engine operation, radio tuning, suspension leveling, climate control, and more. Each of these microprocessors contains random access memory (RAM) that stores information relevant to its job. To "remember", RAM requires a constant supply of power, and therefore puts a continuous drain on the car's electrical system.

The combined drain of several computer memories can discharge a battery to the point where there is insufficient cranking power after only a few weeks. Vehicles with these systems that are driven infrequently, put into storage, or awaiting parts for repair will require battery charging more often than older cars with lower parasitic voltage losses.

Because of the higher parasitic current drains on late-model cars, the old test of removing a battery cable connection and tapping it against the terminal while looking for a spark is both dangerous and no longer a valid check for excessive current drain. Furthermore, every time the power source to the computer is interrupted, the information programmed into memory is lost and will have to be reprogrammed when the battery is reconnected.

On engine control systems with learning capability, like GM's Computer Command Control, driveability may also be affected until the computer relearns the engine calibration modifications that were erased from its memory when the battery was disconnected.

The battery's condition is caused either by a battery defect or by a problem in the charging system. If the battery and the charging system are all right, the problem may be excessive current draw through the starting circuit, not leaving enough energy for the ignition system even with a fully charged battery.

Quits under Electrical Load

If the engine quits at idle or under acceleration when many accessories are being used, it is because the ignition voltage has dropped below the minimum requirement. This is caused by either a battery defect or a charging system problem that has weakened the battery.

Review Questions

Choose the single most correct answer.
Compare your answers with the correct answers on page 451.

1. Which of the following statements is *not* true of a replacement battery?
   a. It may have the same rating as the original battery
   b. It may have a higher rating than the original battery
   c. It may have a lower rating than the original battery
   d. It should be selected according to an application chart

2. The correct ratio of water to sulfuric acid in battery electrolyte is *approximately*:
   a. 80 percent water to 20 percent sulfuric acid
   b. 60 percent water to 40 percent sulfuric acid
   c. 40 percent water to 60 percent sulfuric acid
   d. 20 percent water to 80 percent sulfuric acid

3. Each cell of an automobile battery can produce about _____ volts.
   a. 1.2
   b. 2.1
   c. 4.2
   d. 6

4. Batteries are rated in terms of:
   a. Ampere-hours
   b. Reserve capacity
   c. Cranking performance at 0° F
   d. Any of the above

5. Battery electrolyte is a mixture of water and:
   a. Lead peroxide
   b. Sulfuric acid
   c. Lead sulfate
   d. All of the above

6. The electrolyte in a fully charged battery will generally not freeze until the temperature drops to:
   a. 32° F (0°C)
   b. 0° F (–18°C)
   c. –20° to –30° F (–29° to –34°C)
   d. Below –60° F (–51°C)

7. Alternating current in an alternator is rectified by:
   a. Brushes
   b. Diodes
   c. Sliprings
   d. Transistors

8. The principal cause of battery water loss is:
   a. Spillage from the vent caps
   b. Leakage through the battery case
   c. Conversion of water to sulfuric acid
   d. Evaporation due to heat of the charging current

9. Alternator output voltage is directly related to:
   a. Field strength
   b. Rotor speed
   c. Both field strength and rotor speed
   d. Neither field strength nor rotor speed

10. Which of the following is *not* used to monitor the charging system?
    a. Ammeter
    b. Ohmmeter
    c. Voltmeter
    d. None of the above

11. Which of the following statements is true?
    a. The generator rotates a looped conductor inside a fixed magnetic field
    b. The generator rotates a fixed magnet inside a fixed, looped conductor
    c. The alternator rotates a looped conductor inside a fixed magnetic field
    d. None of the above

12. During cranking, all electrical energy for the automobile system is supplied by the:
    a. Alternator
    b. Battery
    c. Generator
    d. None of the above

13. Which of the following does *not* convert mechanical energy to electrical energy?
    a. Alternator
    b. Battery
    c. Generator
    d. None of the above

14. Which of the following is true of solenoids?
    a. They use the electromagnetic field of a coil to pull a plunger into the coil
    b. They are generally used to engage the starter motor with the engine flywheel
    c. They operate with a movable plunger and usually do a mechanical job
    d. All of the above

15. Which of the following is *not* part of the starter control circuit?
    a. The ignition switch
    b. The starting safety switch
    c. The starter relay
    d. The starter motor

16. The ignition switch will *not* remain in which of the following positions?
    a. Accessories
    b. Off
    c. On (run)
    d. Start

17. The grid material used in a maintenance-free battery is alloyed with:
    a. Silicon
    b. Antimony
    c. Calcium
    d. Germanium

18. Low-maintenance batteries:
    a. Have no cell caps or vent
    b. Do not require additional water
    c. Both a and b
    d. Neither a nor b

19. Recombinant batteries are:
    a. Rebuilt units
    b. Completely sealed
    c. Vented to release gassing
    d. Unable to produce a higher cell voltage

8

The Ignition Primary Circuit and Components

This chapter explains the components of the low-voltage primary ignition circuit and how the circuit operates. Breaker points were used to open and close the low-voltage primary circuit until the mid-1970s, when solid-state electronic switching devices took their place. Whether breaker points or electronic switches are used, however, the principles of producing high voltage by electromagnetic induction remain the same, as we will see.

NEED FOR HIGH VOLTAGE

Energy is supplied to the automotive electrical system by the battery. The battery can supply about 12 volts, but the voltage required to ignite the air-fuel mixture can range from 5,000 to more than 25,000 volts, depending upon engine operating conditions.

This high voltage is required to cause an arc across the spark plug air gap. The required voltage level increases when the:
1. Spark plug air gap increases
2. Engine operating temperature increases (resistance increases with greater temperature)
3. Air-fuel mixture contains less fuel (fewer volatile fuel particles)
4. Air-fuel mixture is at a greater pressure (resistance increases with an increase in pressure).

Since part of the ignition system's job is to provide a high-voltage spark, battery voltage must be greatly increased to meet the needs of the ignition system. This can be done by using electromagnetic induction, which we studied in Chapter 7.

HIGH VOLTAGE THROUGH INDUCTION

We know that a current-carrying conductor or coil is surrounded by a magnetic field. As current in the coil increases or decreases, the magnetic field expands or contracts. If a second coiled conductor is placed within this magnetic field, figure 8-1, the expanding or contracting magnetic flux lines will cut the second coil, causing a voltage to be induced in the second coil. This transfer of energy between two unconnected conductors is called **mutual induction**.

Induction in the Ignition Coil

The ignition coil uses the principle of mutual induction to step up or transform low battery voltage to high ignition voltage. The ignition coil, figure 8-1, contains two windings of copper wire around a soft iron core. The primary winding is made of a hundred or so turns of

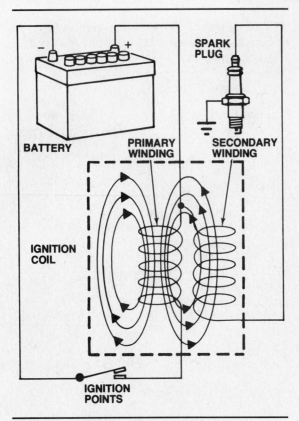

Figure 8-1. Mutual induction in the ignition coil supplies voltage to the spark plugs.

heavy wire. It is connected to the battery so that current flows through it. The secondary winding is made of many thousand turns of fine wire. When current flow in the primary winding increases or decreases, a voltage is induced in the secondary winding.

The ratio of the number of turns in the secondary winding to the number of turns in the primary winding can be between 100 and 200 to 1. This ratio is the voltage multiplier. That is, any voltage induced in the secondary winding will be 100 to 200 times the voltage present in the primary winding.

Several factors govern the coil's induction of voltage. Only two of these factors can be controlled easily in an ignition system. Induced voltage will increase with:
• More magnetic flux lines (a stronger magnetic field caused by greater current flow)
• More rapid movement of flux lines (faster collapse of the field caused by an abrupt end to current flow).

Normal voltage applied to the coil primary winding is about 9 to 10 volts (at high speeds, voltage may rise to 12 volts or more). This voltage causes from 1 to 4 amperes of current to flow in the primary winding. When this current

is flowing, a magnetic field builds up around the windings. Building up a complete magnetic field is called **magnetic saturation**, or coil saturation. When this current flow stops, the primary winding's magnetic field collapses. A greater voltage is self-induced in the primary winding by the collapse of its own magnetic field. This self-induction creates from 250 to 400 volts in the primary winding. If it develops 250 volts and the turns ratio multiplies this by 100, then 25,000 volts will be induced in the secondary winding. This is enough voltage to ignite the air-fuel mixture under almost all operating conditions.

This kind of ignition system, based on the induction of a high voltage in a coil, is called an **inductive-discharge ignition** system. An inductive-discharge system using a battery as the source of low-voltage current has been the standard automotive ignition system for about 80 years.

We have seen that the ignition system can transform low battery voltage into high ignition voltage. Now we can look at the ignition system circuitry to see how the system works.

BASIC CIRCUITS AND CURRENT FLOW

The ignition system, figure 8-2, consists of two interconnected circuits:
1. The primary (low-voltage) circuit
2. The secondary (high-voltage) circuit.
    When the ignition switch is turned on, battery current flows:
• Through the ignition switch and the primary resistor
• To and through the coil primary winding
• Through a switching device (breaker points or solid-state device)
• To ground and the grounded terminal of the battery.
    Low-voltage current flow in the coil primary winding creates a magnetic field. When the switching device interrupts this current flow:
• A high-voltage surge is induced in the coil secondary winding
• Current flows through an ignition cable from the coil to the distributor
• Current passes through the distributor cap, rotor, across the rotor air gap, and through another ignition cable
• Current flows to the spark plug, where it arcs to ground.
    The inductive-discharge battery ignition system was invented by Charles F. Kettering in 1908. He used a set of contact points as a mechanical switch to open and close the circuit to

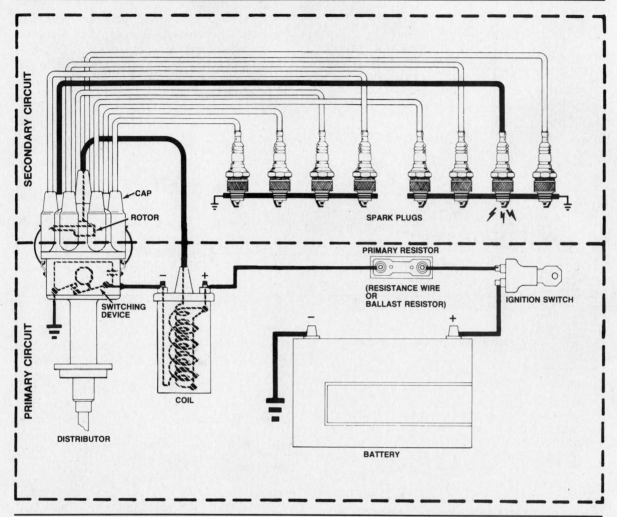

Figure 8-2. The ignition system is divided into the primary circuit and the secondary circuit. (Prestolite)

the primary winding of the ignition coil. These contacts are opened by the rotation of a cam on the distributor shaft. They are called **breaker points** because they continually break the primary circuit.

Kettering's ignition system was quickly adopted as the standard for the automotive industry and was used virtually unchanged for over 60 years. By the early 1970s, though, solid-state electronic components began to replace breaker points as switching devices for the primary circuit. The electronic or breakerless ignitions on late-model cars still use the inductive-discharge principles to produce a high-voltage spark. However, the primary circuits are controlled by electronic rather than mechanical switching devices.

Mutual Induction: The transfer of energy between two unconnected conductors, caused by the expanding or contracting magnetic flux lines of the current-carrying conductor.

Magnetic Saturation: The condition when a magnetic field reaches full strength and maximum flux density.

Inductive-Discharge Ignition: A method of igniting the air-fuel mixture in an engine cylinder. It is based on the induction of a high voltage in the secondary winding of a coil.

Breaker Points: The metal contact points that act as an electrical switch in a distributor. They open and close the ignition primary circuit.

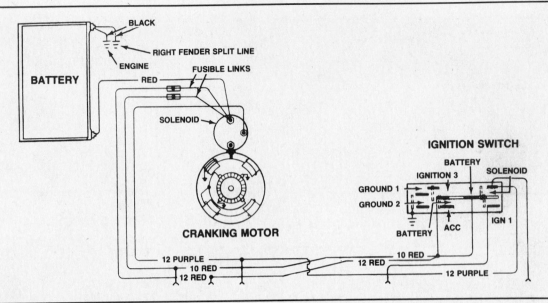

Figure 8-3. General Motors products draw current from a terminal on the starter solenoid. (Buick)

PRIMARY CIRCUIT COMPONENTS

The primary circuit, figure 8-2, contains the:
1. Battery
2. Ignition switch
3. Primary (ballast) resistor (in some systems)
4. Starting bypass (in some systems)
5. Switching device in the distributor
6. Coil primary winding.

Battery

The battery supplies low-voltage current to the ignition primary circuit. This current flows when the ignition switch is in the Start or the Run position.

Ignition Switch

The ignition switch controls low-voltage current through the primary circuit. This current can flow when the ignition switch is in the Start or the Run position. Other switch positions route current to accessory circuits and lock the steering wheel in position.

Manufacturers use differing ignition switch circuitry. The differences lie in how battery current is routed to the switch. Regardless of variations, full system voltage is always present at the switch, as if it were connected directly to the battery.

General Motors automobiles draw ignition current from a terminal on the Delco-Remy starter motor solenoid, figure 8-3. Ford Motor Company systems draw ignition current from a terminal on the Motorcraft starter relay. In Chrysler Corporation cars, ignition current comes through a wiring splice installed between the battery and the alternator. American Motors cars use the Delco-Remy starter system on some 4-cylinder and V-6 GM engines. AMC vehicles with AMC engines use the Motorcraft starter relay with one of two different alternators. Ignition current is drawn through a wiring splice between the battery and the starter relay to simplify the circuitry. Older imported and domestic automobiles may use different connections, such as drawing ignition current from a terminal on the voltage regulator.

Ballast (Primary) Resistor

For an ignition coil to have uniform secondary voltage capabilities over a wide range of engine speeds, complete saturation of its magnetic fields must be developed at these varying speeds. Magnetic saturation depends on the amount of voltage applied to the coil and the amount of current flowing in the windings. It also depends on the length of time the current flows.

An automotive ignition system does not operate with uniform current and voltage or current flow time. When the starter is cranking, the high current draw of the starter motor drops system voltage to about 10 or 11 volts. For this reason, the ignition coil must be able to produce enough secondary voltage to fire the engine with only 10 volts of primary voltage applied. Also, at high engine speeds, primary current flow time is reduced to only a few milliseconds. Therefore, uniform coil saturation must develop under extremes of low voltage

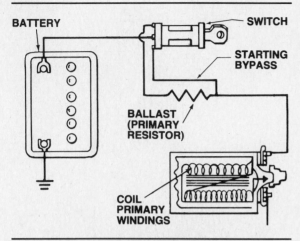

Figure 8-4. A ballast (primary) resistor can protect the primary circuit from excessive voltage.

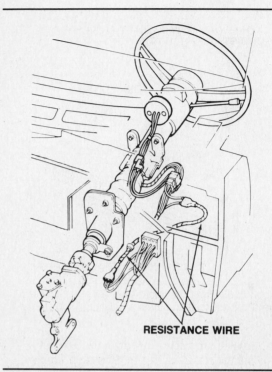

Figure 8-5. Ford products have a length of resistance wire installed near the ignition switch. (Ford)

and short current flow time. To achieve this, most 12-volt ignition coils are designed to operate on 9 or 10 volts under most conditions.

As we have mentioned, the starter motor drops ignition system voltage to about 10 volts when the engine is cranking. As soon as the engine starts, however, system voltage rises to 12 volts or more. To maintain the ignition primary voltage at the desired level, a resistor is installed in the primary circuit of all domestic automobile breaker-point ignitions. This is called the **ballast (primary) resistor**, figure 8-4.

The ballast resistor compensates for changes in voltage and current caused by engine speed and temperature changes. The resistor provides about one-half of the total primary circuit resistance (the coil is the other half).

At low speeds, current flows through the circuit for relatively long periods of time. As the current heats the resistor, its resistance increases, dropping the applied voltage at the coil. At higher speeds, the breaker points open more often and current flows for shorter periods of time. As the ballast resistor cools, its resistance drops. Higher voltage is applied to the coil but the shorter current flow duration results in about the same magnetic saturation of the coil.

The ballast resistor simply evens out the voltage and current of the primary circuit. In doing so, it reduces peak voltage at the coil and thus reduces current that would burn the breaker points faster. This is its most noticeable effect.

During cranking, the ballast resistor is bypassed to provide full available battery voltage to the primary circuit. This is done with a low-resistance starting bypass circuit in parallel with the ballast resistor, figure 8-4. When the engine starts, the bypass circuit opens and primary

current flows through the resistor. Ignition primary voltage is reduced to the desired level. The ignition, breaker points, and coil are not damaged by this because:
• The ballast resistor is bypassed for a very short time
• The battery voltage available during cranking is already reduced to a safe level.

Bypassing the ballast resistor at times other than cranking would cause rapid burning of the breaker points and could damage the coil primary winding.

Electronic ignitions with fixed dwell use a ballast resistor in the primary circuit to limit current and voltage. Variable-dwell electronic ignitions do not require one, because the ignition module or computer regulates primary current and voltage to the coil. The following are descriptions of the installation in late-model domestic cars:
• Ford products (except those with Dura Spark I or TFI electronic ignitions) and American Motors cars using Ford ignitions have a length of resistance wire installed near the ignition switch, figure 8-5.

Ballast (Primary) Resistor: A resistor in the primary circuit that stabilizes ignition system voltage and current flow.

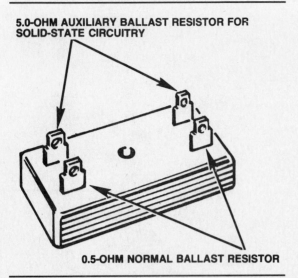

5.0-OHM AUXILIARY BALLAST RESISTOR FOR SOLID-STATE CIRCUITRY

0.5-OHM NORMAL BALLAST RESISTOR

Figure 8-6. Chrysler's dual ballast resistor protects both the primary circuit and the solid-state ignition circuitry.

• Chrysler products built through 1977 have two ballast resistors in one ceramic holder mounted on the firewall, figure 8-6. A 0.5-ohm resistor is connected between the ignition switch and the coil; a 5-ohm resistor is part of the electronic ignition control module circuitry.

The 1977 318-cid V-8 and all 1977 and later Chrysler electronic lean burn (ELB) and electronic spark control (ESC) systems have only the 0.5-ohm ballast resistor. With the change from an analog to a digital computer in 1980, Chrysler eliminated the ballast resistor from its 6- and 8-cylinder ignitions.

Chrysler front-wheel-drive (FWD) cars from 1978 through 1979 (California) and 1980 (Federal) used an analog computer and the 0.5-ohm ballast resistor. The resistor was eliminated on 1980 California and 1981 Federal FWD cars with the introduction of a digital spark control computer.

• General Motors and those American Motors vehicles using the Prestolite BID or Delco-Remy HEI breakerless ignitions have no ballast resistor.

Starting Bypass

When the ballast resistor is bypassed during cranking, battery current flows to the primary circuit through a parallel circuit branch called the **starting bypass**. Current through this parallel branch can be controlled either by the ignition switch or by the starter relay or solenoid.

When the starting bypass is controlled directly by the ignition switch, figure 8-7, the ballast resistor is connected between the Run position contacts and the coil primary winding.

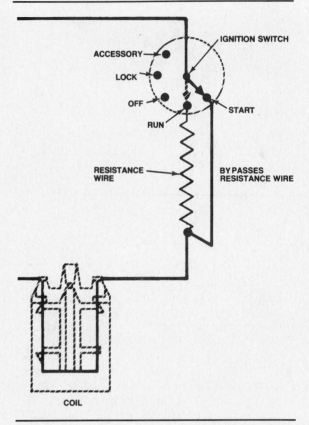

Figure 8-7. The ignition switch can control the starting bypass circuit.

When the ignition switch is in the Start position, full battery voltage is applied to the coil primary winding. Larger Ford automobiles and pre-1977 Chrysler products use this starting bypass method.

When the starting bypass is controlled by a starter relay or solenoid, figure 8-8, the ballast resistor is again connected between the Run ignition switch contacts and the coil. When the ignition switch is turned to Start, current through the starter relay or solenoid closes a set of contact points. Battery current will flow through the relay or solenoid to the coil primary winding through a parallel circuit.

Small Ford automobiles and 1977 and later Chrysler products control the starting bypass through the starter relay. The starting bypass on GM cars is controlled through the starter solenoid.

Switching Devices

The magnetic field of the coil primary winding must collapse totally in order to induce a high voltage in the secondary winding. For the field to collapse, current through the primary winding must stop very rapidly. Current must then

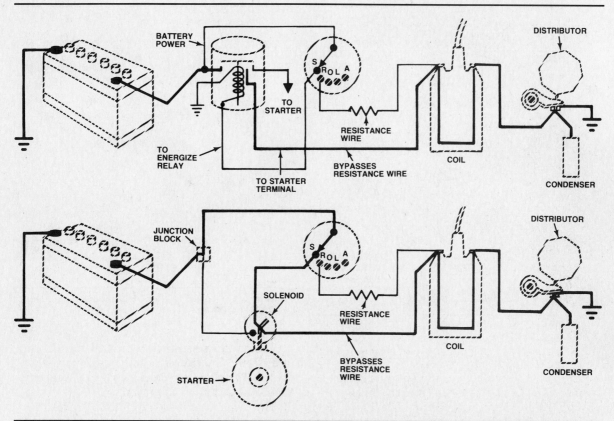

Figure 8-8. The starting bypass circuit can be controlled by the starter relay (top) or the solenoid-point (bottom).

start and stop again, to induce the next high-voltage discharge. The primary circuit needs a switching device that *rapidly* breaks and com-

Starting Bypass: A parallel circuit branch that bypasses the ballast resistor during engine cranking.

■ Charles Franklin Kettering (1876-1958)

Charles F. Kettering was a leading inventor and automotive engineer. After graduating from Ohio State University, he became chief of the inventions department at the National Cash Register Company. While there he designed a motor used in the first electrically operated cash register.

In 1909, he helped form a company called Dayton Engineering Laboratories Company, later to be known as Delco. In 1917, he became the president and general manager of the General Motors Research Corporation.

Kettering invented both the automobile self-starter and the inductive-discharge battery ignition system. The accompanying illustration is an early sketch by Kettering of his design for an ignition system. He was involved in the invention and perfection of high-octane gasoline; improvements for engines, especially diesel engines; elec-

tric refrigeration; and much more. He also helped establish the Sloan-Kettering Institute For Cancer Research in New York City.

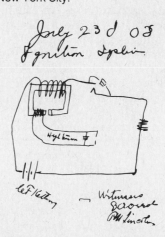

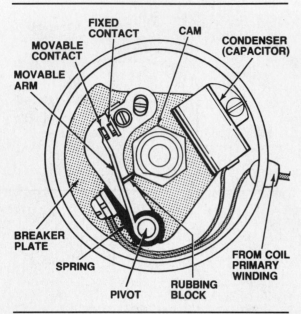

Figure 8-9. Ignition breaker-point (contact) assembly.

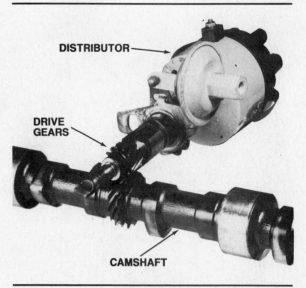

Figure 8-10. The gear on the distributor shaft is driven by another gear on the engine camshaft.

pletes the circuit to start and stop the current. For more than 60 years, ignition systems used breaker points as a mechanical switch. Since the mid-1970s, solid-state electronic devices have replaced breaker points.

Breaker points
The ignition breaker-point assembly, figure 8-9, includes the:
1. Fixed contact
2. Movable contact
3. Movable arm
4. Rubbing block
5. Pivot
6. Spring
7. Breaker plate.

Both breaker points are made from tungsten, an extremely hard metal with a high melting point. The fixed contact is grounded through the distributor housing. The movable contact is insulated from the distributor housing and is connected to the negative terminal of the coil primary winding. Because current flows from the movable to the fixed contact, the movable contact can be labeled + and the fixed contact can be labeled – in a negative-ground system.

The movable contact is mounted on a movable arm. The arm also holds a rubbing block, a small piece of plastic or other synthetic nonconductive material that rides on the surface of the distributor cam. As the cam rotates, the lobes push the arm to open the breaker points. The spring closes the points when the cam lobes move away from the rubbing block.

The pivot and spring control the movement of the arm. The entire assembly is mounted on the breaker plate, which is attached to the distributor housing with screws.

The distributor cam is mounted on the centrifugal advance shaft, or driven assembly, which is driven through the centrifugal advance weights by the distributor shaft. The distributor shaft is driven by the engine camshaft through gears, figure 8-10. Every opening of the breaker points induces a pulse of high-voltage current in the secondary circuit, and a spark plug fires. The breaker points must open as many times during one rotation of the cam as the engine has spark plugs. The cam, therefore, has as many lobes as the engine has spark plugs. The cam and points shown in figure 8-9 would be installed on a 6-cylinder engine.

When the breaker points open, a voltage is still present at the movable arm. This voltage can cause current to arc across the opening point gap. This would damage the points and affect the ignition system's operation. To avoid this, a **condenser**, a type of **capacitor**, is connected to the movable arm, figure 8-11. The condenser consists of two conducting surfaces separated by an insulator. A condenser can store voltage without using any of the voltage. The voltage at the movable point arm is stored in the condenser instead of causing an arc across the point gap. We will study condensers in more detail later in this chapter.

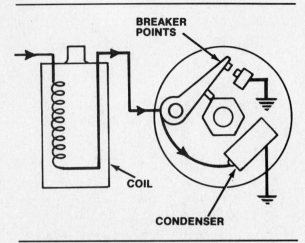

Figure 8-11. The condenser or capacitor prevents arcing as the breaker points open.

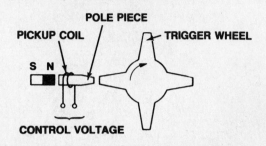

Figure 8-12. A simple magnetic pulse generator. (Bosch)

Solid-state switching devices

Breaker-point ignitions make it difficult for engines to meet today's exhaust emission control standards. Such standards not only require maximum system performance, they also require *consistent* performance. Because breaker points wear during normal operation, ignition system settings and performance change.

Since solid-state switching devices do not wear, ignition system performance remains consistent and emission control can be effectively maintained. Virtually all carmakers now use solid-state ignition systems. Although we will study the more common ignitions in detail in Chapter 11, we will look now at the most widely used solid-state switching devices.

A solid-state control module is responsible for switching the primary current on and off. The module must be signalled *when* to turn the current off. Two devices are commonly used to do this:

• Magnetic pulse generators
• Hall-effect switches.

The **magnetic pulse generator** is installed in the distributor housing where the breaker points used to be. The pulse generator, figure 8-12, consists of a trigger wheel, a permanent magnet, a pole piece affected by the permanent magnet, and a pickup coil wound around the pole piece. The only moving part is the trigger wheel, which rotates as a distributor cam would.

The trigger wheel is made of steel with a low **reluctance** that cannot be permanently magnetized. Therefore, it provides a low-resistance path for magnetic flux lines. The trigger wheel has as many teeth as the engine has cylinders.

As the trigger wheel rotates, its teeth come near the pole piece. Flux lines from the pole piece concentrate in the low-reluctance trigger wheel, increasing the magnetic field strength and inducing a voltage in the pickup coil. The pickup coil is connected to the electronic control module, which senses this voltage and switches the primary current off. Each time a trigger wheel tooth comes near the pole piece, the control module is signalled to switch off the primary current. Solid-state circuitry in the module determines when the primary current will be turned on again.

The simple pulse generator shown in figure 8-12 would be installed in a 4-cylinder engine. Figure 8-13 shows the typical construction of a pulse generator for an 8-cylinder engine.

We have used the terms "trigger wheel" and "pickup coil" in describing the magnetic pulse generator. Various manufacturers have

Condenser: A capacitor used in breaker-point ignition systems to prevent arcing across the points.

Capacitor: A device that can store voltage without affecting the voltage in any way. Formed by bringing two conductive surfaces close together, separated only by an insulator. Also called a condenser.

Magnetic Pulse Generator: A signal-generating switch that creates a voltage pulse as magnetic flux changes around a pickup coil.

Reluctance: An object's resistance to magnetic lines of force. Magnetic lines will concentrate in areas of low reluctance, and avoid areas of high reluctance.

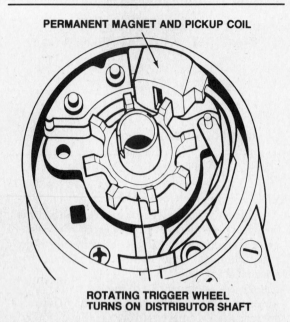

PERMANENT MAGNET AND PICKUP COIL

ROTATING TRIGGER WHEEL
TURNS ON DISTRIBUTOR SHAFT

Figure 8-13. A magnetic pulse generator installed in the distributor housing. (Ford)

Manufacturer	Stationary Pickup Coil	Rotating Trigger Wheel
AMC	Sensor	Trigger wheel
Bosch	Pickup coil & pole piece	Trigger wheel
Chrysler	Pickup coil	Reluctor
Ford	Stator	Armature
General Motors	Magnetic pickup & pole piece	Timer core
Nissan	Stator	Reluctor
Toyota	Pickup coil	Signal rotor

Figure 8-14. Manufacturers have different names for the trigger wheels and pickup coils or sensors in breakerless distributors, but all devices serve the same purpose.

different names for these components, figure 8-14, but all serve the same purpose.

A **Hall-effect switch** also uses a stationary sensor and rotating trigger wheel (shutter), figure 8-15. Unlike the magnetic pulse generator, it requires a small input voltage in order to generate an output or signal voltage. As used in some Chrysler distributors, the rotor has a shutter blade for each cylinder (Ford and GM use a separate ring of metal blades). The pickup plate in the distributor housing contains a gate which the shutter blades pass as the distributor shaft rotates. An integrated circuit (IC) mounted on the plate faces the switch. As a shutter blade enters the air gap between the IC and the Hall-effect switch, it bypasses the magnetic field around the pickup, causing the Hall-effect output voltage to change. This changes the bias to the ignition module, just as a magnetic pulse generator signal does.

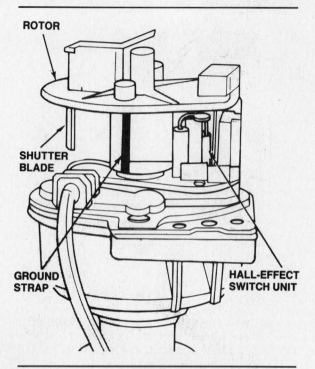

Figure 8-15. Shutter blades rotating through the Hall-effect switch air gap bypass the magnetic field around the pickup and drop the voltage output to zero. (Chrysler)

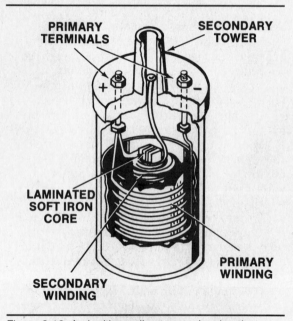

Figure 8-16. An ignition coil cutaway showing the primary and secondary windings.

Coil Primary Winding

The coil primary winding, figure 8-16, is made of about 100 to 150 turns of a relatively heavy copper wire. The coil turns are insulated from

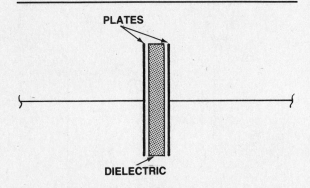

Figure 8-17. A simple condenser.

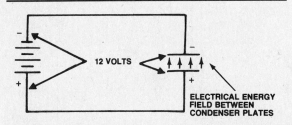

Figure 8-18. When a condenser is connected to a battery, voltage is stored in the field between the condenser plates.

each other by a thin coat of enamel. The two ends of the winding are connected to two terminals on the top of the coil. With a **negative-ground electrical system**, the coil + terminal is connected to the battery + terminal; the coil – terminal is connected to the ignition breaker points and through the points to ground. With a **positive-ground electrical system**, the coil primary connections are reversed.

Condensers

As we learned earlier, a condenser, or capacitor, is a device that is able to store voltage. It consists of two conductive plates with an insulating material between them, figure 8-17. The insulation is called the **dielectric**. When a condenser is placed in a circuit, figure 8-18, the battery's voltage will force current to flow around the circuit. Because the current cannot flow through the dielectric insulator, one of the condenser's plates becomes positively charged and the other plate becomes negatively charged. An electric charge (voltage) exists in the field between the two plates. The voltage stored in the condenser is equal to the battery's voltage.

If the condenser is removed from the circuit right now, the energy field between the plates would still exist. The voltage stored inside the condenser is not changed or used in any way. If

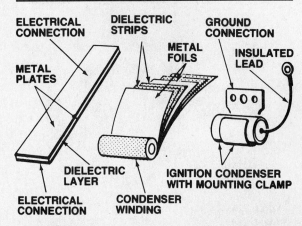

Figure 8-19. The construction of an ignition condenser.

the charged condenser is installed in another circuit, it will act like a battery. The voltage in the condenser will force current to flow through the new circuit until the condenser's plates become discharged.

Condenser ratings
Condensers are measured in terms of how much energy they can store. Condensers are rated in units called **farads**. The abbreviation for farad is F. One farad is a very big unit, and a condenser rated at one farad might be the size of a hot-water heater. Condensers used in automotive systems are rated in microfarads, abbreviated μF. A microfarad is one-millionth (0.000001) of a farad. Typical ignition system condensers have capacities from 0.18 to 0.32 μF.

Condenser construction and installation
Most automotive condensers are formed from two thin foil strips and separated by several layers of insulating paper, figure 8-19. These lay-

Hall-Effect Switch: A signal-generating switch that develops a transverse voltage across a current-carrying semiconductor when subjected to a magnetic field.

Negative-Ground Electrical System: An automotive electrical system in which the battery negative terminal is connected to ground.

Positive-Ground Electrical System: An automotive electrical system in which the battery positive terminal is connected to ground.

Dielectric: The insulating material between the two plates of a condenser, or capacitor.

Farad: The unit of measurement of a condenser's ability to store electrical energy.

Figure 8-20. A condenser installed inside the distributor housing.

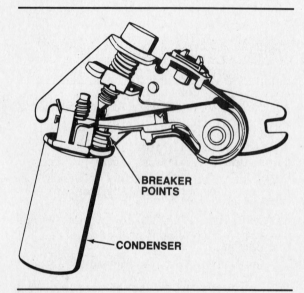

BREAKER POINTS

CONDENSER

Figure 8-21. Delco-Remy's Uni-Set point and condenser assembly.

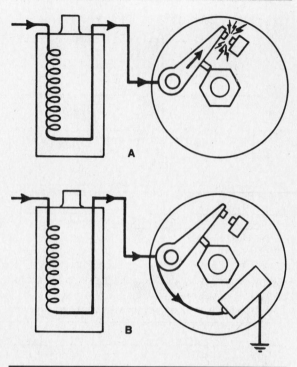

Figure 8-22. In position A, primary current arcs at the breaker points as they open. In position B, primary current flows to the condenser when the breaker points open, eliminating the arc.

ers, each more than eight feet long, are tightly rolled into a cylinder. The foil strips are offset, so that the top edge of one strip protrudes past the paper on one end of the cylinder and the bottom edge of the other strip protrudes from the other end of the cylinder. These edges provide an electrical contact with foil strips. The edges are flattened and the cylinder is installed in a metal canister. The bottom of the canister contacts one foil edge and grounds it. The other foil edge is connected to an insulated lead at the top of the canister.

To ensure ample insulation between the foil strips, the canister is placed in a vacuum. Wax or oil is drawn into the canister and the entire unit sealed. Condensers cannot be adjusted or repaired, but must be replaced if defective.

An assembled condenser is usually installed inside the distributor housing on the breaker plate, figure 8-20. The bracket is held to the breaker plate by a screw. This is the ground connection. The insulated lead from the top of the condenser is attached to the spring of the movable point arm, giving it an electrical connection to the movable breaker point.

The condenser can also be attached to the outside of the distributor housing. The wiring connections look different but provide the same electrical paths.

Some Delco-Remy distributors use a combined points and condenser unit called a Uni-Set, figure 8-21. This is a condenser as described above already attached to the point assembly. The assembly is installed and replaced as one unit. A similar product, the Prestolite Capaci-Point, attaches a ceramic capacitor to the point assembly. Both of these units eliminate the condenser wire lead, a principal cause of radio interference.

Condenser purpose
Self-induction in the coil primary winding can increase the primary voltage to as much as 400 volts. When the breaker points open, figure 8-22, position A, the high voltage would cause current to arc across the air gap. The unwanted spark would:
• Consume energy at the expense of the secondary circuit energy

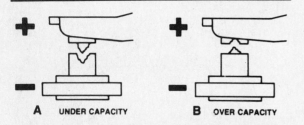

Figure 8-23. Incorrect condenser capacity can cause point pitting.

• Burn and pit the contacts, causing rapid point failure
• Leave an oxidized coating on the points, increasing primary circuit resistance.

To prevent these problems, the ignition condenser is installed in parallel with the breaker points, figure 8-22, position B. When the points open, the condenser is charged by the inductive current from the primary winding. It requires a small amount of time, about 0.1 millisecond, to charge the condenser to the peak voltage of the primary winding. By the time the condenser is fully charged, the contact points have opened far enough so that the current cannot arc across the air gap.

The energy in the condenser is then discharged, **oscillating** between the condenser and the coil primary winding, and dissipated as heat.

Since the condenser allows the primary circuit to be broken quickly and completely, the coil's magnetic field collapses rapidly. The field collapses about 20 times faster than if there were no condenser in the circuit. The faster the collapse, the greater the induced voltage in the secondary winding. The field has fully collapsed by the time the condenser begins its first discharge into the primary circuit.

At low engine speeds, the breaker points open relatively slowly. At engine speeds requiring fewer than 3,000 sparks per minute, the primary winding's induced voltage is great enough to cause a slight arc across the slowly opening point air gap, despite the condenser. Automobiles driven mostly at low engine speeds will show more rapid point failure than those used for high-speed travel.

It is important to follow manufacturers' recommendations when installing ignition condensers. If a condenser with too little capacity is used, primary current will charge the condenser and still be able to arc across the point gap. This causes pitting at the points, with metal transfer from the grounded (–) point to the movable (+) point, figure 8-23, position A. If the condenser has too great a capacity, pitting

and metal transfer can occur in the opposite direction, figure 8-23, position B. The "**Minus Rule**" may help you to remember these relationships:

Minus metal on the minus point means a minus-capacity condenser.

BREAKER-POINT DISTRIBUTORS

Great demands are placed on the ignition breaker points by the rest of the ignition system. Points must be correctly installed and accurately adjusted.

Oscillating: Moving back and forth with a steady rhythm.

Minus Rule: Minus metal on the minus side of the distributor breaker points means a minus-capacity condenser.

■ **Dual-Point, Dual-Coil, Dual-Plug Ignition**

Some early Nash automobiles used a "Twin Ignition" system. This system had two ignition coils, two sets of spark plugs and cables, a distributor with 16 plug terminals and two coil wire terminals, a rotor with offset tips, two sets of breaker points and two condensers.

The inline engines were designed with the spark plugs on both sides of the cylinders. The overhead valves were located directly over each cylinder in a vertical position.

The breaker points were synchronized by using a dual-bulb test lamp. With the ignition switch on, the distributor cam was turned to just break a stationary set of points, thereby lighting one bulb. A movable set of points was then adjusted to break contact, and light the second bulb, at the same instant. This adjustment assured that both sparks would occur in a cylinder at the same time.

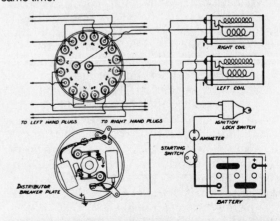

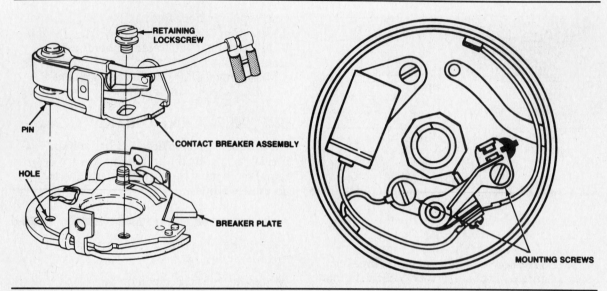

Figure 8-24. Point assemblies are usually mounted with either one screw and a locating pin (left) or with two screws (right). (Ford)

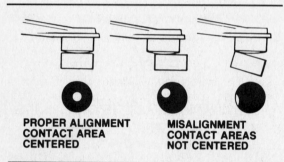

Figure 8-25. Breaker points must be properly aligned for proper ignition system performance.

Breaker-Point Installation

Ignition breaker points are normally supplied as a complete unit, figure 8-24. This assembly is fastened to the distributor breaker plate. The fasteners are either two screws or one screw and a small pin, as illustrated.

One of the mounting holes of the point assembly is elongated, so that the position of the points on the breaker plate can be adjusted. This adjustment has a great effect on breaker-point operation, as we will soon see.

The wiring connections between the points, the condenser, and the primary circuit can be made at one of two places. When the condenser is mounted inside the distributor, the connection is usually made at the bracket where the movable arm's spring is braced, figure 8-24. In some distributors, a nut and bolt hold the two wiring terminals to the bracket. Other distributors have push-on terminals.

When the condenser is mounted outside the housing, the primary lead and the condenser lead may be attached to a single slide terminal. A lead from the movable breaker point attaches to this terminal.

The stationary breaker point and the condenser canister are grounded through the distributor housing and the engine.

Correct ignition point alignment and spring tension are essential for proper ignition operation and long service life. Points are correctly aligned, figure 8-25, when the mating surfaces are in the center of both contacts, the faces are parallel, and the diameters are **concentric**. This ensures maximum contact area and precise switching action by the points.

Correct spring tension also ensures precise point action. Too much spring tension causes rapid cam and rubbing block wear. In some cases, it even can cause distributor shaft bushing wear or broken points. If spring tension is too light, the points will bounce as they open and close at high speed. This generally results in a loss of engine power. Spring tension is normally between 15 and 25 ounces (425 and 710 grams).

Point Dwell Angle

Point **dwell angle**, or cam angle, is a measurement of how far the distributor cam rotates while the points are closed. In figure 8-26, the points closed when line A was at the rubbing block. The points will open when line B reaches the rubbing block. Between line A and line B,

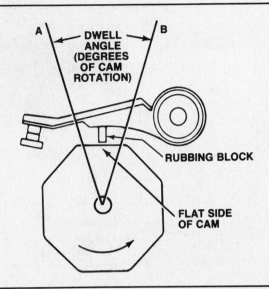

Figure 8-26. Dwell angle is the period during which the ignition points are closed. (Ford)

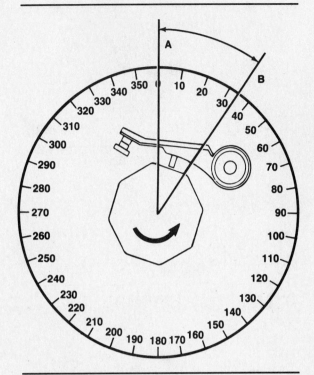

Figure 8-27. Dwell angle is measured in degrees of cam rotation. In this case, dwell is about 33 degrees.

the points stay closed. The number of degrees that the cam rotates between the point closing (line A) and the point opening (line B) is called the dwell angle.

Distributor rotation, like crankshaft rotation, is measured in degrees. If we superimpose a degree scale onto the point assembly, figure 8-27, we see that this particular dwell measures about 33 degrees.

The cam illustrated has eight lobes, so it is used with an 8-cylinder engine. Four-cylinder or 6-cylinder engines require 4-lobe or 6-lobe cams. This means that the points open four or six times during each cam revolution. The more times the points must open, the less time they can remain closed.

The ignition dwell angle is directly related to an engine's firing intervals. There are 90 degrees of crankshaft rotation between the firing intervals in an 8-cylinder engine. Because the distributor rotates at one-half the crankshaft speed, the distributor cam rotates half as far as the crankshaft between firing intervals, or 45 degrees. The theoretical dwell angle of an 8-cylinder engine would be 45 degrees, but the points must be open during part of that time, and dwell equals the number of degrees during which the points are *fully closed*. About 12 to 17 degrees are required for the points to open and close on an 8-cylinder engine. Therefore, a typical dwell angle for an 8-cylinder engine is about 28 to 33 degrees.

An even-firing 6-cylinder engine fires every 120 degrees of crankshaft rotation (60 degrees of distributor rotation). A 4-cylinder engine fires every 180 degrees of crankshaft rotation (90 degrees of distributor rotation). Dwell on a 6-cylinder engine could be around 45 degrees; on a 4-cylinder engine, it could be about 75 degrees. However, large dwell angles mean that the primary current flows for a long time at low engine speeds. This is not necessary for full coil saturation and could lead to coil overheating. For this reason, 4- and 6-cylinder distributors are designed for less dwell than the maximum amount they could have. Dwell on a typical 4-cylinder engine is usually about 50 degrees; on a 6-cylinder engine, it is about 38 degrees.

Concentric: Having the same center.

Dwell Angle: Also called cam angle, or dwell. The measurement in degrees of how far the distributor cam rotates while the breaker points are closed.

NORMAL DWELL

POINTS OPEN AND CLOSE AS SPECIFIED

SMALL DWELL

WIDE GAP

POINTS CLOSE LATE AND OPEN EARLY

LARGE DWELL

SMALL GAP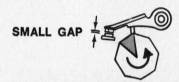

POINTS CLOSE EARLY AND OPEN LATE

 = DWELL ANGLE. POINTS ARE CLOSED
          DURING THIS PERIOD OF CAM
          ROTATION

Figure 8-28. Point gap and dwell angle are related; when one increases, the other decreases.

Dwell and point gap

Point gap is the maximum distance between the breaker points when they are open. Figure 8-28 shows the relationship between point gap and dwell. A small point gap means a large dwell angle. A large point gap means a small dwell angle. Point gap is usually measured in thousandths of an inch or hundredths of a millimeter. Typical point gaps range from 0.015 to 0.025 inch or 0.40 to 0.60 millimeter.

Point gap is adjusted by shifting the position of the breaker point assembly. This changes the position of the points relative to the cam, altering the point gap and the dwell. Point assemblies have elongated mounting holes so that the point gap can be adjusted.

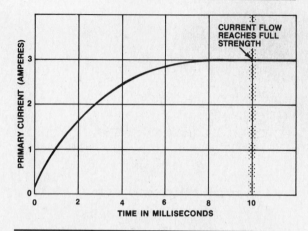

Figure 8-29. Primary winding current flow does not immediately reach full strength. (Bosch)

Effect of dwell on the coil

As long as the points are closed, current flows through the coil primary winding. This creates a magnetic field within the coil and makes induction possible.

However, the primary winding magnetic field does not appear instantly. When current first flows through the primary winding, self-induction causes a countervoltage within the winding. This countervoltage opposes primary current flow. The magnetic field of the primary winding does not immediately reach full strength, because the primary current does not immediately reach full strength, figure 8-29. It generally takes from 10 to 15 milliseconds (0.010 to 0.015 second) for the primary current to reach full strength.

The breaker points must remain closed long enough for the primary winding's magnetic field to reach nearly full strength. If the field is not at full strength, secondary voltage will be reduced. The point dwell must be great enough to allow nearly maximum coil strength.

However, if the point dwell is too great, the point gap will be very small. Primary current will be able to arc across the air gap, and the magnetic field will not collapse quickly and completely. Point dwell and gap must be adjusted exactly to the manufacturer's specifications if the ignition system is to perform most efficiently.

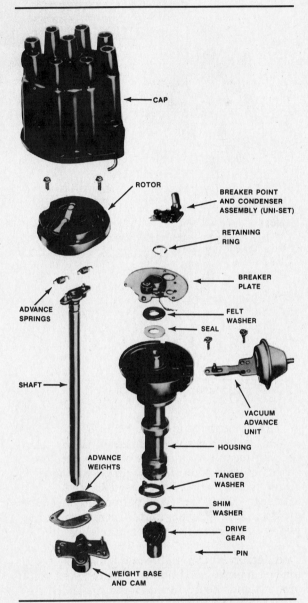

Figure 8-30. An exploded view of the Delco-Remy external-adjustment distributor. (Delco-Remy)

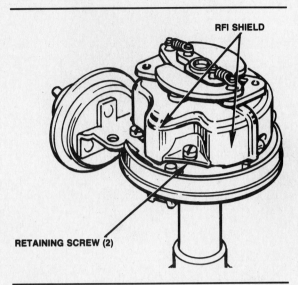

Figure 8-31. Some Delco-Remy distributors have a shield to reduce radio interference from the ignition system.

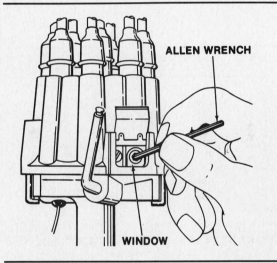

Figure 8-32. The point gap and dwell adjustment can be made from outside the distributor.

Dwell and engine speed

As engine speed increases, the distributor cam rotates faster. Dwell angle is unchanged, but the *time* it takes the cam to rotate through this angle is decreased. That is, the amount of time that the points are closed is reduced as engine speed increases.

We have seen that it takes a specific amount of time — about 0.010 second — for primary current flow to reach full strength, figure 8-29. At a 625-rpm idle speed, the 33-degree dwell angle of an 8-cylinder engine lasts about 0.0165 second. Primary current flow can reach its full strength before the points open to interrupt it.

■ Dual Breaker Points

Some high-performance engines have a special breaker point installation to counteract the reduction of dwell time at high speed, typically above 4,500 or 5,000 rpm. Two sets of ignition points are connected in parallel. The point sets open and close at different times. One set opens the primary circuit; the other closes it. This provides an overlapping action that extends the dwell angle. The increased dwell allows higher coil voltage output during high-speed operation.

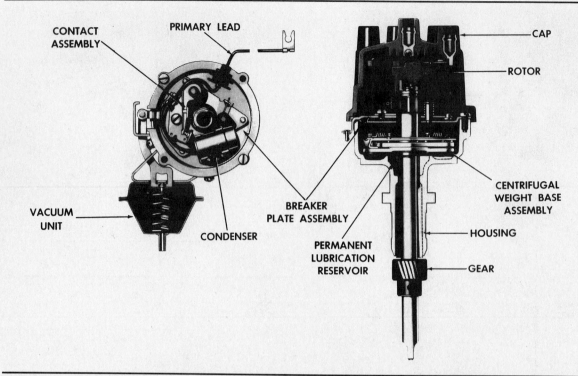

Figure 8-33. A cross-section view of the Delco-Remy internal-adjustment distributor. (Delco-Remy)

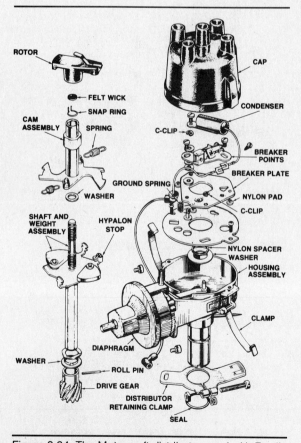

Figure 8-34. The Motorcraft distributor used with Ford's 1,600-cc engine. (Ford)

As engine speed increases to 1,000 rpm, the 33-degree dwell period decreases to 0.0099 second. Primary current is interrupted just before it reaches its maximum strength. Available secondary voltage will be decreased slightly.

At 2,000 rpm, the dwell period is reduced to 0.0045 second. Primary current is interrupted well before it reaches its maximum strength. Available secondary voltage will be reduced considerably. If the engine and ignition system are not in excellent condition, the required voltage level may be greater than the available voltage level. If this occurs, the engine will misfire.

SPECIFIC DISTRIBUTORS

The following paragraphs describe the various distributors used by major manufacturers. We will learn more about servicing these units in the *Shop Manual*.

Delco-Remy

All domestically built General Motors products used Delco-Remy breaker-point distributors until 1975, when the Delco-Remy High Energy Ignition (HEI) system became standard equipment. Many AMC products built before 1975 also used Delco-Remy breaker-point distributors.

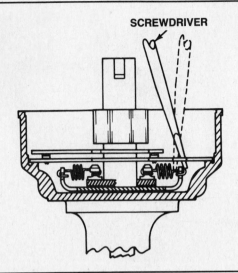

Figure 8-35. Adjusting the centrifugal advance on a Motorcraft distributor. (Ford)

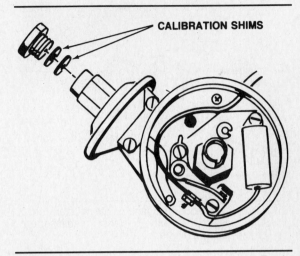

Figure 8-36. The vacuum advance units on early Ford distributors are adjusted by inserting or removing shims.

External-adjustment distributor

The V-6 and V-8 engine distributor, figure 8-30, had the following unusual design features:
• Cap held to housing by two spring-loaded latches
• Large circular rotor keyed to weight base by locators
• Centrifugal advance weights installed above the cam and breaker plate
• RFI shield, figure 8-31, installed on cars with windshield-mounted radio antennas (not used if equipped with Uni-Set assembly)
• Point assembly held to breaker plate by two screws; condenser retained by an additional screw
• Gap and dwell adjustment made with Allen wrench through sliding window in cap, figure 8-32, while engine is running.

Internal-adjustment distributor

The Delco-Remy distributor used with inline 4- and 6-cylinder engines is more similar to other manufacturer's designs, figure 8-33:
• Cap held to housing by two clips
• Rotor is press-fit onto distributor shaft
• Centrifugal advance located under the breaker plate
• Point assembly held to breaker plate by single screw
• Gap and dwell adjustment made by loosening screw, shifting point assembly, and tightening screw.

Motorcraft

Domestically built Ford products used Motorcraft (Autolite) breaker-point distributors until 1975, when a Motorcraft solid-state ignition became standard. Early Capris, manufactured in Germany, used a Bosch breaker-point distributor on all but the 1,600-cc engine, figure 8-34. Some AMC V-8 engines used a Motorcraft dual-diaphragm distributor. Common features of these distributors include:
• Cap held to housing by two clips
• Rotor is press-fit onto distributor shaft
• Centrifugal advance located under the breaker plate and adjusted by bending spring brackets, figure 8-35
• Single and dual vacuum advance units used
• Vacuum advance adjusted with calibrated shims on early models, figure 8-36, or an Allen-head screw on later models, figure 8-37

■ **Useful Distributor Tool**

When you're timing an engine and want to rotate the distributor to advance or retard the spark, you may find that the distributor does not want to budge. This can occur even after the holddown bolt has been loosened. If it does, try using an oil filter wrench around the distributor. It may give you the grip and leverage you need.

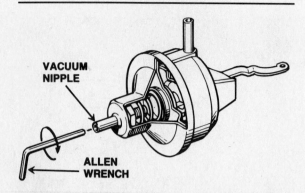

Figure 8-37. The vacuum advance units on later Ford distributors are adjusted with an Allen wrench inserted through the vacuum nipple.

- Point assembly held to breaker plate by two screws; condenser retained by additional screw
- Gap and dwell adjustment made by loosening both screws, shifting point assembly, and tightening screws
- Dual breaker points used on some high-performance V-8 engines are adjusted separately.

Chrysler

Chrysler products used breaker-point distributors made by Chrysler, figure 8-38, and Prestolite. High-performance V-8 engines used Prestolite dual-point distributors. Some AMC 6-cylinder engines before 1969 used Prestolite distributors. Common features include:
- Cap held to housing by two clips
- Rotor is press-fit onto distributor shaft
- Centrifugal advance located under the breaker plate. Chrysler advance units are nonadjustable; Prestolite units are adjusted by bending spring brackets
- Breaker plate in Chrysler-built distributor pivots eccentrically so dwell changes as engine speed increases
- Point assembly held to breaker plate by single screw; condenser held by separate screw
- Gap and dwell adjustment made by loosening screw, shifting point assembly, and tightening screw
- Dual breaker points used on some high-performance V-8 engines are adjusted separately.

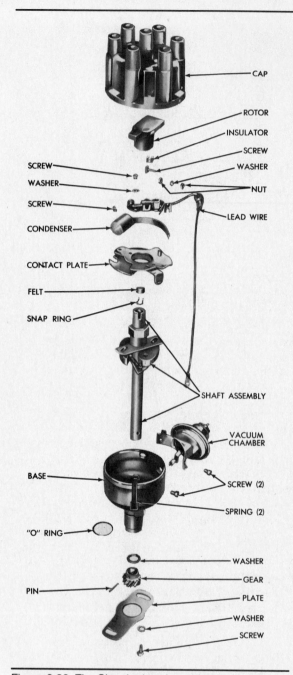

Figure 8-38. The Chrysler breaker-point distributor used with 6-cylinder engines. (Chrysler)

Bosch

A dual-diaphragm Bosch distributor is used in Ford's German-built Capri on all but the 1,600-cc engine. Volkswagen models have used a similar unit with either a single- or dual-diaphragm unit.

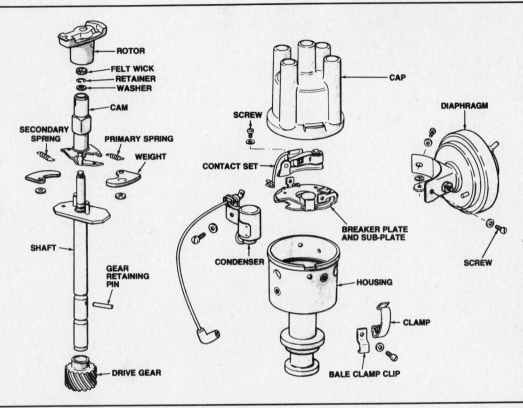

Figure 8-39. Typical Bosch 4-cylinder distributor. (Bosch)

A typical Bosch breaker-point distributor, figure 8-39, has the condenser mounted on the outside of the housing. Some rotors have a high-resistance carbon insert. The centrifugal advance can be adjusted by bending the spring brackets, but neither type of vacuum unit is adjustable. Point gap is adjusted by loosening the single holddown screw, shifting the point assembly and tightening the screw.

Because of the opposed cylinder engine design, distributors on air-cooled Volkswagen engines are driven by a gear on the crankshaft, rather than by the camshaft.

SUMMARY

Through electromagnetic induction, the ignition system transforms the low voltage of the battery into the high voltage required to fire the spark plugs. Induction occurs in the ignition coil where current flows through the primary winding to build up a magnetic field. When the field collapses rapidly, high voltage is induced in the coil secondary winding. All domestic original-equipment ignitions are the battery-powered, inductive-discharge type.

The ignition system is divided into two circuits: the primary and the secondary. The pri-

mary circuit contains the battery, the ignition switch, the ballast (primary) resistor, the starting bypass, the coil primary winding, and a switching device in the distributor.

For over 60 years, mechanical breaker points were used as the primary circuit switching device. Solid-state electronic components replaced breaker points as the switching device in the mid-1970s. The two most common solid-state switching devices are the magnetic pulse generator and the Hall-effect switch.

The ignition condenser is a capacitor that absorbs primary voltage when the points open. This prevents arcing across the points and premature burning. Typical ignition condensers are rated at 0.18 to 0.32 microfarad.

The breaker points are a mechanical switch that opens and closes the primary circuit. The period during which the points are closed is called the dwell angle. The dwell angle varies inversely with the gap between the points when they are open. As the gap decreases, the dwell increases.

Domestic carmakers used breaker-point distributors made by Delco-Remy, Motorcraft, Chrysler, Prestolite, and Bosch. Although slightly different in construction, all operate on the same principles.

Review Questions

Choose the single most correct answer.
Compare your answers with the correct answers on page 451.

1. The voltage required to ignite the air-fuel mixture can range from _____ volts.
   a. 5 to 25
   b. 50 to 250
   c. 500 to 2,500
   d. 5,000 to 25,000

2. Which of the following does not require higher voltage levels to cause an arc across the spark plug gap?
   a. Increased spark plug gap
   b. Increased engine operating temperature
   c. Increased fuel in air-fuel mixture
   d. Increased pressure of air-fuel mixture

3. The coil transforms low voltage from the primary circuit to high voltage for the secondary circuit through:
   a. Magnetic induction
   b. Capacitive discharge
   c. Series resistance
   d. Parallel capacitance

4. Voltage induced in the secondary winding of the ignition coil is how many times greater than the self-induced primary voltage?
   a. 1 to 2
   b. 10 to 20
   c. 100 to 200
   d. 1,000 to 2,000

5. The two circuits of the ignition system are:
   a. The "Start" and "Run" circuits
   b. The point circuit and the coil circuit
   c. The primary circuit and the secondary circuit
   d. The insulated circuit and the ground circuit

6. Which of the following components is part of both the primary and the secondary circuits?
   a. The ignition switch
   b. The distributor rotor
   c. The condenser
   d. The coil

7. Which of the of the following is *not* contained in the primary circuit of an ignition system?
   a. Battery
   b. Spark plugs
   c. Ignition switch
   d. Coil primary winding

8. When the cranking system is operating, the ballast resistor:
   a. Reduces coil primary voltage to about 7 volts
   b. Heats up, increasing resistance and reducing voltage
   c. Is bypassed to provide full available voltage
   d. Cools, and increases primary current flow

9. Which of the following is true of the coil primary windings?
   a. They consist of 100 to 150 turns of very fine wire
   b. The turns are insulated by a coat of enamel
   c. The negative terminal is connected directly to the battery
   d. The positive terminal is connected to the breaker points and to ground

10. Current flow through the starting bypass can be controlled by the:
    a. Ignition switch
    b. Starter relay
    c. Solenoid
    d. Any of the above

11. In order to collapse the magnetic field of the coil, the primary circuit requires a:
    a. Ballast resistor
    b. Switching device
    c. Condenser
    d. Starting bypass circuit

12. Breaker points are usually made of:
    a. Silicon
    b. Tungsten
    c. Aluminum
    d. Copper

13. Which of the following statements is true?
    a. Breaker points wear during operation, changing settings and performance
    b. An engine with a breaker-point ignition system has difficulty meeting exhaust emission control standards
    c. Solid-state switching devices do not wear, keeping ignition performance consistent
    d. All of the above

14. In the solid-state ignitions used as original equipment on late-model domestic cars, the breaker points and distributor cam have been replaced by:
    a. RFI filter capacitors
    b. Auxiliary ballast resistors
    c. Magnetic pickup triggering devices
    d. Integrated coil and distributor cap assemblies

15. The accompanying illustration shows:

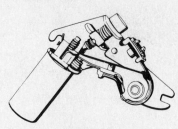

   a. Delco-Remy's Uni-Set point and condenser assembly
   b. Prestolite's Capaci-Point assembly
   c. Ignition condenser assembly, with mounting bracket
   d. None of the above

16. Condensers are rated in:
    a. Ohms
    b. Milliohms
    c. Farads
    d. Microfarads

17. The accompanying illustration shows which of the following situations with respect to the breaker points?

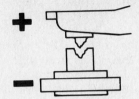

  a. Condenser with too little capacity used
  b. Condenser with too much capacity used
  c. Normal wear of points with correct condenser used
  d. None of the above

18. The accompanying illustration shows:

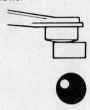

  a. Properly aligned breaker points
  b. Properly offset breaker points
  c. Misaligned breaker points
  d. Breaker points with excessive spring tension

19. Dwell angle is the period during which the ignition points:
  a. Are fully open
  b. Are fully closed
  c. Are opening and closing
  d. None of the above

20. The point gap is _____ related to the dwell angle:
  a. Directly
  b. Inversely
  c. Proportionately
  d. Reciprocally

21. The distributor rotates at _____ the speed of the crankshaft.
  a. One-half
  b. The same speed as
  c. Twice
  d. None of the above

9

The Ignition Secondary Circuit and Components

We have explained the general operation of the ignition primary circuit and have studied some of the system components. In this chapter, we will look at the secondary circuit and its components.

The secondary circuit must conduct surges of high voltage. To do this, it has large conductors and terminals, and heavy-duty insulation. The secondary circuit, figure 9-1, consists of the:
1. Coil secondary winding
2. Distributor cap and rotor
3. Ignition cables
4. Spark plugs.

The secondary circuit has the same components and function whether the primary circuit uses breaker points or a solid-state switching device.

IGNITION COILS

As we have seen, the ignition coil steps up voltage in the same way as a transformer. When the magnetic field of the coil primary winding collapses, it induces a high voltage in the secondary winding.

Coil Secondary Winding and Primary-to-Secondary Connections

Two windings of copper wire compose the ignition coil. The primary winding of heavy wires consists of 100 to 150 turns; the secondary winding is 15,000 to 30,000 turns of a fine wire. The ratio of secondary turns to primary turns is usually between 100 and 200. To increase the strength of the coil's magnetic field, the windings are installed around a laminated core of soft iron, figure 9-2.

The coil must be protected from the underhood environment to maintain its efficiency. Two coil designs are used:
• Traditional oil-filled coil
• Laminated E-core coil.

Traditional Oil-Filled Coil

In the oil-filled coil (used with both breaker-point and breakerless ignitions), the coil windings are insulated by layers of paper and the entire case is filled with oil for greater insulation. The top of the coil is molded from an insulating material such as Bakelite. Metal inserts for the winding terminals are installed in the cap. Primary and secondary terminals are generally marked with a + and –, figure 9-2. Leads are attached with nuts and washers on some coils; others use push-on lead connectors. The entire unit is sealed to keep out dirt and moisture.

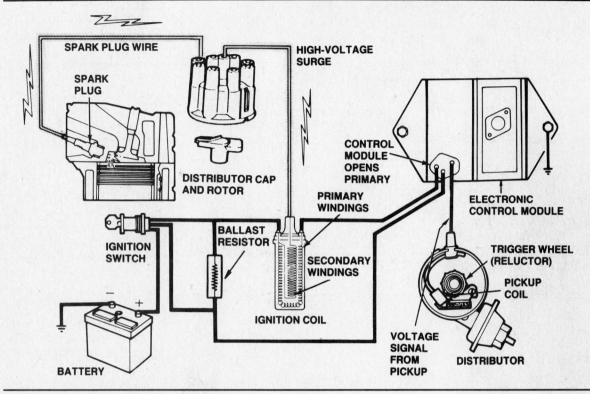

Figure 9-1. Operation of the ignition secondary circuit. (Chrysler)

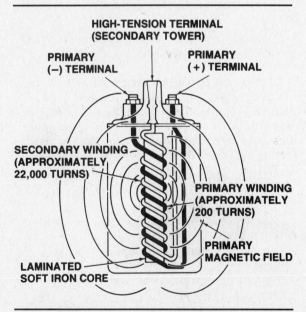

Figure 9-2. The laminated iron core within the coil strengthens the coil's magnetic field.

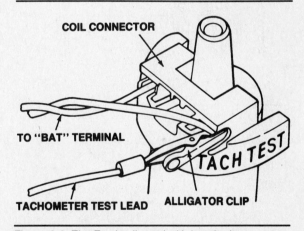

Figure 9-3. The Ford coil used with breakerless ignitions has a polarized slide-on primary terminal connector with a tachometer connection. (Ford)

In 1977, Ford introduced a "high-output" version of the oil-filled coil. Because its windings have a much lower resistance, more current is conducted through the windings. This coil is used without a ballast resistor, applying the entire 12-volt supply voltage across the coil primary. This increases the strength of the magnetic field around the windings, which results in a higher voltage in the secondary circuit. The primary leads connect to the coil terminals with a polarized slide-on connector that allows a tachometer to be connected using an alligator clip, and without removing the coil connector, figure 9-3.

Figure 9-4. The E-core coil is used without a ballast resistor.

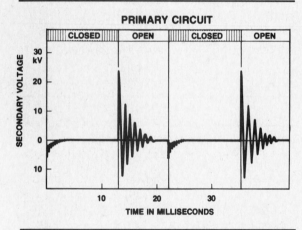

PRIMARY CIRCUIT

Figure 9-5. A secondary circuit no-load voltage trace. (Bosch)

Laminated E-Core Coil

Unlike the oil-filled coil just described, the E-core coil uses an iron core laminated *around* the windings and potted in plastic, much like a small transformer, figure 9-4. The coil is named because of the "E" shape of the laminations making up its core. Since the laminations provide a closed magnetic path, the E-core coil has a higher energy transfer. The secondary connection looks much like a spark plug terminal. Primary leads are housed in a single snap-on connector that attaches to the coil's blade-type terminals. The E-core coil has very low primary resistance and is used without a ballast resistor in Ford TFI and some GM HEI ignitions.

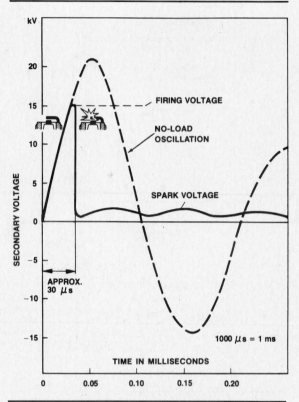

Figure 9-6. The dashed line shows no-load voltage; the solid line shows the voltage trace of firing voltage and spark voltage. (Bosch)

Coil Voltage

A coil must supply the correct amount of voltage for any system. Since this amount of voltage varies, depending on engine and operating conditions, the coil's **available voltage** is generally more than the system's required voltage. If it is less, the engine may not run.

Available voltage

The ignition coil can supply much more secondary voltage than the average engine requires. The peak voltage that a coil can produce is called its available voltage.

Three important coil design factors determine available voltage level:
- Secondary-to-primary turns ratio
- Primary voltage level
- Primary circuit resistance.

The turns ratio is a multiplier that creates high secondary voltage output. The primary voltage level that is applied to a coil is determined by the ignition circuit's design and condition. Installing a ballast resistor of the wrong value will affect this voltage level, as will loose and corroded connections. Generally, a primary circuit voltage loss of 1 volt can decrease available voltage by 10,000 volts.

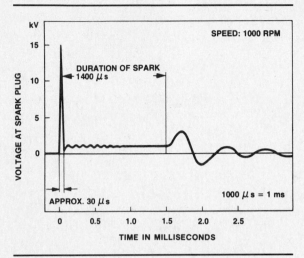

Figure 9-7. The voltage trace of an entire secondary ignition pulse. (Bosch)

Available Voltage: The peak voltage that a coil can produce.

No-Load Oscillation: The rapid, back-and-forth, peak-to-peak oscillation of voltage in the ignition secondary circuit when the circuit is open.

Firing Voltage (Required Voltage): The voltage level that must be reached to ionize and create a spark in the air gap between the spark plug electrodes.

Spark Voltage: The inductive portion of a spark that maintains the spark in the air gap between a spark plug's electrodes. Usually about one-quarter of the firing voltage level.

Voltage Decay: The rapid oscillation and dissipation of secondary voltage after the spark in a spark plug air gap has stopped.

■ The Lincoln-Zephyr V-12 Ignition System

The ignition system for the Lincoln-Zephyr V-12 engines used two coils contained in a single housing mounted on top of a distributor with two distributor caps, two sets of breaker points, a rotor with two contacts, and two condensers. The distributor was mounted on the front of the engine and was connected directly to the camshaft.

Looking at the distributor from the driver's seat position, the right-hand coil and a fixed set of breaker points fired the right bank of cylinders, numbers 2-4-6-8-10-12. The left-hand coil and an adjustable set of breaker points fired the left bank of cylinders, numbers 1-3-5-7-9-11.

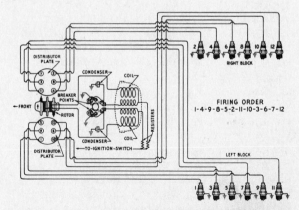

If there were no spark plug in the secondary circuit (that is, if the circuit were open), the coil secondary voltage would have no place to discharge quickly. The voltage would oscillate in the secondary circuit, dissipating as heat. The voltage would be completely gone in just a few milliseconds. Figure 9-5 shows the trace of this no-load, open-circuit voltage. This is called secondary voltage **no-load oscillation**. The first peak of the voltage trace represents the maximum available voltage from that particular coil. Available voltage is usually between 20,000 and 50,000 volts.

Required voltage

When there is a spark plug in the secondary circuit, the coil voltage creates an arc across the plug air gap. Figure 9-6 compares a typical no-load oscillation to a typical secondary firing voltage oscillation. At about 15,000 volts, the spark plug air gap ionizes and becomes conductive. This is the ionization voltage level, also called the **firing voltage**, or **required voltage**.

As soon as a spark has formed, the energy demands of the spark cause the secondary voltage to drop to the much lower spark voltage level. This is the inductive portion of the spark. **Spark voltage** is usually about one-quarter of the firing voltage level.

Figure 9-7 shows the entire trace of the spark. When the secondary voltage falls below the inductive air-gap voltage level, the spark can no longer be maintained. The spark gap becomes nonconductive. The remaining secondary voltage oscillates in the secondary circuit, dissipating as heat. This is called secondary **voltage decay**. At this time, the primary circuit

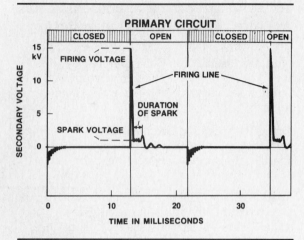

Figure 9-8. As the primary circuit opens and closes, the ignition cycle repeats. (Bosch)

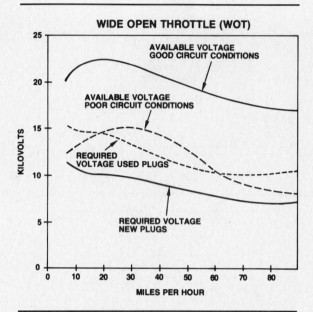

Figure 9-9. Available and required voltage levels under different system conditions.

closes and the cycle repeats, figure 9-8. The traces shown in figures 9-7 and 9-8 are similar to the secondary circuit traces you will see on an oscilloscope screen.

Some conditions that cause required voltage levels to increase are:
- Eroded electrodes in the distributor cap, rotor, or spark plug
- Damaged ignition cables
- Reversed plug polarity
- High compression pressures
- A lean air-fuel mixture that is more difficult to ionize.

Voltage reserve

The physical condition of the automotive engine and ignition system can affect both available and required voltage levels, as we have seen. Figure 9-9 shows available and required voltage levels in a particular ignition system under various operating conditions. **Voltage reserve** is the amount of coil voltage available in excess of the voltage required.

Under certain poor circuit conditions, there may be no voltage reserve. At these times, some spark plugs will not fire, and the engine will run poorly or not at all. Ignition systems must be properly maintained to ensure that there is always some voltage reserve. A well-tuned ignition system should have a voltage reserve of about 60 percent of available voltage under most operating conditions.

Coil Installations

Ignition coils are usually mounted with a bracket on a fender panel in the engine compartment or on the engine, figure 9-10.

Some ignition coils have an unusual design and location. The Delco-Remy High Energy Ignition (HEI) solid-state ignition system used on V-6 and V-8 engines has a coil mounted in the distributor cap, figure 9-11. The coil output terminal is connected directly to the center electrode of the distributor cap. The connections to the primary winding are made through a multiple-plug connector.

The computer-controlled coil ignition (C^3I) used on some 1984 and later GM engines has an assembly containing three separate ignition coils and an electronic control module, figure 9-12. Control circuits in the module discharge each coil separately in sequence, with each coil serving two cylinders 360 degrees apart in the firing order. We will learn more about this system in Chapter 11.

In any system, the connections to the primary winding must be made correctly. If spark plug polarity is reversed, greater voltage is required to fire the plug. Plug polarity is established by the ignition coil connections.

One end of the coil secondary winding is connected to the primary winding, figure 9-13, so that the secondary circuit is grounded through the ignition primary circuit. When the coil terminals are properly connected to the battery, the grounded end of the secondary circuit is electrically positive. The other end of the secondary circuit, which is the center electrode of

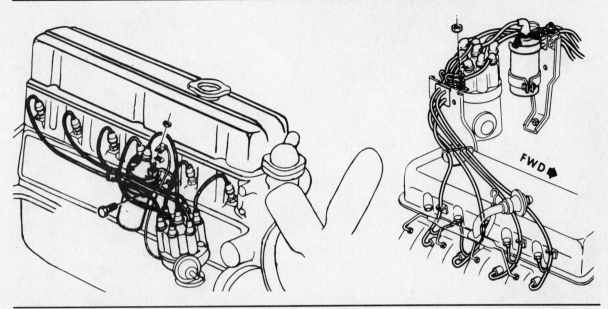

Figure 9-10. Ignition coils are commonly mounted on the engine (left) or on a fender panel (right). (Chevrolet)

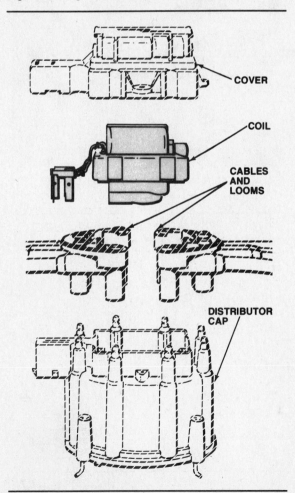

Figure 9-11. Many Delco-Remy HEI solid-state ignition systems used on V-6 and V-8 engines have a coil mounted in the distributor cap.

the spark plug, is electrically negative. The plug's grounded side electrode is positive, and plug polarity is correct. Whether the secondary winding is grounded to the primary + or – terminal depends on whether the windings are wound clockwise or counterclockwise.

If the coil connections are reversed, figure 9-14, spark plug polarity is reversed. The grounded end of the secondary circuit is electrically negative. The plug center electrode is electrically positive, and the side electrode is negative. When plug polarity is reversed, 20 to 40 percent more secondary voltage is required to fire the spark plug.

Coil terminals are usually marked BAT or +, and DIST or –. To establish the correct plug polarity with a negative-ground electrical system, the + terminal must be connected to the positive terminal of the battery (through the ignition switch, starter relay, and other circuitry). The – coil terminal must be connected to the distributor breaker points and condenser or to the ignition control module.

Voltage Reserve: The amount of coil voltage available in excess of the voltage required to fire the spark plugs.

Figure 9-12. The Buick C³I distributorless ignition uses three separate ignition coils, each of which serves two cylinders 360 degrees apart in the firing order.

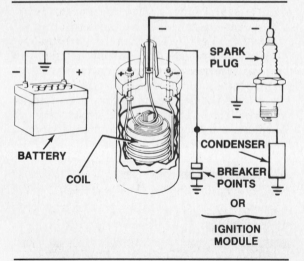

Figure 9-13. When coil connections are made properly, the spark plug center electrode is electrically negative.

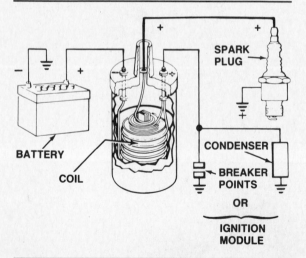

Figure 9-14. When coil connections are reversed, spark plug polarity is reversed.

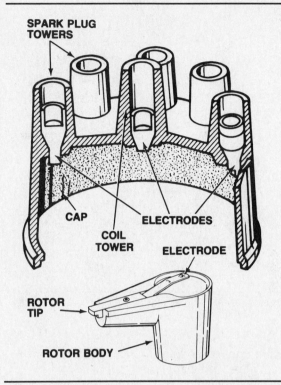

Figure 9-15. A distributor rotor and a cutaway view of the distributor cap.

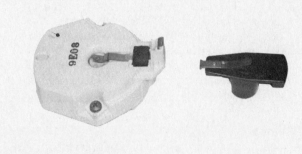

Figure 9-16. Typical distributor rotors.

DISTRIBUTOR CAP AND ROTOR

The distributor cap and rotor, figure 9-15, receive high-voltage current from the coil secondary winding. Current enters the distributor cap through the central terminal, called the coil tower. The rotor carries the current from the coil tower to the spark plug electrodes in the rim of the cap. The rotor is mounted on the distributor shaft and rotates with it, so that the rotor electrode moves from one spark plug electrode to another in the cap to follow the designated firing order.

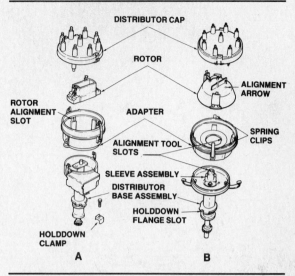

Figure 9-17. Ford's bilevel rotor used with the 1978 EEC-I distributor (left) requires alignment when installed; the style used with 1979 and later EEC-I, -II, and -III distributors (right) normally does not. (Ford)

Distributor Rotor

A rotor is made of silicone plastic, **Bakelite**, or a similar synthetic material that is a very good insulator. A metal electrode on top of the rotor conducts current from the carbon terminal of the coil tower.

The rotor is keyed to the distributor shaft to maintain its correct relationship with the shaft and the spark plug electrodes in the cap. The key may be a flat section or a slot in the top of the shaft. Delco-Remy V-6 and V-8 (shown at the left in figure 9-16) and Ford TFI distributor rotors are keyed in place by two locators and secured by two screws. Most other rotors (shown at the right in figure 9-16) are pressed onto the shaft by hand. The rotor in Chrysler's optically triggered distributor is retained by a horizontal capscrew.

The Ford EEC-I, -II, and -III ignitions have rotors with two pickup arms and two electrodes, figure 9-17. The electrodes are on different levels that correspond to two levels of distributor cap electrodes, which minimizes

Bakelite: A synthetic plastic material that is a good insulator. Distributor caps are often made of Bakelite.

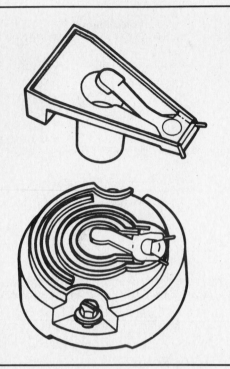

Figure 9-18. Typical Ford multiwire or "cat-whisker" rotors used in some 1983-85 systems. (Ford)

high-voltage **cross-firing** in the distributor. When the rotor is removed or replaced on 1978 EEC-I systems, figure 9-17A, it requires alignment. A modification of this design is used on 1979 and later EEC-I, -II, and -III distributors, figure 9-17B. Rotor alignment is not normally required when replacing this rotor.

Ford's basic rotor design uses a blade-type rotor tip. This was changed to a multiwire or "cat-whisker" rotor tip, figure 9-18, in some 1983-86 systems. This was an attempt to further reduce RFI interference from the secondary circuit without using silicone grease on the rotor tip. However, arcing from the multiwire tip formed ozone and nitrogen oxides from the air inside the distributor. Over a period of time, these combined to form nitric acid that reacted with the distributor cap to create a short-circuit path for secondary voltage.

Ford released replacement caps of a different material in 1985 to counteract the cross-firing problem and discontinued the cat-whisker rotors in 1986. Replacement rotors for 1983-85 models are the blade-type design.

Except for the multiwire-tip rotors, Ford and Chrysler breakerless distributor rotors are coated at the factory with a silicone grease. As the silicone ages, it may look like contamination, but it is not. Do not remove or reapply any

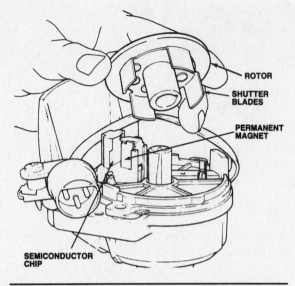

Figure 9-19. A Hall-effect triggering device attached to the rotor. (Chrysler)

coating on a used Ford rotor. Chrysler recommends removing any excess on the tip of the rotor. When a new Ford rotor is installed, apply a $1/8$-in. (3-mm) coating of silicone grease (Dow Corning 111, GE G-627, or equivalent) on all sides of the electrode, including the tip. The Ford multiwire-tip rotor *does not* require the silicone grease used on the blade-type rotors.

Rotors used with Hall-effect switches often have the shutter blades attached, figure 9-19, serving a dual purpose. In addition to distributing the secondary current, the rotor blades bypass the Hall-effect magnetic field and create the signal for the primary circuit to fire.

Rotor air gap

An air gap of a few thousandths of an inch, or a few hundredths of a millimeter, exists between the tip of the rotor electrode and the spark plug electrode of the cap. If they actually touched, both would wear very quickly. Because the gap cannot be measured when the distributor is assembled, it is usually described in terms of the voltage required to create an arc across the electrodes. Only about 3,000 volts are required to create an arc across most breaker-point distributor air gaps, but some Delco-Remy distributors require as much as 9,000 volts. The voltage required to jump the air gap in electronic distributors generally is higher than that required for breaker-point ignitions. As the rotor completes the secondary circuit and the plug fires, the rotor air gap adds resistance to the circuit. This raises the plug firing voltage, suppresses secondary current, and reduces RFI.

Distributor Cap

The distributor cap is also made of silicone plastic, Bakelite, or a similar material that resists chemical attack and protects other distributor parts. Metal electrodes in the spark plug towers and a carbon insert in the coil tower provide electrical connections with the ignition cables and the rotor electrode, figure 9-20. The cap is keyed to the distributor housing and is held on by two or four spring-loaded clips or by screws.

Delco-Remy HEI caps and all Ford Dura-Spark and TFI caps have male connectors rather than female spark plug towers. When removing a cap from an early-1977 Dura-Spark distributor, unlatch the cap from the adapter ring first. Do not try to lift the cap and adapter from the body together, because the adapter will jam on the rotor. On later Dura-Spark distributors, the adapter ring is held to the body by two screws inside the ring.

HEI distributor caps with an integral coil, figure 9-11, are secured by four spring-loaded clips. When removing this cap, be sure that all four clips are disengaged and clear of the housing. Then lift the cap straight up to avoid bending the carbon button in the cap and the spring that connects it to the coil. If the button and

Cross-Firing: Ignition voltage jumping from the distributor rotor to the wrong spark plug electrode inside the distributor cap. Also, ignition voltage jumping from one spark plug cable to another due to worn insulation.

■ Making Tracks

You often read instructions to inspect ignition parts for carbon tracks. Although you may have heard about or seen carbon tracks, have you ever thought about what they are and what causes them?

Carbon tracks are deposits or defects on distributor rotors, caps, spark plugs, and cables that create a short-circuit path to ground for secondary high voltage. They also cause crossfiring, in which the high voltage jumps from the distributor rotor to the wrong terminal in the cap.

The problems caused by carbon tracks are all pretty similar, but the causes for these defects are rather complex. A distributor cap or rotor may develop a hairline crack because of rough handling, a manufacturing defect, or some other problem. Under certain conditions, moisture can collect in the crack and create a lower resistance path for high voltage. High voltage arcing to ground in a distributor ionizes air molecules and can form conductive deposits along its path. If any dirt or grease is in the short-circuit path, the combination of high voltage and its accompanying current causes carbon deposits to form around the crack. Thus, a carbon track develops.

Carbon tracks can form even without a crack in a cap or rotor. High voltage ionizes air and oil molecules in the distributor and causes deposits to form. The deposits have high resistance, but if they are the least bit conductive, secondary voltage can arc to them. Over a period of time, the deposits build up and can create a short circuit.

Outside a distributor, similar carbon tracks can form on spark plug insulators and ignition cables due to grease deposits and weak points in damaged cable insulation.

Carbon tracks inside a distributor cap often can be tricky to diagnose. Sometimes an engine will run smoothly at idle but misfire at high speed. As the distributor advance mechanisms operate, the rotor moves farther away from the cap terminals as the coil discharges. The high-voltage current must cross an increasing air gap. If a nearby carbon track provides lower resistance, the voltage will jump to ground and the engine will misfire.

A typical carbon track has about the same, or a little less, resistance as a TVRS ignition cable. That's quite conductive enough to cause a misfire or a no-start problem. The accompanying photo shows a classic set of carbon tracks inside a distributor cap.

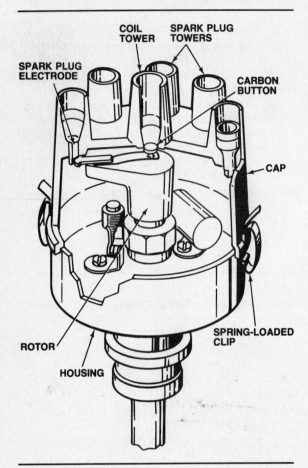

Figure 9-20. The distributor cap and rotor assembled with the distributor housing.

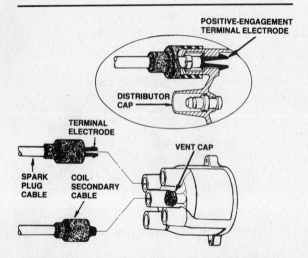

Figure 9-21. Chrysler 4-cylinder distributors have used positive locking terminal electrodes as part of the ignition cable since 1980. (Chrysler)

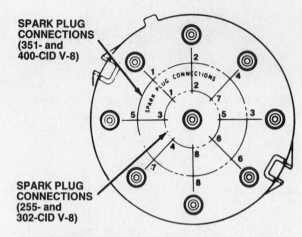

Figure 9-22. Spark plug cable installation order for V-8 EEC systems.

spring are distorted, arcing can occur that will burn the cap and rotor.

Positive-engagement spark plug cables are used with some Chrysler and Ford 4-cylinder ignition systems. There are no electrodes in distributor caps used with these cables. A terminal electrode attached to the distributor-cap end of the cable locks inside the cap to form the distributor contact terminal, figure 9-21. The secondary terminal of the cable is pressed into the cap.

Ford Motorcraft Dura-Spark III distributors used with some of Ford's electronic engine control (EEC) systems have caps and rotors with the terminals on two levels to prevent secondary voltage arcing. Spark plug cables are not connected to the caps in firing order sequence, but the caps are numbered with the engine cylinder numbers, figure 9-22. The caps have two sets of numbers, one set for 302-cid (5-liter) standard engines, and the other for 351-cid (5.7-liter) and 302-cid high-performance engines. Cylinder numbers must be checked carefully when changing spark plug cables.

Distributor caps used on some late-model Ford and Chrysler vehicles have a vent to prevent the buildup of moisture and reduce the accumulation of ozone inside the cap, figure 9-21.

IGNITION CABLES

Secondary ignition cables carry high-voltage current from the coil to the distributor (coil wire) and from the distributor to the spark plugs (spark plug cables). They use heavy insulation to prevent the high-voltage current from jumping to ground before it reaches the spark plugs. Ford, GM, and some other electronic ignitions use an 8-mm cable; all others use a 7-mm cable.

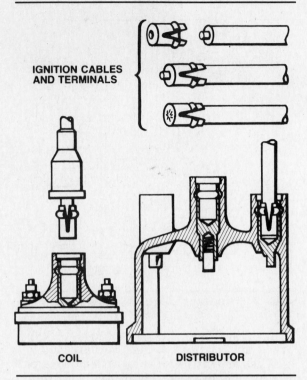

Figure 9-23. Ignition cables and terminals.

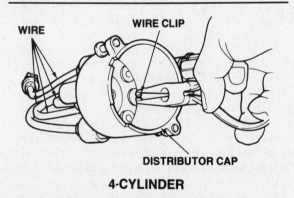

Figure 9-24. Positive locking terminal electrodes are removed by compressing the wire clips with pliers and removing the wire from the cap.

Conductor Types

Spark plug cables originally used a solid steel or copper wire conductor. Cables manufactured with these conductors were found to cause radio and television interference. While this type of cable is still made for special applications such as racing, most spark plug cables have been made of a high-resistance, nonmetallic conductor for the past 30 years. Several nonmetallic conductors may be used, such as carbon, and linen or fiberglass strands impregnated with graphite. The nonmetallic conductor

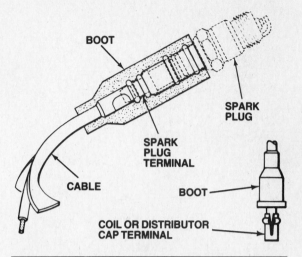

Figure 9-25. Ignition cables, terminals and boots work together to carry the high-voltage secondary current.

acts as a resistor in the secondary circuit and reduces RFI and spark plug wear due to high current. Such cables are often called **television-radio-suppression (TVRS) cables**, or just suppression cables.

When replacing spark plug cables on vehicles with computer control systems, be sure that the resistance of the new cables used is within the specifications provided by the carmaker to avoid possible electromagnetic interference with the operation of the computer.

Terminals and Boots

Secondary ignition cable terminals, figure 9-23, are designed to make a strong contact with the coil and distributor electrodes. They are, however, subject to corrosion and arcing if not firmly seated and protected from the elements.

Positive-engagement spark plug cable terminals, figure 9-24, lock in place inside the distributor cap and cannot come loose accidentally. They can only be removed with the cap off the distributor. The terminal electrode then is compressed with pliers and the wire is pushed out of the cap, figure 9-24.

The ignition cables must have special connectors, often called spark plug boots, figure 9-25. The boots provide a tight and well-insulated contact between the cable and the spark plug.

Television-Radio-Suppression (TVRS) Cables: High-resistance, carbon-conductor ignition cables that suppress RFI.

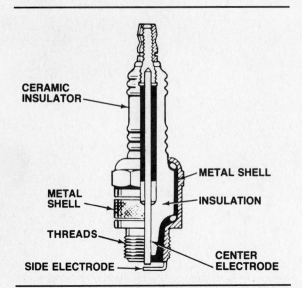

Figure 9-26. A cutaway view of the spark plug.

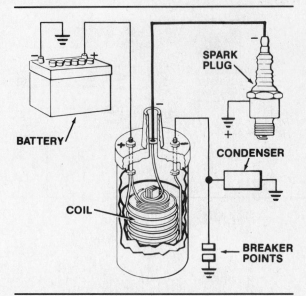

Figure 9-27. The spark plug should have a negative charge at the center electrode and a positive charge at the side electrode.

SPARK PLUGS

Spark plugs allow the high-voltage secondary current to arc across a small air gap. The three basic parts of a spark plug, figure 9-26, are:
1. A ceramic core, or insulator, which insulates the center electrode and acts as a heat conductor
2. Two electrodes, one insulated in the core and the other grounded on the shell
3. A metal shell that holds the insulator and electrodes in a gas-tight assembly and which has threads to hold the plug in the engine.

The metal shell grounds the side electrode against the engine. The other electrode is encased in the ceramic insulator. A spark plug boot and cable are attached to the top of the plug. High-voltage current flows through the center of the plug and arcs from the tip of the insulated electrode to the side electrode and ground. This spark ignites the air-fuel mixture in the combustion chamber to produce power.

The burning gases in the engine can corrode and wear the spark plug electrodes. Electrodes are made of metals that resist this attack. Most electrodes are made of high-nickel alloy steel, but platinum and silver alloys have also been used.

Spark Plug Firing Action

The arc of current across a spark plug air gap provides two types of discharge:
• Capacitive
• Inductive.

When a high-voltage surge is first delivered to the spark plug center electrode, the air-fuel mixture in the air gap cannot conduct an arc. The spark plug acts as a capacitor, with the center electrode storing a negative charge and the grounded side electrode storing a positive charge. The air gap between the electrodes acts as a dielectric insulator. This is the opposite of the normal negative-ground polarity, and results from the polarity of the coil secondary winding, as shown in figure 9-27.

Secondary voltage increases, and the charges in the spark plug strengthen until the difference in potential between the electrodes is great enough to **ionize** the spark plug air gap. That is, the air-fuel mixture in the gap is changed from a nonconductor to a conductor by the positive and negative charges of the two electrodes. The dielectric resistance of the air gap breaks down and current flows between the electrodes. The voltage level at this instant is called ionization voltage. The current that flows across the spark plug air gap at the instant of ionization is the capacitive portion of the spark. It flows from negative to positive and uses the energy stored in the plug itself when the plug was acting as a capacitor, before ionization. This is the portion of the spark that starts the combustion process within the engine.

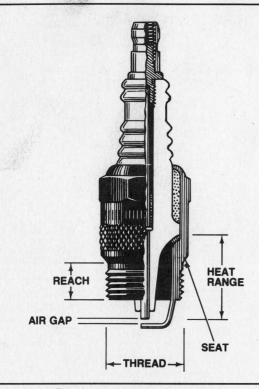

Figure 9-28. The design features of a spark plug.

The ionization voltage level is usually less than the total voltage produced in the coil secondary winding. The remainder of the secondary voltage (that voltage not needed to force ionization) is dissipated as current across the spark plug air gap. This is the inductive portion of the spark discharge, which causes the *visible* flash or arc at the plug. It contributes nothing to the combustion of the air-fuel mixture, but is the cause of electrical interference and severe electrode erosion. High-resistance cables and spark plugs suppress this inductive portion of the spark discharge.

SPARK PLUG CONSTRUCTION

Spark Plug Design Features

Spark plugs are made in a variety of sizes and types to fit different engines. The most important differences among plugs are:
1. Reach
2. Heat range
3. Thread and seat
4. Air gap.
These are illustrated in figure 9-28.

Reach
The **reach** of a spark plug is the length of the shell from the seat to the bottom of the shell, including both threaded and unthreaded portions. If an incorrect plug is installed and the reach is too short, the electrode will be in a

Ionize: To break up molecules into two or more oppositely charged ions. The air gap between the spark plug electrodes is ionized when the air-fuel mixture is changed from a non-conductor to a conductor.

Reach: The length of the spark plug shell from the seat to the bottom of the shell.

Spark Plug Design

Many people have tried to redesign the spark plug. Not all of the "new" designs have worked out. For example, a plug manufactured before World War I had an insulated handle at the top. By pulling this handle up, an auxiliary gap was opened, presumably to create a hotter spark and stop oil fouling. A window in the side of the plug showed whether the gap was open or closed.

Another "revolutionary" type of plug had a screw connector that allowed the inner core assembly to be removed and cleaned quickly.

Still another design had threads and electrodes at each end of the plug. The plug could be removed, the terminal cap installed on the other end, and then reinstalled upside down. All of the photos were provided by Champion Spark Plug Company.

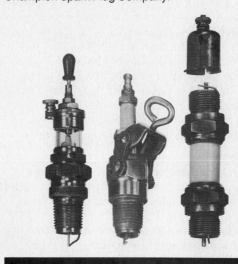

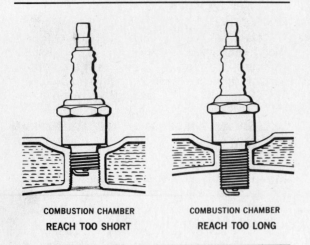

Figure 9-29. Spark plug reach.

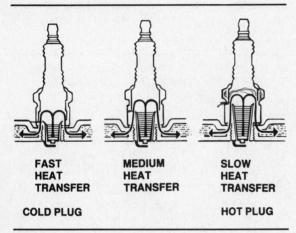

Figure 9-30. Spark plug heat range.

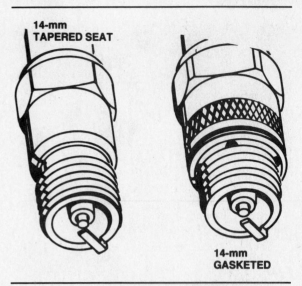

Figure 9-31. Spark plug thread and seat types.

pocket and the spark will not ignite the air-fuel mixture very well, figure 9-29.

If the spark plug reach is too long, the exposed plug threads could get hot enough to ignite the air-fuel mixture at the wrong time. It may be difficult to remove the plug due to carbon deposits on the plug threads. Engine damage can also result from interference between moving parts and the exposed plug threads.

Heat range
The **heat range** of a spark plug determines its ability to dissipate heat from the firing end. The design of the insulator core controls the plug's heat dissipation ability, figure 9-30. A "cold" spark plug has a short insulator tip that provides a short path for heat to travel, and permits the heat to dissipate rapidly to maintain a lower firing tip temperature. A "hot" spark

plug has a long insulator tip that creates a longer path for heat to travel. This slower heat transfer maintains a higher firing tip temperature. Heat range is extremely important because the firing end of the spark plug must run hot enough to burn away fouling deposits at idle, but must also remain cool enough at highway speeds to avoid preignition.

Thread and seat
Automotive spark plugs are made with one of two thread diameters: 14 or 18 millimeters, figure 9-31. All 18-mm plugs have tapered seats that match similar tapered seats in the cylinder head. No gaskets are used. The 9-mm plugs are made either with a flat seat that requires a gasket or with a tapered seat that does not. The gasket-type 9-mm plugs are still quite common, but the 9-mm tapered-seat plugs are now used in most late-model engines.

The steel shell of a spark plug is hex-shaped so that a wrench will fit it. The 9-mm tapered-seat plugs have shells with a $5/8$-inch hex; 9-mm gasketed and 18-mm tapered-seat plugs have shells with a $13/16$-inch hex.

Air gap
The correct spark plug air gap is important to engine performance and plug life. A gap that is too narrow will cause a rough idle and a change in the exhaust emissions. A gap that is too wide will require higher voltage to jump it; if the required voltage is greater than the available ignition voltage, misfiring will result.

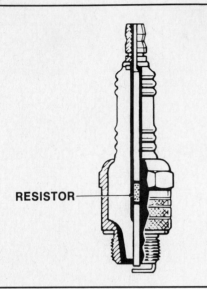

Figure 9-32. A resistor-type spark plug.

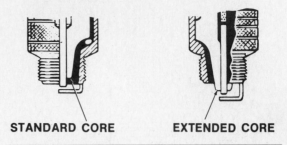

STANDARD CORE　　　　EXTENDED CORE

Figure 9-33. A comparison of a standard and an extended-core spark plug.

Special-Purpose Spark Plugs

Specifications for all spark plugs include the design characteristics just described. In addition, many plugs have other special features to fit particular requirements.

Resistor-type spark plugs

This type of plug contains a resistor in the center electrode, figure 9-32. The resistor generally has a value of 7,500 to 15,000 ohms and is used to reduce radiofrequency interference (RFI). **Resistor-type spark plugs** can be used in place of nonresistor plugs of the same size, heat range, and gap without affecting engine performance.

Extended-tip spark plugs

Sometimes called an **extended-core spark plug**, this design uses a center electrode and insulator that extend farther into the combustion chamber, figure 9-33. The extended-tip operates hotter under slow-speed driving conditions to burn off combustion deposits and cooler at high speed to prevent spark plug overheating. This greater efficiency over a wide temperature range has led to increased use in the smaller and less powerful engines used in the 1980s.

Wide-gap spark plugs

The electronic ignition systems on some late-model engines require spark plug gaps in the 0.045- to 0.080-inch (1.0- to 2.0-mm) range. Plugs for such systems are made with a wider gap than other plugs. This wide gap is indicated in the plug part number. Do not try to open the gap of a narrow-gap plug to create the wide gap required by such ignitions.

Copper-core spark plugs

Many plug manufacturers are making plugs with a copper segment inside the center electrode. The copper provides faster heat transfer from the electrode to the insulator and then to the cylinder head and engine coolant. Copper-core plugs are also extended-tip plugs. The combined effects are a more stable heat range over a greater range of engine temperatures and greater resistance to fouling and misfire.

Platinum-tip spark plugs

Platinum-tip plugs are used in some late-model engines to increase firing efficiency. The platinum center electrode increases electrical conductivity, which helps prevent misfiring with lean mixtures and high temperatures. Since platinum is very resistant to corrosion and wear from combustion chamber gases and heat, recommended plug life is double that of other plugs.

Long-reach, short-thread spark plugs

Some late-model GM engines, Ford 4-cylinder engines, and Ford 5.0-liter (302-cid) V-8 engines use 9-mm, tapered-seat plugs with a 3/4-inch reach but which only have threads for about half of their length, figure 9-34. The plug part number includes a suffix that indicates the special thread design, although a fully threaded plug can be substituted if necessary.

Heat Range: The measure of a spark plug's ability to dissipate heat from its firing end.

Resistor-Type Spark Plug: A plug that has a resistor in the center electrode to reduce the inductive portion of the spark discharge.

Extended-Core Spark Plug: Also called power tip. The insulator core and the electrodes in this type of spark plug extend further into the combustion chamber than they do on other types.

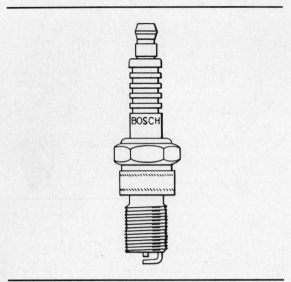

Figure 9-34. A long-reach, short-thread spark plug.

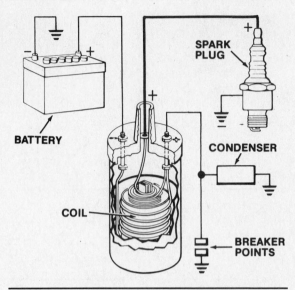

Figure 9-36. Reverse, or positive, ignition polarity.

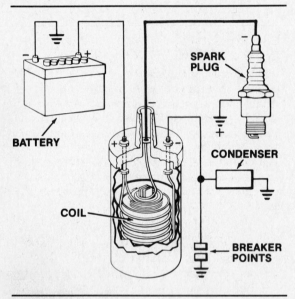

Figure 9-35. Negative, or ground, ignition polarity.

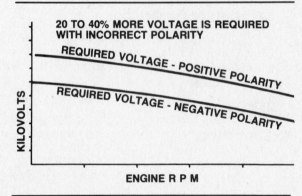

Figure 9-37. More voltage is required to fire a spark plug that has reverse polarity. (Prestolite)

IGNITION POLARITY

If the ignition coil is correctly connected, figure 9-35, voltage will be delivered to the spark plug so that the center electrode is negatively charged and the grounded electrode is positively charged. Electrons will move from the hotter center electrode to the cooler side electrode at a relatively lower voltage. This is called **negative polarity**. If the coil is incorrectly connected, figure 9-36, electrons will be forced to move from the cooler side electrode to the hotter center electrode. This is called **positive polarity**, or reverse polarity. Figure 9-37 shows

how much more voltage is required to fire a spark plug with positive polarity than one with negative polarity.

Negative Polarity: Also called ground polarity. A correct polarity of the ignition coil connections. Coil voltage is delivered to the spark plugs so that the center electrode of the plug is negatively charged and the grounded electrode is positively charged.

Positive Polarity: Also called reverse polarity. An incorrect polarity of the ignition coil connections. Coil voltage is delivered to the spark plug so that the center electrode of the plug is positively charged and the grounded electrode is negatively charged.

SUMMARY

The ignition secondary circuit generates the high voltage and distributes it to the engine's spark plugs. This circuit contains the coil secondary winding, the distributor cap and rotor, the ignition cables, and the spark plugs.

The ignition coil produces the high voltage necessary to ionize the spark plug gap through electromagnetic induction. Low-voltage current flow in the primary winding induces high voltage in the secondary winding. A coil must be installed with the same primary polarity as the battery to maintain proper secondary polarity at the spark plugs.

Available voltage is the amount of voltage the coil *can* produce. Required voltage is the voltage necessary to ionize and fire the spark plugs under any given operating condition. Voltage reserve is the difference between available voltage and required voltage. A well-tuned ignition system should have a 60-percent voltage reserve.

The spark plugs allow the high voltage to arc across an air gap and ignite the air-fuel mixture in the combustion chamber. Important design features of a spark plug are its reach, heat range, thread and seat size, and the air gap. Other special features of spark plugs are the use of resistors, extended tips, wide gaps, and copper cores. For efficient spark plug firing, ignition polarity must be established so that the center electrode of the plug is negative and the ground electrode is positive.

Review Questions
Choose the single most correct answer.
Compare your answers with the correct answers on page 451.

1. Which of the following is used as insulation to protect the windings of coils?
   a. Oil
   b. Plastic potting
   c. Paper
   d. All of the above

2. Which of the following statements about ignition coils is true?
   a. They are easily repaired
   b. Adjustments are made by set-screws
   c. They cannot be replaced
   d. None of the above

3. Many of Delco-Remy's solid-state ignition systems have a coil mounted:
   a. On the engine
   b. On a fender panel
   c. On the distributor cap
   d. None of the above

4. When the coil terminals are properly connected to the battery, the grounded end of the secondary circuit is electrically:
   a. Positive
   b. Negative
   c. Neutral
   d. None of the above

5. A loss of one volt in the primary circuit can decrease available secondary voltage by _____ volts.
   a. 10
   b. 100
   c. 1,000
   d. 10,000

6. The accompanying illustration shows:

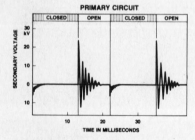

   a. Secondary circuit firing pulse trace
   b. Secondary circuit ignition pulse trace
   c. Secondary circuit no-load voltage trace
   d. Secondary circuit spark voltage trace

7. Firing voltage is usually about _____ as high as spark voltage.
   a. One-fourth
   b. One-half
   c. Four times
   d. Two times

8. The voltage delivered by the coil is:
   a. Its full voltage capacity under all operating conditions
   b. Approximately half of its full voltage capacity at all times
   c. Only the voltage necessary to fire the plugs under any given operating condition
   d. Its full voltage capacity only while starting

9. The voltage reserve is the:
   a. Voltage required from the coil to fire a plug
   b. Maximum secondary voltage capacity of the coil
   c. Primary circuit voltage at the battery side of the ballast resistor
   d. Difference between the required voltage and the available voltage of the secondary circuit

10. A well-tuned ignition system should have a voltage reserve of about _____ of available voltage, under most operating conditions.
    a. 30 percent
    b. 60 percent
    c. 100 percent
    d. 150 percent

11. Bakelite is a synthetic material used in distributors because of its good:
    a. Permeability
    b. Conductance
    c. Insulation
    d. Capacitance

12. Which of the following are basic parts of a spark plug?
    a. Ceramic core
    b. Two electrodes
    c. Steel shell
    d. All of the above

13. That part of the energy that flows through a spark plug and causes the visible flash or arc:
    a. Contributes nothing to the combustion of fuel mix
    b. Causes electrical interference and electrode corrosion
    c. Is called the inductive portion of the spark
    d. All of the above

14. Which of the following is *not* an important design feature among types of spark plugs?
    a. Reach
    b. Heat range
    c. Polarity
    d. Air gap

15. In the illustration below, the dimension arrows indicate the:

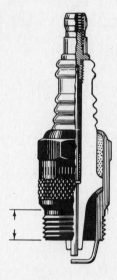

    a. Heat range
    b. Resistor portion of the electrode
    c. Extended core length
    d. Reach

16. All spark plugs have:
    a. A resistor
    b. An extended core
    c. A ceramic insulator
    d. A series gap

Chapter

10

Ignition Timing and Spark Advance Control

Chapter 1 dealt with ignition intervals and how the ignition must be synchronized with crankshaft rotation and cylinder firing order. We also have seen that the initial ignition timing is set for the best engine operation at a specific engine speed, usually at or near slow-idle speed. When engine speed changes, ignition timing also must change.

In this chapter, we will learn how ignition timing changes as engine speed and load change and how timing changes are made. This chapter also covers the centrifugal and vacuum advance units and the emission control systems that have been used to modify the vacuum advance operation. With the latest generation of electronic ignition systems, the computer has taken the place of the more familiar mechanical and vacuum advance devices previously used. Early electronic spark timing controls are discussed at the end of the chapter.

REVIEWING BASIC TIMING AND BURN TIME

Engine speed and load changes require the ignition timing to advance or to retard. As we have seen, the burn time of an air-fuel mixture is about 3 milliseconds. Maximum combustion pressure should occur with the piston, connecting rod, and crankshaft in position to produce the most power. At low engine speeds, relatively little spark advance is required to achieve this. However, as engine speed increases, the process of combustion must be started earlier to provide enough burn time.

We have said that burn time is *about* 3 milliseconds. This means that it does vary somewhat with engine load. When the fuel system provides a lean air-fuel mixture under light load, it takes longer to ignite and burn the mixture. Conversely, richer mixtures ignited under a heavy load will burn a little faster.

SPARK ADVANCE

There are two basic factors that govern ignition timing: engine speed and load. All changes in timing are related to these two factors:
• Timing must increase, or advance, as engine speed increases; it must decrease, or retard, as engine speed decreases.
• Timing must decrease, or retard, as load increases; it must increase, or advance, as load decreases.

Optimum ignition timing under any given combination of these basic factors will result in maximum cylinder pressure. In turn, this delivers maximum power with a minimum of exhaust emissions and the best possible fuel economy.

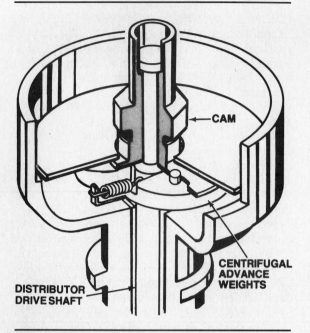

Figure 10-1. The centrifugal advance weights transfer the rotation of the distributor drive shaft to the cam, or trigger wheel, and the rotor.

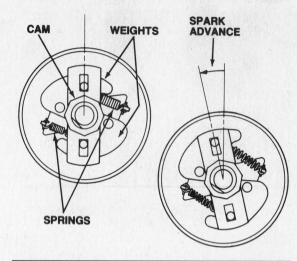

Figure 10-2. When the centrifugal advance weights move, the position of the cam, or trigger wheel, and of the rotor changes.

When ignition takes place too early, the combustion pressure slows down the piston. If timing is too far advanced, the increased combustion pressure will cause an engine knock. When ignition takes place too late, the piston is too far down on its power stroke to benefit from the combustion pressure, resulting in a power loss.

Before the introduction of computer-controlled timing, most automotive distributors had two spark advance mechanisms to react to engine operating changes and alter ignition timing:
1. The centrifugal advance changes ignition timing to match engine speed by altering the position of the distributor cam or trigger wheel on the distributor shaft.
2. The vacuum advance changes ignition timing to match engine load by altering the position of the breaker points or the magnetic pickup coil (electronic sensor).

These changes in position alter the time, relative to crankshaft position, at which the primary circuit is opened.

Centrifugal Advance — Speed

The **centrifugal**, or **mechanical**, **advance** mechanism consists of two weights connected to the distributor drive shaft by two springs, figure 10-1. The distributor cam, or electronic trigger

wheel, and the distributor rotor are mounted on another shaft. The second shaft fits over the drive shaft like a sleeve. Drive shaft motion is transmitted to the second shaft through the centrifugal advance weights. When the weights move, the relative position of the drive shaft and the second shaft is changed.

As engine speed increases, distributor shaft rotation speed increases. The advance weights move outward because of **centrifugal force**. The outward movement of the weights shifts the second shaft and the cam or the trigger wheel, figure 10-2. The primary circuit opens earlier in the compression stroke, and the spark occurs earlier.

Each advance weight is connected to the distributor drive shaft by a control spring. These springs are selected to allow the correct amount of weight movement and ignition advance for a particular engine.

At low engine speeds, spring tension holds the weights in, so that initial timing is maintained. As engine speed increases, centrifugal force overcomes spring tension and the weights move outward. The advance is not a large, rapid change, but rather a slow, gradual shift. Figure 10-3 shows a typical centrifugal advance curve. The advance curve can be changed by changing the tension of the control springs. Remember that centrifugal advance responds to engine speed.

In most distributors, the centrifugal advance mechanism is mounted below the cam and breaker points, figure 10-1, or below the trigger wheel and pickup coil. Delco-Remy V-6 and V-8

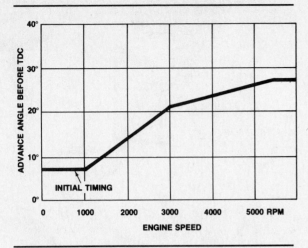

Figure 10-3. A typical distributor advance curve.

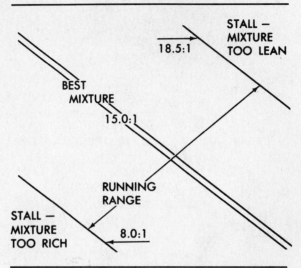

Figure 10-5. Air-fuel ratio limits for a 4-stroke gasoline engine. (Chevrolet)

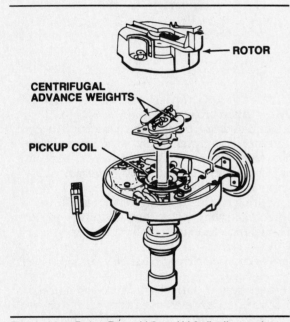

Figure 10-4. Delco-Remy V-6 and V-8 distributors have the centrifugal advance mechanism above the cam and rotor, or above the pickup coil and trigger wheel, as shown.

distributors, as well as some distributors made in Japan, have the advance mechanism above the cam or trigger wheel, just below the rotor, figure 10-4.

Vacuum Advance — Load

The **vacuum advance** mechanism allows efficient engine performance within a range of air-fuel ratios. These ratios are important, since there are limits to how rich or how lean they can be and still remain fully combustible. The air-fuel ratio with which an engine can operate efficiently ranges from 8 to 18.5 to 1 by weight, figure 10-5.

These ratios are generally stated as eight parts of air combined with one part of gasoline (8:1), which is the richest mixture that an engine can tolerate and still fire regularly. A ratio of 18.5 parts of air mixed with one part of gasoline (18.5:1) is the leanest mixture that an engine can tolerate without misfiring.

An average air-fuel ratio is about 15:1. This mixture takes about 3 milliseconds to burn. A lean mixture (one with more air and less fuel) will require more time to burn. The ignition timing must be advanced to provide maximum combustion pressure at the correct piston position. A rich mixture (one with more fuel and less air) will burn more quickly and emit more exhaust pollutants. Ignition timing should be retarded for complete combustion and emission control.

Centrifugal (Mechanical) Advance: A method of advancing the ignition spark using weights in the distributor that react to centrifugal force.

Centrifugal Force: The natural tendency of objects, when rotated, to move away from the center of rotation.

Vacuum Advance: The use of engine vacuum to advance ignition spark timing by moving the distributor breaker plate.

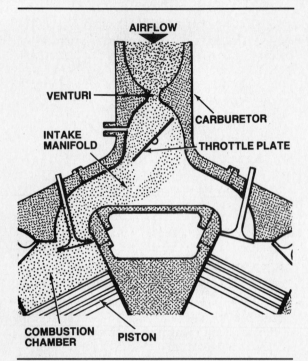

Figure 10-6. Air flows through the carburetor and intake manifold to reach the combustion chamber.

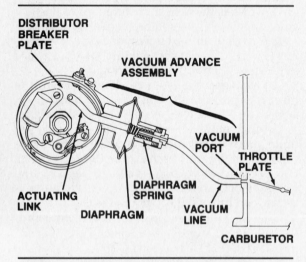

Figure 10-7. The vacuum advance assembly is connected to a port in the carburetor.

Engine Vacuum

The reciprocating engine can be considered as an air pump. As a piston moves downward, air pressure in the cylinder decreases. Air from the atmosphere rushes in to fill the void.

The fuel delivery system uses this air movement to carry fuel to the cylinders. On many cars, the air must travel through a carburetor, figure 10-6, to reach the cylinders. Under several operating conditions, air movement caused

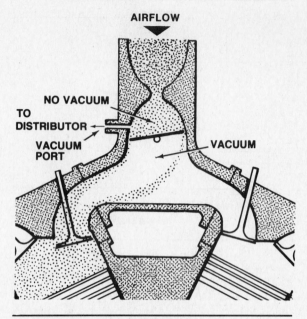

Figure 10-8. When the throttle is closed during idle or deceleration, there is no vacuum at the port.

by the downstroke of a piston is not great enough to draw fuel into the cylinder. The carburetor forces the air to flow through a restriction called a **venturi**. This increases the speed of the airflow and creates a low-pressure (vacuum) area. Fuel is drawn into the airflow by the vacuum, and the resulting air-fuel mixture enters the cylinder combustion chambers. The air-fuel ratio changes as the vacuum in the carburetor changes.

The ignition timing must be changed as the air-fuel ratio changes, so that the mixture has enough time to burn. The vacuum advance mechanism is connected to a small hole or port in the carburetor, figure 10-7, just above the throttle plate. This is called **ported vacuum**. When vacuum exists at the port, timing is advanced. When no vacuum exists at the port, the timing remains at a basic setting or is affected only by the centrifugal advance. The vacuum advance mechanism will be explained in more detail later. The following paragraphs explain the relationship between carburetor vacuum and the need for advanced timing.

The driver of an automobile controls engine load and carburetor vacuum through the action of the throttle plate, which is a variable restriction in the carburetor airflow. When the engine is at idle, figure 10-8, the throttle plate is almost closed. Very little air flows through the carburetor to mix with the fuel. With this rich air-fuel mixture, no spark advance is necessary. High vacuum exists in the intake manifold, but there

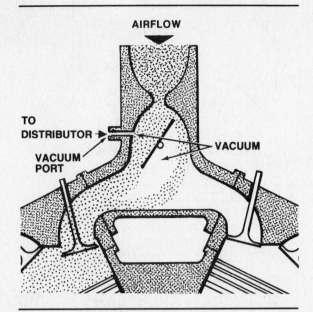

Figure 10-9. When the throttle is partially open, the port is exposed to manifold vacuum.

is no vacuum at the port because it is above the closed throttle plate. There is no vacuum-controlled spark advance with a closed throttle. The large amount of vacuum *below* the throttle plate exists because of the small amount of air entering the engine. This is called **manifold vacuum**.

When the throttle plate is partially open, figure 10-9, more air can flow through the carburetor. The air-fuel mixture becomes lean and requires an advanced spark. Since the port is now exposed to vacuum, ignition timing is advanced.

Venturi: A restriction in an airflow, such as in a carburetor, that increases the airflow speed and creates a reduction in pressure.

Ported Vacuum: Vacuum immediately above the throttle plate in a carburetor.

Manifold Vacuum: Low pressure in an engine's intake manifold, below the carburetor throttle.

Vacuum Measurement

When you work with vacuum devices on late-model cars, you will encounter several different units of measurement used to gauge vacuum. The U.S. auto industry customarily has measured air pressure in pounds per square inch (psi) and vacuum in inches of mercury (in. Hg). This can be confusing right away because we are using two different kinds of units to measure essentially the same thing: air pressure. The reason we use both is based on scientific tradition.

Air pressure and vacuum are measured in a laboratory with a device called a manometer. This is a U-shaped glass tube with each end connected to a different pressure source. One end can be open to the atmosphere, and the other can be connected to a pump or other source of low pressure. The tube is filled with liquid that moves up and down the two columns formed by the two legs of the U. Using two columns joined in a U-shape eliminates the effects of gravity and the weight of the liquid. Displacement caused by changes in pressure is read in marks graduated on the columns.

Laboratory manometers customarily are filled with mercury because it is stable and flows freely when exposed to pressure differentials. When low pressure on one side drops enough for air pressure on the other side to move the mercury column one inch, vacuum (low pressure) equals one inch of mercury (1 in. Hg).

When atmospheric pressure is removed completely from one side of the manometer, the mercury column will be displaced 29.921 inches at 32°F (0°C). Thus, 29.921 inches of mercury equals one atmosphere of

negative pressure, or is equivalent to 14.696 pounds per square inch.

If the manometer column were graduated in millimeters instead of inches, one atmosphere of displacement would equal 760 millimeters of mercury. Car service vacuum specifications are often given in metric units of mm Hg.

Another unit you will encounter often is the "bar". A bar equals one unit of atmospheric pressure. This is barometric pressure, and that is where we get the term "bar". A standard bar equals one kilogram of force applied to one square centimeter. This equals 750 mm Hg or 14.2 psi. These values are close to the customary atmospheric pressure values of 14.7 psi and 760 mm Hg. All standard pressures are calculated at 32°F (0°C) because pressure drops as temperature rises, and vice versa.

In automobile service, we work with pounds per square inch (psi) and kilopascals (kPa) to measure positive pressure. The most common units of vacuum measurement are in. Hg., mm Hg, and bar. Here are some handy conversion factors that you can use to switch from one unit to another. All equivalent measurements are at a standard temperature of 32°F (0°C), but the conversions are quite close enough for car service work.

    1 in. Hg = 0.4912 psi
    1 psi = 2.036 in. Hg = 51.72 mm Hg
    29.9 in. Hg = 14.7 psi = 760 mm Hg = 1 bar
    1 psi = 6.895 kPa (usually rounded off to 6.9
        or 7 kPa)

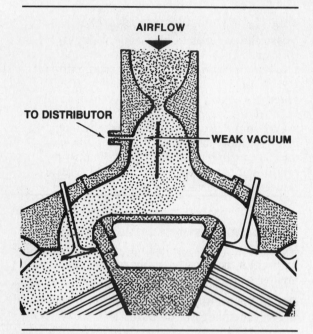

Figure 10-10. When the throttle is fully open, the vacuum at the port is too weak to cause any vacuum advance.

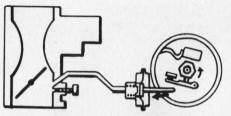

THROTTLE OPENED
VACUUM PORT   UNCOVERED
VACUUM SPARK   ADVANCE INTRODUCED

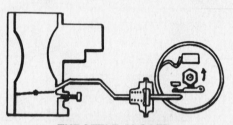

THROTTLE CLOSED
VACUUM PORT COVERED
NO VACUUM SPARK ADVANCE

Figure 10-11. Vacuum at the carburetor port causes the position of the breaker plate to shift.

At medium cruising speeds, the engine operates with a partly open throttle and an air-fuel ratio of approximately 15:1. Airflow velocity is high, and the vacuum signal at the carburetor port is strong enough to provide vacuum advance for this relatively lean air-fuel mixture.

A lean mixture is not the only factor that affects ignition timing requirements. During part-throttle operation, the cylinders are only partially filled with the air-fuel mixture. Because there is less to compress, the compression pressure is less. A less highly compressed mixture takes a longer time to burn.

At wide-open throttle, figure 10-10, the power circuit in the carburetor provides a richer mixture than at part-throttle cruising. Also, the cylinders are more completely filled because airflow volume increases. These factors cause a faster burn that requires the ignition timing to retard or decrease slightly for proper efficiency. Manifold vacuum and ported vacuum drop at wide-open throttle and become approximately equal. Vacuum may drop to as little as 5 inches of mercury (17 kPa), and typically 7 inches (24 kPa) of vacuum are required to operate a vacuum advance mechanism.

Vacuum advance also decreases when the throttle is opened quickly from idle or a part-throttle position. This occurs because airflow velocity lags behind throttle opening. This reduced vacuum will not draw enough fuel

through the main metering circuit of the carburetor, so the accelerator pump supplies extra fuel. This momentarily rich mixture does not need as much spark advance for complete combustion. Because the vacuum at the vacuum port of the carburetor is low when the throttle is first opened quickly, the vacuum advance decreases or retards to meet the needs of the momentarily rich mixture. Remember that vacuum advance responds to engine load.

Vacuum advance mechanism
The vacuum advance mechanism at the distributor, figure 10-7, consists of the:
• Movable breaker plate on which the points or electronic pickup coil are mounted
• Vacuum assembly, a housing with a flexible diaphragm and a spring
• Actuating link that connects the vacuum diaphragm to the breaker plate
• Tubing to connect the vacuum unit to the vacuum source.

When the **diaphragm** is pulled toward a vacuum, it pulls the actuating link, figure 10-11. This rotates the breaker plate to change the position of the point rubbing block in relation to the cam. Ignition timing increases or advances. In an electronic system, the pickup is shifted relative to the trigger wheel to advance timing.

Some older vacuum advance units can be adjusted by changing spring tension against the diaphragm.

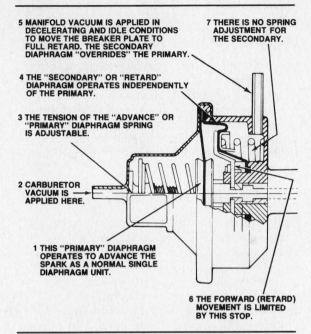

5 MANIFOLD VACUUM IS APPLIED IN DECELERATING AND IDLE CONDITIONS TO MOVE THE BREAKER PLATE TO FULL RETARD. THE SECONDARY DIAPHRAGM "OVERRIDES" THE PRIMARY.

7 THERE IS NO SPRING ADJUSTMENT FOR THE SECONDARY.

4 THE "SECONDARY" OR "RETARD" DIAPHRAGM OPERATES INDEPENDENTLY OF THE PRIMARY.

3 THE TENSION OF THE "ADVANCE" OR "PRIMARY" DIAPHRAGM SPRING IS ADJUSTABLE.

2 CARBURETOR VACUUM IS APPLIED HERE.

1 THIS "PRIMARY" DIAPHRAGM OPERATES TO ADVANCE THE SPARK AS A NORMAL SINGLE DIAPHRAGM UNIT.

6 THE FORWARD (RETARD) MOVEMENT IS LIMITED BY THIS STOP.

Figure 10-12. Operation of a typical dual-diaphragm vacuum advance assembly. (Ford)

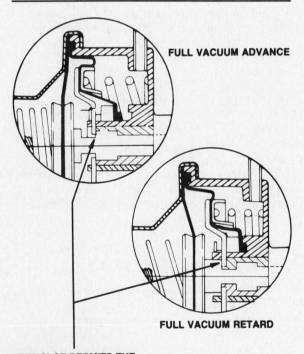

FULL VACUUM ADVANCE

FULL VACUUM RETARD

THIS SLOT PERMITS THE RETARD DIAPHRAGM TO MOVE THE LEVER TO THE BREAKER PLATE, EVEN IF THE ADVANCE DIAPHRAGM IS AT FULL VACUUM ADVANCE.

Figure 10-13. In a dual-diaphragm unit, the retard diaphragm can override the action of the advance diaphragm. (Ford)

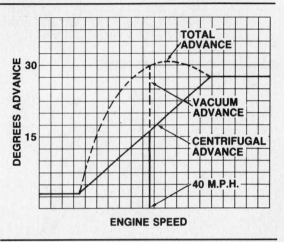

Figure 10-14. This typical advance curve shows that the total advance is the total of vacuum plus centrifugal advances.

Some distributors used by Ford, Volkswagen, and AMC have a dual-diaphragm vacuum unit to retard timing during certain engine operating conditions. In these systems, figure 10-12, one diaphragm acts as described above to advance ignition timing. The second diaphragm is exposed to intake manifold vacuum (between the throttle plate and the combustion chamber), which is high during idle and closed-throttle deceleration. This vacuum acts upon the second diaphragm to shift the breaker plate in the retard direction.

For exhaust emission control, the retard diaphragm can override the advance diaphragm. This causes timing to retard even when the advance diaphragm is at an advanced position, figure 10-13.

Total Ignition Advance

The two types of advance mechanisms work on different parts of the distributor to advance timing. Therefore, their effects are additive: the **total ignition advance** is the sum of the centrifugal advance and the vacuum advance, *plus* the initial ignition timing. This formula determines actual ignition timing under all conditions. Figure 10-14 shows the advance curves of a typical ignition system.

Diaphragm: A thin flexible wall, separating two cavities, such as the diaphragm in a vacuum advance unit.

Total Ignition Advance: The sum of centrifugal advance, vacuum advance, and initial timing; expressed in crankshaft degrees.

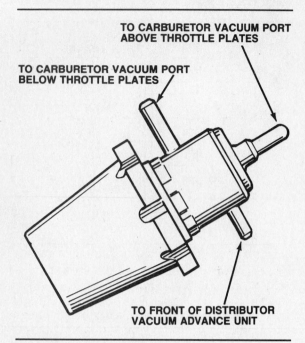

TO CARBURETOR VACUUM PORT
ABOVE THROTTLE PLATES

TO CARBURETOR VACUUM PORT
BELOW THROTTLE PLATES

TO FRONT OF DISTRIBUTOR
VACUUM ADVANCE UNIT

Figure 10-15. A deceleration vacuum advance valve.

EFFECTS OF TIMING ON PERFORMANCE, ECONOMY, AND EMISSIONS

Igniting the air-fuel mixture at exactly the right instant will create the highest possible amount of heat and pressure. This means that the engine is getting the most energy possible from the fuel, leading to good performance and fuel economy. This efficient combustion process uses advanced ignition timing. High-temperature combustion occurs at an early point during the process. Unfortunately, NO_x is created during high-temperature combustion. Later in the combustion process, the exhaust gases are cooler. They do not heat up the exhaust manifold as much. These cool exhaust gases will carry whatever fuel was not burned in the cylinder into the atmosphere as HC.

If ignition timing is retarded, combustion is less efficient. Performance and economy are worse, too, but NO_x emissions decrease. This is because the peak temperature of combustion is reduced, lowering NO_x formation. At the same time, the duration of peak temperature is shifted toward the end of the combustion process. This increases the temperature of the exhaust gases. HC emissions are also reduced because any unburned fuel from the cylinder is burned in the exhaust system.

EARLY SPARK-TIMING EMISSION CONTROLS

Spark-timing control systems were introduced in the 1960s to reduce exhaust emissions. A description of the early systems follows. These types of spark-timing controls were used until late-model, fully integrated electronic engine control systems began to appear in the late 1970s. The late-model systems are covered in Chapters 14 and 15.

Early Distributor Controls

Early emission control equipment advanced or retarded ignition timing under particular engine operating conditions, usually during starting, deceleration, and idle.

The deceleration vacuum advance valve, figure 10-15, was used during the mid-to-late 1960s on Chrysler, Ford, AMC, and Pontiac products with manual transmissions. In a manual transmission car, the air-fuel mixture becomes extremely rich when decelerating or shifting gears.

This valve momentarily switches the vacuum for the vacuum advance from a low vacuum source at the carburetor to a high vacuum source during deceleration, then back to the low vacuum source. This prevents overly retarded timing during deceleration or gear shifting, which could cause some engines to emit a lot of CO.

While the deceleration vacuum advance valve was effective against CO emissions, it did not limit HC and NO_x emissions. As emission limits for these pollutants became tighter in the early 1970s, use of the device ceased and manufacturers developed other devices that worked against all three major pollutants.

PRINCIPLES OF SPARK-TIMING CONTROLS OF THE 1970s

These systems were designed primarily to delay vacuum advance at low and intermediate speeds and allow it during high-speed cruising. The most common types of control systems used in the early to mid-1970s are:
• Distributor solenoids
• Vacuum delay valves
• Speed- and transmission-controlled timing.

Distributor Solenoids

A distributor vacuum retard solenoid was used on some 1970-1971 Chrysler products with V-8

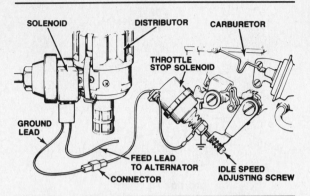

Figure 10-16. A distributor vacuum retard solenoid.

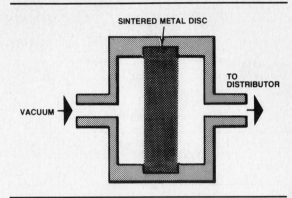

Figure 10-18. A cross-sectional view of a vacuum delay valve containing sintered metal to slow the application of vacuum.

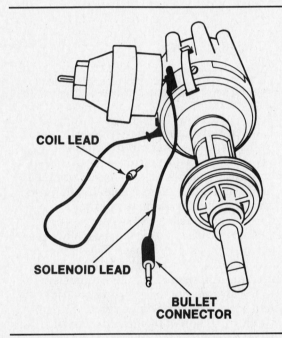

Figure 10-17. The installation of a distributor advance solenoid.

engines and automatic transmissions. This electric solenoid is attached to, and controls the action of, the distributor vacuum advance unit, figure 10-16.

The solenoid is energized by contacts mounted on a carburetor throttle stop solenoid. When the throttle is closed, the idle adjusting screw contacts the carburetor solenoid to complete the ground circuit. The contacts in the carburetor solenoid carry current to the distributor solenoid windings. Since the distributor solenoid plunger is connected to the vacuum diaphragm, solenoid movement shifts the breaker plate in the retard direction.

When engine speed increases, the idle adjusting screw breaks contact with the carburetor

solenoid. Current to the distributor solenoid is stopped, and normal vacuum advance is allowed.

Some 1972-73 Chrysler V-8 distributors have a spark timing advance solenoid that promotes better starting by providing a 7.5-degree spark advance. The solenoid is mounted in the distributor vacuum unit, figure 10-17. It is activated by power from the starter relay at the same terminal that sends power to the starter solenoid. The solenoid is activated only while the engine is cranking.

The starting advance solenoid is not an emission control device by itself, but it allows lower basic timing settings, which help to control emissions while providing advanced timing for quicker starting.

Vacuum Delay Valves

The vacuum delay valve "filters" the carburetor vacuum, slowing its application to the distributor vacuum advance unit. Generally, vacuum must be present in the system for 15 to 30 seconds before it is allowed to affect the advance mechanism.

One method of vacuum delay is used in Ford's spark delay valve (SDV) system, figure 10-18. In this design, vacuum must work its way through a **sintered**, or sponge-like, metal disc to reach the distributor. Many GM engines also use this type of spark delay valve.

Sintered: Welded together without using heat to form a porous material, such as the metal disc used in some vacuum delay valves.

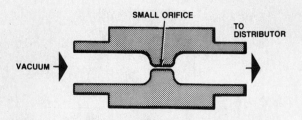

Figure 10-19. A cross-sectional view of a vacuum delay valve using a small orifice to delay the application of vacuum.

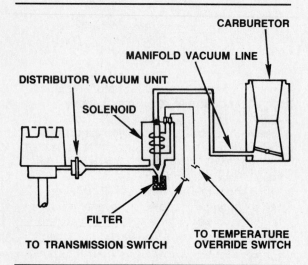

Figure 10-20. A simplified transmission-controlled spark system.

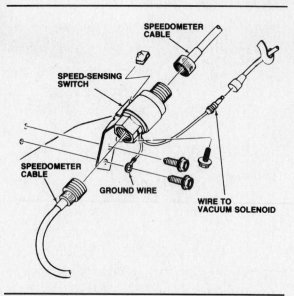

Figure 10-21. Most speed-controlled spark systems use a speed-sensing switch such as this. (Cadillac)

Another method of vacuum delay is used in Chrysler's orifice spark advance control (OSAC) system, figure 10-19. A small **orifice** is placed in the vacuum line to delay vacuum buildup.

Manufacturers often combine the use of vacuum delay valves with other emission control systems. All valves operate on one of the two principles just described.

Speed- and Transmission-Controlled Timing

These systems prevent any distributor vacuum advance when the vehicle is in a low gear or is traveling slowly. A solenoid controls the application of vacuum to the advance mechanism, figure 10-20. Current through the solenoid is controlled by a switch that reacts to various vehicle operating conditions.

A control switch used with a manual transmission reacts to shift lever position. A control switch used with an automatic transmission will usually react to hydraulic fluid pressure. Both systems prevent any vacuum advance when the car is in a low or intermediate gear.

A speed-sensing switch may be connected to the vehicle speedometer cable, figure 10-21. The switch signals an electronic control module when vehicle speed is below a predetermined level. The module triggers a solenoid that controls engine vacuum at the distributor.

Both vacuum-delay systems and speed- and transmission-controlled systems usually have an engine temperature bypass. This allows normal vacuum advance at high and low engine temperatures. Before March 1973, some systems had an **ambient temperature** override switch. Most of these switches were discontinued at the direction of the Environmental Protection Agency (EPA). Later temperature override systems sense engine coolant temperature or underhood temperature.

SUMMARY OF CARMAKERS' SYSTEMS

The systems using the principles described above are known by many different trade names and are all somewhat different. The following paragraphs briefly describe the major systems used by domestic manufacturers.

General Motors

Transmission-controlled spark (TCS)
Introduced by GM in 1970, the TCS system was used to reduce the exhaust emissions of many GM cars and light-duty trucks during all but high gear operation. This was accomplished primarily by a switch in the shift linkage and a solenoid which controlled vacuum to the distributor vacuum advance unit, figure 10-22.

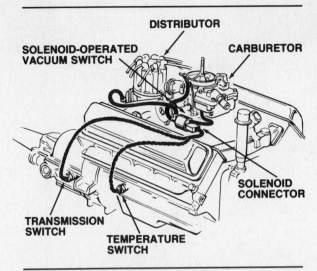

Figure 10-22. Components of a typical General Motors transmission-controlled spark system.

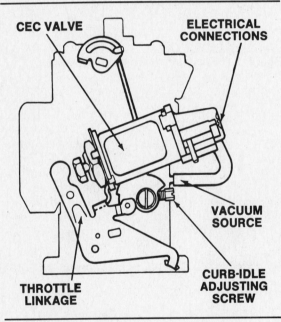

Figure 10-23. The General Motors combination emission control valve.

When the vehicle is in any gear except high, the switch energizes the solenoid, cutting off vacuum to the advance mechanism and retarding the timing. Once the vehicle is shifted into high gear, the switch deenergizes the solenoid. This restores manifold vacuum to the advance mechanism, providing normal vacuum advance. Transmission control switch and solenoid operation on GM systems varies for different models and years. This means that you must refer to GM shop manuals for specific model application, operation, and specifications.

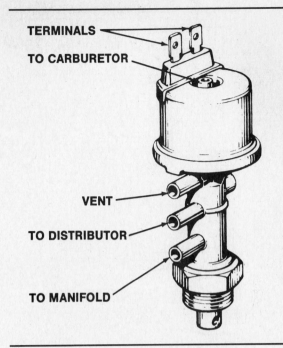

Figure 10-24. A distributor vacuum control switch.

Some vehicles used an additional temperature switch with a time delay relay. The switch acted as a thermal override to allow normal vacuum advance in low gears when the engine coolant was below a predetermined temperature. Various control temperatures were used, depending upon the vehicle. The time delay provides full vacuum advance for about 20 seconds after the ignition is turned on to provide vacuum advance for easier starting and warmup.

Combination emission control (CEC) valve
The CEC valve is part of the TCS system on some 1971-73 GM cars. Mounted on the side of the carburetor, figure 10-23, the CEC valve is a simple solenoid with a vacuum valve at one end and a throttle check rod extending from the other. The valve provides vacuum spark advance control and deceleration throttle position control in high gear.

Distributor vacuum control switch
Some Oldsmobiles used this switch, figure 10-24, along with a normally closed TCS switch. The vacuum control switch does the dual jobs

Orifice: A small opening in a tube, pipe, or valve.

Ambient Temperature: The temperature of the air surrounding a particular device or location.

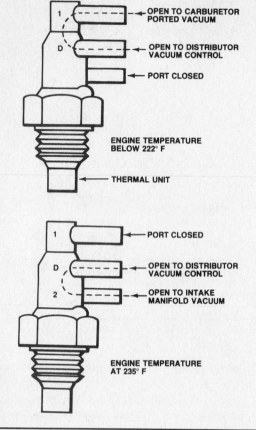

Figure 10-25. The thermostatic vacuum valve (TVV) used by AMC.

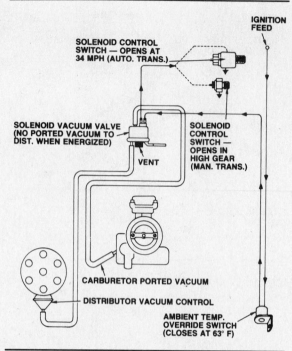

Figure 10-26. The AMC transmission-controlled spark system. (AMC)

of a TCS solenoid and a thermal vacuum switch. When the engine is at normal operating temperature, it permits vacuum spark advance only with the transmission in high gear. As engine coolant temperature increases, the switch applies full manifold vacuum to the distributor regardless of transmission gear position.

With the transmission in other than high gear, the TCS switch closes to energize the solenoid and to seal off the carburetor port, venting distributor vacuum to the atmosphere. In high gear, the deenergized solenoid seals off the vent port, applying carburetor vacuum to the distributor.

Engine overheating due to prolonged idling with a retarded spark is prevented because the thermal part of the switch seals off the vent port and applies manifold vacuum to the distributor.

A combination thermostatic vacuum switch (TVS) and TCS solenoid used on some Buick engines does the same job as the distributor vacuum control switch.

Speed control switch (SCS) system

Distributor vacuum advance on 1972 Cadillacs and Pontiacs is controlled by vehicle speed instead of transmission gear. The principal components of the SCS system are a speed sensor interconnected with the speedometer drive, and a solenoid that prohibits vacuum advance at speeds below 35 mph (56 kph) unless the engine starts to overheat. Vacuum advance is also eliminated at speeds below 25 mph (40 kph) during deceleration.

American Motors

Before 1971, AMC products used dual-diaphragm vacuum units and deceleration valves to control exhaust emissions. Some models had a thermostatic vacuum valve, figure 10-25, that permits normal vacuum advance at low engine temperatures. As engine temperature increases, the valve sends manifold vacuum to the distributor advance unit.

After 1971, many AMC products used a speed- or transmission-controlled spark timing system similar to GM's TCS, figure 10-26. Before March 1973, automatic transmission cars used a speed-sensing control switch. On later models, fluid pressure operates the control switch. On manual transmission models, gear lever position activates the switch.

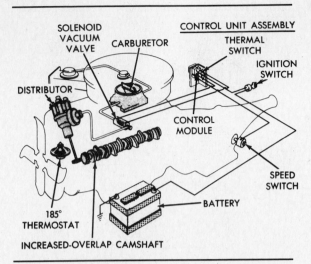

Figure 10-27. Chrysler's NO$_x$ control system. (Chrysler)

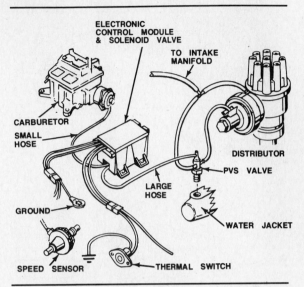

Figure 10-29. Ford's electronic distributor modulator system.

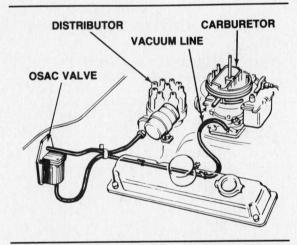

Figure 10-28. The Chrysler orifice spark advance control system.

Some AMC cars have an ambient temperature or coolant temperature override switch. When used with a TCS system, carburetor vacuum application is controlled, but manifold vacuum is *always* applied when coolant temperature is low.

Chrysler

NO$_x$ spark control
Chrysler 1971-72 products sold in California have a TCS system similar to those of GM and AMC. An ambient temperature switch was used only on 1971 cars to permit vacuum advance at all times when the temperature was low.

An electric control unit was used to actuate the solenoid vacuum valve on automatic transmission cars, figure 10-27. This is a reversing relay that receives signals from grounding

switches: a temperature switch, a speed switch, and a vacuum switch (1971 only). All switches must be open to activate the control unit, energize the solenoid, and cut off the vacuum advance.

Orifice spark advance control (OSAC)
The OSAC system was introduced on 1973 models. The principal component of the system is the OSAC valve, figure 10-28. This valve contains a one-way restriction or orifice that delays the rate of vacuum buildup in the vacuum advance unit during acceleration from idle to part throttle. During closed throttle deceleration or wide-open throttle acceleration, there is no spark retard delay.

OSAC valves with ambient temperature control are mounted on the vehicle firewall; those without the temperature control are attached to the air cleaner cover. This system was discontinued on many Chrysler products when the catalytic converter was introduced in 1975.

Ford

Electronic distributor modulator (EDM)
The EDM system, figure 10-29, was used on some 1970-71 Ford vehicles to permit vacuum advance only during high-gear operation. Above a selected speed, the speed sensor sends a voltage signal to the electronic control module. The ambient temperature switch overrides the speed sensor signal at low temperatures to permit normal vacuum advance.

A ported vacuum switch (PVS) overrides the module when coolant temperature is high to

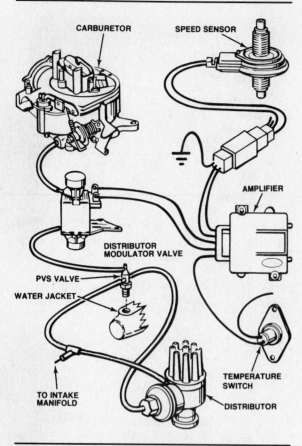

Figure 10-30. The Ford electronic spark control system.

apply intake manifold vacuum to the distributor. The module is mounted under the dash in the passenger compartment and determines whether or not the solenoid which it contains will be energized. At speeds above 25 mph (40 kph), the solenoid applies carburetor port vacuum to the vacuum advance unit; during deceleration, it denies vacuum to the advance unit.

Electronic spark control (ESC)
The ESC system used on some 1972 Ford products is very similar to the EDM system just described. It differs primarily in that the ESC module and solenoid are separate, figure 10-30, while the earlier EDM module contained the solenoid.

Spark delay valve (SDV)
This system uses a spark delay valve to restrict the vacuum control applied to the carburetor during acceleration, figure 10-31. Since the valve is installed between the carburetor and the distributor, vacuum must pass through a sintered metal disc to reach the advance unit.

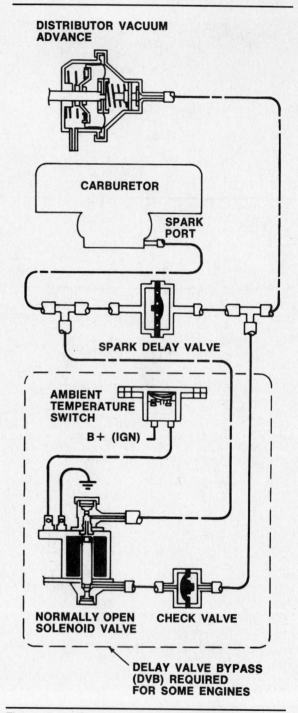

Figure 10-31. Ford's spark-delay valve system.

When carburetor vacuum decreases, a check valve in the SDV opens to relieve vacuum from the advance unit.

On engines built before 1973, an ambient temperature switch energizes a solenoid to apply vacuum to the distributor through a delay valve bypass.

The cold-temperature-activated vacuum (CTAV) system is a variation of TAV. The ambient temperature switch is located in the air cleaner. The temperature required to energize the solenoid is greater than in the TAV system, and a latching relay allows only one cycle of the temperature switch each time the ignition is turned on.

DECLINE AND FALL OF EARLY SPARK-TIMING CONTROLS

Many spark-timing control systems were discontinued when catalytic converters were introduced in 1975. Converters reduce HC and CO emissions, and exhaust gas recirculation (EGR) provides more effective control of NO_x emissions.

Emission standards continued to tighten during the mid-1970s. During this period, fuel mileage requirements also became important. Meeting the challenge of more stringent emission standards and better fuel economy required far more accurate ignition system performance than mechanical devices could deliver. Centrifugal and vacuum advance mechanisms simply could not respond quickly enough to changes in engine operating conditions to provide the necessary accuracy, so major manufacturers turned to computer-controlled ignition systems.

EARLY ELECTRONICALLY CONTROLLED TIMING

In a computer-controlled ignition system, an electronic control module receives signals from various system sensors. These signals may include information on coolant temperature, atmospheric pressure and temperature, throttle position and rate of change of position, and crankshaft position. The central processing unit (CPU) in the control module is programmed to interpret this information and calculate the proper ignition timing for each individual spark.

Early systems worked with the manufacturers' existing solid-state ignition systems. Some changes were made to these ignition systems because they no longer had to control spark timing, but many components remained the same.

Early computer-controlled ignition systems used by domestic manufacturers can be divided into two types. In one type, rotation of the distributor shaft sends a crankshaft position signal to the control module. The other type receives crankshaft position information from a sensor

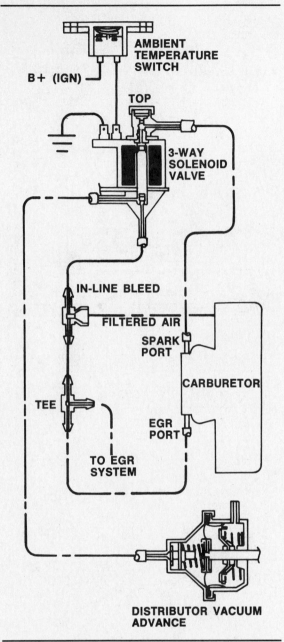

Figure 10-32. Ford's temperature-activated vacuum system.

Temperature-activated vacuum (TAV)

Some Ford products use the TAV system to match vacuum spark advance to engine requirements by switching between two vacuum sources, figure 10-32. The 3-way vacuum solenoid valve is connected to the distributor and the carburetor spark and EGR ports. An ambient temperature switch controls the 3-way valve. At high temperature, the EGR vacuum controls spark advance; at low temperature, the spark port vacuum controls advance.

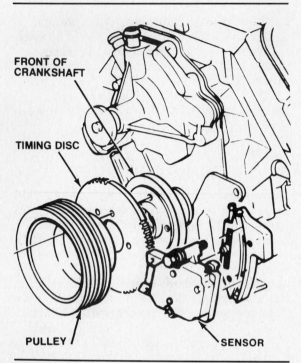

Figure 10-33. Crankshaft position signals can be taken directly from the crankshaft.

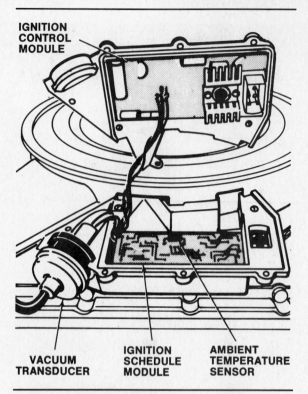

Figure 10-34. The early Chrysler ELB computer contains two separate modules. Later models use one module to perform all functions.

mounted near the crankshaft, figure 10-33. The sensor reacts to a trigger attached to the crankshaft itself.

Signals taken directly from the crankshaft are more accurate than those taken from the distributor shaft. The gears or chain driving the camshaft and the gears driving the distributor shaft are manufactured within tolerances. Although the actual measurements are small, these tolerances can combine to cause a significant difference between crankshaft position and ignition timing.

Early systems used by Chrysler, GM, and Ford were called:
• Chrysler Electronic Lean-Burn (ELB)
• GM Microprocessed Sensing and Automatic Regulation (MISAR)
• Ford Electronic Engine Control (EEC).

These early electronic timing control systems were partial-function engine control systems. They controlled ignition timing only. They were not fully integrated systems that controlled fuel metering with feedback signals from various engine sensors. Nevertheless, these early systems were the ancestors of the late-model engine control systems.

The electronic timing-regulation function of all three systems is similar, but the electronics are fundamentally different. The Lean-Burn

system uses an analog computer, while MISAR and EEC use digital microprocessors.

The practical difference between analog and digital electronics in this kind of application is that a digital computer can instantly alter timing from 1 to 65 degrees. An analog computer must calculate through all the points on a theoretical curve to make such an adjustment. Since an electronic spark advance adjustment takes only a few milliseconds, this fact is not really significant to the driver or serviceman. However, a digital system is more flexible and more economical to build than an analog system.

Chrysler

Chrysler's ELB was introduced on some 1976 models and used through 1978. The spark control computer is mounted on the air cleaner, figure 10-34. Early models have two printed circuit boards: the ignition schedule module and the ignition control module. Computers used with 1977 5.2L (318-cid) engines and all 1978 systems have only one circuit board to do both jobs.

The ignition schedule module receives signals from various engine sensors and computes them to determine the exact spark timing required. It then directs the ignition module to advance or retard the timing accordingly.

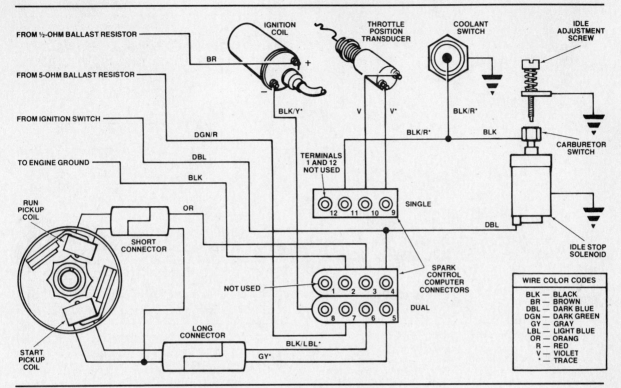

Figure 10-35. 1976-77 (except 318 V-8) ELB system wiring diagram, showing sensors.

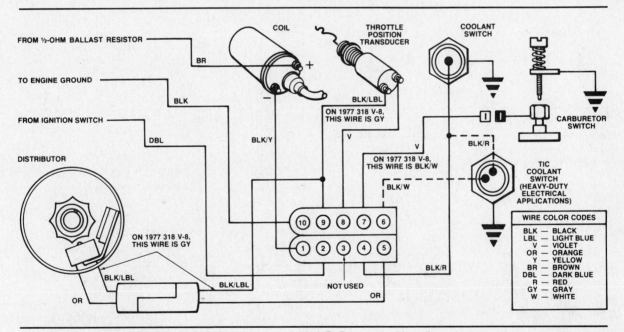

Figure 10-36. 1977 318 V-8 and all 1978 (except 4-cylinder) ELB system wiring diagram.

Six or seven sensors, figures 10-35 and 10-36, feed information to the computer.
• The Start pickup coil in the distributor provides a fixed amount of advance during cranking.
• The Run pickup coil supplies a basic timing

signal and allows the computer to determine engine speed. The single circuit board computer system uses only one pickup coil to provide all timing signals.
• The coolant temperature sensor on the water pump housing signals the computer when coolant temperature is low.

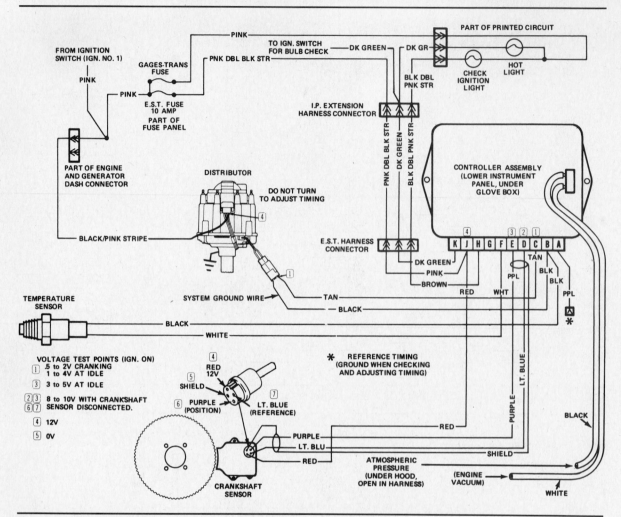

Figure 10-37. A circuit diagram of the 1977 General Motors MISAR system. (Oldsmobile)

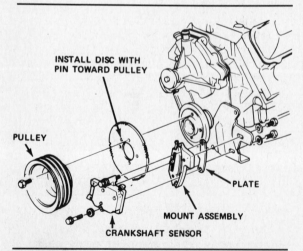

Figure 10-38. The MISAR system takes crankshaft position signals from a special disc on the front of the crankshaft.

• The air temperature sensor is located inside the computer. It is a **thermistor** that provides varying resistance with changing air temperature.
• The carburetor switch sensor tells the computer if the engine is at idle or off idle.

The remaining two sensors are **transducers**, devices that change mechanical movement to an electrical signal. The transducer has a coil and a movable metal core. A small amount of voltage applied to the coil will vary in strength as the core moves within the coil. This varying voltage signal is interpreted by the computer.
• The throttle position transducer has a core connected to the throttle lever. Core movement tells the computer the position and the rate of position change of the throttle plates.
• The vacuum transducer contains a diaphragm that is exposed to engine vacuum. Movement of the diaphragm moves the core and signals the computer of changes in engine vacuum.

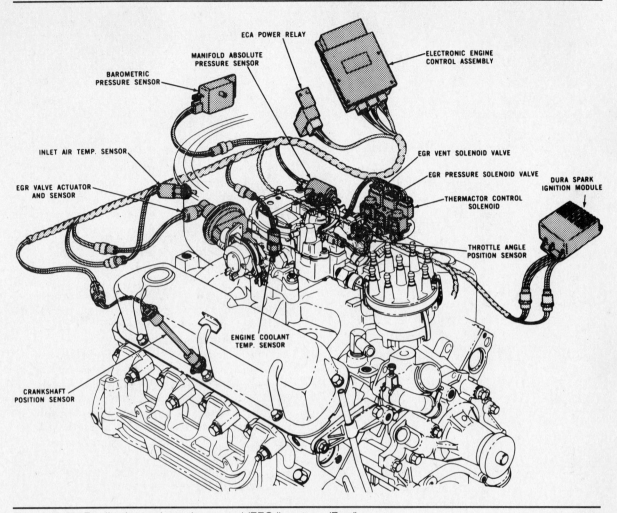

Figure 10-39. Ford's electronic engine control (EEC-I) system. (Ford)

General Motors

The MISAR system, figure 10-37, was used only on 1977-78 Oldsmobile Toronados. The microprocessor is contained in a control module mounted under the instrument panel. The module monitors signals from these engine sensors:

- Coolant temperature
- Manifold vacuum
- Atmospheric pressure
- Crankshaft speed and position.

The coolant sensor is not a simple on-off switch, but rather a thermistor which supplies varying resistance with changes in temperature.

The vacuum sensor is located in the control module. The sensor is a solid-state unit connected to the intake manifold by a vacuum line. A second line connected to the module is open in the engine compartment to provide an atmospheric pressure signal.

Crankshaft speed and position signals are provided by a rotating disc and a stationary sensor on the front of the engine, figure 10-38. These components replace the distributor pickup coil and trigger wheel. In 1978, the crankshaft speed and position sensor was moved into the distributor.

Ford

Ford introduced its electronic engine control (EEC) system, figure 10-39, on the 1978 Lincoln

Thermistor: An electrical conductor that changes its resistance as the surrounding temperature changes.

Transducer: A device that converts (transduces) one form of energy into another. In an ignition system, it may sense a mechanical movement and change it to an electrical signal.

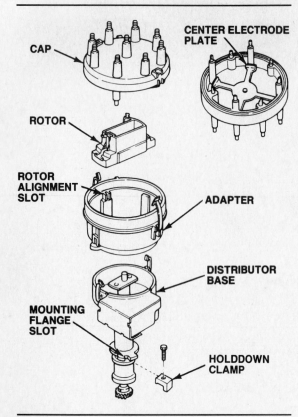

CAP

CENTER ELECTRODE PLATE

ROTOR

ROTOR ALIGNMENT SLOT

ADAPTER

DISTRIBUTOR BASE

MOUNTING FLANGE SLOT

HOLDDOWN CLAMP

Figure 10-40. Components of Ford's EEC-I distributor. (Ford)

Versailles. This system controls both spark timing and EGR valve operation. A digital microprocessor installed in the passenger compartment receives signals from various sensors.

An electromagnetic pickup at the flywheel end of the crankshaft provides crankshaft position and speed signals. It also replaces the distributor pickup coil and trigger wheel. Other information is fed into the computer by a throttle position sensor, a coolant temperature sensor, a barometric pressure sensor, an inlet temperature sensor, a manifold pressure sensor, and an EGR valve position sensor.

The module determines the optimum spark timing and EGR valve operating mode. A spark timing signal is sent to the Dura-Spark solid-state ignition control module. This module is similar to that used with the standard Ford Dura-Spark ignition, as we will see in Chapter 11.

The EEC-I distributor, figure 10-40, is different from the standard distributor. Since its only function is to distribute the ignition spark, it contains only a rotor, coil electrode, and spark plug electrodes. The distributor cap and rotor are designed to minimize the chances of crossfiring (when the spark jumps to the incorrect spark plug electrode).

SUMMARY

Most ignition distributors have two devices to advance or retard spark timing in response to changing conditions of engine operation. The two primary factors which determine spark advance are engine speed and load. The centrifugal advance alters the position of the distributor cam or trigger wheel on the distributor shaft and changes engine timing as engine speed changes. The vacuum advance alters the position of the breaker points or magnetic pickup coil with respect to the cam or trigger wheel. It changes timing as engine load changes.

Many different spark timing emission control systems have been used. Regardless of their design and operation, these systems all regulate distributor vacuum advance. Vacuum advance is generally allowed only at cold start-up, during high gear operation, or if the engine overheats.

Auxiliary spark timing control systems are not used on all engines. Development of the exhaust gas recirculation (EGR) systems, catalytic converters and the expanded use of air injection systems eliminated the use of TCS and SCS systems on most late-model engines.

Electronic spark timing systems appeared because more accurate control was required. They all regulate ignition timing for the best combination of emission control, fuel economy and driveability. Early electronic spark timing systems were the forerunners of late-model, fully integrated electronic engine control systems that we will study in Chapters 14 and 15.

Review Questions

Choose the single most correct answer.
Compare your answers with the correct answers on page 451.

1. Which of the following affect ignition timing?
   a. Valve timing
   b. Compression ratio
   c. Engine load
   d. All of the above

2. Distributors commonly have two automatic spark advance mechanisms, which are:
   a. Initial advance and mechanical advance
   b. Initial advance and dynamic advance
   c. Dynamic advance and static advance
   d. Centrifugal advance and vacuum advance

3. Centrifugal advance responds directly to engine:
   a. Load
   b. Horsepower
   c. Speed
   d. Torque

4. The purpose of the venturi in the carburetor is to:
   a. Mix the air and fuel mixture
   b. Speed the airflow and create a low-pressure area
   c. Carry fuel to mix with air
   d. Raise the air pressure sufficiently

5. Vacuum advance responds directly to engine:
   a. Load
   b. Horsepower
   c. Speed
   d. Torque

6. The richest air-fuel ratio with which an engine can operate efficiently is:
   a. 4:1
   b. 6:1
   c. 8:1
   d. 16:1

7. At medium cruising speeds, the engine operates with a partially open throttle and an air-fuel ratio of about:
   a. 8:1
   b. 12:1
   c. 15:1
   d. 18.5:1

8. Which of the following is *not* a component of the vacuum advance mechanism?
   a. Movable breaker plate
   b. Throttle valve
   c. Diaphragm
   d. Actuating link

9. Automotive emission control equipment is designed to reduce exhaust emissions of which pollutants?
   a. Hydrocarbons
   b. Oxides of nitrogen
   c. Carbon monoxide
   d. All of the above

10. The most common types of recent spark timing control systems do *not* include:
    a. Decelerator vacuum advance valves
    b. Vacuum delay valves
    c. Speed-controlled timing
    d. Transmission-controlled timing

11. Which of the following is *not* part of the General Motors TCS system?
    a. A CEC valve
    b. A spark delay valve
    c. A solenoid-operated vacuum switch
    d. A transmission control switch

12. The accompanying illustration shows a:

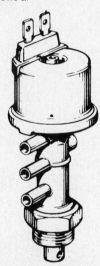

    a. Spark delay valve
    b. OSAC valve
    c. Deceleration vacuum advance valve
    d. Distributor vacuum control switch

13. Almost all spark timing emission control systems work with the vacuum advance units to:
    a. Increase vacuum advance at low and intermediate vehicle speeds
    b. Cut off vacuum advance during high-speed acceleration
    c. Retard the timing during high-speed deceleration
    d. Cut off vacuum advance at low and intermediate vehicle speeds

14. The Ford EDM and ESC spark timing control systems have vehicle speed sensors mounted in the:
    a. Transmission
    b. Distributor housing
    c. Speedometer cable
    d. None of the above

15. Chrysler's Electronic Lean-Burn computer-controlled ignition system incorporates _____ sensors to feed information to the computer.
    a. 3 or 4
    b. 6 or 7
    c. 12 or 13
    d. 17 or 18

16. The distributor on Ford's Electronic Engine Control system:
    a. Contains a rotor, a coil electrode, and spark plug electrodes
    b. Has only the function of distributing ignition spark
    c. Is designed to minimize chances of cross-firing
    d. All of the above

17. The dual-diaphragm vacuum unit provides:
    a. Twice as much vacuum advance as a single-diaphragm unit
    b. Faster vacuum retard than does a single-diaphragm unit
    c. Both vacuum advance and vacuum retard
    d. All of the above

11

Solid-State Electronic Ignition Systems

During the 1960s, solid-state ignition systems were used only on a few high-performance engines. Solid-state systems were not standard on domestic automobiles until the early 1970s; foreign carmakers followed a few years after with their versions. Within less than a decade, solid-state systems completely replaced breaker-point ignitions. The major driving force behind this rapid transition was their ability to help meet stringent emission control standards.

Although solid-state systems are more expensive to produce than breaker-point systems, their advantages greatly outweigh the drawback of increased cost:
• Greater available voltage, especially at high engine speeds
• Reliable system performance at all engine speeds
• Potential for more responsive and variable advance curves
• Decreased maintenance.
In addition, engine operation and exhaust emissions are more accurately controlled by solid-state circuitry.

BASIC SOLID-STATE SYSTEMS

Solid-state systems differ from breaker-point systems in the devices used to control primary circuit current. Breaker-point systems use mechanical breaker points to open and close the primary circuit. The points are operated by a cam on the distributor shaft. Most solid-state systems use an electronic switch in the form of a sealed module to control primary circuit current. This module contains one or more transistors, integrated circuits, or other solid-state control components. A triggering device in the distributor functions with the control module.

As we learned in Chapter 8, this triggering device is usually a magnetic pulse generator or a Hall-effect switch. Solid-state ignitions also can be triggered by a set of breaker points, as will be explained later in this chapter.

Solid-state ignitions can be classified in terms of their primary circuit operation. There are two general types:
1. Inductive discharge
2. Capacitive discharge.
The difference between these types lies in how they use primary current to produce a high-voltage secondary current.

Inductive Discharge

The inductive discharge system uses battery voltage to create current through the coil primary winding. When a signal is sent by the

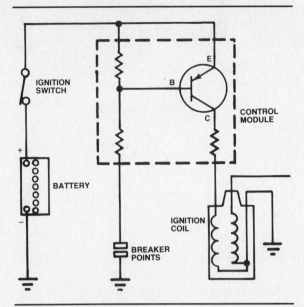

Figure 11-1. A typical breaker-point-triggered electronic ignition system.

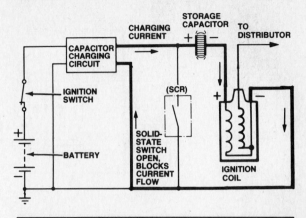

Figure 11-2. When the SCR blocks current, the capacitor is charged. (Bosch)

triggering device, primary current is interrupted. This sudden *decrease* in primary current collapses the coil's magnetic field and induces a high-voltage surge in the secondary circuit.

In an electronic ignition, primary current passes through the ignition control **module**, not through the distributor. Most modules contain one or more large power transistors which switch the primary current. A power or a switching transistor can transmit as much as 10 amperes of current — far more than a set of breaker points can. The power transistor is controlled by a driver transistor that receives voltage signals from the distributor signal generator.

Original equipment solid-state ignitions use inductive discharge to provide about 30,000 volts of available voltage and sustain a spark for about 1.8 milliseconds (a millisecond is one-thousandth of a second, or 0.001 second).

Breaker points

Inductive discharge is used in both electronic and breaker point systems; only the device used to open the circuit differs. The earliest transistorized ignitions used breaker points as a mechanical switch to control voltage applied to a power transistor. Battery voltage causes current to flow through the control module to the breaker points, figure 11-1. This current flow biases the transistor base so that current can also flow through the coil primary winding. When the points open, current stops. The power transistor will no longer conduct current to the coil primary winding, and an ignition spark is produced.

While full primary current flowed through the transistor, the points carried less than one ampere of current. This minimized the pitting and burning problems encountered with breaker points. However, the points were still subject to mechanical wear and bounced at high speeds. Electronic ignitions replaced the points with a solid-state signal generator containing no moving parts.

Capacitive Discharge

The capacitive discharge system uses battery voltage to charge a large capacitor in the control module. The capacitor charging time while the module is on corresponds to dwell in the inductive discharge system. Current flows to the storage capacitor instead of to the coil during this period. The module charging circuit uses a transformer to increase the voltage in the capacitor to as high as 400 volts. The module also contains a **thyristor**, or silicon-controlled rectifier (SCR), which functions as an open switch to prevent the capacitor from discharging as it charges, figure 11-2.

Module: A self-contained, sealed unit that houses the solid-state circuits which control certain electrical or mechanical functions.

Thyristor: A silicon-controlled rectifier (SCR) that normally blocks all current flow. A slight voltage applied to one layer of its semiconductor structure will allow current flow in one direction while blocking current flow in the other direction.

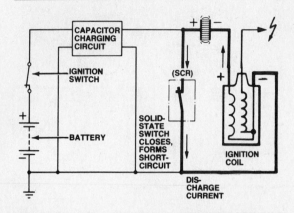

Figure 11-3. When a signal voltage makes the SCR conduct current, the capacitor discharges through the coil primary winding. (Bosch)

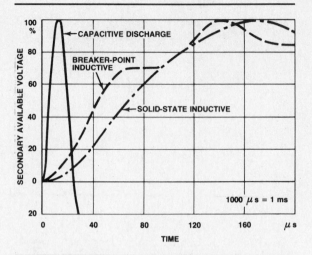

Figure 11-4. A major difference in ignition system performance is the *time* at which maximum secondary voltage is developed. (Bosch)

When the triggering device signals the module, the SCR closes the capacitor discharge circuit, figure 11-3, which allows the capacitor to discharge through the coil primary winding. This sudden *increase* in primary current expands the coil's magnetic field and induces a high-voltage surge in the secondary circuit.

Capacitive discharge systems are available in the automotive aftermarket, but no major domestic manufacturer installs them as original equipment. A few imported cars such as Audi and Mercedes-Benz have used these ignition systems in the past. They provide a greater available voltage than inductive discharge systems, but can sustain a spark for only about 200 microseconds. The spark is much more intense than that produced by an inductive discharge system and will fire plugs that are in very poor condition. Under certain engine operating conditions, however, a longer spark time is required or the air-fuel mixture will not burn completely.

Figure 11-4 shows the time and voltage characteristics of a breaker-point ignition system, a capacitive discharge system, and a solid-state inductive system.

CONTROL MODULES AND PRIMARY CIRCUITRY

Although various manufacturers use different circuitry within their ignition system control modules, the basic function of all modules is the same. The following paragraphs explain how these electronic ignition modules work. Because the electronic components within the module are delicate and complex, the modules are sealed during manufacture. If any individual component within the module fails, the entire unit is replaced rather than repaired. Our

explanation of module circuitry and operation will be brief, because you will never need to service module components.

Solid-State Devices

We learned about one solid-state device, the diode, in Chapter 7. Two other parts are commonly used in ignition system control modules:
• Transistors
• Silicon-controlled rectifiers (thyristors).

Transistor operation
Transistors act like relays because they allow a small amount of current flow to control the flow of a large amount of current. Figure 11-5 shows a relay installed in a circuit. When the contact points are open, position A, no current can flow through the circuit. When the switch is closed, position B, a small amount of current flows through the relay's electromagnetic coil. This closes the contact points, and a large amount of current can flow through the relay armature. If the switch is opened again, current flow through the coil will stop. The contact points will be opened by a spring, and the large amount of current flow will stop.

Figure 11-6 shows a transistor installed in the same circuit, in place of the relay. The transistor symbol shows that it has three parts:
• The **base**
• The **emitter**
• The **collector**.

In its normal state, position A, the transistor will not allow any current flow through the emitter and collector. When the switch is closed, position B, there is a complete circuit

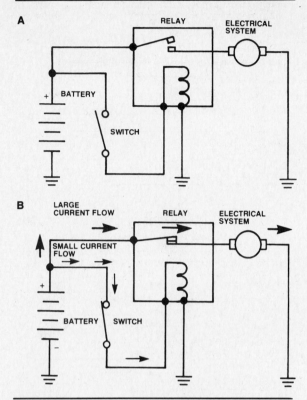

Figure 11-5. A relay in a circuit allows a small amount of current to control the flow of a large amount of current.

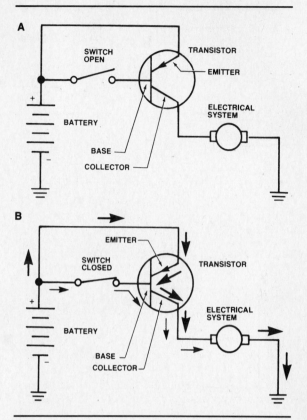

Figure 11-6. This transistor is made conductive by base-to-collector current flow.

through the base and collector. A small amount of current will flow through the base-to-collector circuit. This current flow makes the emitter-to-collector circuit complete, because when a small amount of current flows through the base, the emitter and collector become conductive. A larger amount of current can flow through the emitter-to-collector circuit. When the switch is opened and base-to-collector current flow stops, the emitter-collector circuit current flow also stops.

The switch in figure 11-6 controls base-collector current flow by opening and closing the circuit. The flow can also be controlled by varying the voltage present in the circuit. A certain amount of voltage is needed to force current to flow through the base and collector. If not enough voltage is present, or if too much voltage is present, no current will flow through any of the transistor's circuits.

Silicon-controlled rectifier operation

The silicon-controlled rectifier (SCR) is also called a thyristor. Figure 11-7 shows an SCR installed in a circuit. In its normal state, position A, the SCR blocks current flow in both directions. When a small amount of battery voltage is applied to the SCR's gate, position B, the

SCR acts like a diode. That is, it allows current to flow in one direction while still blocking current flow in the opposite direction. When voltage is taken away from the gate, the SCR will again block all current flow in either direction.

Now we can see how transistors and SCRs are used in ignition system control module circuitry.

Transistor: A 3-terminal semiconductor used for current switching, detection, and amplification. Low current flow between one pair of terminals can control high current flow between another pair of terminals, with one common terminal.

Base: The center layer of semiconductor material in a transistor.

Emitter: The outside layer of semiconductor material in a transistor that conducts current to the base.

Collector: The outside layer of semiconductor material in a transistor that conducts current away from the base.

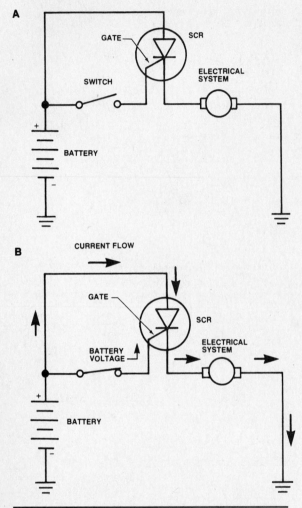

Figure 11-7. An SCR in a circuit can be changed from a total nonconductor to a diode by applying a small amount of voltage to the SCR gate.

Inductive-Discharge System

Figure 11-8 is a simple inductive-discharge ignition control module circuit. The various triggering devices that can be used in this system all produce the same type of signal: a pulsating voltage. In the illustration, the signal comes from the pickup coil of a magnetic pulse generator. This pulsating voltage is applied to the control module's transistor and signals the module to turn primary current off.

Primary Circuit Control

Primary circuit control is made possible in an electronic ignition by the ability of transistors to control a high current flow in response to a very small current. The transistor is like a solid-state relay. It has a base of one type of semiconductor material and an emitter and collector of

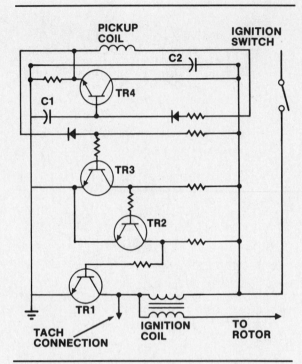

Figure 11-8. A simplified inductive discharge control module. (Chevrolet)

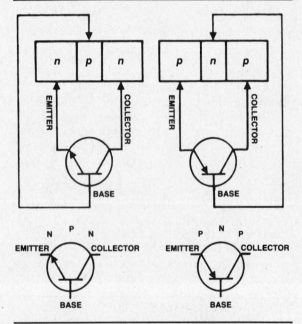

Figure 11-9. Transistor construction and symbols.

the other type of material, figure 11-9. A certain amount of current must flow through the base-to-emitter or base-to-collector circuit before any current will flow through the emitter-to-collector circuit. In this way, a small amount of current controls the flow of a large amount of current.

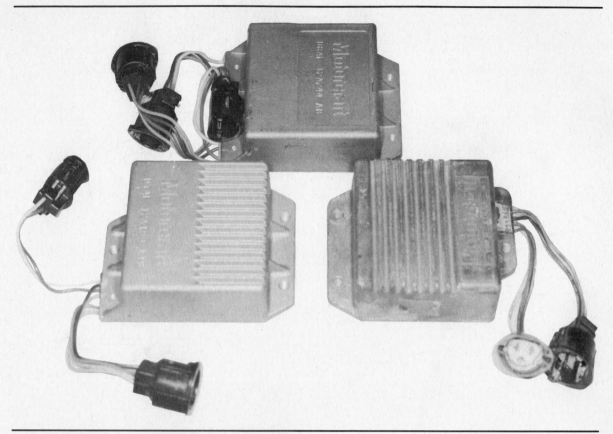

Figure 11-10. Typical external ignition modules from Ford.

Figure 11-11. The ignition module may be installed inside the distributor, as in the HEI system.

Ignition Transistor Operation

In our illustration, figure 11-8, the module can either be in the dwell mode (when primary current flows) or in the firing mode (when primary current stops).

During the dwell mode, TR1 and TR3 are conducting. TR2 is nonconducting. A signal from the pickup coil turns TR3 off, charges C1, and turns TR4 on. This results in the firing mode, as reduced primary current flow causes a high-voltage secondary surge.

TR4 stays on until C1 is discharged. When C1 is discharged, TR3 turns on and the module returns to the dwell mode. At higher engine speeds, C1 will be charged less and less. This results in reduced firing times and longer dwell periods. C2 is a capacitor in the distributor for radio noise suppression.

Actual electronic ignition modules take various forms, but all work on these principles. Some modules are large units, figure 11-10. Others are relatively small integrated circuit (IC) units mounted in the distributor, figure 11-11.

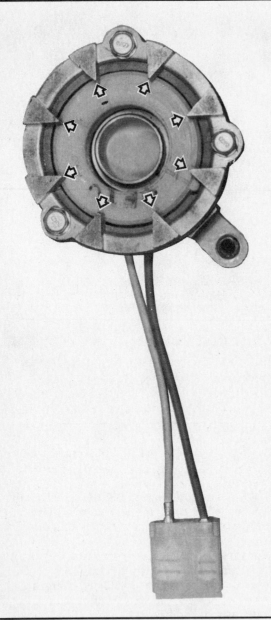

Figure 11-12. This Delco-Remy magnetic pulse generator has a pole piece for each cylinder (arrows), but operates in the same manner as single pole piece units.

TRIGGERING DEVICES AND IGNITION TIMING

We have seen that all triggering devices produce a pulsating voltage that signals the generation of an ignition spark. Four triggering devices are commonly used in a solid-state ignition:
1. Magnetic pulse generator
2. Hall-effect switch
3. Metal detection
4. Optical (light detection) signal generator.

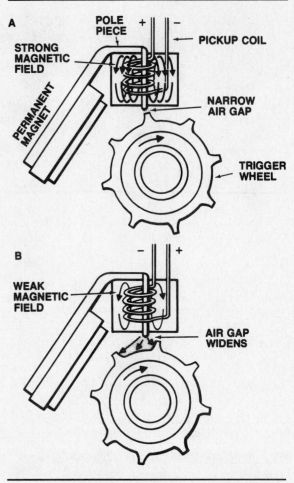

Figure 11-13. The magnetic field expands and collapses as the trigger wheel's teeth move past. This induces a varying strength voltage in the pickup coil.

Magnetic Pulse Generator

Magnetic pulse generators are the most common type of original equipment triggering device. They were used in the original Chrysler, GM, and Ford electronic ignitions and are still used today, both by domestic and foreign carmakers.

Most manufacturers use the rotation of the distributor shaft to time voltage pulses. Distributor-mounted magnetic pulse generator designs may have a single pole piece or as many pieces as the trigger wheel has teeth, figure 11-12. Regardless of the design, the pickup coil works in the same way. The pickup coil is wound around the permanent magnet or between the magnet and the pole pieces.

As the nonmagnetic trigger wheel turns with the shaft, figure 11-13, teeth on the wheel approach, align with, and move away from the pole piece of the permanent magnet. The low reluctance of the trigger wheel teeth causes the

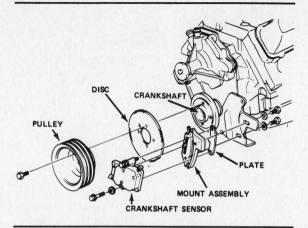

Figure 11-14. This magnetic pulse generator reacts to the movement of a disc mounted on the crankshaft. (Oldsmobile)

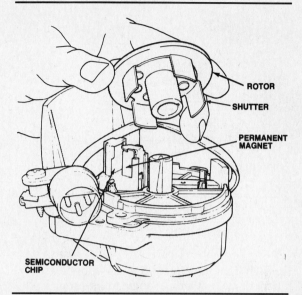

Figure 11-15. A Hall-effect triggering device.

magnet's field to expand as a tooth approaches, figure 11-13, position A. The field collapses as the tooth moves away, figure 11-13, position B. This motion of the magnetic field induces a signal voltage in the pickup coil wound around the pole piece.

Although magnetic field strength is strongest when the trigger wheel tooth is aligned with the pole piece, the rate of expansion or contraction is zero. Pickup coil voltage drops to zero at this point and changes the bias voltage on the ignition module driver transistor to turn it off. The driver transistor turns off the power transistors to interrupt primary current. The coil then discharges secondary voltage to fire a spark plug.

The point at which the trigger wheel tooth aligns with the pole piece is the ignition timing point for one cylinder and corresponds to the point where breaker points open.

As mentioned in Chapter 10, GM, Ford, and some other carmakers have used magnetic pulse generators that rely on engine crankshaft rotation (instead of distributor shaft rotation) to produce a signal voltage. In the 1977 GM microprocessed sensing and automatic regulation (MISAR) system, the pickup coil, pole piece, and permanent magnet are mounted near a disc that is on the end of the crankshaft, figure 11-14. Teeth on the disc act like the teeth on a distributor-mounted trigger wheel to induce a single voltage in the pickup coil. In the 1978 MISAR system, the pickup coil and trigger wheel were installed in the distributor.

Ford's EEC-I system takes its crankshaft rotation signal from the flywheel end of the crankshaft. As we will see later in this chapter, Buick's C³I system uses a Hall-effect crankshaft sensor.

Hall-Effect Switch

The Hall-effect switch is the latest switching technology in electronic ignitions. The Hall-effect triggering assembly uses a small chip of **semiconductor** material, a permanent magnet, and a ring of low-reluctance shutters, figure 11-15.

The Hall-effect switch does not generate a signal voltage in the same way as a magnetic pulse generator, however. In fact, it requires an input voltage to generate an output voltage.

The Hall effect is the generation of a small voltage in a semiconductor by passing current

Semiconductor: A material that is neither a good conductor nor a good insulator. Semiconductors are the raw material used to make solid-state devices such as diodes and transistors. Silicon and germanium are common semiconductors.

■ **Mind Those Magnets**

When you are servicing a distributor from an electronic ignition system, be sure that no metal particles or iron filings get inside. The magnetic pickup coils and pole pieces in the breakerless distributors used by many carmakers will attract metal debris which can really foul up ignition performance. Use a clean, soft-bristled brush or low-pressure compressed air to clean the inside of a distributor and keep scrap metal off the pickup coil.

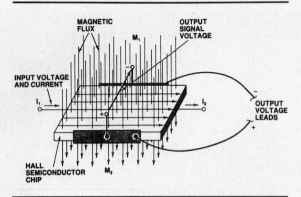

Figure 11-16. The Hall-effect output voltage varies with the strength of the magnetic field, while the input current remains constant.

through it in one direction while applying a magnetic field at a right angle to its surface, figure 11-16. When current flows from I_1 to I_2 through the semiconductor and a magnetic field intersects the chip from M_1 to M_2, voltage develops across the semiconductor as shown in figure 11-16. If the input current remains constant and the magnetic field is varied, the signal voltage will vary proportionally to the field strength.

When the shutter blade of a Hall-effect switch enters the gap between the magnet and the Hall semiconductor element, it creates a magnetic shunt that varies the Hall field strength. This changes the Hall signal voltage, which changes the bias on an ignition driver transistor similarly to the signal from a magnetic pulse generator.

A Hall-effect switch is a complex electronic circuit. Figure 11-17 shows the relationships of the Hall-effect switch and ignition operation. An important point to understand is that ignition occurs when the Hall shutter *leaves* the gap between the Hall semiconductor element and the magnet.

The Hall-effect voltage is not affected by changing engine speed. Magnetic pulse generators (and metal-detection units) depend upon induction to create the signal voltage. The strength of an induced voltage varies if the magnetic lines move more quickly or slowly. The Hall effect is not induction, and the speed of the magnetic lines has no effect on the signal voltage. This constant-strength signal voltage offers more reliable ignition system performance throughout a wide range of engine speeds. Moreover, a Hall-effect switch provides a uniform digital voltage pulse regardless of rotation speed. This makes a Hall-effect switch ideal as a digital engine sensor for fuel injection timing and other functions besides ignition control.

Metal Detection

This triggering device is a variation of the magnetic pulse generator. Instead of a permanent magnet affecting the pole piece, an **electromagnet** supplies the magnetic field, figure 11-18. The control module applies a small amount of battery voltage to the electromagnetic coil. The metal teeth on the trigger wheel affect the electromagnetic field and the voltage within the electromagnetic coil. These voltage changes are sensed by the control module.

This device produces a more reliable signal voltage at lower engine speeds than a magnetic pulse generator. A metal-detection triggering device is used in the Prestolite electronic ignition used by American Motors from 1975 to 1977.

Optical (Light Detection) Signal Generator

The optical signal generator uses a **light-emitting diode (LED)** and a light-sensitive **phototransistor** (photocell) to produce signal voltage pulses. When the LED light beam strikes the photocell, voltage is generated. A slotted disc rotating on the distributor shaft, figure 11-19, interrupts the light beam, sending an on-off voltage signal to the control module.

The optical signal generator provides a more reliable signal voltage at much lower engine speeds than either a magnetic pulse or metal-detection unit. However, periodic LED and photocell cleaning may be required. Several aftermarket, or add-on, ignition systems have been produced using this switching device. Until Chrysler introduced one on some 1987 models, no major carmaker had used an optical signal generator as original equipment.

Electromagnet: A soft iron core wrapped in a coil of a current-carrying conductor. Current flow in the conductor induces a magnetic force around the core.

Light-emitting diode (LED): A gallium-arsenide diode that emits energy as light. Often used in automotive indicators.

Phototransistor: Also called a photocell. A type of solid-state device that will generate a voltage when exposed to light.

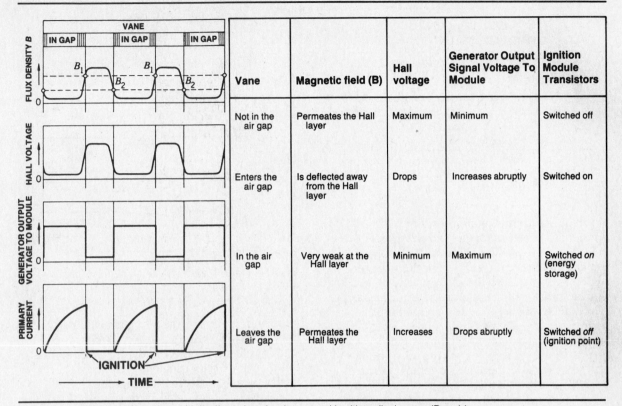

Vane	Magnetic field (B)	Hall voltage	Generator Output Signal Voltage To Module	Ignition Module Transistors
Not in the air gap	Permeates the Hall layer	Maximum	Minimum	Switched off
Enters the air gap	Is deflected away from the Hall layer	Drops	Increases abruptly	Switched on
In the air gap	Very weak at the Hall layer	Minimum	Maximum	Switched *on* (energy storage)
Leaves the air gap	Permeates the Hall layer	Increases	Drops abruptly	Switched *off* (ignition point)

Figure 11-17. The relationship of Hall-effect signal voltage and ignition discharge. (Bosch)

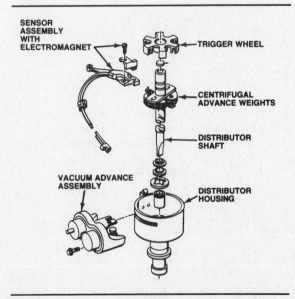

Figure 11-18. A metal-detection triggering device.

ELECTRONIC IGNITION DWELL, TIMING, AND ADVANCE

As you learned in Chapter 8, dwell is the period of time when the breaker points are closed and current is flowing in the primary winding

Figure 11-19. Chrysler introduced an optical distributor on some 1987 models. The slotted disc (arrow) interrupts the light beam from the phototransistor to produce an on/off signal.

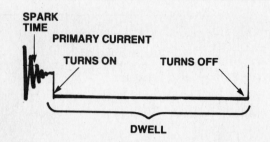

Figure 11-20. Dwell measured in degrees of distributor rotation remains relatively constant at all engine speeds in a fixed-dwell system.

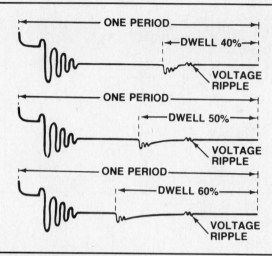

Figure 11-21. The dwell period increases with engine speed in the variable-dwell Delco HEI and some Motorcraft systems.

of the coil. Although solid-state ignitions require a dwell period for the same purpose, the period is controlled by a timing or current-sensing circuit in the ignition module, rather than by a signal from the distributor.

The initial timing adjustment for most basic electronic ignitions is similar to that for breaker-point ignition systems. Timing is set by rotating the distributor housing with the engine idling at normal operating temperature.

The first generation of electronic ignitions used the same centrifugal and vacuum advance mechanisms to advance timing as breaker-point ignitions use. As carmakers began to equip their engines with computer-controlled systems in the late 1970s, however, timing advance became a function of the computer. Since a computer can receive, process, and send information very rapidly, it can change ignition timing with far more efficiency and accuracy than any mechanical device.

The distributor in an electronic ignition used with a computer engine control system contains a triggering device for basic timing. Because the computer actually controls ignition timing, however, the distributor's primary function is to distribute secondary voltage.

Fixed vs. Variable Dwell

Although dwell is not adjustable in electronic distributors, electronic ignitions may have one of two kinds of dwell control:
1. Fixed dwell
2. Variable dwell.

Fixed dwell
A ballast resistor is placed in the primary circuit of a **fixed-dwell** electronic ignition to limit current and voltage. Dwell is the length of time the switching transistor sends current to the primary coil windings. It begins once the secondary voltage and current have fallen below predetermined levels. The ballast resistor functions just as it does in a breaker-point system to

control primary voltage and current. Dwell measured in distributor degrees remains constant at all engine speeds. Figure 11-20 shows the primary circuit oscilloscope pattern of a typical fixed-dwell electronic ignition.

Chrysler's original electronic ignition is a good example of a fixed-dwell system. The original Ford solid-state ignition (SSI) and Dura-Spark II are other examples of fixed-dwell systems with ballast resistors, as are some Bosch and Japanese electronic ignitions.

Variable dwell
A ballast resistor is not used in a **variable-dwell** system. The coil and ignition module receive full battery voltage. A module circuit senses primary current to the coil and reduces the current when the magnetic field is saturated. Unlike a breaker-point or fixed-dwell electronic ignition, dwell measured in distributor degrees changes with speed in a variable-dwell ignition, but the dwell *time* remains relatively constant. Figure 11-21 shows the primary circuit oscilloscope pattern of a typical variable-dwell electronic ignition.

In general, ignition coils used with variable-dwell systems have a higher available voltage capability, lower primary resistance, and a higher turns ratio than the coils used with fixed-dwell systems.

All variations of the GM Delco-Remy High Energy Ignition (HEI) are variable-dwell systems, as well as Ford Dura-Spark I and thick-film integrated (TFI) ignition systems. Other examples are the AMC-Prestolite ignitions, most Chrysler Hall-effect ignitions, some Bosch, Marelli, and several Japanese electronic ignitions.

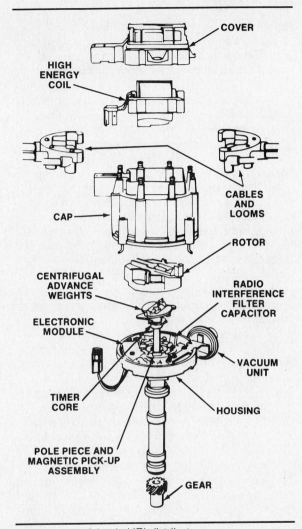

HIGH ENERGY COIL

COVER

CABLES AND LOOMS

CAP

ROTOR

CENTRIFUGAL ADVANCE WEIGHTS

RADIO INTERFERENCE FILTER CAPACITOR

ELECTRONIC MODULE

VACUUM UNIT

TIMER CORE

HOUSING

POLE PIECE AND MAGNETIC PICK-UP ASSEMBLY

GEAR

Figure 11-22. A basic HEI distributor.

Basic Timing and Advance Control

We learned in Chapter 10 that ignition takes place at a point just before or just after top dead center is reached during the compression stroke of a piston. This time is measured in degrees of crankshaft rotation and is established by the mechanical coupling between the crankshaft and distributor. Basic or initial ignition timing is usually set at idle speed.

As engine speed increases, however, ignition must take place earlier. This is necessary to ensure that maximum compression pressure from combustion develops as the piston starts downward on its power stroke. This change in ignition timing is called spark advance and is controlled in basic electronic ignitions (those not used with electronic engine controls) by the same mechanical devices used with a breaker-point ignition: centrifugal advance weights and a vacuum advance diaphragm.

The centrifugal advance mechanism responds to changes in *engine speed* and moves the position of the trigger wheel relative to the distributor shaft. The vacuum advance mechanism responds to changes in engine *load* and moves the position of the pickup coil. These changes in position alter the time, relative to crankshaft position, at which the primary circuit is opened.

In electronic ignitions used with electronic engine control systems, the computer monitors engine speed and load changes, engine temperature, manifold pressure (vacuum), airflow, exhaust oxygen content, and other factors. The computer then changes ignition timing to produce the most efficient combustion. Electronic engine controls are used on most late-model vehicles and will be discussed in the next chapter.

ORIGINAL EQUIPMENT ELECTRONIC IGNITIONS

This section contains brief descriptions of the major electronic ignitions used by domestic and foreign carmakers. All are inductive-discharge systems, but their triggering devices and module circuits vary somewhat from manufacturer to manufacturer.

Because these systems have been under constant development, they have been modified from year to year and model to model. The descriptions given in this section summarize the basic changes resulting from this on-going development. Whenever an electronic ignition requires service, you should always refer to the carmaker's shop manual or an appropriate repair manual to determine the exact specifications and whether the system has any unique features you should know about.

Delco-Remy

High energy ignition (HEI)
The Delco-Remy High Energy Ignition (HEI) system, figure 11-22, was introduced on some 1974 GM V-8 engines and became standard equipment on all GM engines in 1975. The HEI

Fixed dwell: The ignition dwell period begins when the switching transistor turns on and remains relatively constant at all speeds.

Variable dwell: The ignition dwell period varies in distributor degrees at different engine speeds, but remains relatively constant in duration or actual time.

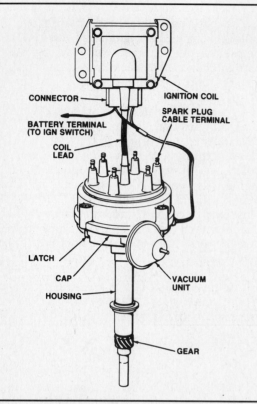

CONNECTOR

IGNITION COIL

SPARK PLUG
CABLE TERMINAL

BATTERY TERMINAL
(TO IGN SWITCH)

COIL
LEAD

LATCH

CAP

HOUSING

VACUUM
UNIT

GEAR

Figure 11-23. The HEI distributor used with some inline and V-6 GM engines.

system was developed from an earlier Delco-Remy Unitized ignition used on a limited number of 1972-74 engines. The HEI and Unitized ignitions have all of the ignition components built into the distributor.

The HEI system was the first domestic original-equipment manufacturer (OEM) electronic ignition to use a variable-dwell primary circuit and no ballast resistor. The control module lengthens the dwell period as engine rpm increases to maintain uniform primary current and coil saturation throughout all engine speed ranges. The HEI module is installed on the breaker plate inside the distributor, and the basic ignition module has four terminals: two connected to the primary circuit and two attached to the pickup coil of a magnetic pulse ignition pickup. The back of the HEI module is coated with a silicone dielectric compound before installation.

The HEI pickup looks different from those of other manufacturers, but it operates in the same basic manner. The rotating trigger wheel of the HEI distributor is called the ''timer core,'' while the coil is attached to a fixed ring-shaped magnet called the ''pole piece.'' The pole piece and trigger wheel have as many

equally spaced teeth as the engine has cylinders, except on uneven-firing V-6 engines, which have three teeth on the trigger wheel and six unevenly spaced teeth on the pole pieces.

The most common HEI system has an integral (built-in) coil mounted in the distributor cap, figure 11-22. Some 4-and 6-cylinder engines have HEI systems with a separate coil, figure 11-23, that provides additional distributor clearance on the engine. Both designs operate in the same way and have similar wiring connections. All HEI systems use 8-mm spark plug cables with silicone insulation to minimize crossfiring caused by the high secondary voltage capability of the HEI coil. Some engines use wide-gap spark plugs to take advantage of the system's high-voltage capability.

In addition to distributing the spark to the appropriate cylinder, the HEI rotor serves as a fuse to protect the module. If an open circuit occurs in the ignition secondary circuit and voltage rises above a certain level, the center of the rotor will burn through and allow the spark to travel to ground rather than arcing through and destroying the module. Early black rotors have a dielectric strength of approximately 70,000 volts; later white ones are designed to ground the secondary circuit at around 100,000 volts.

The newer design rotor may be used in place of the earlier one, but the cap and rotor must be replaced as a matched set. The air gap between the rotor tip and cap electrodes was 0.090 inch (2.29 mm) on the earlier parts, but the later design has an air gap of 0.125 inch (3.18 mm) to better suppress radiofrequency interference (RFI) that could interfere with the engine control computers of the systems discussed in Chapter 12. Caps and rotors from the early and late designs should never be mixed.

In addition to this basic HEI system, GM has used six other HEI versions with electronic engine controls and for certain spark timing requirements:
1. HEI with electronic spark selection (ESS) — This system uses a 5-terminal HEI module and was introduced by Cadillac on the Seville in 1978. The system has an electronic decoder that receives input from the:
● EGR solenoid that signals coolant temperature
● Ignition switch that signals cranking
● The fuel economy switch that signals engine vacuum level.
The decoder uses these signals to determine the appropriate timing alterations. Timing is retarded by a fixed amount during cranking and during cold-engine operation on California models.

EARLY TYPE I

LATE TYPE II

Figure 11-24. The C³I and DIS distributorless ignitions are used with some late-model CCC systems.

Timing is advanced, again by a fixed number of degrees, during cruise.

2. HEI with electronic spark control (ECS) — ECS is a detonation-control system used on 1980 and later turbocharged and high-compression engines. The system consists of a knock sensor, a controller unit, and a special 5-terminal HEI module.

When detonation occurs, the knock sensor sends a signal to the controller, which then instructs the module to retard the ignition timing by a small amount. If the knock sensor continues to detect detonation, the controller instructs the module to further retard timing by another small increment. This sensor-controller-module cycle goes on continuously, and the controller's instructions to the module are updated many times a second until the detonation is eliminated. As soon as that happens,

the process reverses itself and timing is advanced in small steps as long as detonation does not reoccur. Once the detonation-producing conditions have been eliminated, the timing will return to normal within 20 seconds.

3. HEI with electronic module retard (EMR) — This system is a simple 10-degree timing retard system used for cold starts and was also introduced in 1980. The retard circuitry is contained within the special 5-terminal HEI module and is activated by a simple vacuum switch on most models. On cars with the computer-controlled catalytic converter (C-4) system, the module is controlled by the C-4 computer.

4. HEI with electronic spark timing (EST) — This system was introduced on 1981 engines with computer command control (CCC), except those with minimum function CCC systems (Chevette, Pontiac T1000, and Acadian). The 7-terminal module converts the pickup coil signal into a crankshaft position signal used by the electronic control module (ECM) to advance or retard ignition timing for optimum spark timing. HEI-EST distributors have no centrifugal or vacuum advance units.

5. HEI with EST and ESC — Also introduced in 1981, this system combines the electronic spark control of EST with the detonation sensor of ESC and is used primarily with turbocharged engines.

6. HEI with EST and a Hall-effect switch — This system combines the basic magnetic pulse generator of the HEI distributor with a Hall-effect switch and is used with CCC engine control systems. The pickup coil sends timing signals to the HEI module during cranking. Once the engine starts, the Hall-effect switch overrides the pickup coil and sends crankshaft position signals to the computer for electronic control of timing.

Computer-controlled coil ignition (C³I) and direct ignition system (DIS)

This distributorless ignition, figure 11-24, was introduced on some turbocharged, fuel-injected, 3.8-liter Buick V-6 engines in 1984. The system originally was called computer-controlled coil ignition (C³I). Later versions are now called direct ignition system (DIS). Applications of these systems have since been expanded to other 2.5-liter 4-cylinder and 2.8-, 3.0-, and 3.8-liter V-6 engines.

There is no distributor with signal generator, rotor, and cap in the C³I or DIS system. The ignition trigger signal is provided by Hall-effect crankshaft and camshaft position sensors. The

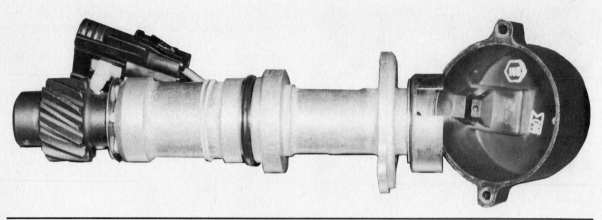

Figure 11-25. The C³I or DIS camshaft sensor contains a Hall-effect switch.

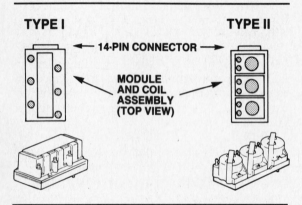

Figure 11-26. Identifying the Type I and Type II coil and ignition module assemblies used by Delco.

crankshaft sensor provides a signal that indicates basic timing, crankshaft position, and engine speed. The camshaft sensor, figure 11-25, provides a firing order signal. On 3.8-liter engines, the camshaft sensor replaces the normal distributor and is mounted in the distributor location to drive the oil pump. On 3.0-liter engines, the camshaft sensor is combined with the crankshaft sensor at the front of the engine.

The C³I or DIS system fires the spark plugs with an assembly containing three separate ignition coils and an electronic control module. Control circuits in the module discharge each coil separately in sequence, with each coil serving two cylinders 360 degrees apart in the firing order. Each coil fires two plugs simultaneously in what GM calls a "waste-spark" method of distribution. One spark goes to a cylinder near tdc on the compression stroke, while the other fires the plug in a cylinder near tdc of the exhaust stroke. The plug in the cylinder on the exhaust stroke requires very little voltage (about 4 kV) to fire and has no effect on engine operation.

Because of "waste-spark" distribution, C³I or DIS is used only on engines with sequential fuel injection. On these engines, fuel is delivered to each cylinder just before the intake valve opens. This means there is no fuel present when the plug fires near the top of the exhaust stroke when there might be valve overlap. This avoids backfiring and other problems that could result from the ignition of fuel in the cylinder or intake manifold.

The operation of the C³I or DIS system is very similar to that of the HEI with EST system described earlier. During starting, the C³I or DIS module controls both ignition timing and spark distribution. When the engine reaches a programmed speed between 200 and 400 rpm, the CCC ECM overrides the C³I or DIS module and assumes control of timing based on signals from the crankshaft sensor and other engine sensors. In case of ECM failure, the C³I or DIS module resumes timing control and operates the ignition with a fixed advance of 10° btdc.

Since introducing the C³I and DIS systems, GM has used three different variations. Type I systems are built by either Motorola or Magnavox, have three spark plug cable terminals on each side of the coil module, figure 11-26, and are called C³I. Type I systems can be further divided into subtypes Ia and Ib. Type Ia modules have the coils molded into a housing with a smooth exterior surface. Type Ib modules have grooves between the coils which make the coils appear to be separate units, although they are 1-piece assemblies. Type Ia and Ib coil modules cannot be interchanged. Type II systems are built by Delco Electronics, have all six spark plug cable terminals on one side of the coil module, and are called DIS. Type II systems also have three separate coils, and each coil can be replaced individually.

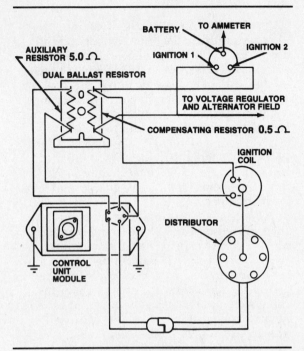

Figure 11-27. A primary circuit diagram of Chrysler's electronic ignition system. (Chrysler)

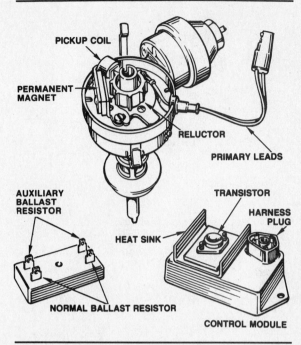

Figure 11-28. The basic Chrysler electronic ignition system.

Chrysler

Electronic ignition

In 1971, Chrysler became the first domestic carmaker to introduce a basic electronic ignition on some models, figure 11-27. The system became standard on all Chrysler Motors's cars in 1973. The same basic system, with very few modifications, has been used on most 6- and 8-cylinder Chrysler engines since.

The Chrysler electronic ignition system, figure 11-28, is a fixed-dwell design using a magnetic pulse distributor, a remote-mounted electronic control module, and a unit-type ballast resistor. The control module is mounted on the firewall or inner fender panel, and has an exposed switching transistor that controls primary current. Don't touch the transistor when the ignition is on, because enough voltage is present to give you a shock. The distributor housing, cap, rotor, and advance mechanisms are all similar to breaker-point components, as are the ignition coil and 7-mm spark plug cables.

All 1972-78 cars and some 1979-80 models have 5-pin modules with a matching 5-terminal wiring harness connector. Early 5-pin module ignition systems used a dual ballast resistor that contained an exposed 0.5-ohm temperature-compensating resistor to control primary circuit current and voltage, and a 5.0-ohm

temperature-compensating resistor to protect the module circuitry from high voltage or current surges. This part was superseded in the mid-1970s by a revised dual resistor using a sealed 1.2-ohm non-temperature-compensating resistor in place of the earlier 0.5-ohm part. The later design is the approved replacement part for all dual-resistor systems.

Some 1979-80 and all 1981 and later vehicles with basic electronic ignition have a 4-pin module and matching wiring harness connector. The 4-pin module contains integral protection circuitry, eliminating terminal 3, which received input voltage from the 5.0-ohm resistor. A single 1.2-ohm unit-type ballast resistor is used in 4-pin module systems to regulate primary circuit current and voltage.

All early Chrysler electronic ignition systems have a single magnetic pickup in the distributor. However, the distributors used with some electronic lean burn (ELB) and electronic spark control (ESC) systems use a dual-pickup distributor containing a start pickup and a run pickup. The run pickup is positioned to advance the ignition trigger signal compared to the start pickup. Under normal engine operation, the module uses the signal from the run pickup. When the ignition switch is in the start position, however, the retarded trigger signal from the start pickup is used to ensure faster starts.

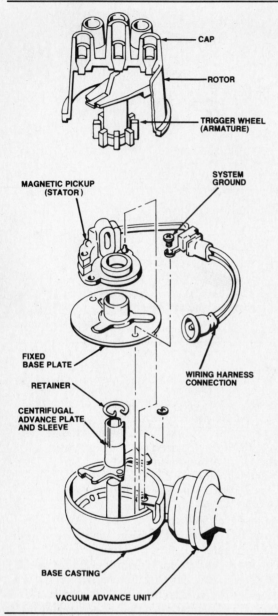

Figure 11-29. Ford's solid-state ignition (SSI) distributor.

Distributors with early ELB systems had only a centrifugal advance mechanism. Those for later ESC systems have neither centrifugal nor vacuum advance mechanisms; all spark advance is controlled by the computer.

The air gap between the reluctor and pickup coil, or coils, is adjustable, but has no effect on the dwell period, which is determined by the control module. The air gap must be set to a specific clearance with a non-metallic feeler gauge when a new pickup unit is installed. Air gap specifications vary according to model year.

Hall-effect electronic ignition system

Chrysler introduced a different electronic ignition in 1978 on their first 4-cylinder, front-wheel-drive (FWD) cars. A Hall-effect switch is used instead of a magnetic pulse generator. The original fixed-dwell ignition on 1978 4-cylinder engines was used with an analog computer and had a 0.5-ohm ballast resistor to control primary current and voltage. The 1978 ELB and 1979 ESC system distributors had both centrifugal and vacuum advance mechanisms and were similar in operation to the 6- and 8-cylinder versions described above.

A changeover to a digital spark-control computer in 1981 resulted in the electronic spark advance (ESA) system. This meant several changes to the system and its operation. Since the computer took over spark control timing, the distributor had no advance mechanisms. The system uses no ballast resistor, and dwell is variable; that is, it increases as engine speed increases. In 1984, the ESA system was incorporated into the electronic fuel injection (EFI) spark control system used on fuel-injected engines. A logic module and a power module replaced the spark control computer, but the ignition portion of this system works essentially the same as in the ESA system.

Ford (Motorcraft)

Solid-state ignition (SSI)

The Ford Motorcraft solid-state ignition system was used in three forms from 1973 through 1976. It consists of a magnetic pulse distributor, figure 11-29, an electronic control module and a special oil-filled coil that can be identified by its blue case or tower. The coil primary terminals are labeled BAT and DEC (distributor electronic control) and a standard primary circuit ballast resistor wire is used, figure 11-30.

The 1973-74 system ignition modules are identified by a black grommet and have seven wires that terminate in 3- and 4-wire connectors. The 1975 versions have a green grommet and the 3-wire connector shape differs from earlier systems. In mid-year, the blue wire for system protection was eliminated, and all later systems (and replacement modules) have a 2-wire connector in place of the earlier 3-wire part. The 1976 versions have a blue grommet and the black and purple wires are reversed in the 4-wire connector.

The 1976 version was adopted by American Motors in 1978 to replace the Prestolite system used from 1975 through 1977.

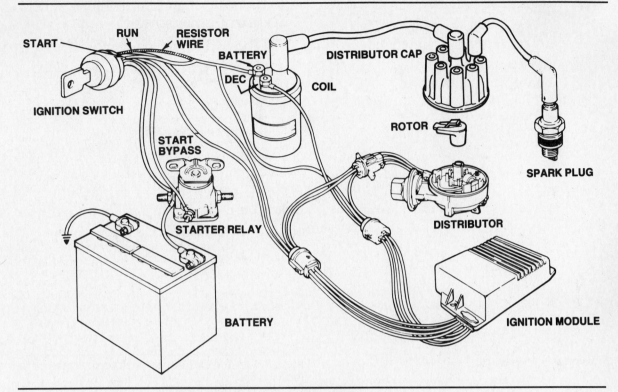

Figure 11-30. Components of Ford's solid-state ignition (SSI). (Ford)

Dura-Spark I and II

Ford introduced its second generation electronic ignitions in 1977. They are direct descendants of the original SSI ignition. The Dura-Spark systems have higher secondary voltage capabilities and the electrical values of some components differ from the earlier Ford systems.

The Dura-Spark I system is used on some 1977-79 California engines and can be identified by a red grommet in the control module. The system does not use a primary resistor and has a new coil with a gray tower and unique terminals that prevent its use in other systems. The Dura-Spark I module adjusts ignition dwell relative to current through the coil at the time of a spark. The module also has a stall-shutdown feature for circuit protection. If the engine stalls, the module opens the primary circuit even though the ignition switch is in the on position. The switch must be turned off and then back to start to close the primary circuit.

Dura-Spark II systems more closely resemble the 1976 solid-state ignition (SSI). They retain a primary resistor wire, but the resistance values are changed to provide higher secondary voltage. The coil is the same as that used with the 1973-76 systems.

Dura-Spark II systems have been produced in several variations. The most basic version,

■ Simple Simulator

If you've done much solid-state ignition service, you know that pinpointing an intermittent problem — a random misfire, for example — can be time-consuming and frustrating. You often spend a lot of time on the road, driving and waiting for the bug to appear. However, there is an ignition pulse simulator as near as your toolbox that may reduce your troubleshooting time considerably.

An electric engraving tool, driven by a vibrating electromagnet, will produce a high-frequency signal that can trigger the pickup coil in some electronic ignitions. It works fine on Ford solid-state ignitions and may work as well on similar systems.

Simply remove the coil high-voltage lead from the distributor cap and set up about a half-inch (13-mm) gap to ground. Then remove the distributor cap and lay the electric engraver across the top of the distributor near the pickup coil. Be sure it doesn't touch the shaft, pickup coil, or armature (reluctor). Then turn the ignition switch to ON and switch on the engraving tool. A strong, high-frequency spark should be produced at the coil lead. You can use your scope to test coil output and you can poke, wiggle, and otherwise check all connectors while the ignition is "running".

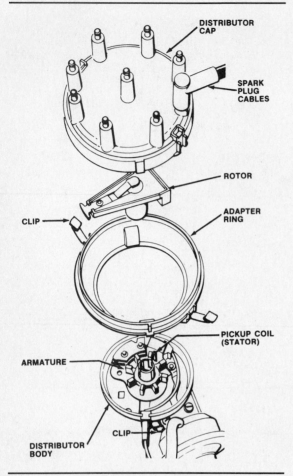

Figure 11-31. A Dura-Spark distributor.

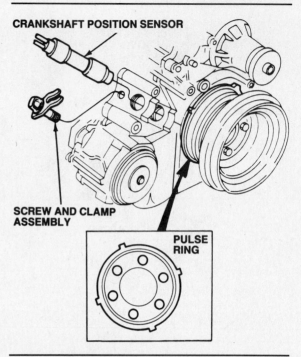

Figure 11-32. The EEC-III crankshaft position sensor replaced the magnetic pulse generator in the Dura-Spark III distributor. (Ford)

produced from 1977 on, has a blue grommet, just like the 1976 SSI system. Some 1979 and later 2.3-liter engines with automatic transmissions have a Dura-Spark II module with a white grommet. This module has "start retard" circuitry that retards the timing up to 18 degrees at cranking speed. Certain 1979-80 engines use a "dual-mode" module with a yellow grommet. This module has three additional wires attached to a third connector. The connector plugs into one of two sensors that affect ignition timing in different ways, depending upon the application. Some models have a vacuum switch for improved fuel economy, while others use a barometric pressure switch for altitude compensation.

From 1981 on, the dual-mode module is replaced by the universal ignition module (UIM) which also has three connectors and a yellow grommet. This module is smaller and more compact than previous Dura-Spark units and contains a factory-programmable retard feature used for fuel economy calibrations, altitude

compensation, or spark knock control, depending upon the application.

All Dura-Spark I and II distributor caps, figure 11-31, use male terminals for the 8-mm spark plug cables. The caps on 6- and 8-cylinder distributors are much larger than previous models and have adapter rings to mate with the distributor housing. Large rotors are also used with the bigger caps.

Dura-Spark III

This system was introduced in late 1979 as part of Ford's second generation electronic engine control (EEC-II) system. The Dura-Spark III ignition module can be identified by its brown grommet. Although it appears similar to other Dura-Spark modules, many of its control circuits were eliminated and their functions incorporated in the EEC-II engine control assembly (ECA).

The Dura-Spark III distributor essentially is nothing more than a device to route the spark from the coil to the proper plug. It has no centrifugal or vacuum advance mechanisms. The magnetic pulse generator was removed from the distributor and relocated to the crankshaft in the form of a crankshaft position sensor (pickup coil) and pulse ring (armature), figure 11-32.

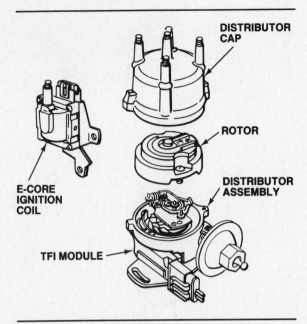

Figure 11-33. Ford TFI ignition system components.

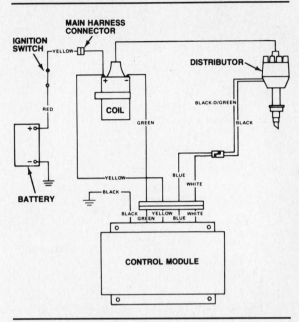

Figure 11-34. Prestolite ignition installation. (AMC)

Thick-film integrated (TFI) ignition
The TFI-I ignition system, figure 11-33, was introduced in 1982 on the 1.6-liter Escort engine. It differs in many respects from the earlier Ford systems already discussed. Instead of a remote-mounted control module, the TFI-I system uses an integrated circuit control module attached to the outside of the distributor housing. The module connects directly to the distributor stator.

Inside the distributor is the familiar magnetic pulse generator, but TFI-I is a variable-dwell system that operates without a ballast resistor. The conventional oil-filled coil is replaced with a special low-resistance E-core part. The distributor cap, rotor, and spark plug cables, however, are similar to those used with Dura-Spark systems.

There are two different versions of the TFI-I control module. Early production parts were made of blue plastic and are called "non-push-start" modules. They contain protection circuitry that will shut off voltage to the coil if an ignition trigger signal is not detected for a period of 10 to 15 seconds. When shutdown occurs, the ignition switch must be turned off and back on again before the engine will start.

All later modules are made of gray plastic and contain revised circuitry that still turns off the voltage to the coil after a preset period, but switches the power back on as soon as a trigger signal is detected.

A revised TFI ignition system appeared in 1983 as part of Ford's fifth generation of electronic engine controls (EEC-IV). Called TFI-IV, this design uses a gray ignition module which appears similar to the TFI-I module, but has a six-wire connector instead of the TFI-I's three-wire connector. The additional three wires connect the module to the ECA. The TFI-IV module is used with a Universal distributor that contains a Hall-effect switch. The TFI ignitions have replaced the Dura-Spark ignitions on virtually all new Ford vehicles.

The TFI module attaches to the distributor with several screws and depends on good contact with the distributor housing for its cooling. Whenever a module is replaced, silicone dielectric compound must be applied to its back to improve heat conductivity and prevent premature module burnout. The module should never be used as a handle to turn the distributor when setting the initial timing. This kind of careless handling can cause it to warp and fail soon after.

Prestolite

Breakerless inductive discharge (BID) ignition
The Prestolite BID ignition was first used on some 1974 International Harvester V-8 engines. A variation was introduced as standard equipment on 1975 AMC 6- and 8-cylinder engines.

The Prestolite system consists of a conventional ignition coil, a control unit, and a breakerless distributor, figure 11-34. Standard spark plugs and cables are used.

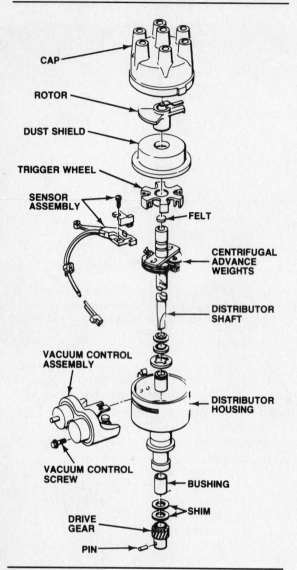

CAP

ROTOR

DUST SHIELD

TRIGGER WHEEL

SENSOR ASSEMBLY

FELT

CENTRIFUGAL ADVANCE WEIGHTS

DISTRIBUTOR SHAFT

VACUUM CONTROL ASSEMBLY

DISTRIBUTOR HOUSING

VACUUM CONTROL SCREW

BUSHING

SHIM

DRIVE GEAR

PIN

Figure 11-35. Prestolite's electronic ignition distributor as used on 1975-77 AMC engines.

The control unit is a solid-state module with protection against reverse polarity and voltage surges. Since the control unit has built-in current regulation, no ballast resistor is required in the primary circuit. The breakerless distributor, figure 11-35, uses conventional centrifugal and vacuum advance mechanisms and its sensor and trigger wheel assembly uses metal detection to provide the signal to the control unit to interrupt primary current flow. Dwell is not adjustable.

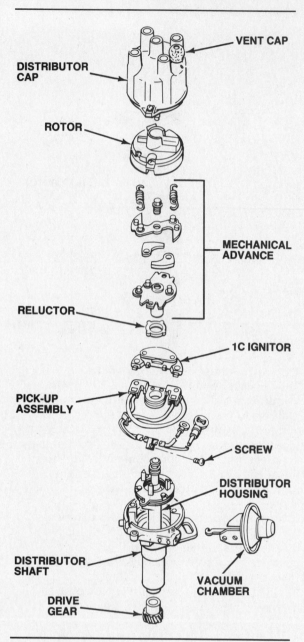

VENT CAP

DISTRIBUTOR CAP

ROTOR

MECHANICAL ADVANCE

RELUCTOR

1C IGNITOR

PICK-UP ASSEMBLY

SCREW

DISTRIBUTOR HOUSING

DISTRIBUTOR SHAFT

DRIVE GEAR

VACUUM CHAMBER

Figure 11-36. The Mitsubishi ignition system used on 2.6-liter engines is typical of the inductive-discharge ignitions used on Japanese vehicles.

Imported Car Electronic Ignitions

Imported vehicles appeared on the automotive scene with electronic ignitions about the same time or shortly after the domestic systems we have discussed. All major imported cars now use an inductive-discharge electronic ignition.

In most of these systems, timing signals are sent to the ignition module from a magnetic pulse generator in the distributor, although Bosch makes a Hall-effect distributor used by Volkswagen.

The electronic ignition used on the Mitsubishi-built 2.6-liter engine in some Chrysler vehicles is typical of most Japanese designs. The distributor contains a magnetic pickup with an integral IC ignitor (control module), figure 11-36 (although some Toyota ignitions use an external ignitor mounted on the coil). The variable-dwell ignition contains no ballast resistor. Full battery voltage is supplied to both the coil and ignitor whenever the ignition switch is in the start or the run position.

SUMMARY

Solid-state electronic ignition systems came into widespread use on both domestic and import vehicles in the early 1970s. Today they are standard on all domestically-built cars and light trucks, as well as imported cars and light trucks. Solid-state ignitions provide greater available voltage, and reliable performance for longer periods under varying operating conditions, with decreased maintenance.

Solid-state ignitions are either the inductive discharge type or the capacitive discharge type. Original equipment systems are the inductive discharge type. The primary circuits of solid-state ignitions can be triggered by breaker points, a magnetic pulse generator, a Hall-effect switch, a metal detector, or an optical triggering device. Original equipment systems generally use a magnetic pulse generator or a Hall-effect switch in the distributor to trigger the primary circuit.

The primary circuit is switched on and off by transistors in the ignition control module. The solid-state ignition module also controls the length of the ignition dwell period. Electronic ignitions with fixed-dwell use a ballast resistor; those with variable dwell have no ballast resistor.

Basic electronic ignition systems use the same centrifugal and vacuum advance devices as breaker point ignitions. Those electronic ignitions used with electronic engine control systems have no advance mechanisms. Spark advance is controlled by the systems computer.

Electronic ignitions have undergone periodic change and improvement since their introduction in the mid-1970s. Most are now a part of an electronic engine control system, which you will study in the next chapter.

Review Questions
Choose the single most correct answer.
Compare your answers with the correct answers on page 451.

1. Which of the following is true of solid-state ignition systems?
   a. They provide greater available voltage than breaker-point systems
   b. They give reliable system performance at all engine speeds
   c. They require less maintenance than breaker point systems
   d. All of the above

2. Inductive discharge systems use a triggering device to provide a sudden _____ in primary current.
   a. Increase
   b. Decrease
   c. High-voltage surge
   d. Low-voltage pulse

3. Which of the following is *not* true of inductive discharge systems?
   a. They are used as original equipment by most car manufacturers
   b. They provide about 30,000 volts of available voltage
   c. They sustain a spark for about 200 microseconds
   d. All of the above

4. Capacitive discharge systems provide _____ secondary voltage when compared to inductive discharge systems.
   a. About the same
   b. Less
   c. Greater
   d. None of the above

5. Transistors have:
   a. A base of one type of material and an emitter and collector of another
   b. An emitter of one type of material and a base and collector of another
   c. A collector of one type of material and a base and emitter of another
   d. None of the above

6. The earliest solid-state ignition systems used which of the following triggering devices?
   a. Metal detectors
   b. Breaker points
   c. Magnetic pulse generators
   d. Light detectors

7. The most common type of original equipment triggering devices are:
   a. Breaker points
   b. Light detectors
   c. Metal detectors
   d. Magnetic pulse generators

8. The accompanying illustration shows a:

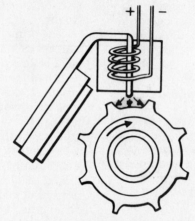

   a. Magnetic pulse generator
   b. Metal detector
   c. Light detector
   d. Breaker point assembly

9. Metal detection triggering devices are used by _____.
   a. General Motors Corporation
   b. Ford Motor Company
   c. American Motors Corporation
   d. Chrysler Motors

10. The dwell period of a solid-state system can be measured with:
    a. A voltmeter
    b. An ammeter
    c. An ohmmeter
    d. An oscilloscope

11. In the Delco High Energy Ignition (HEI) system, the dwell period is controlled by the:
    a. Pole piece
    b. Timer core
    c. RFI filter capacitor
    d. Electronic control module

12. The Delco HEI system uses:
    a. A single ballast resistor
    b. A dual ballast resistor
    c. No ballast resistor
    d. Calibrated resistance wire

13. The Chrysler electronic ignition system uses a:
    a. Dual ballast resistor
    b. Single ballast resistor
    c. No ballast resistor
    d. Calibrated resistance wire

14. The rotating component attached to the distributor shaft in the Chrysler electronic ignition is called the:
    a. Armature
    b. Reluctor
    c. Timer core
    d. Trigger wheel

15. The rotating component attached to the distributor shaft in the Ford electronic ignition is called the:
    a. Armature
    b. Reluctor
    c. Timer core
    d. Trigger wheel

16. Ford's Dura-Spark I system uses:
    a. A single ballast resistor
    b. A dual ballast resistor
    c. No ballast resistor
    d. A calibrated resistance wire

17. A Hall-effect switch requires _____ to generate an output voltage.
    a. A magnetic pulse generator
    b. A varactor diode
    c. A 45-degree magnetic field
    d. An input voltage

18. Thick-film integrated (TFI) ignition modules are:
    a. Mounted inside the distributor
    b. Mounted on the side of the distributor
    c. Mounted on the vehicle fenderwell
    d. Used as a handle to rotate the distributor

19. Dual-mode ignition modules are used with:
    a. Dura-Spark I
    b. TFI-I
    c. Dura-Spark II
    d. TFI-IV

20. A Hall-effect switch is used with which Chrysler electronic ignitions?
    a. 4-cylinder
    b. 6-cylinder
    c. 8-cylinder
    d. All

PART THREE

The Fuel System

12

Fuel System Operation

Fuel and air must be delivered to the carburetor or fuel injection system before the air-fuel mixture can be created. This is the job of the fuel system. The system contains:
- The fuel storage tank
- Fuel delivery lines
- Evaporative emission controls
- The fuel pump
- The fuel filters
- Air cleaners and filters
- Thermostatic air cleaner controls.

This chapter will examine the basic operation of the fuel system and its effects on engine performance, economy, and emission. Chapter 13 describes how the carburetor and intake manifold distribute the air-fuel mixture to the cylinders, while Chapter 16 covers fuel injection.

TANKS AND FILLERS

The automobile fuel tank, figure 12-1, is made of two corrosion-resistant steel halves, which are ribbed for additional strength and welded together. Exposed sections of the tank may be made of heavier steel for protection from road damage and corrosion.

Some cars, sports utility vehicles, and light trucks may have an auxiliary fuel tank. A few of these auxiliary tanks have been made of polyethylene plastic. Greater use of composites in fuel tank construction seems likely in the future.

Tank design and capacity are a compromise between available space, filler location, fuel expansion room, and fuel movement. Some late-model tanks deliberately limit tank capacity by extending the filler tube neck into the tank low enough to prevent complete filling, figure 12-1. A vertical **baffle** in this same tank limits fuel sloshing as the car moves.

Regardless of its size and shape, a fuel tank must have the following:
- An inlet or filler tube through which fuel can enter the tank
- A filler cap
- An outlet to the fuel line leading to the fuel pump
- A vent system.

Tank Location and Mounting

Most domestic sedans and coupes generally use a horizontally suspended fuel tank. It is usually mounted below the rear of the floor pan, figure 12-2, between the frame rails, and just ahead of or behind the rear axle. Many station wagons use a vertically positioned tank located on one side of the car between the outer and inner rear fender panels. To prevent squeaks, some cars

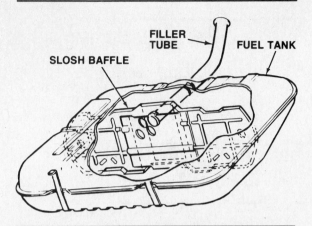

Figure 12-1. The filter tube is located in this tank so that the tank cannot be filled completely. The air space at the top of the tank allows room for fuel expansion. (Oldsmobile)

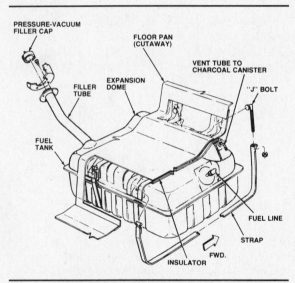

Figure 12-2. Typical fuel tank installation. (Chrysler)

have felt insulator strips cemented on the top or sides of the tank wherever it contacts the underbody.

Location of the fuel inlet depends on the tank design and filler tube placement. It is usually located behind a filler cap or a hinged door in the center of the rear panel or in the outer side of either rear fender panel. Some older cars have their fuel inlet in other positions. The Type 1 Volkswagen's placement of the fuel inlet under the front hood or in the front body panel is an example. On vehicles with a catalytic converter, a decal reading "Unleaded Fuel Only" is located beside the filler cap.

Fuel tanks generally are held in place by a pair of metal retaining straps. The strap ends are bolted to underbody brackets or support

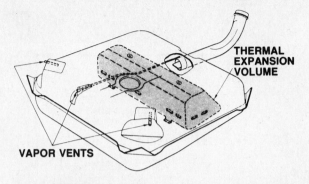

Figure 12-3. This fuel tank has an internal expansion tank to allow for changes in fuel volume due to temperature changes.

panels. The free ends are drawn underneath the tank to hold it in place, and then bolted to other support brackets or to a frame member on the opposite side of the tank. The retaining straps used to hold station wagon tanks often are fastened between the inner wheel well and quarter panel.

Filler Tubes

Two types of filler pipes are used: a rigid, 1-piece tube soldered to the tank, and a 3-piece unit. The 3-piece unit has a lower neck soldered to the tank and an upper neck fastened to the inside of the body sheet metal panel. The two metal necks are connected by a length of hose clamped at both ends.

All 1975 and later cars that require unleaded fuel (cars with catalytic converters and a few without) have a special filler tube inlet. This filler has a restriction in it so that the only nozzles that can be inserted are the smaller-diameter nozzles of pumps dispensing unleaded fuel.

Tank Venting Requirements

Fuel tanks must be vented, or a **vacuum lock** will prevent fuel delivery. Before 1970, tanks were directly vented to the atmosphere with either a vent line or through the filler cap. But those systems added to air pollution by passing fuel vapors into the air. To reduce evaporative

Baffle: A plate or obstruction that restricts the flow of air or liquids. The baffle in a fuel tank keeps the fuel from sloshing as the car moves.

Vacuum Lock: A stoppage of fuel flow caused by insufficient air intake to the fuel tank.

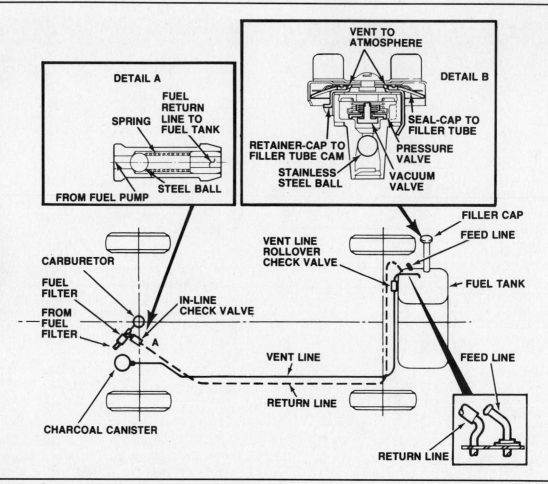

Figure 12-4. One or more rollover leakage protection devices are used in all 1976 and later fuel systems. (AMC)

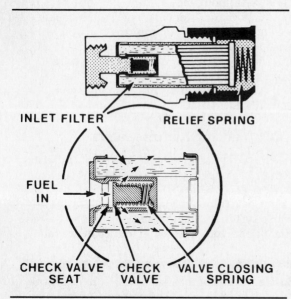

Figure 12-5. The rollover protection check valve is built into the fuel filter used on 1976 and later GM cars. (Chevrolet)

hydrocarbon (HC) emissions, controls have been installed on all 1971 and later model cars. In California, 1970 cars also have controls installed.

Because fuel tanks are no longer vented directly to the atmosphere, the tank must allow for fuel expansion, contraction, and overflow that result from changes in temperature. One way to allow for this is to use a separate expansion tank within the main fuel tank, figure 12-3. Another way is to provide a dome in the top of the tank, figure 12-2. As we mentioned earlier, some tanks are limited in capacity by the angle of the fuel filler tube, figure 12-1. The design used on many GM vehicles usually includes a vertical slosh baffle, and reserves about 12 percent of the tank's total capacity for fuel expansion.

Rollover Leakage Protection

All 1976 and later cars have one or more devices to prevent fuel leaks in case of vehicle rollover. Automakers have met this requirement using two different principles:

- A check valve
- A float valve.

Variations of the basic one-way **check valve** may be installed in any number of places between the fuel tank and the carburetor or throttle body injection unit. The valve can be installed in the fuel return line, vapor vent line, fuel tank filler cap, or carburetor fuel inlet filter. Figures 12-4 and 12-5 show typical locations. This type of rollover leakage protection is used primarily by Chrysler, GM, and AMC.

Ford vehicles use a spring-operated **float valve** in the vapor separator, figure 12-6. It closes whenever the car is at a 90-degree angle or more. Ford also redesigned its mechanical fuel pump on 1976 and later models to reduce fuel spills during an accident.

Vehicles with electric fuel pumps also use these same rollover protection devices, but they have additional features to ensure that the fuel pump shuts off when an accident occurs. Some pumps depend upon an oil pressure or a distributor (rpm) signal to continue operating; these pumps will turn off whenever the engine dies.

Check Valve: A valve that permits flow in only one direction.

Float Valve: A valve that is controlled by a hollow ball floating in a liquid, such as in the fuel bowl of a carburetor.

■ Safety Cells

Most automotive fuel tanks that you service are simple steel tanks that hold liquid fuel. Formed to fit the chassis design and containing some baffles to reduce fuel sloshing, they are pretty straightforward devices. A simple steel tank, however, has some serious disadvantages for vehicles used in hazardous operations. A common fuel tank can be punctured by an impact or leak fuel if overturned. Even with extensive baffling, off-road driving can cause fuel to slosh enough to upset vehicle balance or starve the fuel pickup line. All of these drawbacks to simple fuel tanks led to the development of fuel cells.

A fuel cell is a tank with a rigid shell of steel, aluminum, or some composite material. Inside the shell, a flexible rubber bladder forms a safety liner. The bladder is filled with low-density foam material that absorbs the liquid

fuel. The fuel stays as a liquid within the foam and can be withdrawn easily by the fuel pump and pickup lines. The foam eliminates sloshing by distributing the fuel evenly throughout the tank regardless of the amount of fuel or vehicle motion. The combination of the rubber bladder and the foam prevents — or reduces — leakage in case of impact or tank rupture. Fuel cells also have check valves in the filler and vent lines to prevent leakage in case of rollover.

Fuel cells are mandatory safety equipment in most racecars and are used in many police cars, fire and rescue trucks, ambulances, and off-road equipment. Special cells with self-sealing, antiballistic ("bulletproof") liners are specified by the U.S. Secret Service as standard equipment in presidential limousines.

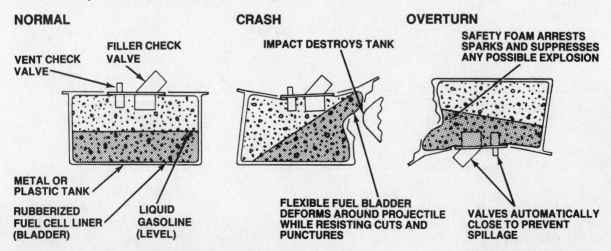

NORMAL
- VENT CHECK VALVE
- FILLER CHECK VALVE
- METAL OR PLASTIC TANK
- RUBBERIZED FUEL CELL LINER (BLADDER)
- LIQUID GASOLINE (LEVEL)

CRASH
- IMPACT DESTROYS TANK
- FLEXIBLE FUEL BLADDER DEFORMS AROUND PROJECTILE WHILE RESISTING CUTS AND PUNCTURES

OVERTURN
- SAFETY FOAM ARRESTS SPARKS AND SUPPRESSES ANY POSSIBLE EXPLOSION
- VALVES AUTOMATICALLY CLOSE TO PREVENT SPILLAGE

Fuel cell construction prevents leakage in case of a crash or a rollover.

THESE VALVES PUSH INTO POSITION IN A GROMMET-TYPE SEAL LIKE A PCV VALVE.

SHARP OBJECTS MUST NOT BE USED BETWEEN THE TANK SEAL AND PUSH-IN SEPARATOR DURING REMOVAL OR INSTALLATION.

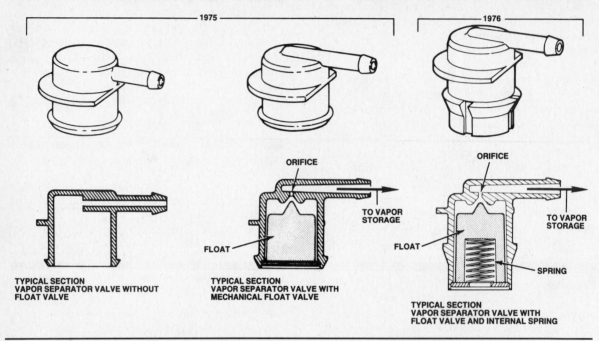

Figure 12-6. Orifice-type vapor separators used on 1974 and later Ford vehicles contain a mechanical check valve that also provides rollover leak protection. (Ford)

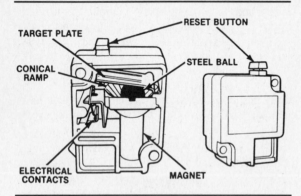

Figure 12-7. Ford uses an inertia switch to turn off the electric fuel pump in an accident.

Late-model Ford vehicles with electronic engine controls and fuel injection have another form of rollover leakage protection. An inertia switch, figure 12-7, is installed in the rear of the vehicle between the electric fuel pump and its power supply. If the car is involved in any sudden impact, the inertia switch contacts will open, shutting off power to the fuel pump. The switch must be reset manually by pushing the button on its top before power can be restored to the pump.

FUEL LINES

The parts of the fuel system are connected by fuel and vapor lines made of steel or nylon tubing and rubber hoses. These are used to supply fuel to the carburetor, throttle body, or fuel rail, to return excess fuel to the tank, and to carry fuel vapors.

The fuel delivery pressure for most carbureted engines is about 5 to 8 psi (34 to 55 kPa). However, the delivery pressure in a low-pressure fuel injection system is between 10 to 15 psi (69 to 103 kPa); and high-pressure systems often operate with 50 psi (345 kPa) or more. In addition, injection systems retain residual pressure in the lines when the engine is off. All of these factors require special fuel lines. All fuel lines, however, must remain as cool as possible. If any part of the line is located near too much heat, the gasoline passing through it will vaporize more rapidly than the fuel pump can create suction, and **vapor lock** will occur. When it does, the fuel pump will pump only vapor, which passes into the carburetor and out through the bowl vent without the engine receiving any gasoline. Depending on their function, fuel and vapor lines may be either rigid or flexible.

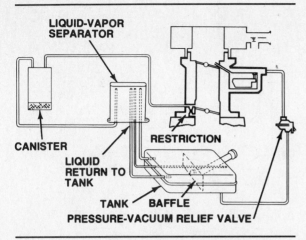

LIQUID-VAPOR SEPARATOR

CANISTER

LIQUID RETURN TO TANK

RESTRICTION

TANK BAFFLE

PRESSURE-VACUUM RELIEF VALVE

Figure 12-8. General Motors EEC system with liquid-vapor separator and constant-purge canister. (Pontiac)

Rigid Lines

All fuel lines that are fastened to the body, frame, or engine are made of seamless steel tubing. Steel springs may be wound around the tubing at certain points to protect against damage.

When rigid fuel line replacement is necessary, only steel tubing should be used. *Copper and aluminum tubing must never be substituted for steel tubing*. These materials will not withstand normal vehicle vibration and they could combine with gasoline to cause a chemical reaction.

Flexible Lines

In most carbureted fuel systems, synthetic rubber hose sections are used where flexibility is needed. Connections between steel fuel lines and other system components often are made with short hose sections. The inside diameter of fuel delivery hose is generally larger ($5/16$ to $3/8$ inch or 8 to 10 millimeters) than that of fuel return hose ($1/4$ inch or 6 millimeters).

Fuel system hoses must be made of special fuel-resistant material. Ordinary rubber hose such as that used for vacuum lines deteriorates when exposed to gasoline. Only hoses made for fuel systems should be used for replacement. Similarly, vapor vent lines must be made of materials that will resist attack by fuel vapors. Replacement vent hoses are usually marked with the designation EVAP to indicate their intended use.

Fuel Line Mounting

Fuel supply lines from the tank to the carburetor are routed to follow the frame along the underbody of the vehicle. Vapor and return lines may be routed with the fuel supply lines, but usually are on the frame rail opposite the supply line. All rigid lines are fastened to the frame rail or underbody with screws and clamps or clips.

EVAPORATIVE EMISSION CONTROL SYSTEMS

California's stringent emission laws brought the first **evaporative emission controls (EEC)** on 1970 cars sold in that state. Use of EEC systems was extended to all 1971 vehicles, regardless of where they were sold.

The purpose of the EEC system is to trap gasoline vapors that would otherwise escape into the atmosphere. The vapors are routed into the intake airflow and burned.

Common Components

The fuel tank filler caps used on cars with EEC systems differ from those used on non-EEC cars. Some early GM EEC systems use a non-vented cap with a pressure-vacuum relief valve in the line between the fuel tank and the carburetor, figure 12-8, but most EEC caps have pressure-vacuum relief built into them, figure 12-9. Whenever pressure or vacuum exceeds the calibration of the valve, it opens. Once the pressure or vacuum has been relieved, the valve closes. If a sealed cap is used on an EEC system that requires a pressure-vacuum relief design, a vacuum lock may develop in the fuel system, or the fuel tank may be damaged by fuel expansion or contraction.

Vapor Lock: A condition in which bubbles are formed in a car's fuel system when the fuel gets hot enough to boil. Flow is stopped or restricted as a result.

Evaporative Emission Control (EEC): A way of controlling HC emissions by collecting fuel vapors from the fuel tank and carburetor fuel bowl vents and directing them through an engine's intake system.

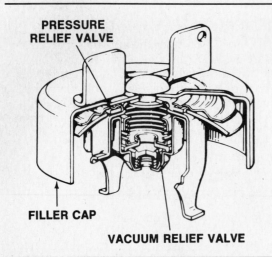

Figure 12-9. Fuel tank caps for EEC systems have vacuum and pressure relief valves.

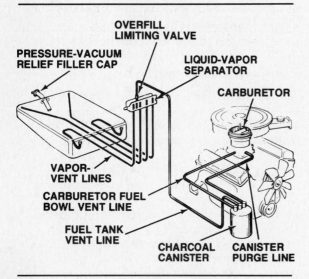

Figure 12-10. This EEC system has a liquid-vapor separator mounted separately from the tank.

Fuel tanks are protected in various ways against fuel expansion and overflow caused by heat. An overfill limiter, or temperature expansion tank, was used on many 1970-73 EEC systems to prevent total filling of the tank. This limiter is attached to the inside of the fuel tank and contains small holes which open it to the fuel area. When the fuel tank appears to be completely full, that is, it will hold no more and the fuel gauge reads full, the expansion tank remains virtually empty. This provides enough space for fuel expansion and vapor collection if the vehicle is parked in the hot sun after filling the tank.

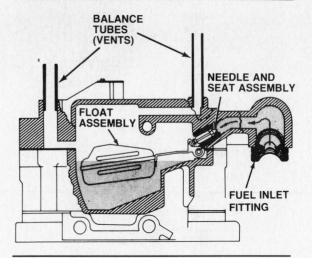

Figure 12-11. Internal carburetor vents. (Chrysler)

The dome design of the upper fuel tank section used in some later-model cars, or the overfill limiting valve contained within the vapor-liquid separator, eliminates the need for the overfill limiter tank used in earlier systems.

All EEC systems use some form of **liquid-vapor separator** to prevent liquid fuel from reaching the engine crankcase or the vapor storage canister. Some liquid-vapor separators are built into the tank and use a single vapor vent line from the tank to the vapor canister. When the separator is not built in, figure 12-10, it usually is mounted on the outside of the tank or on the frame near it. In this case, vent lines run from the tank to the separator and are arranged to vent the tank, regardless of whether the car is level or not. Liquid fuel entering the separator will return to the tank through the shortest line.

Carburetor Venting

Carburetors must be vented to keep atmospheric pressure in the fuel bowl. This provides the pressure differential necessary for precise fuel metering. Two types of vents are used: internal and external.

Internal vents
Carburetors are vented internally through the vent tubes that connect the fuel bowl to the airhorn, figure 12-11. The main purpose of these tubes is to keep atmospheric pressure pushing down on the fuel bowl. This causes the fuel to flow from the bowl, through the circuits and jets, to the lower-pressure area created by the carburetor venturi. The vent tubes also help to compensate for an air pressure drop caused by a dirty air cleaner filter. This helps prevent overly rich air-fuel mixture.

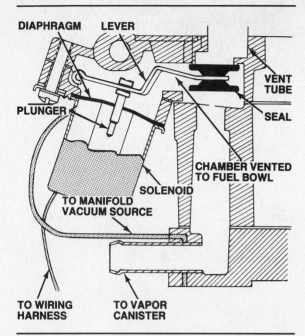

Figure 12-12. A solenoid may be used to switch bowl venting between an internal vent and the canister. (Chrysler)

You will learn more about this in Chapter 13. The balance tubes also allow vapors from the fuel bowl to collect in the air cleaner when the engine is off. This helps control evaporative emissions.

External vents

Many carburetors have external vents for the fuel bowl. On older cars without EEC systems, these vents opened directly to the atmosphere. They released vapors from the fuel bowl to prevent the buildup of vapor pressure, which could cause **percolation**. The carburetor bowl vent on cars with EEC systems is connected to the vapor storage canister by a rubber hose.

Solenoid-operated vent valves may be used on late-model carburetors. The solenoid shown in figure 12-12 is used on a Carter Thermo-Quad to switch the vent passages between the external vent and the internal vent tube.

Vapor Storage

The EEC system traps gasoline vapors from the fuel tank and the carburetor. These trapped vapors are fed into the engine intake system when it is running, or stored until the engine is started. On almost all late-model vehicles, vapors are stored in a charcoal-granule-filled canister.

On a few early EEC systems, vapors were stored in the engine crankcase. When the engine is started, the stored vapors are drawn from the crankcase through the PCV system and added to the incoming air-fuel mixture.

Since 1972, most cars have used a vapor canister for storage. The canister is located under the hood, figure 12-13, and is filled with activated charcoal granules which will hold up to one-third of their own weight in fuel vapors. A vent line connects the fuel tank to the canister. Carburetors with external bowl vents are also vented to the canister.

Vapor Purging

During engine operation, the stored vapors are drawn from the canister to the engine through

Liquid-Vapor Separator Valve: A valve in some EEC fuel systems that separates liquid fuel from fuel vapors.

Percolation: The bubbling and expansion of a liquid. Similar to boiling.

■ Why Vapor Lock?

When gasoline vapors form in the fuel system, vapor lock occurs. This is the partial or complete stoppage of fuel flow to the carburetor. Partial vapor lock will lean the air-fuel mixture and reduce both the top speed and the power of an engine. Complete vapor lock will cause the engine to stall, and make restarting impossible until the fuel system has cooled.

Four factors usually cause vapor lock:
1. High gasoline temperature and pressure in the fuel system.
2. Vapor-forming characteristics of a particular gasoline.
3. The fuel system's inability to minimize vapors.
4. Poor engine operating conditions, such as overheating.

Vapor may form anywhere in the fuel system, but the critical temperature point is the fuel pump.

Engineers have improved fuel pumps and fuel systems to make today's cars less likely to have vapor lock. Oil companies have succeeded in reducing the vapor-locking tendencies of gasoline by adjusting its volatility according to weather requirements. But vapor lock may still occur during long periods of idle (such as in heavy rush-hour traffic) or when the car's fuel system is not properly maintained. Periodically inspect the fuel system and correct all air leaks and defects to prevent vapor lock with today's cars.

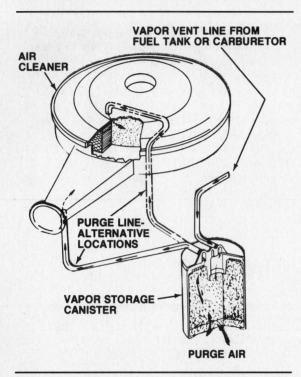

Figure 12-13. Purging the vapor storage canister can be done through either the air cleaner or the carburetor. (Ford)

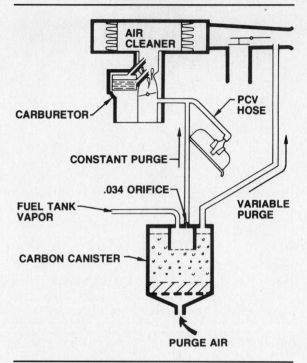

Figure 12-14. In this EEC system, a variable-purge hose runs from the canister to the air cleaner, and a constant-purge hose runs to the intake manifold. (Ford)

a hose connected to either the carburetor base or the air cleaner, figure 12-13. This "purging" process sends vapors to be mixed with the air-fuel mixture, which means that the mixture will be richer. To compensate for the mixture enrichment, carburetors used with an EEC system must be calibrated to take vapor purging into account. If the purge rate is not properly controlled to maintain the correct air-fuel ratio under varying engine operating conditions, engine hesitation and surging will result. This purging process can be done in several ways. The flow rate and purge method are determined by two factors:

1. They must reactivate the charcoal.
2. They must have little effect on the air-fuel ratio and driveability.

Constant purge
In this system, the purge rate remains fixed, regardless of engine air consumption. By "teeing" into the PCV line at the carburetor, intake manifold vacuum is used to draw vapor from the canister. Even though manifold vacuum fluctuates, an orifice in the purge line provides a constant flow rate.

Variable purge
The amount of purge air drawn through the canister is proportional to the amount of fresh

air drawn into the engine. In other words, the more air the engine takes in, the more purge air is drawn through the canister. A simple variable purge system is shown in figure 12-13, which illustrated the two ways used to draw the purge air through the canister. This is done either by using a **pressure drop** across the air filter, or by using the velocity of the air moving through the air cleaner snorkel. In both cases, airflow through the air cleaner varies the air flowing through the canister. The simple variable purge often is combined with a constant purge, figure 12-14.

Two-stage purge
If the air cleaner purge flow is not enough, a vacuum-operated **purge valve** may be used, figure 12-15, in addition to the constant airflow to the manifold. Ported vacuum from the carburetor controls the purge valve line which opens a second passage from the canister to the intake manifold to provide additional purging.

During idle and low engine speeds, spring tension inside the purge valve holds it closed. As the throttle valve moves beyond the carburetor vacuum port, vacuum is applied to the purge valve diaphragm, causing the valve to lift off its seat.

A carburetor purge port also may be used with the constant purge system. This port is

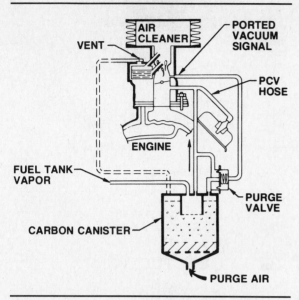

Figure 12-15. The 2-stage purge arrangement in this EEC system uses a vacuum-operated valve to open a second purge line from the canister to the manifold. (Ford)

located above the high side of the carburetor throttle plate so that there is no purge flow at idle, but the flow increases as the throttle opens.

Computer-controlled purge

Canister purging on engines with electronic fuel management control systems may be controlled by the engine control computer. Control of this function is particularly important because the additional fuel vapors sent through the purge line can upset the air-fuel ratio provided by a feedback carburetor or fuel injection system. Since air-fuel ratio adjustments are made many times per second, it is critical that vapor purging be controlled just as precisely.

This is done by a microprocessor-controlled vacuum solenoid mounted on top of the canister, figure 12-16, and one or more purge valves. Under normal conditions, most engine control systems only permit purging during closed-loop operation at cruising speeds. During other engine operation conditions, such as open-loop mode, idle, deceleration, or wide-open throttle, the computer prevents canister purging.

FUEL PUMP OPERATION OVERVIEW

The fuel pump and the fuel lines, figure 12-17, deliver gasoline from the tank to the carburetor or injection system. The fuel pump moves the

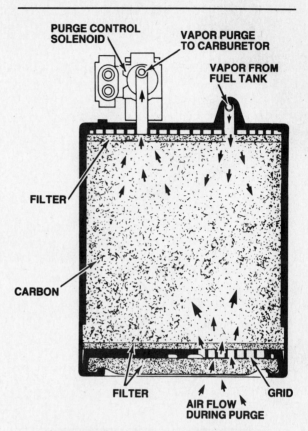

ELECTRIC PURGE VALVE CANISTER

Figure 12-16. In a computer-controlled purging system, the microprocessor controls purge vacuum with a solenoid. (AC-Delco)

fuel with a mechanical action that creates a low-pressure, or suction, area at the pump inlet. This causes the higher atmospheric pressure in the fuel tank to force fuel to the pump. The pump spring also exerts a force on the fuel within the pump and delivers it under pressure to the carburetor or injection system. All pumps, except electric turbine pumps, develop this mechanical action through a reciprocating, "push-pull" motion. The following paragraphs describe various kinds of fuel pumps in detail.

Pressure Drop: A reduction of pressure between two points.

Purge Valve: A vacuum-operated valve used to draw fuel vapors from a vapor storage canister.

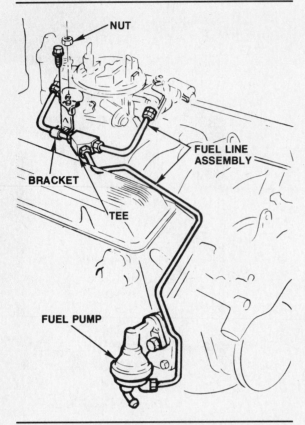

Figure 12-17. Typical fuel pump and line installation on a V-8 engine. (Chevrolet)

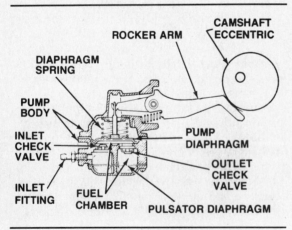

Figure 12-18. Typical diaphragm-type mechanical fuel pump.

PUMP TYPES

While all pumps deliver fuel through mechanical action, they generally are divided into two groups:
1. Mechanical (driven by the car engine)
2. Electrical (driven by an electric motor or vibrating armature).

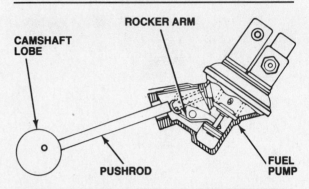

Figure 12-19. Some Chevrolet and Ford engines use a pushrod between the camshaft and pump rocker arm. (Ford)

MECHANICAL FUEL PUMPS

The most common type of fuel pump used by domestic and foreign automakers on carbureted engines is the single-action, diaphragm-type mechanical pump, figure 12-18. The rocker arm is driven by an eccentric lobe on the camshaft. (On some overhead-cam 4-cylinder engines, the eccentric lobe may be on an accessory shaft.) The pump makes one stroke with each revolution of the camshaft. The eccentric lobe (often called simply, ''the eccentric'') may be part of the camshaft.

In some applications, the rocker arm is driven directly by the eccentric, figure 12-18. Other engines have a pushrod between the eccentric and the pump rocker arm, figure 12-19. The most common examples of this arrangement are the small-block Chevrolet V-8 and some 4-cylinder Ford engines.

Mechanical Pump Operation

The fuel intake stroke begins when the rotating camshaft eccentric pushes down on one end of the pump rocker arm. This raises the other end, which pulls the diaphragm up, figure 12-18, and tightens the diaphragm spring. Pulling the diaphragm up creates a vacuum, or low-pressure area, in the fuel chamber. Since there is a constant high pressure in the fuel lines, the inlet check valve in the pump is forced open and fuel enters the fuel chamber.

As the camshaft eccentric continues to turn, it allows the outside end of the rocker arm to ''rock'' back up. Along with the push given by the diaphragm spring, this allows the diaphragm to relax back down. This is the start of the fuel output stroke. As the diaphragm relaxes, it causes a pressure buildup in the fuel chamber.

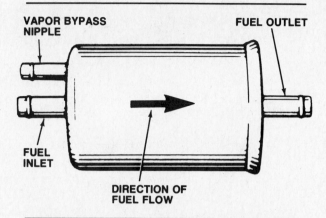

VAPOR BYPASS NIPPLE

FUEL OUTLET

FUEL INLET

DIRECTION OF FUEL FLOW

Figure 12-20. A vapor bypass filter combines the fuel filter and vapor relief functions in one unit.

This pressure closes the inlet check valve and opens the outlet check valve. The fuel flows out of the fuel chamber and into the fuel line on the way to the carburetor. The outlet check valve keeps a constant pressure in the outlet line and prevents fuel from flowing back into the pump.

We measure fuel pump output by the *pressure* and the *volume* of the fuel it delivers. Delivery pressure is controlled by the diaphragm spring. Delivery rate, or volume, is controlled by the carburetor.

The fuel pump delivery rate is proportional to the fuel required by the carburetor. When the carburetor inlet needle valve is open, fuel will flow from the pump, through the lines, and into the carburetor. When the carburetor fuel bowl is full, the needle valve closes and no fuel flows through the lines.

With the needle valve closed and the pressure in the fuel line increasing, the fuel pump diaphragm stays up, even though the rocker arm continues to move up and down in a ''freewheeling'' motion. No fuel is pumped until the fuel level in the carburetor bowl drops enough for the inlet needle valve to open again.

During different operating conditions, the fuel level in the carburetor bowl varies. Therefore, the position of the inlet needle valve varies between being fully open and fully closed. The opening of the needle valve and the rate of fuel flowing into the carburetor is always controlled by, and proportional to, the rate of fuel flow out of the carburetor.

When an engine with a mechanical fuel pump is shut off, pressure in the fuel line to the carburetor is maintained by the pump diaphragm spring. If engine compartment heat expands the gasoline in the fuel line, the fuel will push the carburetor inlet needle valve open and

pass through. The result is too much fuel in the carburetor, and the engine will not restart easily. This is known as **flooding** the carburetor. Also, since fuel expands when it's hot, it may turn from a liquid into a vapor. This causes vapor lock in the pump and lines. Four methods (described in the following paragraphs) are used to maintain fuel pressure and to prevent flooding and vapor lock.

Some older pumps used an air chamber on the outlet side of the pump to separate vaporized fuel and return it to the tank through a separate line.

A vapor separator can be installed between the pump and the carburetor. The carburetor draws liquid fuel from the bottom of the separator while the vapor at the top is returned to the tank.

A vapor bypass filter is often used on air-conditioned cars. It combines a fuel filter and vapor separator into a single unit, figure 12-20.

Many pumps have small bleed-down holes drilled through each check valve, allowing excess pressure in the outlet line to bleed back to the inlet line.

ELECTRIC FUEL PUMPS

Sometimes called a turbine, roller cell, roller vane, or rotary vane pump, the **impeller** pump, figure 12-21, is driven by a small electric motor which draws fuel into the pump, then pushes it out through the fuel line to the carburetor or injection system. Since this type of pump uses no valves, the fuel is moved in a steady flow rather than the pulsating motion of all other electrical and mechanical pumps.

Figure 12-22 shows the pumping action of a roller vane pump. The pump consists of a central impeller disc, several rollers that ride in notches in the impeller, and a pump housing that is offset from the impeller centerline. The impeller is mounted on the end of the motor armature and spins whenever the motor is running. The rollers are free to travel in and out

Flooding: A condition caused by heat expanding the fuel in a fuel line. The fuel pushes the carburetor inlet needle valve open and fills up the fuel bowl even when more fuel is not needed. Also, the presence of too much fuel in the intake manifold.

Impeller: A rotor or rotor blade used to force a gas or liquid in a certain direction under pressure.

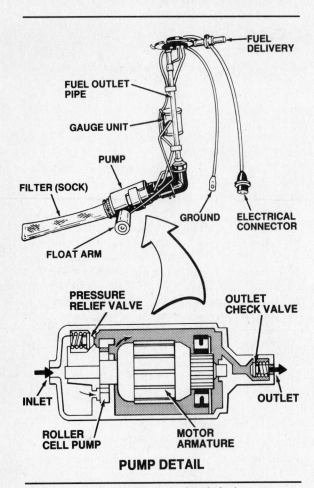

Figure 12-21. An impeller-type electric fuel pump.

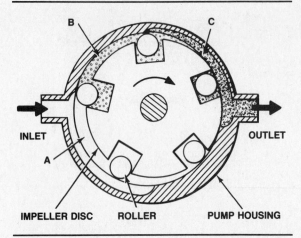

Figure 12-22. The pumping action of an impeller, or rotary vane, pump.

within the notches in the impeller to maintain sealing contact with the pump housing. Unpressurized fuel enters the pump and fills the spaces between the rollers, figure 12-22A. As the impeller rotates, a portion of the fuel is trapped between the impeller, the housing, and two rollers, figure 12-22B. Further rotation toward the offset side of the housing compresses the fuel and forces it out of the pump under pressure, figure 12-22C.

Electric Fuel Pump Location

The electric fuel pump is principally a pusher unit: it pushes the fuel through the supply line. Because it does not rely on the engine camshaft for power, an electric pump can be mounted in the fuel line anywhere on the vehicle — including inside the fuel tank.

Pusher pumps are most efficient when they are mounted as near as possible to the fuel tank and at or below its level. This allows the pump to use gravity to transfer fuel from the tank to

the pump. It also eliminates the problem of vapor lock under all but the most severe conditions. With the pump mounted at the tank, the entire fuel supply line to the carburetor is pressurized. Regardless of how hot the fuel line gets, it is unlikely that vapor bubbles will form to interfere with fuel flow. Having the pump close to or inside the tank also allows the pump to remain cooler because it is away from engine heat. It is therefore less likely to overheat during hot weather.

In-tank pumps

Carbureted GM compacts such as the Monza, Astre, Skyhawk, and Vega use an impeller-type electric fuel pump located in the fuel tank, as do all fuel-injected engines. This is part of the fuel pickup unit and is similar to the in-tank pump used on early Buick Rivieras and some 1972-74 Fords.

Electric Fuel Pump Operation

Late-model electric fuel pumps generally receive current through two parallel circuits and may be controlled by the engine fuel management microprocessor.

Oil pressure switch

Most original equipment electric fuel pumps of the 1970s were controlled by a pressure switch in the engine oil system. This switch opens the electric circuit to the pump motor when the engine is off, and controls the operation of the pump when the engine is started and while it is running.

The pressure switch has two sets of contact points. One set is normally closed and allows current to flow from the battery through the starter solenoid or relay to the fuel pump. The

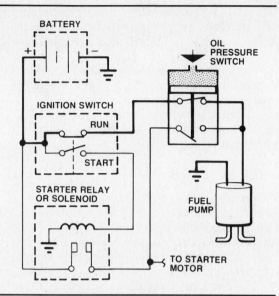

Figure 12-23. When the engine starts, the oil pressure switch opens one set of contacts and closes another. Current then flows through the ignition switch, through the oil pressure switch, and to the fuel pump — as long as the oil pressure remains above a minimum level.

other set is normally open. When closed, it allows current to flow from the battery, through the ignition switch, to the fuel pump.

Turning the ignition key to Start energizes the pump by providing current through the normally closed contact points, figure 12-23. Once the engine is running, the pump receives current through the normally open contacts (which have been closed by engine oil pressure), figure 12-24.

Engine oil pressure opens the normally closed contacts and closes the normally open contacts to keep the pump energized. When the ignition switch is turned off, the pump circuit is deenergized. If oil pressure drops below the specified level for any reason (usually 2 psi or 14 kPa), contact is broken at the pressure switch and the fuel pump stops immediately.

Computer and relay control
Late-model electric fuel pumps used with engine fuel management systems have a relay, figure 12-25, and use the oil pressure switch circuit as a backup in case the relay malfunctions.

■ **Vibrating-Armature Electric Fuel Pumps**

Rotary electric fuel pumps are virtually standard equipment on late-model fuel-injected engines. The rotary (roller vane or roller cell) pump delivers the steady volume and pressure needed for reliable injection operation.

The other general type of electric fuel pump — the vibrating-armature pump — has always been a popular aftermarket item for high-performance engines. Many also were used on older imported cars. Vibrating-armature pumps make a distinctive buzzing and clicking sound as they pressurize the fuel lines when the ignition key is turned on.

The vibrating-armature pump operates a plunger, a bellows, or a diaphragm in pulses. The action is similar to that of a mechanical pump. An armature within an electromagnetic coil operates the bellows, plunger, or diaphragm. Current is applied to the coil to move the armature downward and develop pump suction. This opens an inlet check valve, similarly to the action in a mechanical pump.

When the armature nears the bottom of its stroke, it opens electrical contacts that deenergize the coil. A spring then forces the plunger, diaphragm, or bellows upward to force fuel through the outlet check valve.

Fuel output is regulated as it is in a mechanical pump. As pressure rises in the outlet line, it overcomes spring force and keeps the plunger, diaphragm, or bellows from moving on an output stroke.

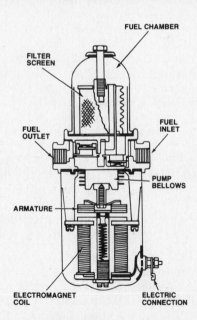

The electrical contacts on some older pumps of this kind would pit and stick together from the continuous arcing as they operated. Many owners of old British sports cars wondered why the small ball peen hammer was included in their car's tool kit. They wondered, that is, until the first time they had to beat on a Lucas electric fuel pump to free the stuck contacts so they could drive on home.

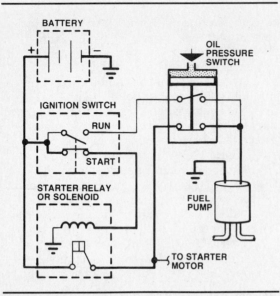

Figure 12-24. During cranking, the fuel pump receives current through the starter relay (solenoid) and the normally closed contacts of the oil pressure switch.

On Chrysler cars, the logic module must receive a distributor (rpm) signal during cranking before it can energize a relay inside the power module to activate the fuel pump, ignition coil, and injectors. If the distributor signal to the logic module is interrupted, the module signals the power module to activate the automatic shutdown relay (ASD) and turn off the pump, coil, and injectors.

Ford and GM systems energize the pump with the ignition switch to initially pressurize the fuel lines, but then deactivate the pump if a distributor (rpm) signal is not received within one to two seconds. The pump is reactivated as soon as engine cranking is detected. The oil pressure sending unit serves as a backup to the fuel pump relay. In case of pump relay failure, the oil pressure switch will operate the fuel pump once oil pressure reaches about 4 psi (28 kPa).

Inertia safety switch
Fords with fuel injection have an inertia switch between the fuel pump relay and fuel pump, figure 12-25. When the ignition switch is turned to the On position, the electronic engine control (EEC) power relay is energized, providing current to the fuel pump relay and a timing circuit in the EEC module.

If the ignition key is not turned to the Start position within about one second, the timing circuit opens the ground circuit to deenergize the fuel pump relay and shut down the pump. This circuit is designed to pre-pressurize the

system. Once the key is turned to the Start position, power to the pump is sent through the relay and inertia switch.

The inertia switch opens under a specified impact, such as a collision. When the switch opens, power to the pump is shut off. The switch must be reset manually by depressing the button on its top before current flow to the pump can be restored.

FUEL FILTERS

Despite the care generally taken in refining, storing, and delivering gasoline, some impurities get into the automotive fuel system. Fuel filters remove dirt, rust, water, and other contamination from the gasoline before it can reach the carburetor or injection system.

The useful life of all filters is limited, although Ford specifies that its filters used with injection systems should last the life of the vehicle. If fuel filters are not cleaned or replaced according to the manufacturer's recommendations, they will become clogged and restrict fuel flow.

Several different types of fuel filters are used, and some systems may contain two or more. Filters can be located in several places within the fuel system.

Fuel Tank Filters and Strainers

A sleeve-type filter of woven Saran is usually fitted to the end of the fuel pickup tube inside the fuel tank. This filter "sock" prevents sediment, which has settled at the bottom of the tank, from entering the fuel line. It also protects against water contamination by plugging itself up. If enough water somehow enters the fuel tank, it accumulates on the outside of the filter and forms a jelly-like mass. If this happens, the filter must be replaced. Otherwise, no maintenance is required for this filter.

Inline Filters

The inline filter, figure 12-20, is located in the line between the fuel pump and carburetor. This protects the carburetor from contamination, but does not protect the fuel pump. The inline filter usually is a throwaway plastic or metal container with a pleated paper element sealed inside.

Some fuel injection systems use inline filter canisters. These are larger units than are generally used with carbureted engines, figure 12-26. They may be mounted on a bracket on the

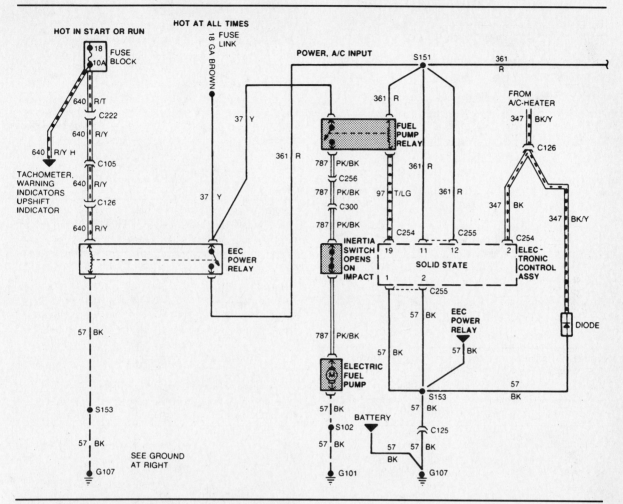

Figure 12-25. Late-model electric fuel pumps used with engine fuel management systems are controlled through a pump relay. This Ford system also uses an inertia switch.

Figure 12-26. Fuel injection systems use large capacity inline fuel filters.

fender panel, a shock tower, or another convenient place in the engine compartment; or they may be installed on a frame rail under the vehicle near the electric fuel pump.

Inline filters must be installed so that gasoline flows through them in the direction shown by the arrow, figure 12-20. If an inline filter is installed backwards, it will restrict fuel delivery to the carburetor or injectors.

An inline filter may have a built-in vapor bypass system. These filters have a third nipple, figure 12-20, that connects a fuel return line back to the fuel tank.

Some older domestic and imported cars have a sediment bowl between the fuel pump and carburetor. The bowl contains a pleated paper, ceramic, fiber, or metal filter element. The filter element works much like an inline filter. The bowl cover is held in place by a wire bail and clamp screw. It can be removed for filter cleaning or replacement, figure 12-27. Ceramic and metal elements can be cleaned and reused, if necessary. Paper and fiber filter elements must be replaced when they are dirty.

Figure 12-27. Older cars may have sediment bowls that contain a paper, fiber, ceramic, or metal filter element.

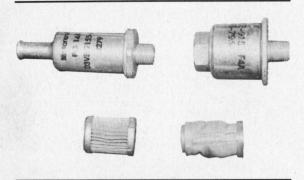

Figure 12-28. A variety of inlet filters used with Motorcraft and Holley carburetors.

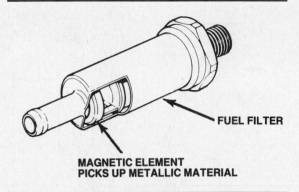

Figure 12-29. This Ford inlet filter contains a magnetic element to remove metallic contamination from the fuel. (Ford)

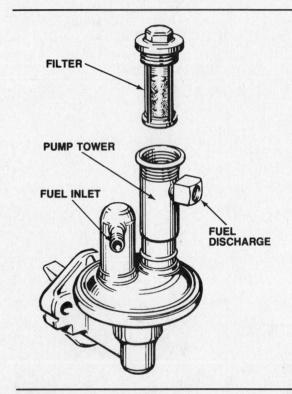

Figure 12-30. Older 6-cylinder Chrysler engines have a filter in the fuel pump outlet tower.

Carburetor Inlet Filters

Ford and General Motors equip most of their carbureted engines with inlet filters, figure 12-28. The Ford filter is a 1-piece throw-away metal unit containing a filter screen and magnetic washer, figure 12-29, to trap dirt and metal particles. The filter generally screws into the carburetor fuel inlet at one end, and clamps to the inlet hose at the other end. One Ford version used in the mid-1970s, however, was designed specifically as an inline filter.

Some Motorcraft, Holley, and Rochester carburetors use a throw-away pleated paper element. Older cars had a bronze filter element, but reuse is not recommended. Filters on 1976

and later Rochester carburetors must contain the new rollover check valve as described earlier.

Pump Outlet Filters

Some cars have fuel filters in the outlet side of the fuel pump. Those pumps used on Chrysler 6-cylinder engines during the early 1970s, figure 12-30, contain a throwaway filter element installed in the fuel outlet tower. Cadillacs through 1974 use a fuel pump outlet filter located on the bottom of the pump, figure 12-31.

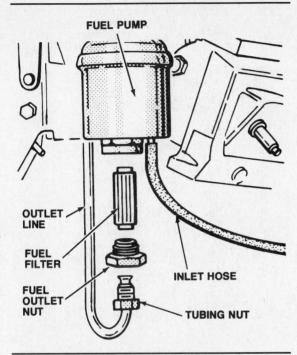

Figure 12-31. Some Cadillacs have a filter in the outlet side of the fuel pump.

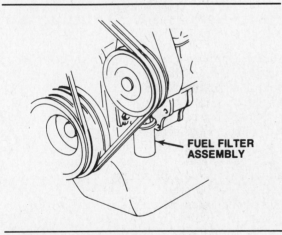

Figure 12-32. Disposable element filters may be mounted on the engine or near the fuel tank.

Disposable Element Filters

Screw-on, throw-away element filters, figure 12-32, look much like a replaceable oil filter. Ford has used this type on the fuel pump of some V-8 engines. The first Cadillac Seville models used a disposable filter mounted to the frame near the left rear wheel. Other fuel-injected Cadillacs have the filter mounted to a bracket on the lower left front of the engine.

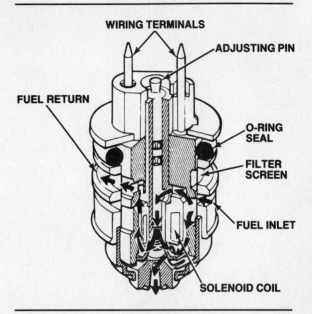

Figure 12-33. Injectors used in throttle body units have one or more external filter screens. (Chrysler)

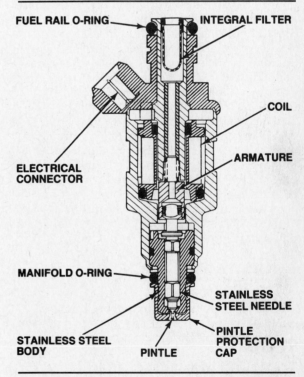

Figure 12-34. Port fuel injectors generally use an integral filter screen. (Ford)

Fuel Injection and Filters

Proper filtering of gasoline is essential to fuel injection operation, because particles smaller

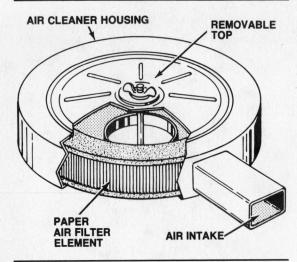

Figure 12-35. A simple air cleaner housing and filter assembly.

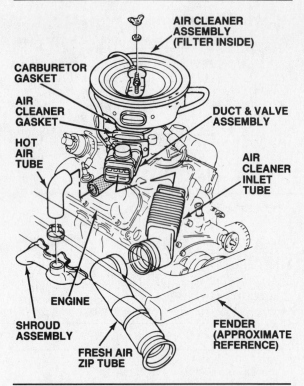

Figure 12-36. Air cleaner housing location on top of the carburetor or throttle body injection (TBI) unit. (Ford)

than one **micron** (0.000025 inch) can interfere with the close tolerances in injectors. Thus, fuel injection systems use various filters:
• The fuel tank filter removes particles larger than 50 microns (0.00125 inch) in size.
• A large-capacity inline filter, figure 12-26, removes particles greater than 10 to 20 microns (0.00025 to 0.00050 inch) in size.
In addition to these filters, some throttle body injection (TBI) units have a filter screen installed in the fuel inlet.

All injectors, throttle body or port, are fitted with one or more filter screens or strainers to remove any particles (generally 10 microns) that might have passed through the other filters. These screens or strainers surround the fuel inlet and thus are external on throttle body injectors, figure 12-33, and internal on port injectors, figure 12-34.

ENGINE AIR FILTERING REQUIREMENTS

The air cleaner and filter have three primary functions:
1. They clean the air before it is mixed with fuel.
2. They silence intake noise.
3. They act as a flame arrester in case of a backfire.

In 1957, engineers at the Lincoln-Mercury Division of Ford Motor Company were searching for ways to improve driveability under cold weather conditions. They discovered that driveability improves when the air cleaner is used to provide warm air to the carburetor at low tem-

peratures. It also allows more efficient carburetor adjustments, which in turn:
• Reduce exhaust emissions without reducing engine performance
• Permit leaner air-fuel ratios
• Give better fuel economy
• Reduce **carburetor icing** in cold weather.

Since then, the air cleaner has become a separate emission control system for intake air temperature control. It also has become a part of other emission controls, such as the PCV system.

The automotive engine burns about 9,000 gallons (34,065 liters) of air for every gallon of gasoline at an air-fuel ratio of 14.7 to 1. With many of today's engines operating on even leaner ratios, the quantity of air consumed per gallon of fuel is closer to 10,000 gallons (37,850 liters). This equals 200,000 gallons (757,000 liters) of air with every 20 gallons (76 liters) of fuel.

Although the basic airborne contaminants — dust, dirt and carbon particles — are found whenever a car is driven, they vary in quantity according to the environment. For example, engine air intake of abrasive carbon particles will be far greater in constant bumper-to-bumper traffic. Intake of dust and dirt particles will be greater in agricultural or construction areas.

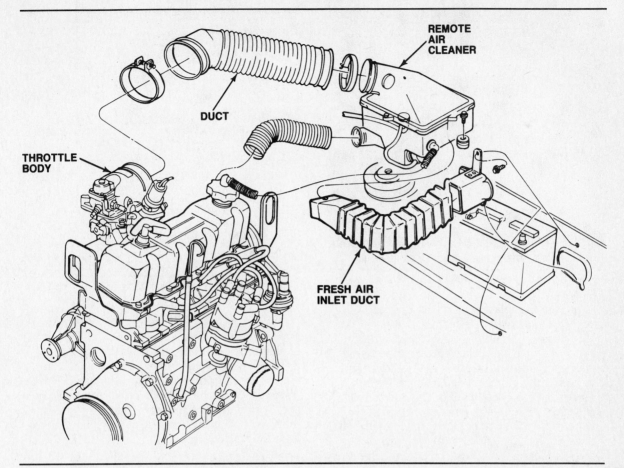

Figure 12-37. Remote air cleaners are positioned to one side of the engine and connected by ducting. (Ford)

THE AIR CLEANER AND FILTRATION

Cleaning of the intake air is done by a filter in a 2-piece air cleaner housing, which is made of either stamped steel or composite materials, figure 12-35. The air cleaner housing is located on top of the carburetor or throttle body injection (TBI) unit, figure 12-36, or is positioned to one side of the engine, figure 12-37.

Older carbureted engine air cleaners had a snorkel or air intake tube which drew fresh air into the housing from the engine compartment, figure 12-35. Snorkels are still used, but they are connected by ducting to a fresh air intake which draws air into the housing from outside the vehicle, figure 12-36. Remote air cleaners are connected to the carburetor or the throttle body by similar ducting and also draw fresh air from outside the vehicle, figure 12-37. The air cleaner housing has a removable top section.

Some air filter elements can be cleaned and reused, but most air filter elements are the disposable (throwaway) type. In areas with high particle concentrations, air filters should be cleaned or replaced at more frequent intervals. A dirty or clogged filter may restrict airflow into the engine, affecting engine performance and life.

Filter Replacement

Automakers recommend cleaning or replacing the air filter element at periodic intervals, usually listed in terms of distance driven or months of service. The distance and time intervals are based on average, or normal, driving. Air filter replacement may be necessary more often when the vehicle is driven under dusty, dirty, or other severe conditions.

Micron: A unit of length equal to one millionth of a meter, one one-thousandth of a millimeter.

Carburetor Icing: A condition that is the result of the rapid vaporization of fuel entering a carburetor; the temperature drops enough to freeze the water particles in the airflow.

Figure 12-38. Some paper filters have an outer polyurethane wrapper.

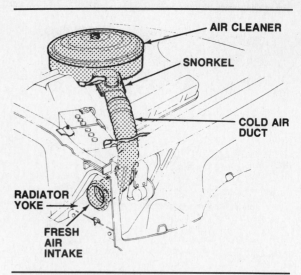

Figure 12-39. Air cleaner with fresh air intake mounted on the radiator yoke.

It is best to replace a filter element before it becomes too dirty to be effective. A dirty air filter will pass contaminants which cause engine wear. A dirty air filter element also can change the air-fuel ratio and affect engine performance. The higher the engine speed, the greater the airflow required. Restricted or clogged filters will greatly affect high-speed operation of the engine. If the element becomes so clogged that it does not let through enough air, it can act as a choke to increase fuel consumption. In severe cases, a clogged air filter can even keep the engine from running.

AIR FILTER ELEMENTS

Three general types of air filter elements have been used on cars and light trucks:
1. Paper filters
2. Polyurethane filters
3. Oil bath filters.
Polyurethane filters are available as aftermarket replacements for OEM filters; oil bath filters are heavy, messy, and inefficient, and have not been in general use for over two decades.

The paper air filter element, figure 12-35, is the most common type of filter used on late-model cars and light trucks. It is made of a chemically treated paper stock containing tiny passages in the fibers. These passages form an indirect path for the airflow to follow. The airflow passes through several fiber surfaces, each of which traps microscopic particles of dust, dirt, and carbon.

Filter paper is pleated and formed into a circle, square, or rectangle (depending upon housing design). Circular filter elements have the top and bottom edges sealed with heat-resistant plastic to prevent unfiltered air from

bypassing the filter. Square and rectangular filter elements generally seal only the top edges. A fine wire mesh screen may be used on the inside of the filter ring to reduce the possibility of the element catching fire from an engine backfire. A similar, but coarser, wire mesh screen may be used on the outside of the filter ring for additional strength.

These filter elements generally are made of dry paper, although an oil-dipped paper stock is sometimes used. The light oil coating helps prevent contaminants from working their way through the paper. It also increases the dirt-holding capacity over the same area of dry paper stock. An outer wrapper of polyurethane, figure 12-38, is used sometimes to make the filter work better. Paper element filters are disposable and should be replaced at the recommended intervals. Some technicians attempt to clean a paper element filter by rapping it on a sharp object to dislodge the dirt, or blowing compressed air through the filter. This tends to clog the paper pores and further reduce the airflow capability of the filter.

AIR INTAKE DUCTS AND FRESH AIR INTAKES

The main source of air intake to the carburetor is the air cleaner snorkel or inlet tube. Some air cleaners use a second snorkel to provide additional air intake at full throttle. Two air cleaner snorkels were common on high-performance engines of the 1960s and early 1970s. They have reappeared on a few high-performance carbureted engines in the 1980s.

The snorkel passes air to the filter and then to the carburetor from the engine compartment.

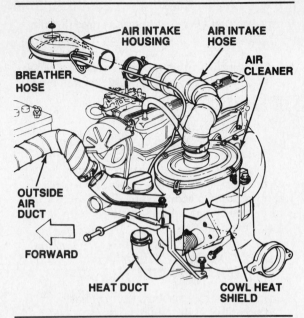

Figure 12-40. Some remote air cleaners are connected to the carburetor or TBI unit by an air intake housing. (Chrysler)

The snorkel also increases the velocity of the air entering the air cleaner housing. Temperatures in the engine compartment will often exceed 200°F (93°C) on a hot day, and hot air can thin out the air-fuel mixture enough to cause detonation and possible engine damage.

Allowing the engine to breathe cooler air from outside the engine compartment prevents such problems. Cooler air is provided by a cold air duct or induction (zip) tube. The tube runs from the snorkel to a fresh air intake at the front of the car, figure 12-39. The fresh air intake normally is open at all times, but may have a screen to prevent insects and other foreign matter from being drawn into the air cleaner. Some fresh air intakes are in the cowl or in the rear area of the hood.

Air cleaner designs used on late-model high-performance engines may have two fresh air inlets, each of which is connected to the air cleaner housing by ducting. This is an updated version of the dual snorkel air cleaner discussed earlier. One inlet provides airflow for general operation; the other opens to provide maximum airflow with the engine at wide-open throttle.

Remotely Mounted Air Filters and Ducts

Air cleaner and duct design depend on a number of factors such as the size, shape, and location of other engine compartment components,

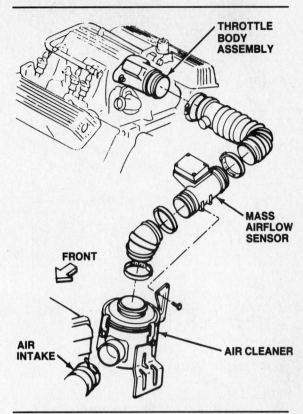

Figure 12-41. Port fuel-injected engines also use a remote air cleaner. If a mass airflow sensor is used, it is inserted in the ducting between the throttle body and the air cleaner. (AC-Delco)

as well as the vehicle body structure. Generally, the air cleaner housing is installed on top of a carburetor or throttle-body injection (TBI) unit, figure 12-36. However, it also can be located away from the engine and connected to the carburetor or TBI unit by an air intake housing, figure 12-40.

Port fuel injection systems generally use a horizontally mounted throttle body. Some systems also have a mass airflow sensor between the throttle body and the air cleaner, figure 12-41. Because placing the air cleaner housing next to the throttle body would cause engine and vehicle design problems, it is more efficient to use this remote air cleaner placement.

Turbocharged engines present a similar problem. The air cleaner connects to the air inlet elbow at the turbocharger. However, the tremendous heat generated by the turbocharger makes it impractical to place the air cleaner housing too close to the turbocharger. For better protection, a mass airflow sensor is installed between the turbocharger and the air cleaner in some vehicles.

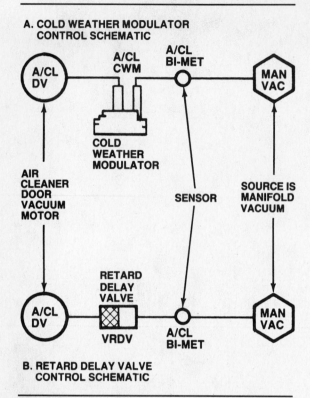

A. COLD WEATHER MODULATOR
CONTROL SCHEMATIC

B. RETARD DELAY VALVE
CONTROL SCHEMATIC

Figure 12-42. A cold weather modulator (top) or a retard delay valve (bottom) prevents a low vacuum condition from overriding the air cleaner temperature control. (Ford)

Turbocharger and fuel injection filters and ducts

Remote air cleaners are connected to the turbocharger air inlet elbow or fuel injection throttle body by composite ducting which is usually retained by clamps. The ducting used may be rigid or flexible, but all connections must be airtight.

Filters used in remote air cleaners vary widely in size and shape, but all are similar to the paper element filters described earlier, and should be serviced in a similar manner.

ENGINE AIR TEMPERATURE REQUIREMENTS

Air temperature regulation requirements differ according to engine, carburetor, or fuel injection system used. Sensors are used to ensure proper intake air temperature. These sensors generally are installed in the air cleaner housing and are calibrated to open a vacuum bleed as low as 50°F (10°C) or as high as 120°F (49°C).

Ford and some other automakers use a vacuum modulator or a retard delay valve, figure 12-42, to trap vacuum to the air cleaner vacuum motor and hold the air control door in the hot-

air position at very low temperatures despite manifold vacuum. Both systems work essentially the same way to prevent low engine vacuum from overriding the temperature control. GM uses a temperature control valve on some engines for the same purpose. Figure 12-43 explains the operation of a vacuum modulator in a typical Ford system.

The retard delay valve, while similar to spark delay valves used in other emission control applications, has an umbrella-type check valve with a sintered steel restrictor to delay vacuum release. Most retard delay valve applications are color coded to indicate the release delay time.

THERMOSTATICALLY CONTROLLED AIR CLEANERS

Some form of **thermostatic** control has been used on automobile air cleaners since 1968 to control intake air temperature for improved driveability. These controls became even more important with the need to maintain the precise air-fuel ratios required for exhaust emission control.

The thermostatically controlled air cleaner has the usual sheet metal or composite housing described earlier. Another sheet metal duct, called a heat stove or shroud, is fastened around the exhaust manifold. The heat stove is connected to the air cleaner intake by a flexible hose or metal tube called a hot air tube, or heat duct. Figures 12-36, 12-40 and 12-44 show examples of various designs. Heat radiating from the exhaust manifold is retained by the heat stove and sent to the air cleaner inlet to provide heated air to the carburetor or the throttle body. However, fuel injection systems using a mass airflow sensor do not use temperature control.

An air control valve or damper permits the intake of:
1. Heated air from the heat stove
2. Cooler air from the snorkel or cold-air duct
3. A combination of both.

While the air control valve generally is located in the air cleaner snorkel, it may be in the air intake housing or ducting of remote air cleaners. The air control valve maintains intake air at a specified temperature, usually 90° to 100°F (32° to 38°C). The air control valve is operated by a vacuum motor or diaphragm, although some older domestic and some imported cars use a thermostatic bulb.

Vacuum Motors

Vacuum motor control of air intake temperature is used on all Chrysler products. Some Ford,

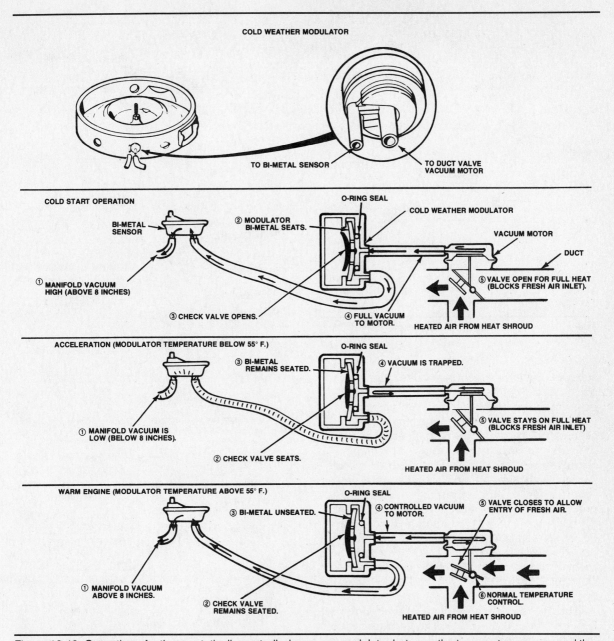

Figure 12-43. Operation of a thermostatically controlled vacuum modulator between the temperature sensor and the vacuum motor. (Ford)

AMC, and smaller GM engines had thermostatic-bulb air cleaners through the mid-1970s. By the 1980s, almost all engines used vacuum motors to control air cleaner damper operation.

In an air cleaner with a vacuum motor, a bimetal temperature sensor and a vacuum bleed in the air cleaner housing regulate vacuum supply to the vacuum motor. Vacuum is supplied from the intake manifold. When intake air temperature is below approximately 100°F (38°C), the temperature sensor holds the vacuum bleed closed and full manifold vacuum is applied to

the vacuum motor. The motor holds the air control valve in the full hot-air position, figure 12-45, position A.

As intake air warms up, the sensor begins to open the vacuum bleed. This decreases the vacuum sent to the motor. A spring in the motor

Thermostatic: Referring to a device that automatically responds to temperature changes in order to activate a switch.

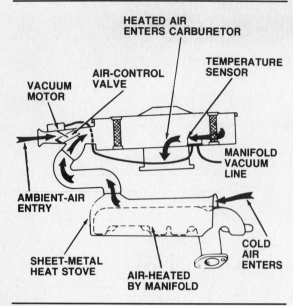

Figure 12-44. A thermostatically controlled air cleaner with a heat stove.

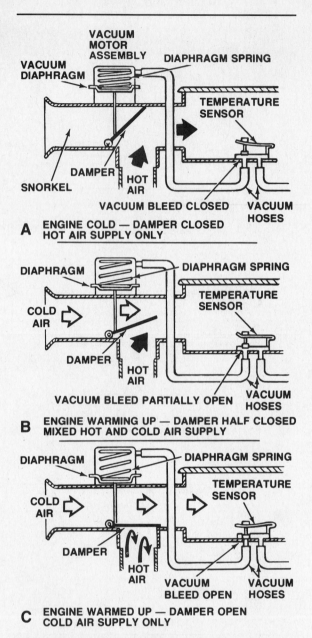

Figure 12-45. A thermostatically controlled air cleaner with vacuum motor control.

starts to move the air control valve from the hot-air to the cold-air position, figure 12-45, position B.

As air temperature continues to rise, the vacuum bleed continues to open, and vacuum to the motor is further reduced. At high air temperatures, vacuum to the air cleaner motor is completely shut off, and the air control valve is in its full cold-air position, figure 12-45, position C. On some engines, the air control valve also opens to the full cold-air position during heavy acceleration, regardless of air temperature. The opening of the valve provides maximum airflow through the air cleaner to the carburetor or throttle body when it is needed the most.

The operating requirements of other engines may be different, however. The vacuum modulator systems described previously trap vacuum in the air motor to hold the damper in the cold-air position. On a cold engine operating close to the 14.7:1 air-fuel ratio, a sudden charge of dense, cold air can cause a lean condition and a hesitation on acceleration.

Thermostatic Bulbs and Coils

Thermostatic bulb operation of the air control was used on many AMC and Ford engines during the 1960s and 1970s. General Motors used a thermostatic coil on small 4-cylinder engines until the mid-1970s. Some import cars also used this method of regulating air intake temperature.

With this type of control, the thermostatic bulb or coil is inside the air cleaner snorkel and connected by linkage to a spring-loaded air control valve. The air control valve is normally held in its closed position by the spring, allowing heated intake air to enter the snorkel, figure 12-46, position A. As the temperature rises, the thermostatic bulb begins to expand. This expansion exceeds air valve spring tension and the valve gradually opens to its cold-air position, figure 12-46, position B.

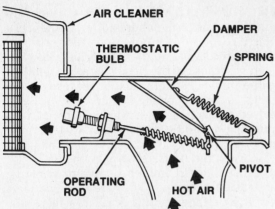

A. COLD ENGINE TEMPERATURE (HOT-AIR POSITION)

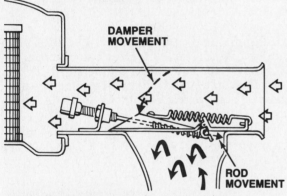

B. NORMAL ENGINE TEMPERATURE (COLD-AIR POSITION)

Figure 12-46. A thermostatically controlled air cleaner with thermostatic bulb control. As the bulb expands, it pushes the rod forward to move the damper downward into the hot-air position.

OTHER AIR CLEANER USES

The air cleaner housing is a convenient place to locate a number of other emission control devices. Here are some that may be found on or in the air cleaner housing:

• The PCV system connects to the air cleaner housing to obtain a source of fresh air. The crankcase ventilation filter usually is in the air cleaner, except on some late-model Ford 4-cylinder and V-6 vehicles and Chrysler 6- and 8-cylinder engines, which have the filter in the oil filler cap or hose.

• GM and other automakers attach the manifold absolute pressure (MAP) sensor to the air cleaner housing.

• Chrysler's orifice spark advance control (OSAC) valve is attached to the air cleaner housing on many models.

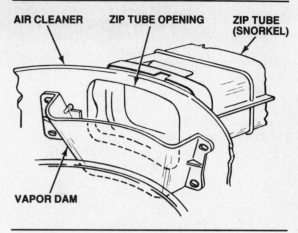

Figure 12-47. Some air cleaners use a vapor dam to trap carburetor fuel vapors when the engine is off. (Ford)

• Ford has mounted an air injection thermal vacuum switch (TVS) in the air cleaner to control air injection operation.

• A vapor dam, figure 12-47, may be used inside some air cleaners to trap carburetor fuel vapors when the engine is off. Since the vapors are heavier than the air, they remain in the bottom of the air cleaner until the engine is started and they are purged.

SUMMARY

Automotive fuel tanks can be mounted either vertically or horizontally, depending on how much room there is under the vehicle. Filler tubes, besides allowing the tanks to be filled, are used as fill limiters, leaving room for fuel to expand. Cars requiring unleaded gasoline will not accept a leaded gas nozzle in the tube.

Tanks must be vented, but evaporative emission control (EEC) requirements state that the fuel vapors must not be vented to the atmosphere. Automakers have devised numerous ways to ensure that all vapors remain within the fuel system. They have provided rollover leak protection, pressure-vacuum relief valves, liquid-vapor separators and positive crankcase ventilation. The EEC systems all use vapor storage canisters. Vapors stored in the canisters are purged into the engine.

Each manufacturer has devised slightly different ways to purge engine vapors, depending on the vehicle and engine requirements. Late-model vehicles with engine control systems have placed the purging function under the control of the computer to ensure that vapor flow does not interfere with air-fuel ratio control or driveability. All EEC systems prevent vapors containing unburned hydrocarbons from reaching the atmosphere, where they pollute the air.

Fuel pumps move the fuel from the tank to the carburetor or injection system. All pumps do this through a mechanical action that creates a low-pressure area into which the fuel will flow. With check valves and high pressure, the fuel is then forced out of the pump and into the carburetor or injector throttle body or fuel rail.

There are two types of fuel pumps: mechanical and electrical. Mechanical pumps use the engine camshaft or auxiliary shaft eccentric for power. Although there are four types of electrical pumps (plunger, diaphragm, bellows, and impeller), only the impeller type has been used in recent fuel system designs. Electric pumps push the fuel rather than pull it, so they are frequently installed in the fuel tank. Some fuel injection systems use a low-pressure intank pump which feeds fuel to a high-pressure external pump that develops system pressure.

Many types of filters are used in the fuel system. They remove contamination from the fuel before it reaches the carburetor or injectors. This is particularly important with fuel injection systems, because of the close tolerances within the injectors. Fuel filters must be replaced or cleaned as directed by the manufacturer. Filters are used as inline filters, at the fuel tank, at the carburetor or throttle body, and on fuel injectors.

Like fuel, the air used by an engine contains tiny particles of dirt and other contaminants that damage an engine if they are allowed to enter it. Air cleaners and their filters screen out this material. Air cleaners also are part of the emission control system, since they help reduce emissions and increase performance and fuel economy.

Since 1968, most domestic cars and light trucks have used thermostatically controlled air cleaners, which provide warm air to the carburetor or throttle body at low temperatures. Each carmaker has a slightly different design, but all these devices work in essentially the same way.

Review Questions

Choose the single most correct answer.
Compare your answers with the correct answers on page 451.

1. When the fuel filter shown below is installed, the arrow must point toward the:

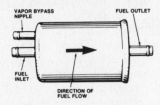

VAPOR BYPASS NIPPLE — FUEL OUTLET
FUEL INLET
DIRECTION OF FUEL FLOW

   a. Carburetor or fuel injectors
   b. Fuel tank
   c. Vapor canister
   d. Fuel pump

2. An electric fuel pump has an advantage over a mechanical pump because:
   a. It is lighter
   b. It requires no maintenance
   c. It overcomes vapor lock by rapid fuel delivery
   d. It does not cause wear to the crankshaft eccentric

3. Inline filters generally:
   a. Are used on both carbureted and fuel injected engines
   b. Are located in the fuel line between the pump and carburetor
   c. Protect the carburetor or injectors but not the pump
   d. All of the above

4. If the fuel pump relay fails in a fuel injection system, the computer continues to operate the fuel pump according to a signal from:
   a. The oil pressure switch
   b. The inertia switch
   c. A timing circuit
   d. The EGO sensor

5. The primary source of air intake to the carburetor or throttle body is the:
   a. Air cleaner snorkel or intake duct
   b. Venturi
   c. Fuel bowl
   d. Heat stove

6. A heat stove is located on the:
   a. Carburetor
   b. Snorkel
   c. Exhaust manifold
   d. Intake manifold

7. When intake air temperature is low in a thermostatic air cleaner:
   a. The vacuum bleed is closed
   b. The vacuum bleed is open
   c. The air control valve is in the cold-air position
   d. Little vacuum is applied to the vacuum motor

8. To prevent a paper air filter element from catching fire:
   a. It is chemically treated
   b. It is soaked in oil
   c. A fine wire mesh screen is used on the inside of the filter ring
   d. A coarse wire mesh screen is used on the outside

9. Airborne contaminants can:
   a. Change air-fuel ratios
   b. Damage piston rings and cylinder walls
   c. Enter the engine oil
   d. All of the above

10. Mechanic A says that heated intake air reduces carburetor icing in cold weather.
    Mechanic B says that a bimetal temperature sensor and vacuum bleed in the air cleaner regulate vacuum to the vacuum motor.
    Who is right?
    a. A only
    b. B only
    c. Both A and B
    d. Neither A nor B

11. All fuel tanks must:
    a. Be vertically mounted
    b. Be horizontally mounted
    c. Have a vent system
    d. Contain a vertical baffle

12. Filler necks with restricted openings:
    a. Provide better venting
    b. Prevent entry of leaded fuel dispensers
    c. Reduce emissions
    d. Act as rollover check valves

13. Fuel lines fastened to the frame, body, or engine are made of:
    a. Steel
    b. Aluminum
    c. Copper
    d. Rubber

14. Ordinary rubber hose can be used for:
    a. Fuel supply lines
    b. Vapor vent lines
    c. Vacuum lines
    d. Fuel return lines

15. Electric fuel pumps are most efficient when located near:
    a. The engine
    b. The fuel tank
    c. The carburetor or injectors
    d. The camshaft

16. Safety control of an electric fuel pump can be provided by:
    a. An oil pressure switch
    b. The starter relay
    c. The ignition switch
    d. Fuel line pressure

17. All EEC systems eliminate vapors containing:
    a. NO_x
    b. CO
    c. SO_2
    d. Unburned hydrocarbons

18. The most common type of fuel pump used on carbureted engines is:
    a. The double-action diaphragm type
    b. The single rocker arm type
    c. The single-action diaphragm type
    d. The pushrod rocker arm type

19. The intake stroke in the fuel pump:
    a. Exerts pressure in the fuel tank line
    b. Creates a vacuum in the fuel chamber
    c. Opens the outlet valve
    d. All of the above

20. The output stroke of the fuel pump:
    a. Increases pressure on the diaphragm spring
    b. Opens the inlet valve
    c. Increases pressure in the pump chamber and opens the outlet valve
    d. Draws fuel into the fuel tank line

21. Fuel pump pressure is controlled by:
    a. The carburetor inlet needle valve
    b. The strength of the diaphragm spring
    c. The carburetor float
    d. None of the above

13

Basic Carburetion and Manifolding

So far in our study of a car's fuel system, we have examined enough hardware to be able to dump raw fuel into the combustion chambers. But adding a spark to that raw fuel will not produce the combustion needed to create the power to move the car.

Something more is required: the fuel first must be changed to a vapor by mixing it with air, and then fed to the cylinders in precise air-to-fuel ratios. This is the job of the carburetor, figure 13-1, or the electronic fuel injection (EFI) system. Fuel injection systems will be studied in detail in Chapter 16. This chapter will cover carburetor function, and delivery of the air-fuel mixture to the cylinders by the intake manifold.

Carburetor designs vary tremendously, from the simple devices used on older cars to the highly complex and expensive versions used on racing engines. Regardless of design, however, all carburetors operate on the same basic principle of air pressure differential, and all manifolds have the same design factors.

In this chapter, you will learn how differences in air pressure apply to a carburetor, how carburetors operate under all types of driving conditions, and how assist devices are used to modify their operation. We will cover the similarities in designs for carburetors and for manifolds, and discuss how proper carburetor and assist-device adjustments can improve driveability and lower the polluting emissions in the engine's exhaust.

Once you understand how the carburetor and manifolding systems work, and what the similarities are, you can then make carburetor adjustments properly and diagnose carburetor problems more accurately.

PRESSURE DIFFERENTIAL

Since air is a substance, the air outside an engine has a specific weight, and so does the air inside the engine. The weight of air exerts pressure on whatever it touches. The greater this weight, the greater the pressure. When the weight of air outside the engine is greater than the weight of air inside the engine, we say that there is a pressure difference, or differential, between the two.

Atmospheric Pressure

The weight of air is not always the same, but changes with temperature and height above sea level (altitude). Air pressure is measured in pounds per square inch (psi) at sea level at an average temperature of 32°F. In metric units, atmospheric pressure at sea level is measured in millimeters of mercury (mm Hg) at 20°C.

Figure 13-1. The modern carburetor is a complex device, but works on two simple principles: airflow and pressure differential.

At sea level and at an average temperature, one cubic foot of air weighs about one and a quarter ounces (36 grams). This seems light enough, but remember that the earth's atmosphere is quite thick, figure 13-2. Therefore the column of air pressing down on an object at sea level is equal to about 14.7 psi (101 kPa).

Effects of temperature

Air expands and becomes lighter as its temperature rises, reducing the pressure it exerts. As its temperature falls, air contracts, making it heavier and increasing its pressure. Variations in air temperature account for changing weather conditions. Direct heat from the sun and reflected heat from the earth's surface warm the air. As its temperature increases, air becomes lighter and rises. Cooler air sinks and takes its place, resulting in a constant motion. This motion creates wind and weather patterns.

Effects of altitude

As you climb above sea level, the amount of air pressing down on you becomes smaller. Since a smaller amount of air weighs less, it exerts less pressure. Air pressure gradually decreases with increased distance above sea level. At 30,000 feet or approximately 9 kilometers above sea level, air pressure is only about 5 psi (34 kPa). A few hundred miles or several hundred kilometers above the earth, the atmosphere ends in a vacuum, or complete lack of pressure.

Manifold Pressure — Vacuum

With each intake stroke of an engine piston in its cylinder, a partial vacuum is produced. As the piston moves down, it creates a larger space in which the air molecules can move. Since the molecules spread out to occupy this increased space, the distance between them increases.

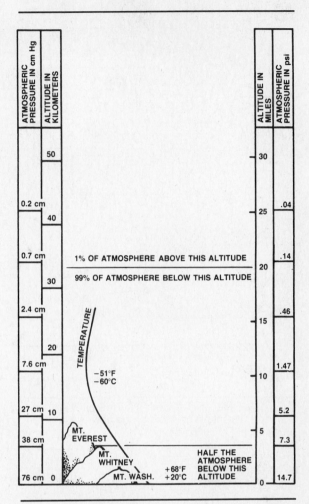

Figure 13-2. The blanket of air surrounding the earth extends many miles into the atmosphere. Atmospheric pressure decreases at higher altitudes.

The greater the space between the air molecules, the greater the vacuum created.

As the piston moves farther down, it increases the vacuum and lowers the air pressure in the cylinder and intake manifold above it, causing a pressure differential between the air inside and the air outside the engine. To offset this differential, outside air rushes into the engine. As it passes through the carburetor, it is mixed with gasoline to form an air-fuel mixture. This combustible vapor is then drawn by vacuum through the intake manifold and the open intake valve into the cylinder, figure 13-3. Here it is compressed, burned, and exhausted.

AIRFLOW AND THE VENTURI PRINCIPLE

Opening the carburetor throttle valve causes air to move from the higher pressure area outside the engine through the carburetor and into the

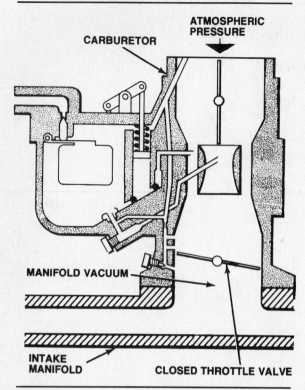

Figure 13-3. Manifold vacuum is the low pressure created in the intake manifold by the downward movement of the engine's pistons.

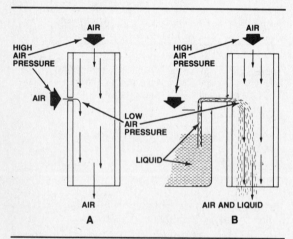

Figure 13-4. Airflow through a tube creates low pressure along the sides of the tube that can draw in more air (A). The low pressure can also draw liquid into the tube (B).

lower pressure area of the manifold. How much and how fast the air travels is determined by the opening of the throttle valve.

The pressure of air passing rapidly through a carburetor barrel is lower along the sides of the barrel than it is in the center of the airflow. By putting a small hole in the side of the barrel,

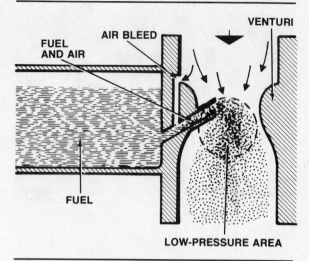

Figure 13-5. Air flowing through the venturi increases in speed, lowering the pressure within the venturi to draw in more fuel.

more air can be drawn into the stream of air rushing through the barrel, figure 13-4A. If a hose is used to connect the hole to a liquid-filled container or bowl, then the liquid will be forced through the hose and into the stream of air rushing by, figure 13-4B.

This action is caused by the higher air pressure on the liquid, which forces it into the lower air pressure area inside the barrel. How much liquid passes through the hose depends on the airflow velocity, or how fast the air is flowing through the inside of the barrel. The higher the velocity (speed) of airflow, the lower the pressure will be at the inlet hole and the more liquid will flow.

To make the carburetor work better, the air velocity through the barrel must be increased. This can be done by placing a restriction called a venturi inside the barrel, figure 13-5. When air flows through the venturi restriction, it speeds up. This speed increase lowers the pressure inside the carburetor barrel and forces more liquid fuel to be drawn into the airflow.

In addition to mixing liquid fuel with air, the carburetor must also vaporize the liquid as much as possible. To help break up the liquid fuel for better vaporization, a small opening called an air bleed is put in the fuel inlet passage, figure 13-6.

The carburetor also must change the air-fuel mixture automatically. It must deliver a rich mixture for starting, idle and acceleration, and a lean mixture for part-throttle operation. Engine speed and power are regulated by the position of the carburetor throttle valve, which controls the flow of the air-fuel mixture, figure 13-6.

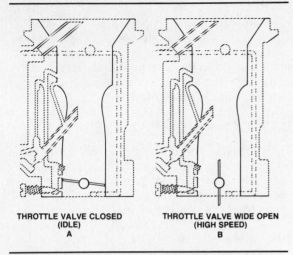

THROTTLE VALVE CLOSED
(IDLE)
A

THROTTLE VALVE WIDE OPEN
(HIGH SPEED)
B

Figure 13-6. The carburetor throttle valve controls engine speed and power by regulating the amount of air and fuel entering the engine.

Carburetor Vacuum

There are four measurements of air pressure, or vacuum, that are important when discussing carburetors:
• Atmospheric pressure
• Manifold vacuum
• Venturi vacuum
• Ported vacuum.

Atmospheric pressure is the pressure of the air outside the carburetor. It is always present, and varies within a narrow range, depending upon altitude and atmospheric conditions.

Manifold vacuum is the low pressure beneath the carburetor throttle valve. Manifold vacuum is produced by the engine and is always present when the engine is running. Manifold vacuum decreases as the throttle valve is opened.

Venturi vacuum is the low-pressure area created by airflow through the venturi restriction in the carburetor barrel. **Venturi vacuum** increases with the speed of the airflow through the venturi. It is present whenever the throttle valve is open and increases as the throttle is opened.

Ported vacuum — the low-pressure area just above the throttle valve — is present whenever the throttle is opened to expose the port in the lower portion of the carburetor barrel to manifold vacuum. Ported vacuum is absent at idle, high at small throttle openings, and decreases as the throttle is opened farther. Vacuum taken from this point often is used to operate distributor vacuum advance units and other vacuum-operated devices. Small ports, or holes, in the side of the carburetor are connected to hoses, which are connected to the vacuum devices.

CARBURETION OPERATING PRINCIPLES

All carburetors must perform three vital functions. They must break up the liquid gasoline into a fine mist, change the liquid into a vapor, and distribute the vapor evenly to the cylinders. These three principles of atomization, vaporization, and distribution of fuel are important principles of carburetion.

Gasoline must be atomized, or broken up, into a fine mist if the fuel is to be properly vaporized. Atomization takes place as the fuel travels from the carburetor discharge nozzles into the moving stream of air.

Vaporization starts as the atomized fuel passes the throttle and enters the intake manifold. Complete vaporization cannot occur unless the fuel is hot enough to boil. Vaporization is affected by the following factors:
• Temperature — vaporization increases as the fuel is heated
• Volatility — the greater the volatility of the fuel, the lower the temperature at which it will vaporize and the faster it will vaporize
• Pressure — a decrease in pressure causes fuel to vaporize faster at a lower temperature.

Low volatility, cold intake air, or a cold manifold can cause poor vaporization. As you learned in Chapter 12, thermostatic air cleaners and heated intake manifolds are ways in which the problems of a cold air-fuel mixture can be overcome. Since manifold vacuum creates a low-pressure area, fuel vaporizes more efficiently in the intake manifold. A poorly designed manifold will result in poor vaporization.

The throttle plate has a direct effect on distribution, since the angle of the throttle sends the mixture against one side of the intake manifold. This tends to feed some cylinders a rich mixture and other cylinders a lean mixture. Cylinders farther away from the carburetor may get less of the mixture than those nearest the carburetor. Engineers must consider the fuel distribution or metering requirements of an engine when they design carburetors and intake manifolds.

Venturi Vacuum: Low pressure in the venturi of a carburetor, caused by fast airflow through the venturi.

Carburetion Air-Fuel Ratio Requirements

A carburetor must serve the varying air-fuel ratio needs of an engine for different operating conditions.

During starting, an engine has low intake manifold vacuum and airflow velocity because the engine is turning slowly. Slow cranking speed and a cold engine combine to reduce fuel vaporization. With reduced vaporization, less gasoline reaches the combustion chamber, and the engine needs a richer air-fuel mixture for starting.

At idle, an engine also needs a rich air-fuel mixture. Manifold vacuum is high, but airflow velocity is low. The combined effects of these factors reduce vaporization. Also, some exhaust remains in the cylinders at idle, which dilutes the air-fuel mixture.

As a vehicle accelerates gradually at low speed, engine speed and airflow increase, while vacuum rises in the carburetor. The engine gradually needs a leaner air-fuel mixture for smooth acceleration and economy with low emissions.

At steady cruising speeds with a light engine load, the engine needs a relatively lean air-fuel ratio of 15 or 16 to 1. At cruising speed, the engine operates at a relatively constant speed and load, with steady (relatively high) vacuum and airflow.

For extra power requirements, such as sudden acceleration, hill climbing, or full-throttle operation at any speed, the engine needs a richer air-fuel mixture. Air-fuel ratios of 12.5 to 13.5 allow an engine to develop maximum power for these conditions. Low vacuum accompanies full-power operation, and a carburetor must provide extra fuel with low airflow velocity for acceleration and low-speed, heavy-load conditions. Low vacuum and high airflow accompany high-speed, full-power operation, and a carburetor must respond to these needs as well. Air-fuel ratios for full power do not vary much except at low speed with low airflow velocity. Between the lean ratios of 15 or 16 to 1 and the rich ratios of 12.5 or 13.5 to 1, a modern carburetor must maintain the stoichiometric ratio of 14.7 for the best combination of power, economy, and emission control. These requirements are maintained on late-model vehicles by electronic controls and closed-loop feedback fuel systems.

All of these variable requirements for carburetor operation may seem overly complex at first. As you study the basic carburetor systems in the following sections, however, you will see how the systems react to engine conditions and meet all of the variable operating needs. Also, if you understand the engine requirements that a carburetor fulfills with its basic systems, you will understand the corresponding operations of fuel injection systems that are explained in Part 4 of this *Classroom Manual*.

BASIC CARBURETOR SYSTEMS

To mix fuel and regulate engine speed, the carburetor has a series of fixed and variable passages, jets, ports, and pumps which make up the fuel metering systems of circuits. There are seven basic systems common to all carburetors:
- Float system
- Idle system
- Low-speed system
- High-speed (main metering) system
- Power system
- Accelerator pump system
- Choke system.

Some engineers and technicians think of the idle and low-speed systems as two halves of a single system because the same carburetor passages are used for both. Whether you think of them as one system or two, the important points to understand are the operations that provide a smooth transition from idle to main metering fuel flow.

Float System

Gasoline from the fuel tank is delivered by the fuel pump to the carburetor fuel bowl, where it is stored for use. Once in the fuel bowl, the gasoline must be kept at a precise, nearly constant level. This level is critical, since it determines the fuel level in all the other passages and circuits within the carburetor. A fuel level that is too high in the bowl will produce an air-fuel mixture that is too rich. A fuel level that is too low will produce an overly lean mixture. For this reason, fuel level is one of the most critical adjustments required by the carburetor.

The main fuel discharge nozzle for the high-speed system is connected directly to the bottom of the fuel bowl. Because liquids seek their own level in any container, the fuel level in the bowl and in the nozzle is the same. If the level is too high, too much fuel will be drawn into the high-speed system. If the fuel level is too low, too little fuel will be drawn in.

Fuel level is controlled by the float and the inlet needle valve, figure 13-7. As gasoline is drawn from the bowl, the float lowers in the remaining fuel. Fuel pump pressure then opens the needle valve and allows more fuel to enter the bowl. As the fuel level rises, so does the float, until it forces the inlet needle back against

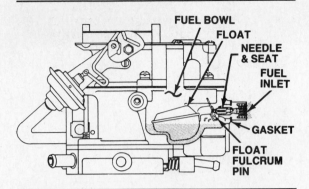

Figure 13-7. Fuel level in the fuel bowl is controlled by the float and needle valve acting against fuel pump pressure.

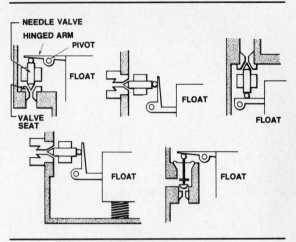

Figure 13-8. Float and needle valve designs vary with different carburetors.

its seat. This closes the inlet valve and shuts off both fuel pump flow and pressure to the carburetor bowl. During many operating conditions, fuel flow into and out of the fuel bowl is about equal. The needle stays in a partly open position to maintain the required flow rate.

The float and needle valve regulate fuel flow, as well as fuel level. Since the needle valve is like a door between the carburetor fuel bowl and the fuel pump, it maintains an air space above the fuel in the bowl. This reduces pressure on the fuel to atmospheric pressure. Atmospheric pressure is maintained in the fuel bowl by a vent or balance tube venting the bowl to the carburetor airhorn. Atmospheric pressure pushing down on the fuel in the bowl provides the pressure differential needed for precise fuel metering into the venturi vacuum area of the carburetor barrel. If the float and the needle valve do not maintain the correct fuel level in the bowl and too much fuel enters, the carburetor will flood.

Float and needle valve design and location in the fuel bowl vary with different carburetor designs, figure 13-8. Some floats have small springs to prevent them from bobbing up and down when the vehicle travels over rough roads. Many fuel bowls have baffles, which keep the fuel from sloshing on rough roads and sharp turns. The needle valves and their seats in older carburetors were usually made of stainless steel. The steel often attracted metallic particles in the fuel. These particles would collect between the needle and seat, allowing the valve to leak. The needles and seats in most modern carburetors are made of brass, and the needles have tips made of Viton or other plastics that conform to any rough spots on the seat and still provide a good seal when the valve is closed.

When the engine is shut off, engine heat causes the fuel in the bowl to evaporate. This was no problem in pre-emission control days, but with the installation of vapor canister systems, the amount of evaporation from a large fuel bowl can easily overload the canister. Therefore, emission carburetors use a somewhat smaller float bowl. Some carburetors, such as the Carter Thermoquad, use a molded plastic float bowl to reduce heat evaporation because plastic does not conduct heat as well as metal. Others use an insulator, figure 13-9, between the intake manifold and the carburetor to reduce heat.

Idle System

When an engine is idling, the throttle is open only slightly and airflow through the carburetor barrel and venturi is reduced. Since there is little or no venturi effect, no fuel flows from the

■ **A Tube Tip**

Sometimes while working on a carburetor that's still in the engine, you'll bust your knuckles trying to reach the idle mixture screws. Most mechanics know that one way to get at those screws is to use a length of rubber tubing. Slip it tightly over the idle screws to make the adjustments. Similar tubing, but with a bit larger inside diameter, can be used to loosen or tighten hard-to-get-at spark plugs.

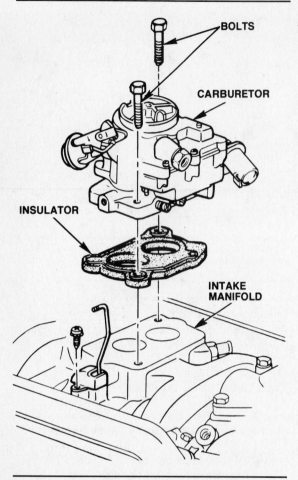

Figure 13-9. This insulator between the carburetor and the intake manifold reduces heat that causes fuel evaporation in the fuel bowl.

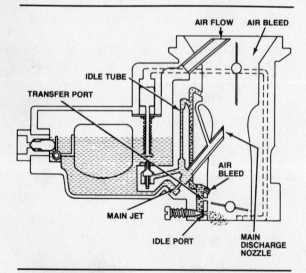

Figure 13-10. Air and fuel for the idle system are mixed inside the carburetor passages and delivered to the idle port below the throttle.

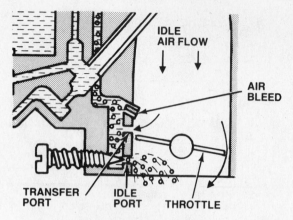

A. IDLE OPERATION

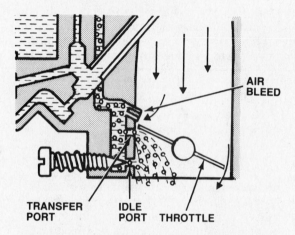

B. LOW SPEED (OFF-IDLE) OPERATION

Figure 13-11. At idle, air flows in through the transfer port to mix with the idle air-fuel mixture. As the throttle opens, flow reverses through the transfer port. Fuel and air now flow out for low-speed operation.

main discharge nozzle. The idle system, figure 13-10, supplies enough air and fuel to keep the engine running under these conditions.

Intake manifold vacuum is high at idle, so idle ports are located just below the closed throttle. The pressure differential between the fuel bowl and the vacuum at the idle ports forces fuel through the ports. Gasoline flows from the bowl, through the main jet, to the idle tube. Because the fuel must be well mixed with air for proper distribution, air bleeds in the idle tube let in air for the idle mixture. The air bleeds also prevent fuel **siphoning** at high speeds or when the engine is stopped.

Extra air for the idle air-fuel mixture can be provided in various ways. In many carburetors, the throttle valve does not close completely, but remains slightly open to let in a small amount of air, figure 13-11. A few designs draw air for

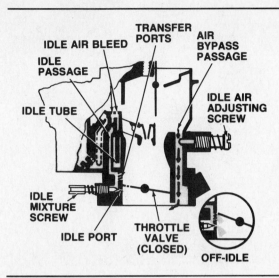

Figure 13-12. Air for the idle circuit in this carburetor passes through a bypass passage and is controlled by an idle air adjusting screw.

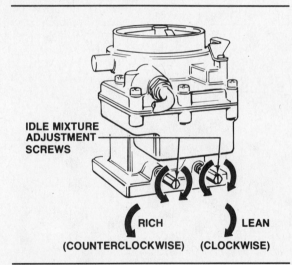

Figure 13-13. Idle mixture screws control the amount of gasoline in the air-fuel mixture.

the idle circuit through a separate air passage in the carburetor body called the idle air bypass, figure 13-12.

Additional small openings called transfer ports, figure 13-11, are located just above the closed throttle valve in the carburetor barrel. At idle, the transfer ports suck air from the barrel into the fuel flow in the idle system. A small amount of air and fuel is released just below the throttle valve. When the engine is under slight acceleration, the throttle valve opens a little and exposes the transfer port to manifold vacuum. This draws the fuel out into the barrel to mix with the air. We will discuss this more completely under the low-speed system.

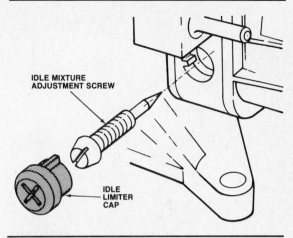

Figure 13-14. Idle limiter caps restrict the amount of adjustment allowed for the idle mixture.

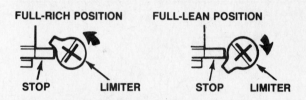

Figure 13-15. Limiter caps allow an adjustment of approximately one turn.

Adjustable needle valves called idle mixture screws, figure 13-13, control the amount of gasoline used in the idle air-fuel mixture. One adjustment screw generally is used for each primary barrel. The screw tips stick out into the idle system passages and are turned inward (clockwise) to create a lean mixture, or outward (counterclockwise) to enrich the mixture.

The idle mixture screws on carburetors used before emission controls could be adjusted from fully closed to fully open. Most carburetors built from the late 1960s to the late 1970s use plastic limiter caps, figure 13-14, on the idle mixture screws. These caps restrict the amount of adjustment to about one turn in or out, figure 13-15. This prevents excessively rich idle mixtures that contain large amounts of HC and CO. Limiter caps must be replaced whenever a carburetor is overhauled.

Regulations set by the Environmental Protection Agency (EPA) in 1979 required manufacturers to make carburetors tamperproof. To

Siphoning: The flowing of a liquid as a result of a pressure differential, without the aid of a mechanical pump.

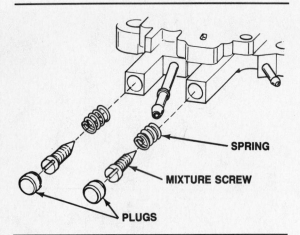

Figure 13-16. The idle mixture screws on late-model carburetors are adjusted and then sealed with plugs or caps. (Carter)

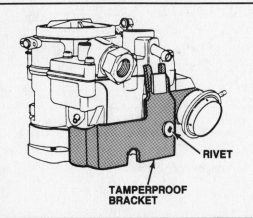

Figure 13-17. Tamper-resistant brackets are used on some carburetors to prevent unauthorized adjustment. (AC-Delco)

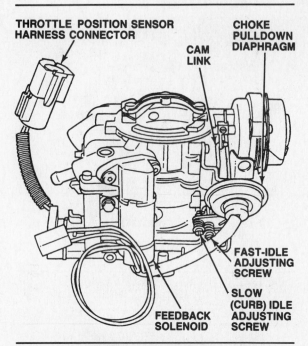

Figure 13-18. The slow (curb) idle screw regulates idle airflow and engine speed by changing the throttle position. (Ford)

Figure 13-19. The idle air bypass speed adjustment screw controls the airflow through a bypass passage to regulate idle speed.

do this, the idle air-fuel ratio of most carburetors made since 1979 is calibrated at the factory, and the mixture screws are covered with caps or plugs, figure 13-16. Other carburetors use a tamper-resistant bracket riveted in place, figure 13-17. The concealment caps, plugs, or brackets prevent any changes in the air-fuel ratio that would affect idle emission control.

Engine idle speed is adjusted by changing the amount of air going to the idle system. This idle speed adjustment is usually done with a screw that changes the position of the throttle valve in the carburetor, figure 13-18. Carburetors which use idle air bypass passages are adjusted by a large screw that varies the opening in the air passage to change the airflow, figure 13-19. Many late-model feedback carburetors used with electronic engine control systems

have an electric motor that controls idle speed and airflow as directed by the system microprocessor.

Low-Speed System

Once the throttle valve begins to open for low-speed operation, the engine needs more fuel than the idle port alone can provide. The airflow passing through the venturi is still not strong enough to develop fuel flow through the main discharge nozzle. To provide more fuel,

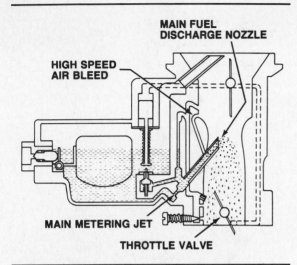

Figure 13-20. Fuel for the high-speed or main metering system flows through the main jet and out the fuel discharge nozzle in the venturi.

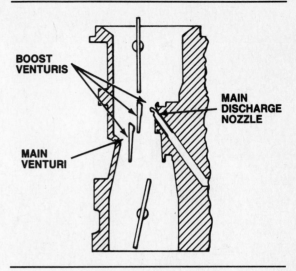

Figure 13-21. Most carburetors have multiple (boost) venturis for better air and fuel mixing.

the transfer port comes into operation as the low-speed system, figure 13-11.

The transfer port is located above the throttle at idle, and the air pressure there is about equal to atmospheric pressure. Air from the barrel flows *into* the transfer port to mix with the fuel going to the idle port. As the throttle opens, the transfer port is exposed to intake vacuum and the flow reverses. Extra fuel flows *out* of the transfer port to meet the engine's needs during the change from idle to low-speed operation. Fuel continues to flow from the idle port, but at a reduced rate. This permits an almost constant air-fuel mixture during this transition period. Some people consider the idle and the low-speed systems to be a single system because they use the same passages in the carburetor.

High-Speed (Main Metering) System

When the throttle valve opens wider, airflow increases through the carburetor. At the same time, the partial vacuum (low-pressure) area of the intake manifold moves up in the carburetor barrel. This airflow and pressure change strengthens the venturi. This is the high-speed or main metering system, figure 13-20.

For better mixing of the fuel and air, most carburetors have multiple, or boost, venturis placed one inside another, figure 13-21. The main discharge nozzle is located in the smallest venturi to increase the partial vacuum effect on the nozzle. Fuel flows from the bowl through

the main jet and main passage into the discharge nozzle. A high-speed air bleed, figure 13-20, mixes air into the fuel before it is discharged from the nozzle.

The primary or upper venturi produces vacuum, which causes the main discharge nozzle to spray fuel. The secondary venturi creates an air stream which holds the fuel away from the barrel walls where it would slow down and condense. The result is air turbulence, which causes better mixing and finer atomization of the fuel.

As the throttle continues to open wider, fuel flow from the low-speed system tapers off, while flow from the high-speed system increases. The engine's fuel needs are now supplied entirely by the main discharge nozzle during high-speed, light-load cruising.

Power System

The main high-speed system delivers the leanest air-fuel mixture of all the carburetor systems. When engine load increases during high-speed operation, the air-fuel mixture is too lean to deliver the power required by the engine. The extra fuel needed is provided instead by another system called the power system, or power valve. It supplements main metering fuel delivery. The power system or valve can be operated by vacuum or by mechanical linkage. The exact type differs according to carburetor design, but all provide a richer air-fuel mixture.

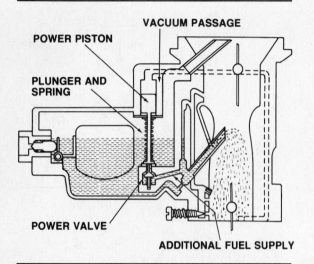

Figure 13-22. This power valve is operated by a vacuum-controlled piston and plunger. When vacuum decreases, the spring moves the plunger to open the power valve.

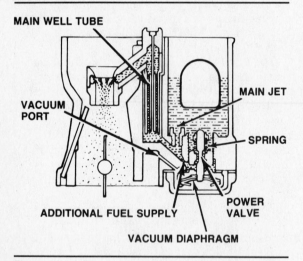

Figure 13-23. The vacuum diaphragm holds the power valve closed. When vacuum decreases, a spring opens the valve to allow more fuel into the main passage.

One type of power valve, figure 13-22, is located in the bottom of the fuel bowl with an opening to the main discharge tube. A spring holds a small poppet valve closed, while a vacuum piston holds a plunger above the valve. Since manifold vacuum decreases as the engine load increases, a large spring moves the plunger downward. This opens the valve and lets more fuel pass to the main discharge nozzle.

Another type of vacuum-operated power valve uses a diaphragm, figure 13-23. Manifold vacuum against the diaphragm holds the valve

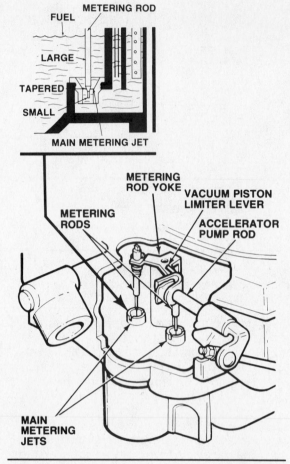

Figure 13-24. Some power systems consist of metering rods placed in the main jets. Mechanical or vacuum linkage moves the rods upward to allow more fuel to flow through the jets when required.

closed. As vacuum decreases under an increased load, a spring opens the valve. This sends more fuel through the power system and main discharge nozzle.

Metering rods also can be used as a power system, figure 13-24. These may be controlled by vacuum pistons and springs, or by mechanical linkage connected to the throttle. The ends of the rods installed in the main jet opening are tapered or stepped to increase the extra fuel gradually. The rods restrict the area of the main jets and reduce the amount of fuel that flows through them during light-load operation of the main metering system. Extra fuel for full-throttle power is provided by moving the rods out of the jets to increase the flow through the jets.

Vacuum-controlled metering rods, also called stepup rods, are held in the jets by manifold vacuum applied to pistons attached to the rods. When vacuum drops under heavy load,

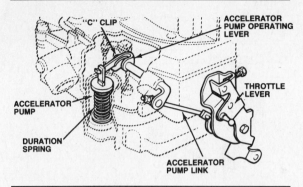

Figure 13-25. Typical plunger-type accelerator pump. (Ford)

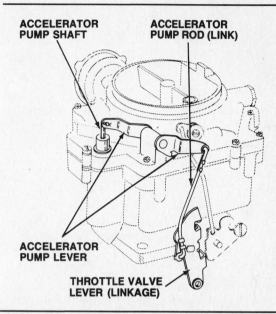

Figure 13-26. The accelerator pump linkage (lever and rod) is connected to the throttle linkage.

springs working against the pistons move the rods out of the jets. Mechanically operated metering rods are controlled directly by mechanical linkage connected to the throttle linkage.

Feedback carburetors used with electronic engine control systems generally do not have a separate power system. A mixture control (MC) solenoid operates the metering rods or air bleeds. When a richer mixture is required for additional power, the engine control microprocessor drives the solenoid to its full-rich position.

Accelerator Pump System

This system provides additional fuel for certain engine operating conditions. If the throttle is opened suddenly from a closed, or nearly closed, position, airflow increases faster than fuel flow from the main discharge nozzle. This "dumping" of air into the intake manifold reduces manifold vacuum suddenly and causes a lean air-fuel mixture. This excessively lean mixture results in a brief hesitation or stumble. This is sometimes called a **flat spot**. To keep the mixture rich enough, extra fuel must be provided by the accelerator pump.

The accelerator pump, figure 13-25, is a plunger or diaphragm in a separate chamber in the carburetor body. It is operated by a linkage connected to the carburetor throttle linkage, figure 13-26. When the throttle closes, the pump draws fuel into the chamber. An inlet check valve opens to allow fuel into the chamber, figure 13-27A, and an outlet check valve closes so

Flat Spot: The brief hesitation or stumble of an engine caused by a momentary overly lean air-fuel mixture due to the sudden opening of the throttle.

■ What's Next in Emission Controls?

When the first edition of this book was published in 1978, it made the statement, "emission control devices and systems now in use have been refined about as much as possible." At that time, we considered the thermal reactor to be the next big advance. Obviously, that could not have been further from the truth. Great changes in emission controls have taken place since that time, mainly the introduction and increasing sophistication of electronic engine control systems.

One major benefit of adding electronics to the automobile has been the elimination of emission control systems, such as spark timing controls, that were once considered permanent automotive features. The entire area of ignition timing, spark advance and retard has been taken over by the computer, which does such a precise job that the old control systems have disappeared. A look under the hood of a late-model car shows the engine compartment to be remarkably clean, compared with the extensive plumbing that "graced" the engines of cars current when this text was first published in 1978.

With fuel injection rapidly making the carburetor a quaint mixing device of the past, automakers have been able to introduce such precision in engine fuel management that heated intake air, air injection, and EGR systems have already disappeared from some engines and may be the next systems to go the way of spark timing controls. We may be going out on a limb again, as we did a decade ago, but it appears that the next trend in emission controls is simply fewer of them.

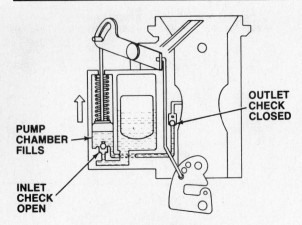

A. PUMP INTAKE STROKE

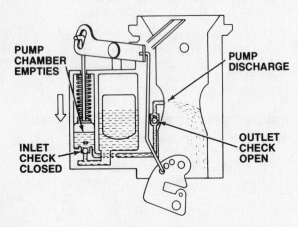

B. PUMP DISCHARGE STROKE

Figure 13-27. Accelerator pump operation.

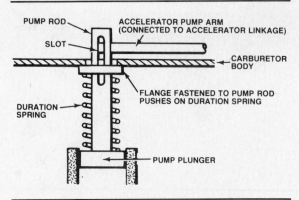

Figure 13-28. The duration spring provides uniform pump delivery regardless of the speed at which the throttle linkage moves.

that air will not be drawn through the pump nozzle. When the throttle is opened quickly, the pump moves down or inward to deliver fuel to the nozzle in the barrel, figure 13-27B. The pump outlet check opens, and the inlet check closes. The inlet check ball is usually (but not always) larger than the outlet check ball.

The pump outlet check may be a steel ball or a plunger. The inlet check may be a steel ball, a rubber diaphragm, or part of the pump plunger. Not all pumps have inlet checks. Some rely on an inlet slot in the pump well, or chamber, that is closed by the plunger on the downward stroke.

Most pump plungers or diaphragms are operated by a duration spring, figure 13-28. The throttle linkage holds the pump in the returned position. When the throttle opens, the linkage releases the pump and the spring moves the plunger for a steady and uniform fuel delivery. The accelerator pump operates during the first half of the throttle travel from the closed to the wide-open position.

During high-speed operation, the vacuum at the pump nozzle in the carburetor barrel may be strong enough to unseat the outlet check and siphon fuel from the pump. This is called pump pullover or siphoning. In a few carburetors, this extra fuel is included in the high-speed system adjustment. In most carburetors, air bleeds are placed in the pump discharge passages to prevent the siphoning. In still other carburetors, an extra weight is added to the outlet check to resist siphoning. The pump plungers in some carburetors have anti-siphon check valves.

Choke System

The choke provides a very rich mixture for starting a cold engine. This extra-rich mixture is needed because:
• Engine cranking speed is slow
• Airflow speed is slow
• Cold manifold walls cause gasoline to condense from the air-fuel mixture, and less vaporized fuel reaches the combustion chambers.

To make the mixture richer, a choke plate or a butterfly valve is positioned above the venturi in the carburetor barrel. This choke plate can be tilted at various angles to restrict the passage of air, figure 13-29. Cranking the engine with the choke plate closed creates a partial vacuum throughout the carburetor barrel below the plate. This airflow reduction and partial vacuum area work together to allow more fuel to be drawn into the mixture.

The choke plate can be controlled manually by a cable running to the driver's compartment, or automatically by a thermostatic coil spring. Chokes on most domestic carburetors since the early 1950s have been operated by a bimetal thermostatic coil spring. The choke plate shaft

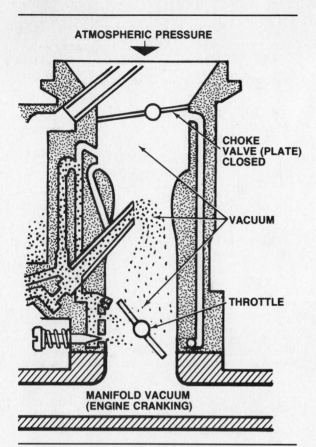

Figure 13-29. Vacuum is present throughout the carburetor barrel below the closed choke. This draws fuel from the idle, low-speed, and high-speed circuits for starting the engine.

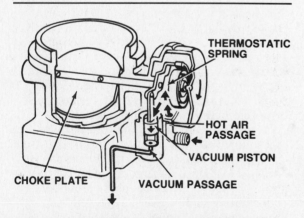

Figure 13-30. An older version of an integral or cap-type choke. The thermostatic bimetal spring is in a housing on the carburetor airhorn. A vacuum piston opens the choke when the engine starts.

is connected to the spring by linkage. The bimetal spring normally is located in one of two places:
1. In a round housing on the carburetor airhorn, figure 13-30. This is called an integral choke.

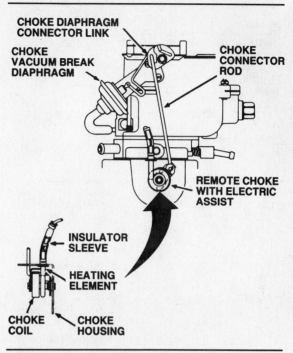

Figure 13-31. In a remote, or well-type choke, the thermostatic bimetal spring is in a heated well on the intake manifold. (Carter)

2. Off the carburetor in a well on the intake manifold, figure 13-31. This is called a remote, or well-type, choke.

Regardless of type and location, the thermostatic coil spring forces the choke closed when the engine is cold. Running the engine heats up the spring, which then opens the choke. With an integral choke, hot air from a source near the exhaust manifold, or hot coolant from the cooling system, may be routed to the choke housing to heat the spring. Remote chokes normally are heated by the exhaust routed through a crossover passage in the intake manifold. Most late-model integral and remote chokes have electric heating elements to heat the spring faster and speed the choke opening.

■ **Check for a Cold Carburetor**

Cold outside air can cause carburetors to freeze up, especially when low temperature combines with high humidity. This carburetor icing can, in turn, cause the choke valve to stick or bind in the carburetor. If you are servicing a car whose owner has complained about poor engine performance during cold weather, always be sure to check for carburetor icing. If it's your car, you can throw a blanket over the engine and carburetor when it is left to sit for a long time in cold weather.

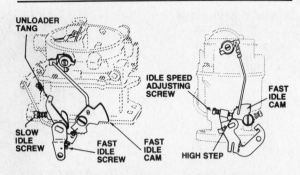

Figure 13-32. The fast-idle cam opens the throttle wider for faster engine speed when the choke is operating. It may work either on the slow-idle speed adjusting screw or on a separate fast-idle screw.

When a cold engine is cranked, the choke must be completely closed. As soon as the engine starts, the choke must open slightly to provide enough airflow. This is done in two ways. First, the choke plate shaft is offset in the carburetor so that airflow will tend to open the plate. Second, manifold vacuum is applied to a vacuum piston or a vacuum-break diaphragm that pulls the choke open a few degrees.

Integral chokes once had a vacuum piston built into the choke housing, figure 13-30, but this design had a tendency to stick. The emission-control requirement for precise choke operation resulted in nearly universal use of the vacuum-break diaphragm on emission carburetors. Most chokes have the vacuum-break diaphragm mounted on the side of the carburetor, figure 13-31.

A cold engine must idle faster than a warm engine, or the lack of air and fuel flow will cause it to stall. A fast-idle cam and screw, figure 13-32, provide enough air and fuel to prevent engine stalling. The cam is linked to the choke plate, and the screw is located on the throttle valve shaft. Depressing the accelerator pedal to start a cold engine allows the choke to close. This moves the fast-idle cam to allow the screw to rest against a high step of the cam. The cam may contact the normal slow-idle adjusting screw, or a separate fast-idle screw.

In both cases, the throttle is held open slightly more than for a normal slow idle, and idle speed increases between 400 and 800 rpm. As the engine gradually warms up, choke spring tension decreases and a weight pulls the fast-idle cam back, returning engine speed to idle rpm. On engines with computer control systems, a motor or a solenoid controlled by the system microprocessor often regulates fast-idle speed.

A mechanical link or choke unloader, figure 13-32, opens the choke about halfway when the

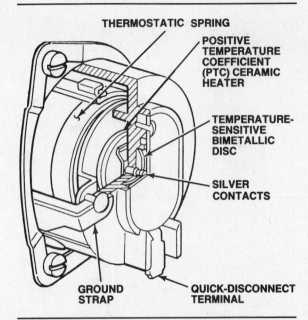

Figure 13-33. An electric choke cap contains a ceramic heater and bimetallic disc to heat the thermostatic spring and release the choke as fast as possible. (Ford)

throttle is fully open. If the engine is accidentally flooded during starting, this provides the extra airflow necessary to clear out the fuel.

Because the choke system provides a very rich mixture, it increases HC and CO emissions. To meet emission control standards, late-model engines must get off the choke as soon as possible. This is done in various ways, but the most common method used is the electric choke cap, figure 13-33. This contains a small heating element connected to the alternator, and a temperature-sensing switch. The switch lets the heating element warm the thermostatic coil spring and open the choke as quickly as possible. Depending upon their design, some carburetors may have 2- or 3-stage choke heaters to deliver specific amounts of heat according to ambient temperature.

The spring tension on older chokes can be adjusted to control the amount of choke closing and the rate at which it opens. Late-model choke housings, however, are sealed with breakaway screws, rivets, or brackets to prevent unauthorized choke adjustment that might change emissions, figure 13-34.

CARBURETOR TYPES

The operation of the basic carburetor systems has been explained in terms of a carburetor which uses a single barrel and throttle valve. But carburetors also are made with two or more barrels. Various carburetor types are used to

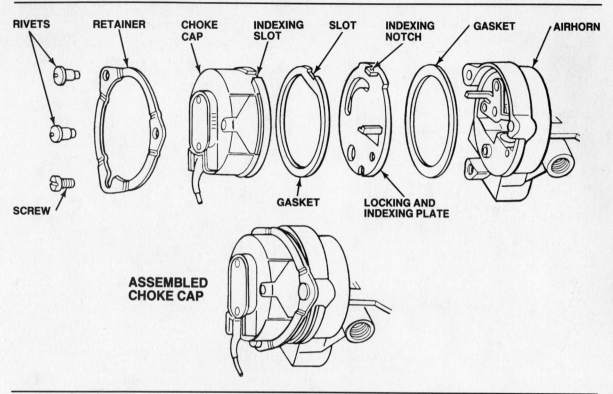

RIVETS   RETAINER   CHOKE   INDEXING   SLOT   INDEXING   GASKET   AIRHORN
                      CAP   SLOT   NOTCH

SCREW   GASKET   LOCKING AND
                                         INDEXING PLATE

ASSEMBLED
CHOKE CAP

Figure 13-34. Tamperproof carburetor design requires a sealed choke housing to prevent unauthorized adjustment. (Ford)

TWO VENTURIS

TWO BARRELS

TWO THROTTLE PLATES

Figure 13-35. A 2-barrel carburetor uses one airhorn but contains two venturis and throttle plates.

match fuel flow to engine requirements. Domestic engines all use downdraft carburetors; older imports often used sidedraft carburetor designs. Carburetors are usually classified by the number of barrels or venturis used. The differences are detailed below.

One-Barrel

The 1-barrel carburetor has a single outlet through which all systems feed to the intake manifold. This type of carburetor may also be known as a single-venturi design. These carburetors flow 150 to 300 cubic feet per minute (cfm) and generally are used on 4-cylinder and smaller 6-cylinder engines.

Single-Stage Two-Barrel

This carburetor design contains two barrels and two throttles which operate together, figure 13-35. Since the various fuel discharge passages in each barrel operate at the same time, it can be considered as two 1-barrel carburetors sharing the same body. The two throttle plates are mounted on the same shaft and operate together. The two barrels share a common float, choke, power system, and accelerator pump. Single-stage 2-barrel carburetors are used on

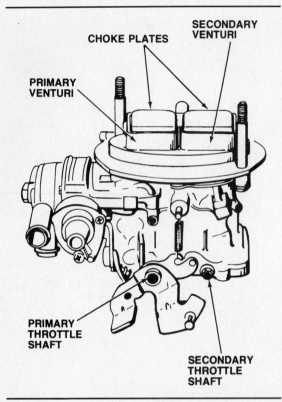

Figure 13-36. The 2-stage, 2-barrel carburetor has both primary and secondary throttles, which operate independently.

many 6- and 8-cylinder engines and generally have an airflow capacity of 200 to 550 cfm.

Two-Stage Two-Barrel

This carburetor design, figure 13-36, resulted from emission control requirements. It differs from the single-stage, 2-barrel design in that its two throttles operate independently. The primary barrel generally is smaller than the secondary, and handles engine requirements at low-to-moderate speeds and loads. The larger secondary opens when needed to handle heavier load requirements.

The primary stage usually includes the idle, accelerator pump, low-speed, main metering, and power systems. The secondary stage usually has a transfer, main metering, and power system. Both stages draw fuel from the same fuel bowl. Some designs use a common choke for both barrels. In others, only the primary stage is choked.

The 2-stage 2-barrel carburetor has an airflow capacity of 150 to 300 cfm and is used primarily on 4-cylinder and smaller 6-cylinder engines.

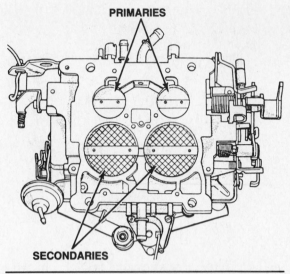

Figure 13-37. Most 4-barrel carburetors have primary and secondary systems that open progressively. (Chrysler)

Four-Barrel

Used primarily on V-8 engines, the 4-barrel, or quad, carburetor contains two primary and two secondary barrels in a single body, figure 13-37. The two primaries operate like a 1-stage 2-barrel at low-to-moderate engine speeds and loads. The secondary barrels open at about half to three-quarters throttle to provide the increased fuel and airflow required for high-speed operation. The primary barrels contain the idle, low-speed, and high-speed systems, as well as an accelerator pump and a power system. The secondary barrels have their own high-speed and power systems, and may use their own accelerator system. Some 4-barrel carburetors use separate fuel bowls and fuel supplies for the primary and secondary barrels; others work with a single fuel bowl and fuel supply for all four barrels.

Two methods are used to provide airflow through the secondary barrels: venturi action, figure 13-38, or air velocity valves, figure 13-39. Air velocity valves look like large choke plates located in the secondary barrels. They are opened by the low pressure created in the secondary barrels when the throttles are opened. Older Rochester and Carter 4-barrel carburetors may have auxiliary air velocity valves inside the secondary barrels. Airflow through the barrels opens the velocity valves; counterweights hold them closed when the throttles are closed. Late-model Rochester Quadrajet carburetors use vacuum diaphragms to modulate air valve movement. Venturis and air valves also may be

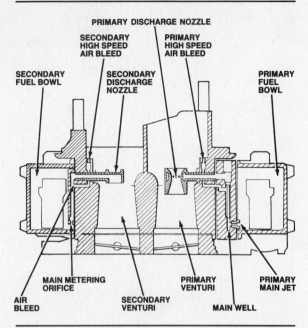

Figure 13-38. Venturi action controls airflow and fuel discharge through the secondary barrels of some 4-barrel carburetors. (Ford)

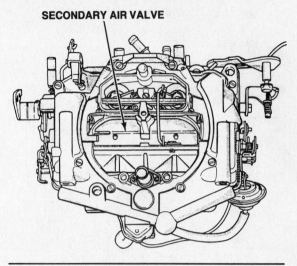

Figure 13-39. Air valves are used to control secondary airflow in many Rochester and Carter carburetors. (Chrysler)

combined in one carburetor to modulate the airflow through the barrels.

The primary barrels supply all eight cylinders during low-to-moderate speeds and loads. The secondary barrels provide additional fuel and airflow for high speeds and heavy loads. The 4-barrel carburetor flows from 400 to more than 900 cfm.

VARIABLE-VENTURI (CONSTANT DEPRESSION) CARBURETORS

As we have seen, carburetors meter fuel by using a venturi to create a partial vacuum in the barrel. Airflow through the venturi increases velocity, which decreases pressure. This pressure drop causes fuel to flow through the discharge nozzle into the barrel. Since both the carburetor barrel and venturi are fixed in size, the volume and velocity of air passing through will be correct for some operating conditions but not correct for others. To produce better performance under *all* operating conditions, auxiliary circuits such as the choke, power, and idle systems must be added to the main metering system.

A carburetor with a venturi whose size changes according to the demands of engine speed and load does not need these extra systems. At the same time, air-fuel mixtures can be controlled more closely for better fuel economy and emission control. Changing the size of the venturi relative to engine speed and load

results in an even pressure drop across the venturi under all operating conditions. This gives a variable-venturi carburetor its other name: a ''constant depression'' carburetor.

Variable-venturi carburetors, such as those manufactured by SU, Solex, Hitachi, and Stromberg, were used on some imported cars for many years. In 1977, Ford Motor Company introduced the Motorcraft 2700 VV, the first variable-venturi carburetor used on domestic cars in 45 years (Ford's first V-8 engines in 1932 had variable venturi, 1-barrel carburetors). This was followed by an electronically-controlled feedback version of the same design, the 7200 VV.

The 2700 VV, figure 13-40, Ford's variable-venturi, 2-barrel carburetor, has a fuel inlet system with a replaceable filter in the inlet housing. Throttle plates and an accelerator pump also are used. However, the variable venturis and the different fuel metering systems make this carburetor unique.

The variable venturis are formed by two rectangular valve plates (actually a single casting) that slide back and forth across the tops of the two barrels. Movement is controlled by a spring-loaded vacuum diaphragm, regulated by a vacuum signal taken below the venturis (but above the throttle plates) in the carburetor barrels. As the throttle opens, the vacuum increases, opening the venturis and allowing more air to enter.

The front edge of each venturi valve has a tapered metering rod. Each rod moves in and out of a fixed main jet on the other side of the

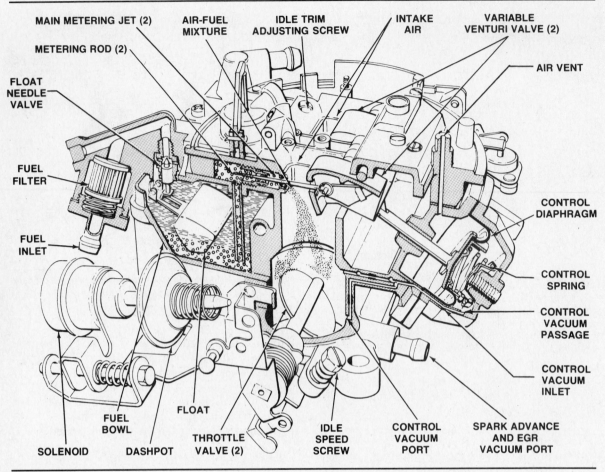

Figure 13-40. The Motorcraft 2700 VV variable-venturi carburetor uses vacuum to control the movement of the venturi valves. (Ford)

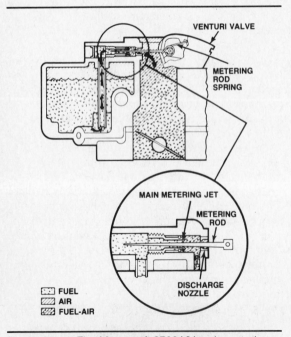

Figure 13-41. The Motorcraft 2700 VV main metering system. (Ford)

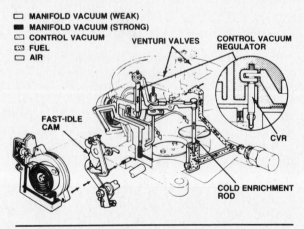

Figure 13-42. The Motorcraft 2700 VV cold enrichment system operation with a cold engine. (Ford)

barrel, figure 13-41. This arrangement meters fuel in proportion to the airflow through the venturis. Because of the variable venturis, this type of carburetor has fewer fuel metering systems than the fixed venturi design. However,

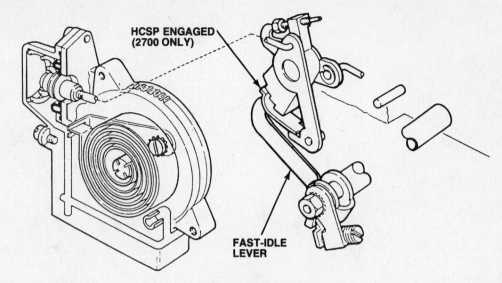

A. ENGINE OFF

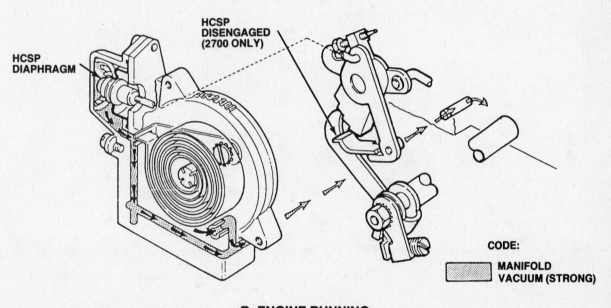

B. ENGINE RUNNING

Figure 13-43. Operation of the HCSP system on 1977-79 Motorcraft 2700 VV carburetors. (Ford)

the main metering system of the 2700 VV carburetor cannot handle all operating conditions without help from secondary systems. For example, at full throttle under heavy load, vacuum may not be strong enough to override the diaphragm spring. In this case, a limiter lever on the throttle shaft pushes the venturi valves fully open. Other auxiliary systems in this carburetor are the accelerator pump, idle trim, cranking enrichment, and cold enrichment systems.

The carburetor's design is innovative, but it requires extremely precise adjustments. A major redesign of some systems took place in 1980, with continuing refinements made through the mid-1980s, when the 2700 VV was discontinued and use of the 7200 VV was restricted to police vehicles.

Cold Enrichment System

The 2700 VV carburetor does not have a traditional choke. Instead, a bimetal thermostatic

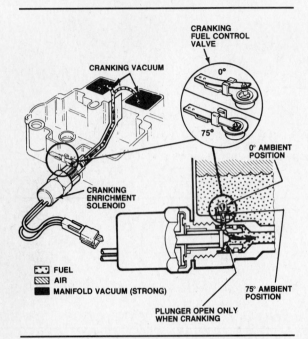

Figure 13-44. The cranking enrichment system used on 1977-79 Motorcraft 2700 VV carburetors. (Ford)

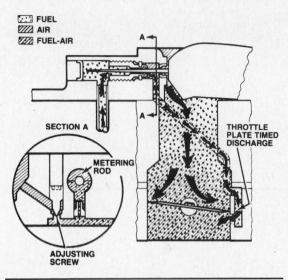

Figure 13-45. The Motorcraft 2700 VV idle trim system. (Ford)

choke control using an electric-assist heater manages the cold enrichment system, figure 13-42. This system contains a fast-idle cam, a cold enrichment auxiliary fuel passage and metering rod, and a control vacuum regulator rod.

A unique feature of the fast-idle cam on 1977-79 2700 VV models is a vacuum-operated high-cam-speed position (HCSP). When a cold engine is started, a lever slides between the fast-idle cam and the fast-idle lever to provide more throttle opening, figure 13-43A. When the engine starts, vacuum applied to the HCSP diaphragm retracts the lever, figure 13-43B.

When the engine is started below 95°F (35°C), the choke spring pushes the control vacuum regulator rod to block the ported control vacuum and send manifold vacuum to the venturi valve diaphragm. This opens the venturis wider than normal. The fast-idle cam is touched by the HCSP for a wider throttle opening. Redesign of the cranking enrichment system eliminated this system on 1980 and later carburetors.

Cranking Enrichment System

The cranking enrichment system also provides extra fuel only for starting a cold engine. On 1977-79 models, figure 13-44, it uses an electric solenoid energized by the ignition switch to open an auxiliary fuel passage. When the engine starts, the solenoid is deenergized and

closes the cranking fuel passage. When this happens, the main metering and cold enrichment systems maintain the fuel flow.

Redesign of the system on 1980 and later models eliminated the solenoid. The cranking enrichment system was changed to provide fuel enrichment both during cranking and cold engine running. This was done with a new linkage which provided an additional stroke for the cranking enrichment rod. The increase in rod travel supplies the additional enrichment fuel that was formerly delivered by the solenoid.

Idle Trim System

On early models, the idle fuel flow is controlled by the main jets, but an additional small amount of fuel is drawn by manifold vacuum through internal passages to discharge ports below the throttles. This is called the idle trim system, figure 13-45, and uses adjustable metering screws. The system was redesigned to eliminate the adjustable metering screws on 1978 carburetors.

CARBURETOR LINKAGE

Vehicle speed is controlled by the accelerator pedal which moves rods, cables, levers, and spring to operate the carburetor throttle valve. The throttle linkage on some vehicles is a combination of solid rods, levers, and links, figure 13-46. Other vehicles use a cable to link the accelerator to the carburetor throttle, figure 13-47.

Other kinds of linkage operate the accelerator pump, the automatic choke, the fast-idle

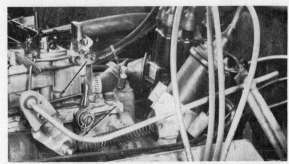

Figure 13-46. This throttle linkage is a combination of solid rods and levers.

Figure 13-47. A cable from the accelerator to the carburetor is used for this throttle linkage.

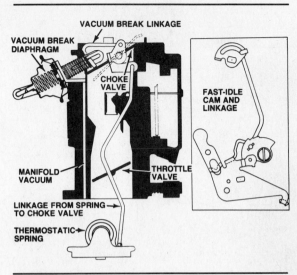

Figure 13-48. Several pieces of linkage are used on this choke system. (Chevrolet)

cam, secondary throttle valves, and the automatic transmission downshift points on some cars.

Accelerator Pump Linkage

The accelerator pump piston or plunger is connected to the throttle by a small rod, or rods, and levers. On some carburetors, the linkage holds the pump in the retracted position against a compressed duration spring. When the throttle opens all the way, the linkage releases the spring and the duration spring moves the pump piston through its stroke.

On some carburetors, the accelerator pump linkage also opens a vent for the fuel bowl when the throttle is closed. On other carburetors, the accelerator pump linkage operates a diaphragm to deliver fuel to the pump system. The accelerator pumps on yet other carburetors are operated directly by mechanical linkage. Pump operation may be balanced by a duration spring and a return spring.

Accelerator pump and linkage designs vary from carburetor to carburetor, but all work on these same principles. On most carburetors, the accelerator pump ends its stroke at the half-throttle position. From this point to the full-throttle position, the high-speed and the power systems can supply enough fuel. The pump linkage on some carburetors can be installed in two or three positions on the carburetor throttle linkage to provide different pump strokes.

Automatic Choke Linkage

Automatic chokes vary in design, but all require connecting linkage between the thermostatic spring that closes the valve and the vacuum piston or diaphragm that opens it. A remote or well-type choke with a vacuum-break diaphragm is shown in figure 13-48. The rod linkage from the spring to the choke valve closes the choke. The vacuum-break diaphragm opens the choke through its linkage as soon as the engine starts.

With most integral, piston-type chokes, the thermostatic spring acts directly on a lever on the end of the choke shaft inside the choke housing, figure 13-32. The vacuum piston also acts directly on this lever to open the choke when the engine starts. Some carburetors are built with an integral choke housing mounted away from the choke valve. This arrangement requires an external linkage rod from the thermostatic spring to the choke valve, as well as a separate vacuum-break diaphragm.

Fast-Idle Cam Linkage

The fast-idle cam is linked to the choke valve, figure 13-48, to provide a faster than normal idle and prevent stalling when the engine is cold. A fast-idle operating lever is attached to the choke shaft and connected to the fast-idle cam by a link. When the choke closes, the linkage turns the fast-idle cam so that a high step of the cam touches the idle speed adjusting screw or a separate fast-idle screw. As the choke opens, the fast-idle cam continues to follow the choke movement and reduces idle speed step

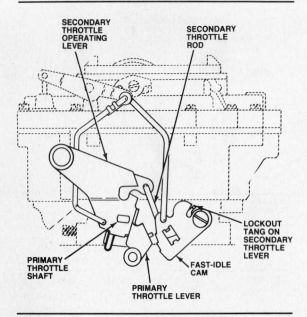

Figure 13-49. Mechanical secondary throttle linkage on a 4-barrel carburetor.

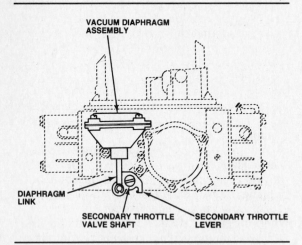

Figure 13-50. Vacuum-operated secondary throttle valves are controlled by a vacuum diaphragm.

by step. When the choke is fully open, gravity keeps the fast-idle cam away from the idle speed screw. However, when the engine is shut off, the idle speed screw blocks the cam and keeps it from turning back to the fast-idle position as long as the throttle is closed. This also keeps the choke thermostatic spring from closing the choke valve as the engine cools. To begin the choking operation with a cold engine, the accelerator must be depressed to release the fast-idle cam and linkage and allow the choke to close.

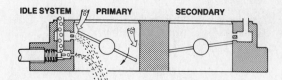

A. THROTTLE PLATES AT IDLE

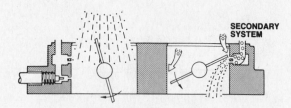

B. SECONDARY PROGRESSION AS THROTTLE IS OPENED

Figure 13-51. Secondary throttle valves are closed during low cruising speeds but open progressively as more fuel and air are required at higher speeds. (Ford)

Secondary Throttle Linkage

The secondary throttles of 4-barrel and 2-stage, 2-barrel carburetors may be operated by mechanical linkage or by vacuum. Secondary throttle valves operated by mechanical linkage have an operating rod to connect the primary throttle shaft to the secondary throttle shaft, figure 13-49. Secondary throttles begin to open when the primary throttles are about half open. The secondaries continue to open along with the primaries, but at a faster rate. The primary and secondary throttles then reach the fully open position at the same time.

On some carburetors, the primary and secondary throttle shafts are mechanically linked, but the secondary throttles are not visible through the carburetor airhorn. This type of carburetor has secondary air velocity valves, called auxiliary throttle valves, figure 13-39. These valves have offset shafts and counterweights so that they remain closed until air velocity through the carburetor barrels is strong enough to open them. These auxiliary throttle valves operate only when the mechanical secondary throttles are open, but they do not rely on the mechanical movement of the secondary throttles.

Vacuum-operated secondary throttle valves are controlled by a vacuum diaphragm mounted on the side of the carburetor, figure 13-50. At low cruising speeds, the secondary throttle valves are closed and the engine's air-fuel requirements are met by the primary half of the carburetor, figure 13-51A. At higher speeds,

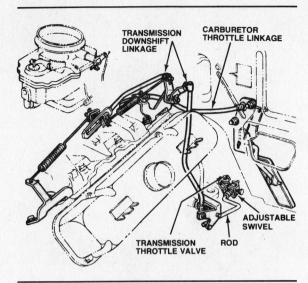

Figure 13-52. The secondary diaphragm responds to vacuum from ports within the carburetor barrels.

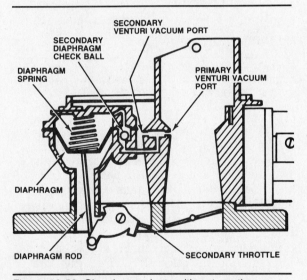

Figure 13-53. Chrysler products with automatic transmissions have mechanical linkage between the carburetor and transmission throttle valve to control shift points. (Chrysler).

when more fuel and air are needed, the secondary throttles are opened by linkage connected to the vacuum diaphragm, figure 13-51B.

The vacuum diaphragm responds to increasing vacuum within the primary venturi as engine airflow increases, figure 13-52. Linkage from the diaphragm opens the secondary throttles. Diaphragm action is changed by another vacuum port, or air bleed, in the secondary barrels.

The amount and rate at which the secondary throttles open are determined by the vacuum signal at the diaphragm. When the secondaries are closed, the air bleed in the secondary

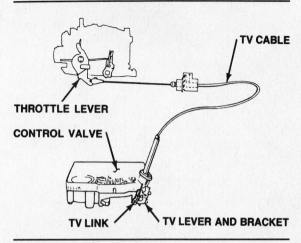

Figure 13-54. Some GM vehicles control automatic transmission shifting by a cable between the carburetor and the transmission throttle valve (TV). (Buick)

barrels weakens the vacuum signal at the diaphragm a set amount. As the secondaries open, the air bleed becomes a vacuum port as vacuum develops within the secondary barrels. This vacuum signal is then added to the vacuum from the port within the primary venturis to open the secondary throttles completely.

Sudden secondary throttle opening is prevented by a ball check valve in the vacuum chamber passage which allows a gradual vacuum buildup. As engine speed decreases, the weaker vacuum signal allows the diaphragm spring to close the secondary throttles.

All secondary throttle linkage, whether mechanically or vacuum operated, includes a secondary throttle or air valve lockout device to keep the secondary throttle from opening when the choke is closed, figure 13-49.

Transmission Linkage

Some vehicles with an automatic transmission or transaxle may use an adjustable throttle rod, figure 13-53, or a cable linkage, figure 13-54, between the transmission and the carburetor or throttle body. This controls shift points and shift quality. Other automatic transmissions do this with vacuum control.

CARBURETOR CIRCUIT VARIATIONS AND ASSIST DEVICES

Variations in the basic carburetor systems we just discussed are used by all automakers. One or more add-on devices also may be used to improve economy, driveability, and emission control. Those most commonly used are covered in the following sections.

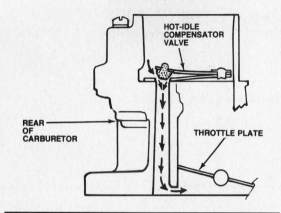

Figure 13-55. The hot-idle compensator is a thermostatic valve that opens at high temperature to admit more air to the idle circuit.

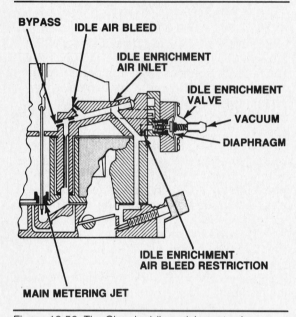

Figure 13-56. The Chrysler idle enrichment valve.

Hot-Idle Compensator Valves

High carburetor inlet air temperature causes gasoline to vaporize rapidly, which can cause an overly rich idle mixture. To prevent this, many carburetors use a hot-idle compensator valve, figure 13-55. The compensator is a thermostatic valve consisting of a bimetal spring, bracket, and small poppet. The compensator valve usually is located either in the carburetor barrel or in a chamber on the rear of the carburetor bowl. A dust cover is placed over the chamber. A third location (used primarily in Autolite 2-barrel carburetors on air-conditioned Ford vehicles of the late 1960s) is an external mounting in the PCV valve hose near the carburetor.

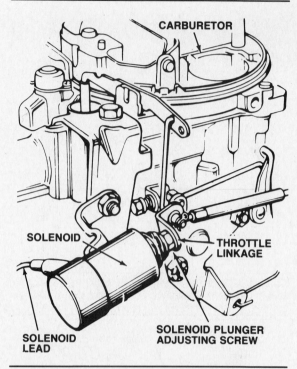

Figure 13-57. The throttle stop solenoid holds the throttle open for normal slow idle and allows the throttle to close farther when the engine is shut off.

The hot-idle compensator valve normally is closed by spring tension and engine vacuum. As temperature rises, the bimetal strip bends. This uncovers an auxiliary air passage or air bleed through which air enters the carburetor below the throttle plates. As this extra air mixes with excess fuel to lean out the idle mixture, it prevents stalling and rough idling. Once the carburetor temperature returns to normal, the compensator valve closes to shut off the extra air. If the valve does not close fully, it causes a high idle speed with high CO emissions.

Idle Enrichment Valves

Emissions carburetors run on leaner mixtures. For good cold-engine operation, the idle mixture must be enriched in some cases. Some 1975 and later carburetors used by Chrysler have an idle enrichment system. This system works opposite to a hot-idle compensator valve.

A small vacuum diaphragm mounted near the carburetor top, figure 13-56, controls idle circuit air. When control vacuum is applied, the diaphragm reduces idle system air. This increases fuel and reduces the air in the air-fuel mixture. Diaphragm vacuum is controlled by a

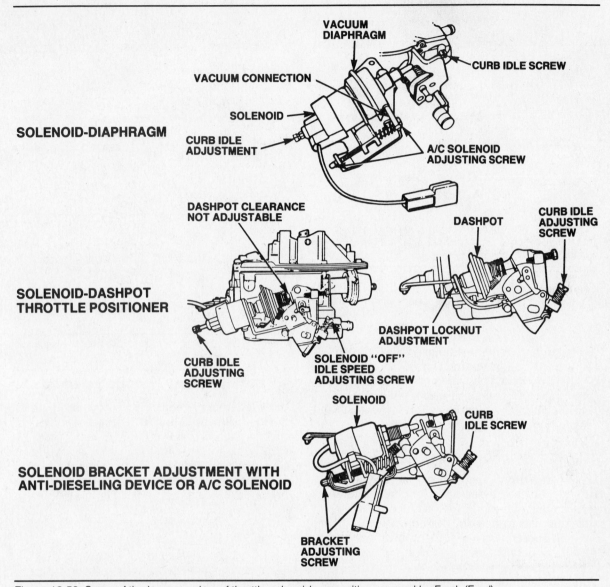

VACUUM DIAPHRAGM

CURB IDLE SCREW

VACUUM CONNECTION

SOLENOID

A/C SOLENOID ADJUSTING SCREW

SOLENOID-DIAPHRAGM

CURB IDLE ADJUSTMENT

DASHPOT CLEARANCE NOT ADJUSTABLE

CURB IDLE ADJUSTING SCREW

DASHPOT

SOLENOID-DASHPOT THROTTLE POSITIONER

DASHPOT LOCKNUT ADJUSTMENT

CURB IDLE ADJUSTING SCREW

SOLENOID "OFF" IDLE SPEED ADJUSTING SCREW

SOLENOID

CURB IDLE SCREW

SOLENOID BRACKET ADJUSTMENT WITH ANTI-DIESELING DEVICE OR A/C SOLENOID

BRACKET ADJUSTING SCREW

Figure 13-58. Some of the large number of throttle solenoids or positioners used by Ford. (Ford)

temperature switch in the radiator. As the engine warms, this switch stops the vacuum signal, returning the air-fuel mixture to its normal lean level.

Fast-Idle Pulloff (Choke Pulloff)

The rich air-fuel mixtures resulting from long periods of choke and fast idle can damage catalytic converters. Some converter-equipped GM cars use a fast-idle pulloff to avoid converter overheating. In one system, manifold vacuum acts on a vacuum-break diaphragm at the rear of the carburetor. This diaphragm will drop the fast idle cam to a lower step 35 seconds after engine coolant temperature reaches 70°F

(21°C). Vacuum to the diaphragm is controlled by a vacuum solenoid operated by a coolant temperature switch and delay timer.

Another system uses the front vacuum diaphragm to pull the throttle down one step on the fast-idle cam as soon as engine coolant temperature reaches 150°F (66°C). Vacuum to the diaphragm is controlled by a temperature vacuum switch.

A third method uses an electric solenoid instead of a vacuum diaphragm to open the choke. This pulls the fast-idle screw off the cam whenever the engine is started with the coolant below a specified temperature. A temperature switch on the engine and a firewall-mounted relay provide current for the pulloff solenoid.

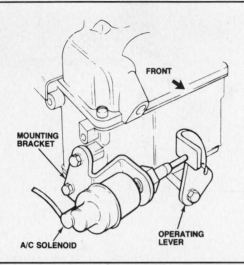

Figure 13-59. An air conditioning throttle solenoid opens the throttle slightly when the air conditioner is on. This maintains a uniform idle speed, even with the increased engine load.

Regardless of the system used, fast-idle pulloff has no effect on engine warmup during ordinary operation because normal throttle movement will disengage the fast-idle cam. The fast-idle pulloff system only operates when the engine is warming up while parked.

Throttle Stop Solenoids

Engine **dieseling**, or after-run, results when combustion chamber temperatures remain hot enough to ignite an idle air-fuel mixture after the ignition is turned off. Dieseling is caused by several aspects of late-model engines:
- Higher operating temperatures
- Faster idle speeds
- Retarded ignition timing at idle
- Lean air-fuel mixtures.

Closing the throttle more than it would close for the engine's normal slow idle speed will prevent dieseling. Shutting off airflow past the throttle valve closes the idle circuit.

A throttle stop solenoid, figure 13-57, provides the new stop position for the throttle during normal slow idle. Turning on the ignition energizes the solenoid, and its plunger moves out to contact the idle speed adjusting screw or a bracket on the throttle shaft. This holds the throttle open slightly for a normal slow idle until the ignition is shut off. The solenoid is then deenergized, its plunger retracts, and the throttle closes to block airflow.

Since a variety of different throttle solenoids or positioners have been used over the years, figure 13-58, you should check the manufacturer's adjustment procedures before attempting to service any throttle solenoid.

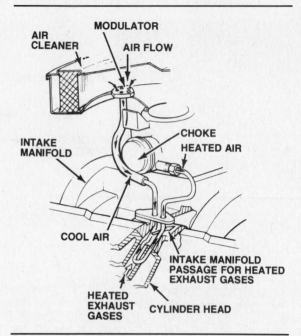

Figure 13-60. General Motors' choke hot air modulator.

Air Conditioning Throttle Solenoids

Many late-model vehicles with air conditioning may use a solenoid that looks exactly like a throttle solenoid, figure 13-59. In many cases, it is the same solenoid and may even carry the same part number. However, it should not be confused with the throttle stop solenoid just discussed, since it performs an entirely different function.

This solenoid is energized *only* through the air conditioner switch. Its plunger moves forward to contact a bracket on the throttle shaft *only* when the air conditioning is turned on. This maintains or slightly raises engine idle speed to prevent the engine from stalling due to the increased load. It also helps to prevent overheating from the air conditioning condenser heat load by speeding up the radiator fan.

Choke Hot Air Modulators

Some GM engines of the mid-1970s used a choke hot air modulator check valve (CHAM-CV) in the air cleaner, figure 13-60. The valve is closed at air cleaner temperatures below 68°F (20°C). Air that is to be heated by the heater coil passes through a tiny hole in the modulator. This restricts hot airflow over the bimetal thermostatic coil and results in a slower choke warmup. When air cleaner temperature rises above 68°F (20°C), the modulator opens to permit more airflow for a faster choke warmup.

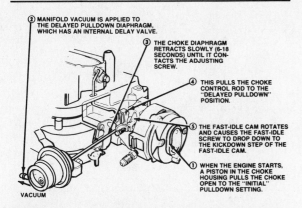

Figure 13-61. The delayed choke pulldown diaphragm provides rich initial choking, rapid choke release, and fast-idle modulation. (Ford)

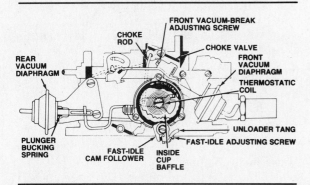

Figure 13-62. Temperature-controlled vacuum break used on some GM V-8 engines. (Pontiac)

Staged Choke Pulldowns

Found only on 1972 Ford engines, this system has a small double-chamber housing connected to the choke linkage at one end and to manifold vacuum at the other. A divider with an orifice separates the two chambers inside the housing. The chamber facing the carburetor contains a spring and silicone fluid; the other chamber holds a diaphragm and bimetal valve. The valve controls the application of manifold vacuum to the diaphragm. The orifice controls the time interval of choke opening and varies between 15 to 54 seconds, depending upon engine model.

Delayed Choke Pulldowns

A delayed choke pulldown operated by a vacuum diaphragm is used on some Motorcraft carburetors beginning in 1975. This opens the choke to a wider setting 6 to 18 seconds after the engine starts. As the pulldown diaphragm operates, the fast-idle screw is pulled from the

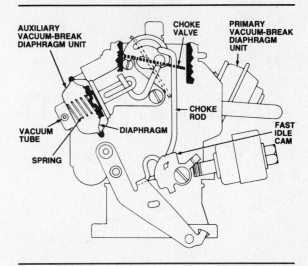

Figure 13-63. Temperature-controlled vacuum break used on some GM 6-cylinder engines. (Chevrolet)

top to the second step of the fast-idle cam to reduce cold-engine idle speed. Figure 13-61 shows the exact sequence of operation.

Temperature-Controlled Vacuum Breaks

Many Rochester carburetors since 1975 use two vacuum-break diaphragms to provide better mixture control by choking the engine more when it is cold and less when warm. Slightly different systems are used on GM V-8 engines, figure 13-62, and 6-cylinder engines, figure 13-63.

On V-8 engines, the primary (front) diaphragm opens the choke to keep the engine from stalling when first started. The secondary (rear) diaphragm opens the choke wider when air cleaner temperature exceeds 62°F (17°C). The rear diaphragm operates on manifold vacuum provided by a temperature vacuum valve on the air cleaner. The vacuum-break diaphragm has an inside restriction to delay diaphragm movement by several seconds.

On 6-cylinder engines, the primary diaphragm (choke coil side) opens the choke to keep the engine from stalling when first started. The auxiliary diaphragm (throttle lever side) opens the choke wider when engine coolant temperature exceeds 80°F (27°C). The auxiliary

Dieseling: A condition in which extreme heat in an engine's combustion chamber continues to ignite fuel after the ignition has been turned off.

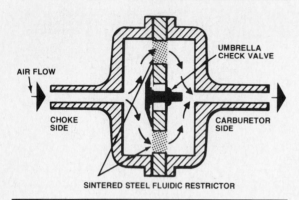

Figure 13-64. Ford's choke delay valve.

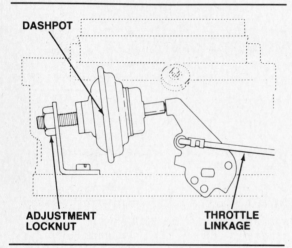

Figure 13-65. The dashpot slows throttle closing.

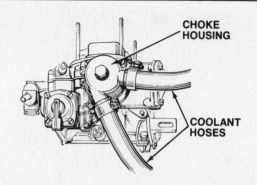

Figure 13-66. This type of hot-water heated choke routes engine coolant through the choke housing.

diaphragm operates on manifold vacuum provided by a two-nozzle temperature vacuum switch on the cylinder head.

Choke Delay Valves

Choke delay valves have various designs, but all delay the opening of the choke for a period of time to improve driveability and cold engine warmup.

Ford uses the same valve for choke delay, figure 13-64, that it uses for spark delay in the ignition system. The valves are color coded to indicate delay interval and can be used for either purpose. When used as a choke delay valve, it is installed in a hose between the intake manifold and the choke vacuum piston or diaphragm. The black side must face the vacuum source (manifold) and the colored side faces the choke.

GM uses an internal bleed check valve in the rear vacuum break diaphragm unit.

A slightly different system is used on some 2.5L (151-cid) 4-cylinder GM engines. The engine has a choke vacuum-break and a vacuum-delay valve. The valve delays manifold vacuum against the choke vacuum-break unit for about 40 seconds when starting the engine. If the engine stalls after being started, a relief feature in the valve permits immediate release of vacuum to let the choke close quickly.

Dashpots

These small chambers containing a spring-loaded diaphragm and plunger have been used for over 30 years. Before that hydraulic and magnetic dashpots were used.

As the throttle closes, a link from the throttle contacts the dashpot plunger, figure 13-65. As force is applied to the plunger, air slowly bleeds out of the diaphragm chamber through a small hole.

Dashpots originally were used to prevent an excessively rich mixture on deceleration which can cause stalling. They now function as emission control devices on late-model engines by reducing HC emissions on deceleration.

Choke Heaters

The need to keep exhaust emissions low means that choking the engine can only be done for a brief time. Prompt choke release can be done in several ways, all of which apply heat to the thermostatic coil spring to warm it up quickly.

Hot water choke

One way to apply heat to the thermostatic coil spring is by routing part of the engine coolant through the choke housing, figure 13-66. Once the engine reaches normal operating temperature, coolant heat helps release the choke. Older Ford models used an external coolant bypass hose held against the choke housing cap by a

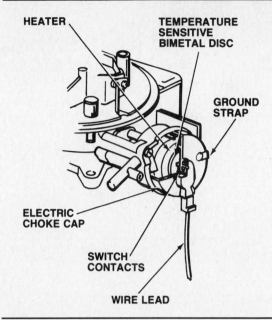

Figure 13-67. The Ford and AMC automatic choke electric heater.

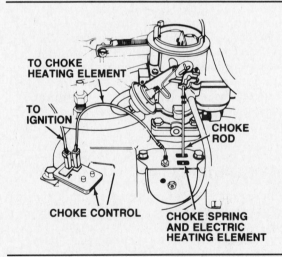

Figure 13-68. Chrysler's electric-assist choke.

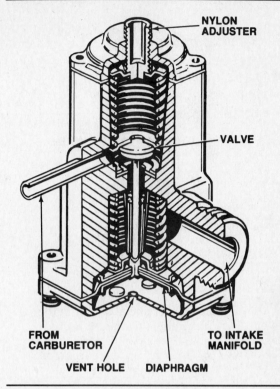

Figure 13-69. Fuel deceleration (decel) valve. (Ford)

the choke opening when underhood temperature is above about 60°F (16°C), by heating the choke bimetal thermostatic coil spring.

Ford and older AMC choke heater elements are located in the integral choke cap on the carburetor choke housing, figure 13-67. Electric current is supplied continuously from the alternator directly to the choke cover temperature-sensing switch. At underhood temperatures above 60° to 65°F (16° to 18°C), the switch closes to pass current to the choke heater. The circuit is grounded through a strap connected to the carburetor.

The Chrysler electric-assist choke heater is located in the intake manifold choke well and is regulated by a control switch which receives power from the ignition switch, figure 13-68. The control switch energizes the heater at temperatures above 63° to 68°F (17° to 20°C), and deenergizes it when the switch warms to between 110° and 130°F (43° to 54°C). A 2-stage heater control is used on some engines to provide three levels of heat, depending upon ambient temperature. The low heat level is provided by a resistor on the control switch.

Some GM engines from 1975 on use an electric choke heater. This 2-stage heater receives current from the engine oil pressure switch. Below specified air temperatures (usually 50° to

spring clip. This supplemented the exhaust manifold air passed through the choke housing.

Hot water chokes reduce over-choking when an engine is restarted. Since water holds heat longer than air, the choke coil will remain warm longer when exposed to heat from hot coolant. This reduces the amount of choking on a restart.

Electric-assist choke
Electrically assisted heater elements are used on almost all late-model engines. These speed up

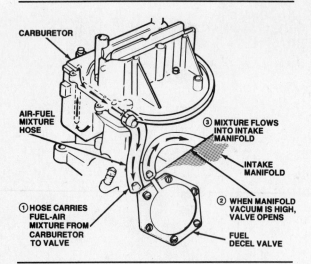

Figure 13-70. Decel valve operation. (Ford)

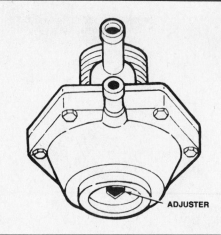

Figure 13-71. Ford's decel valve was redesigned in 1975 but its operation remained unchanged. (Ford)

70°F or 10° to 21°C), a bimetal sensor in the cover turns off current to the larger heater stage. Both stages operate at higher temperatures. This choke heater receives current as long as the engine is running.

Fuel Deceleration (Decel) Valves

The decel valve, figure 13-69, was used primarily by Ford on some 4-cylinder and V-6 engines during the 1970s to momentarily provide extra fuel and air during deceleration. Decel valves also have been used on some GM and imported-car engines. The valve prevents cylinders from misfiring during deceleration and sending an unburned charge of hydrocarbons through the exhaust. The extra air and fuel provided by the valve ensure complete combustion.

When the throttle is closed, increased manifold vacuum opens the valve diaphragm, figure 13-70. This, in turn, opens a passage between the carburetor and the manifold, allowing an additional air-fuel charge to enter the intake system. The extra air-fuel charge slows deceleration speed and reduces HC emissions. When vacuum drops, spring action and an air bleed to the diaphragm reseat the valve.

Some decel valves are adjustable. A nylon screw in the valve top, figure 13-69, can be adjusted to control the valve's opening time and duration. A round valve design, first used in 1974, figure 13-71, was not adjustable but was modified to permit adjustment on 1975 and later engines.

Deceleration Throttle Openers

This is a solenoid which holds the throttle open during deceleration to prevent excess fuel from being pulled through the idle system by high manifold vacuum. It is used on catalytic converter-equipped cars to prevent converter overheating. GM cars with the combination emission control (CEC) system use a throttle positioning solenoid that is energized on deceleration. Some Chrysler Corporation cars with converters have a solenoid to keep the throttle from closing completely at engine speeds above 2,000 rpm.

ALTITUDE-COMPENSATING CARBURETORS

Earlier in this chapter, you learned that atmospheric pressure is greatest at (or below) sea level. Suppose that you drive a car from a low elevation into an area where the elevation is 7,000 feet (2,134 meters). As the altitude increases, atmospheric pressure decreases and less air enters the carburetor. This means that the air-fuel mixture passing into the engine becomes richer as altitude increases. The result is poor driveability and high CO emissions at the higher elevation. For the driver who is only passing through high-elevation areas, the poor driveability is mainly a temporary inconvenience. But for driving at that elevation for an extended time, the car will run better if the engine is tuned for high elevation by leaning the air-fuel mixture.

However, if the retuned engine is driven back to lower elevations without once again adjusting the mixture, performance will suffer. As the car descends from the higher elevation to

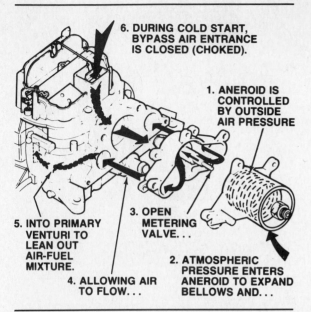

Figure 13-72. Motorcraft 2150 and 4350 automatic altitude compensator.

6. DURING COLD START, BYPASS AIR ENTRANCE IS CLOSED (CHOKED).

1. ANEROID IS CONTROLLED BY OUTSIDE AIR PRESSURE

3. OPEN METERING VALVE...

2. ATMOSPHERIC PRESSURE ENTERS ANEROID TO EXPAND BELLOWS AND...

5. INTO PRIMARY VENTURI TO LEAN OUT AIR-FUEL MIXTURE.

4. ALLOWING AIR TO FLOW...

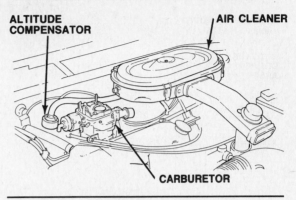

ALTITUDE COMPENSATOR

AIR CLEANER

CARBURETOR

Figure 13-73. Some Ford and Chrysler engines use remote altitude compensators to bleed air from the clean side of the air cleaner into the idle fuel system. (Ford)

sea level, the air-fuel mixture receives increasing amounts of air, leaning the mixture too much. If the engine is to operate properly at the lower elevation, it will have to be retuned to restore the proper air-fuel mixture. Unfortunately, it is not always possible or even desirable to tune the engine for such driving conditions. As a result, performance suffers, driveability is impaired, and emissions are excessive.

To maintain an appropriate air-fuel mixture while the car is driven in an altitude other than that for which it is adjusted, GM and Chrysler introduced the altitude compensating carburetor on some 1975 models. During the 1977 model year, the Environmental Protection Agency designated 167 counties in 10 western states (not including California) as high-altitude emission control areas. These counties are entirely above 4,000 feet (1,219 meters) in elevation. These high-altitude emission control requirements were suspended in 1978 but were reintroduced later in a modified form.

Because the major problem at high altitude is CO emission due to richer mixtures, the center of the special emission controls is the carburetor. Feedback carburetors used with electronic engine control systems continuously adjust the air-fuel ratio and automatically compensate for changes in atmospheric pressure, as we will see when we study them later in this chapter. But nonfeedback carburetors used in

high altitude areas require auxiliary systems or devices to provide more air or less fuel when operating at higher elevation than when operating at sea level. Most of the altitude-compensating systems are automatic, responding to changes in atmospheric pressure. There are, however, systems that require manual adjustment or operation.

Automatic Compensation

The most widely used altitude compensating device is the aneroid bellows. An aneroid bellows is an accordion-shaped bellows that responds to changes in atmospheric pressure by expanding and contracting. As pressure decreases at high altitude, the bellows expands.

The air bypass passage on Motorcraft 2150 and 4350 altitude carburetors has its own air intake and choke valve, figure 13-72. The aneroid bellows on these carburetors have adjusting screws and locknuts that appear to be for adjusting the tension on the bellows. However, these screws are for original factory adjustments only, and should not be changed while adjusting or overhauling the carburetor. The bellows and air valve can be removed for carburetor cleaning without upsetting the adjustment.

The altitude compensator used with Motorcraft 740 carburetors is a unit remotely mounted on the bulkhead, figure 13-73. It leans the mixture by drawing air from the clean side of the air cleaner filter and bleeding it into the primary and idle fuel systems at altitudes above 3,000 feet (914 meters). Chrysler uses a similar system with many late-model 4-cylinder engines.

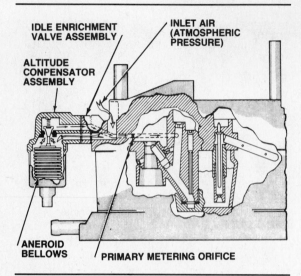

Figure 13-74. The Carter Thermo-Quad automatic altitude compensator. (Chrysler)

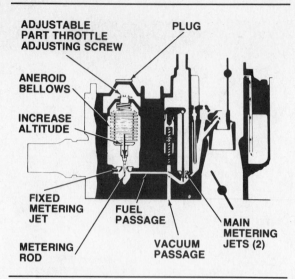

Figure 13-75. The Rochester Quadrajet automatic altitude compensator.

The altitude compensator on the Carter Thermo-Quad, figure 13-74, was introduced on 1975 models. It also is automatic and requires no service.

The aneroid bellows is also part of the Rochester M4MEA Quadrajet used on 1976 and later high-altitude engines. The aneroid bellows controls the position of the metering rods in the primary main jets, figure 13-75. At high altitude, the bellows expands and moves the rods into the jets to reduce fuel flow and keep the mixture from becoming excessively rich. This unit requires adjustment only when it is replaced.

Manual Compensation

The American Motors high altitude 6-cylinder engines from the mid- and late-1970s use a Carter YF 1-barrel carburetor with a manually adjusted auxiliary air bleed. The adjustment plug is located on the side of the airhorn near the fuel inlet.

Some Carter BBD 2-barrel carburetors also have manually adjusted air bleeds. The adjustment screw for this air bleed is inside the airhorn above the venturi clusters.

Holley 5200 2-stage, 2-barrel carburetors used on some 1977 Ford 2.3-liter engines have a driver-controlled fuel valve to compensate for altitude changes. Located in the carburetor base, the fuel valve is controlled by a 2-position lever (SEA LEVEL and ALTITUDE) mounted under the instrument panel. A cable and swivel linkage opens and closes the fuel valve. Under normal use, the system requires no adjustment.

FEEDBACK-CONTROLLED CARBURETORS

The first engine fuel management systems appeared in 1978 on California engines. Ford's feedback carburetor electronic control system (FCECS), figure 13-76, was used on 2.3-liter Pinto and Bobcat engines. The system contained a modified Holley 5200 carburetor (redesignated the Model 6500) in which the power and fuel enrichment pistons were replaced by a metering valve and diaphragm controlled by the system's electronic control unit (ECU). Other components were vacuum and temperature switches, a vacuum solenoid regulator, exhaust gas oxygen (EGO) sensor, and a dual-bed catalytic converter.

The system was called "feedback" because the EGO sensor installed in the exhaust manifold sent a voltage signal to the ECU indicating amount of oxygen in the exhaust. The ECU responded to this signal by cycling a vacuum solenoid regulator on and off. The solenoid in turn regulated vacuum to the feedback metering valve diaphragm which established the metering valve position, thus controlling the fuel flow into the carburetor's main well tube. This solenoid cycling action allowed the ECU to maintain the air-fuel ratio at approximately 14.7 to 1.

The GM electronic fuel control (EFC) system introduced on 1978 California engines contained similar parts and worked about the same to control the air-fuel ratio.

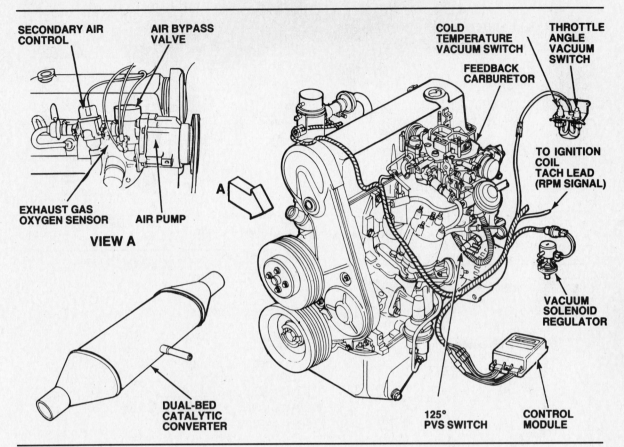

SECONDARY AIR CONTROL
AIR BYPASS VALVE
COLD TEMPERATURE VACUUM SWITCH
THROTTLE ANGLE VACUUM SWITCH
FEEDBACK CARBURETOR
TO IGNITION COIL TACH LEAD (RPM SIGNAL)
EXHAUST GAS OXYGEN SENSOR
AIR PUMP
VIEW A
A
VACUUM SOLENOID REGULATOR
DUAL-BED CATALYTIC CONVERTER
125° PVS SWITCH
CONTROL MODULE

Figure 13-76. Ford's first electronic fuel management system appeared in 1978. (Ford)

Principles of Operation

Electronic control of fuel metering involves the ability of the engine control computer to turn a solenoid on and off more rapidly than any mechanical device can. This solenoid on-off sequence is called a cycle. The part of the time the solenoid is on is called the **duty cycle**. The solenoid can be designed to operate at any number of cycles per second. A complete cycle requires a specific length of time, but the duty cycle is a variable percentage of the complete cycle.

For example, a solenoid may operate 10 times per second. Each operating cycle is thus 1/10th of a second. But of that 1/10th second portion of the cycle, the solenoid may be on 10 percent of the time and off 90 percent, or on 90 percent of the time and off 10 percent, or any combination in between. This variable percentage of the complete cycle during which the solenoid is *on* is the solenoid's duty cycle.

The duty cycle is used by the engine control computer to precisely meter air (air bleed control) or fuel (fuel flow control) into the mixture according to the input it receives from the exhaust gas oxygen (EGO) sensor. The metering of air or fuel can be done by either a stepper motor or a solenoid. The EGO sensor tells the computer how much the mixture varies from the desired 14.7 ratio. The computer then signals the carburetor to correct its performance, if necessary.

This process is repeated many times per second, allowing the computer to fine-tune carburetor operation and the air-fuel mixture, according to engine speed and load conditions. This makes it possible for the catalytic converter to work effectively to reduce exhaust emissions. Since the carburetor constantly responds to information about its past performance (feedback information from the EGO sensor to the computer), it is called a feedback carburetor.

The computer does not control the air-fuel mixture under all conditions at all times through the duty cycle. For example, when the

Duty Cycle: The percentage of total time in one complete on-off cycle during which a solenoid is energized.

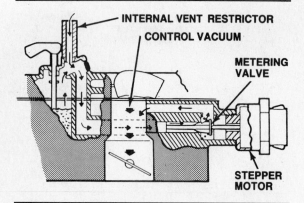

Figure 13-77. Early models of the Motorcraft 7200 VV carburetor use a stepper motor to vary air pressure on the fuel bowl.

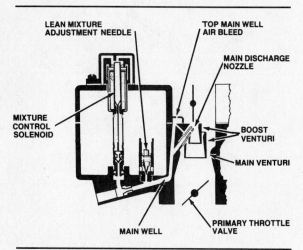

Figure 13-78. The mixture control solenoid in Rochester carburetors controls metering rod position. (Buick)

engine is first started, the fuel management system operates in an **open-loop** mode. This means that the computer ignores any signals from the EGO sensor and operates the stepper motor or solenoid with a programmed, fixed duty cycle. Various fixed duty cycles may be programmed into the computer for open-loop conditions, ranging from cold starts to hot wide-open throttle acceleration. When certain conditions are met, such as normal engine coolant temperature, the microprocessor switches system operation into the **closed-loop** mode. At this time, it evaluates the EGO sensor signals and varies the duty cycle of the stepper motor or solenoid to manage the air-fuel ratio. You will learn more about the operation of an engine management system in Part 4.

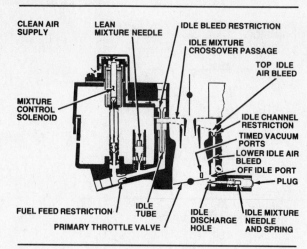

Figure 13-79. The same idle mixture solenoid may also control an idle air bleed passage. (Buick)

Stepper Motors

A **stepper motor** is used with some feedback carburetors. This dc motor moves in a specified number of incremental steps (usually 100 to 120) according to the voltage applied. Each step is tiny (approximately 0.004 inch or 0.1 mm), with motor speed varying from 12 to 100 steps per second.

The stepper motor is connected to tapered metering pins positioned either in air bleed orifices or in the main metering jets. When power is applied to the stepper motor, it moves the metering pins inward (rich position) to an end stop. This gives the engine control computer a stable reference. The stepper motor then backs the pins out to a position calculated to deliver a 14.7 to 1 air-fuel ratio and the computer takes over its operation. This is called initialization.

Stepper motors are used in early Motorcraft 7200 VV and some Carter carburetors. In the 7200 VV, the stepper motor moves a valve which lets control vacuum into the fuel bowl. Since this lowers the pressure above the fuel bowl, less fuel is pushed into the main metering system, figure 13-77. The result is a leaner air-fuel mixture. This design is sometimes called the "backsuction" system. The Carter carburetors use a stepper motor to position the metering pins in the air bleeds, controlling the amount of air in the air-fuel ratio.

Mixture Control Solenoids

Mixture control (MC) solenoids are used to control the air-fuel ratio in various ways, but all work on the variable duty cycle principle just

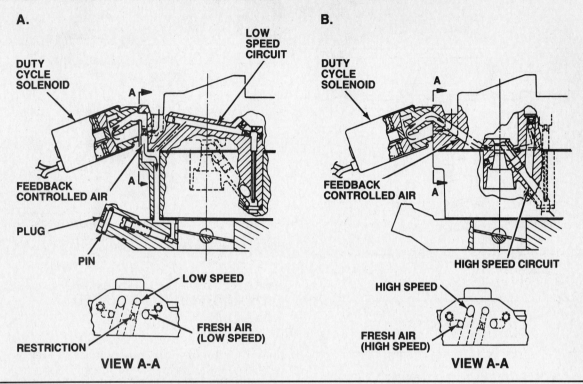

Figure 13-80. The Chrysler Thermo-Quad pulse solenoid opens and closes low-speed and high-speed air bleeds. (Chrysler)

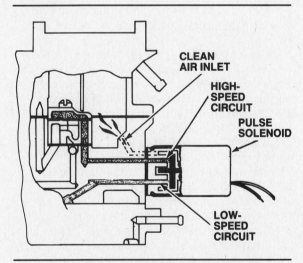

Figure 13-81. The Chrysler BBD pulse solenoid bleeds air to both the low- and high-speed circuits. (Carter)

discussed. The MC solenoid installed in Rochester carburetors regulates fuel flow directly by controlling a metering rod in the main jet, figure 13-78. The MC solenoid also controls a rod, figure 13-79, that opens and closes an idle air bleed.

Some Carter Thermo-Quad carburetors use the variable duty cycle of an MC solenoid to open and close the low-speed air bleed, figure 13-80A, and the high-speed air bleed, figure 13-80B. The Carter BBD carburetor uses a similar solenoid, figure 13-81, which bleeds air to both the low-speed and the high-speed circuits when energized, or shuts off air to both circuits when deenergized. Since solenoids used in this application are either on or off, they are called pulse solenoids.

Open-Loop: An operational mode in which the engine control microprocessor adjusts the system to function according to predetermined instructions and does not respond to feedback signals from the EGO sensor.

Closed-Loop: An operational mode in which the engine control microprocessor reads and responds to feedback signals from the EGO sensor, adjusting system operation accordingly.

Stepper Motor: A direct current motor that moves in incremental steps from deenergized to fully energized.

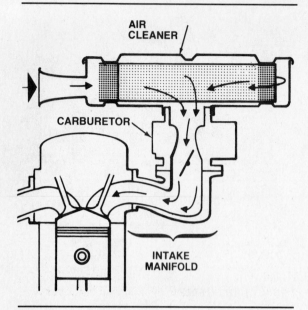

Figure 13-82. Intake manifold passages route the air-fuel mixture from the carburetor (or throttle body) to the intake valve ports.

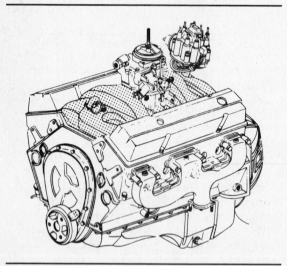

Figure 13-83. V-type engines normally have the intake manifold between the two banks of cylinders (shaded area in the illustration). (Chevrolet)

Vacuum Control Solenoids

Other carburetors may use an external solenoid that controls vacuum to an internal diaphragm in the carburetor. The internal diaphragm may regulate fuel flow by changing the position of the metering rods in the carburetor jets. It can also open and close air bleeds used in the idle and main metering circuits.

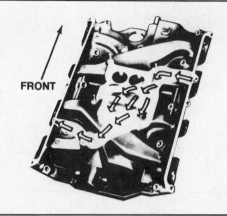

Figure 13-84. Exhaust gases are routed from ports in the cylinder heads through separate passages in the intake manifold to form the manifold hot spot. (Ford)

INTAKE MANIFOLDS AND CARBURETOR-TO-MANIFOLD RELATIONSHIP

The vaporized air-fuel mixture flowing through the carburetor or throttle body must be evenly distributed to each cylinder. The intake manifold does this with a series of carefully designed passages that connect the carburetor or throttle body with the engine's intake valve ports, figure 13-82. To do its job, the intake manifold must provide efficient vaporization and air-fuel delivery.

As you learned in Chapter 2, liquid gasoline is composed of various hydrocarbons which vaporize at different temperatures. If all of the hydrocarbons in gasoline vaporized at the same rate, the job of the intake manifold would be simple. But they do not, and so the intake manifold must be heated to keep the air-fuel mixture properly vaporized. This is done with exhaust manifold heat, engine coolant heat, or both, depending on engine design. Some engines also use electric grid heaters.

V-type engines have the intake manifold in the valley between the cylinder banks, figure 13-83. An exhaust crossover passage inside the manifold carries hot exhaust gases near the base of the carburetor or throttle body, figure 13-84. In a few manifolds, engine coolant is routed through the manifold near the carburetor or throttle body to heat the air-fuel mixture.

Most inline engines have both manifolds on the same side of the engine, with the intake manifold on top of the exhaust manifold, figure 13-85. A chamber between the two manifolds fills with exhaust gases and creates a hot spot to improve fuel vaporization in the intake manifold passages. Some inline engines use a "crossflow" design in which the two manifolds are mounted on opposite sides of the cylinder

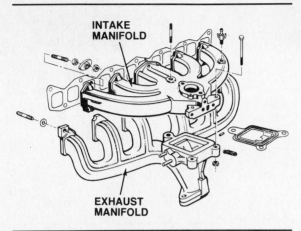

Figure 13-85. Most inline engines have both manifolds on one side of the engine. (Chrysler)

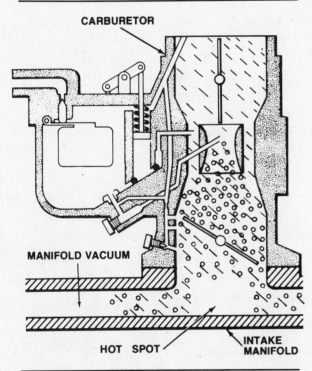

Figure 13-86. The angle of the carburetor throttle plate can affect the flow of the air-fuel mixture above the hot spot.

head. Coolant passages and a heat jacket on the intake manifold supply the heat.

Even with the help of heat from the exhaust manifold engine coolant, the air-fuel mixture usually does not completely vaporize in the intake manifold. This results in unequal mixture distribution among the cylinders, with some cylinders receiving more fuel and developing more power than others. This problem is greater during engine warmup, when less than normal heat is available to vaporize the fuel.

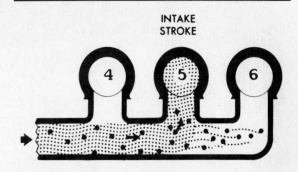

Figure 13-87. An intake manifold with large passages and sharp angles will cause liquid fuel to separate out of the air-fuel mixture. (Chevrolet)

Causes of Unequal Distribution

The air-fuel mixture reaching the engine cylinders may vary in amount and ratio for several reasons:

• The mixture flow is directed against one side of the manifold by the throttle valve in the carburetor or throttle body, figure 13-86. To some extent, the carburetor choke plate can influence flow in a similar manner.

• Lighter particles of the air-fuel mixture will turn corners in the manifold more easily, while heavier particles tend to continue in one direction, figure 13-87.

• Cylinders closer to the carburetor will receive a richer mixture than those farther away from the carburetor or throttle body. However, this can be minimized by careful carburetor or throttle body placement and good manifold design. Depending on manifold design, using a 2- or 4-barrel carburetor, or 2-bore throttle body, can improve mixture distribution, because each barrel or bore supplies fewer cylinders.

The efficiency of a manifold is determined by the shape, interior surface, and size of its passages. Passages, or manifold **runners**, should be as short as possible and without sharp corners, bends or turns to interfere with mixture flow. Smooth surfaces speed mixture flow. Rough surfaces aid vaporization by slowing down and breaking up mixture flow. Passages must be large enough in diameter to supply all cylinders with equal amounts of mixture, as passages that are too large or too small will slow down flow.

Runners: The passages or branches of an intake manifold that connect the manifold's plenum chamber to the engine's inlet ports.

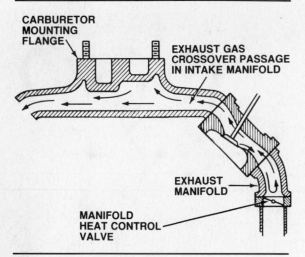

Figure 13-88. A thermostatic heat control valve or heat riser can be installed between the manifold and the exhaust pipe.

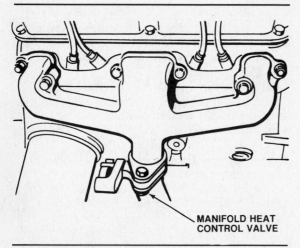

Figure 13-89. The heat control valve also can be within the manifold itself.

INTAKE MANIFOLD HEAT CONTROL

When the engine is cold, the incoming air-fuel mixture must be heated for complete vaporization. Hot exhaust gases are the most efficient heating source. A heat control valve, or heat riser, in the exhaust system routes a small part of the exhaust through passages in the intake manifold in order to provide the heat.

Heat control valves can be operated by:
• A thermostatic spring
• A vacuum diaphragm.
Each of these reacts to engine heat to control the valve operation, as you will see.

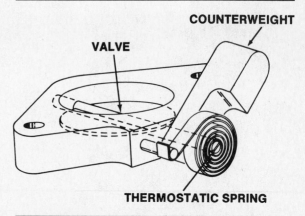

Figure 13-90. The manifold heat control valve can be operated by a thermostatic spring and a counterweight.

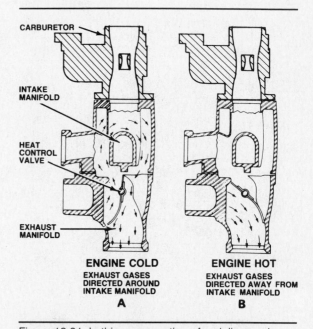

Figure 13-91. In this cross section of an inline engine manifold, the heat control valve forces the exhaust gases to flow either around the intake manifold (A), or directly out the exhaust system (B).

Thermostatic Heat Control Valve

Used by automakers for decades, the thermostatic heat control valve is located between the exhaust manifold and the exhaust pipe, figure 13-88, or in the manifold itself, figure 13-89. The valve is held closed by a thermostatic spring when the engine is cold, figure 13-90. This directs the hot exhaust gases around the intake manifold to preheat and help vaporize the air-fuel mixture, figure 13-91A. As the engine warms up, the thermostatic spring unwinds.

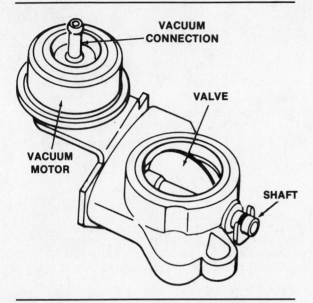

Figure 13-92. A vacuum-operated heat control valve.

The counterweight and the pressure of exhaust gas open the valve. Exhaust gases now pass directly out through the exhaust system, figure 13-91B.

The thermostatic heat control valve has a tendency to stick, because the exhaust gases rust and corrode it. If the valve sticks open, it can cause increased fuel consumption, poor performance during warmup, and excessive emissions because the choke remains on. If the valve sticks closed, it can cause poor acceleration, a lack of power, and poor high-speed performance.

Vacuum-Operated Heat Control Valve

GM and Ford introduced vacuum-operated manifold heat control valves, figure 13-92, on some 1975 engines. Chrysler followed in 1977 with vacuum-operated valves on its California V-8 engines. AMC remained with the thermostatic valves on all of its engines until the early 1980s. GM calls its device a vacuum-servo early fuel evaporation (EFE) valve; Ford's is called a vacuum-operated heat control valve (HCV); Chrysler's is a power heat control valve. All work in the same way to provide more precise control of the manifold heat and to reduce emissions while improving driveability.

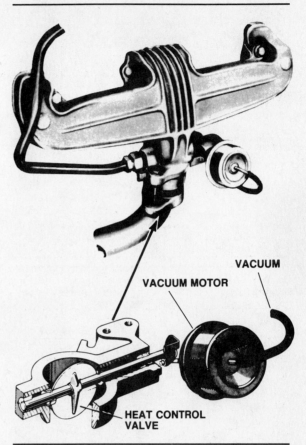

Figure 13-93. A vacuum-operated heat control valve installed in the exhaust manifold. (Chrysler)

A rotating flapper valve is contained in a cast iron body, figure 13-93. This valve body is installed between the manifold and the exhaust pipe. The valve shaft extends through the valve body and is linked to a diaphragm in a vacuum motor. Intake manifold vacuum operates the vacuum diaphragm. The manifold vacuum source is controlled by a switch that reacts to either coolant temperature or to oil temperature. Ford, Chrysler, and some GM engines have a thermal vacuum switch (TVS) installed in the cooling system; GM's inline 6-cylinder engines of the late 1970s use an oil temperature switch.

When an engine is cold, vacuum is applied to the heat control valve diaphragm to close the valve. This directs exhaust gas through the intake manifold passage. As the engine reaches normal operating temperature, vacuum is shut

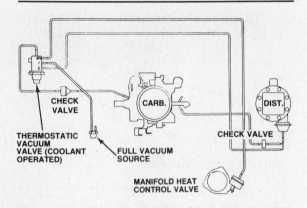

Figure 13-94. A vacuum diagram of the heat control valve installation. This valve responds to engine coolant temperature. (Buick)

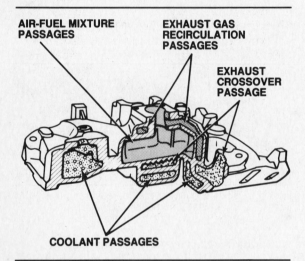

Figure 13-95. Hot engine coolant can also be used to pre-heat the air-fuel mixture. (Chrysler)

off from the valve. In systems using a thermostatic vacuum switch, the TVS closes when coolant temperature reaches a specified level, figure 13-94. This blocks vacuum from the valve. Where an oil temperature switch is used, the rising oil temperature opens a normally closed thermostatic switch. This opened switch deenergizes the vacuum solenoid, and a spring in the diaphragm opens the valve. Exhaust now flows through the exhaust system instead of bypassing to the intake manifold.

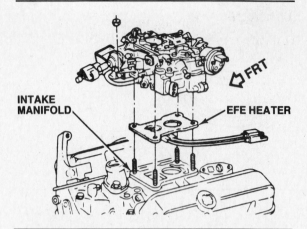

Figure 13-96. An electric heater grid can be installed between the carburetor and the intake manifold to improve cold engine driveability. (Buick)

Coolant-Heated Intake Manifolds

Engine exhaust is not always used to heat intake manifolds. In some designs, hot engine coolant circulating through passages in the intake manifold preheats the air-fuel mixture, figure 13-95. A thermostat shuts off coolant flow to remove manifold heat when the engine is at normal operating temperature.

Electric Grid Heaters

A rubber insulator containing a ceramic heater grid is installed between the carburetor and the intake manifold of many late-model engines to improve cold engine driveability, figure 13-96. GM also calls this device an early fuel evaporation (EFE) system.

The ceramic heater grid is underneath the primary throttle of the carburetor. When engine coolant is below a specified temperature, electrical current is sent to the grid by a TVS on noncomputer-controlled engines, or by the engine control computer through a relay on computer-controlled engines. The heater grid temperature is self-regulating at a calibrated value and remains on until the engine coolant reaches a specified temperature, at which time current to the grid is shut off.

SUMMARY

The carburetor is the all-important device that converts air and gasoline into an air-fuel mixture that can be burned in the cylinders. Carburetors must operate under all types of conditions and in all temperatures. Although there are dozens of carburetor designs available, all operate on the same basic principle of pressure differential. Pressure differential is the difference in air pressure between the relatively high pressure of the atmosphere outside the engine, and the low pressure of the carburetor and intake manifold. A partial vacuum is created by the downward stroke of the piston, which draws air in through the manifold and the carburetor.

For a carburetor to operate efficiently, the gasoline must be properly atomized, vaporized, and distributed to the cylinders through the intake manifold.

In spite of different designs, most carburetors have the same seven basic systems of passages, ports, jets, and pumps. Venturis, or restrictions, help speed the airflow through the throat, and throttle valves help control the rate of flow.

Most carburetors made since 1979 are of a tamperproof design in which the idle mixture and choke adjustment are set at the factory and sealed according to U.S. government regulations. This was done to prevent unauthorized adjustments that would affect emissions.

Many late-model carburetors are part of an electronic fuel management system. An exhaust gas oxygen (EGO) sensor in the exhaust manifold measures the oxygen content in the exhaust gas and signals the engine control computer. To maintain the desired 14.7 to 1 air-fuel ratio, the computer signals a mixture control (MC) solenoid or stepper motor in the carburetor to enrich or lean the mixture as required. Since they respond to this feedback information from the EGO sensor through the computer, they are called feedback carburetors.

Once the air-fuel charge leaves the carburetor, it enters the intake manifold on its way to the cylinders. Good manifold design is critical for smooth performance and low emissions required of today's engines. To promote better fuel vaporization, a heat control valve is used to route exhaust gases through the intake manifold while a cold engine warms up. Instead of exhaust gases, hot engine coolant may be routed through the manifold. Some late-model engines use an electric heater grid underneath the carburetor for this purpose.

Review Questions

Choose the single most correct answer.
Compare your answers with the correct answers on page 451.

1. Which of the following is *not* true
   of air pressure?
   a. It is measured in millimeters of
      mercury (mm Hg)
   b. It is measured in pounds per
      square inch (psi)
   c. It is always constant
   d. It results from the weight of air
      pressing on a surface

2. Air pressure:
   a. Increases with altitude
   b. Decreases with altitude
   c. Remains the same regardless
      of altitude
   d. Increases with warming
      temperature

3. A pressure differential is created
   between outside air and engine air
   by:
   a. An increase in cylinder volume
   b. A decrease in cylinder volume
   c. Air rushing through the
      carburetor
   d. The intake manifold

4. The restriction in an airflow tube or
   barrel is called:
   a. A throttle
   b. An air bleed
   c. A vaporizer
   d. A venturi

5. The air pressure along the sides of
   a barrel in which there is an airflow:
   a. Is higher than at the center of
      the flow
   b. Is higher than atmospheric or
      outside pressure
   c. Is lower than at the center of
      the flow
   d. Increases with airflow velocity

6. Ported vacuum:
   a. Is the low-pressure area in the
      carburetor just above the throt-
      tle valve
   b. Is the low pressure beneath
      the throttle valve
   c. Is the air pressure in the
      venturi
   d. Is equal to atmospheric
      pressure

7. At idle:
   a. Venturi vacuum is high
   b. Manifold vacuum is high
   c. Ported vacuum is high
   d. All of the above

8. Which is *not* a fuel-metering
   system?
   a. Float system
   b. Idle system
   c. Power system
   d. EEC system

9. The carburetor float controls fuel
   level:
   a. By closing the needle valve
      when the level is low
   b. By opening the needle valve
      when the level is high
   c. By closing the needle valve
      when the level is high
   d. All of the above

10. At engine idle:
    a. Venturi vacuum is high
    b. Fuel enters the carburetor bar-
       rel above the throttle
    c. Air is provided by an air bleed
       in the idle tube
    d. The throttle is one-third open

11. Which is *not* used to provide extra
    air at idle?
    a. The throttle valve
    b. The choke
    c. Transfer ports
    d. Idle air bypass

12. At low off-idle speeds, extra fuel is
    provided by:
    a. The transfer port
    b. The main nozzle
    c. The idle air bleed
    d. The idle air adjust screw

13. In a high-speed system, better fuel
    and air mixtures are obtained with:
    a. Transfer ports
    b. A single venturi
    c. Multiple venturis
    d. None of the above

14. Power circuits are operated by:
    a. Vacuum diaphragms
    b. Vacuum pistons
    c. Mechanical metering rods
    d. All of the above

15. Which is *not* part of the accelera-
    tor pump circuit?
    a. The metering rod
    b. The inlet check
    c. The outlet check
    d. The duration spring

16. Which carburetor circuit makes
    the fuel mixture richer when start-
    ing an engine?
    a. Power circuit
    b. Choke circuit
    c. High-speed circuit
    d. Accelerator pump circuit

17. The illustration below shows:

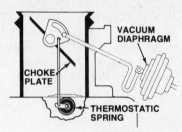

    a. A power valve diaphragm
    b. An integral choke
    c. A remote choke
    d. None of the above

18. Which of the following allows feed-
    back carburetors used with elec-
    tronic fuel management systems
    to compensate for changes in
    altitude?
    a. A remote compensator
    b. An aneroid bellows
    c. The microprocessor
    d. An EGO sensor

19. Feedback carburetors control fuel
    flow with some type of:
    a. Hot-idle compensator
    b. Mixture control solenoid
    c. Decel valve
    d. Aneroid bellows

20. The intake manifold is heated by:
    a. Exhaust manifold heat
    b. Engine coolant heat
    c. Both a and b
    d. Neither a nor b

21. Unequal distribution of the air-fuel
    mixture occurs because of:
    a. Fuel flow from the throttle
    b. Sharp turns in the manifold
    c. Distance of travel to the
       cylinders
    d. All of the above

22. Manifold heat control valves:
    a. Can be located between the
       carburetor and the intake
       manifold
    b. Can be located between the
       exhaust manifold and exhaust
       pipe
    c. Are open when the engine is
       cold
    d. None of the above

23. GM's thermostatic vacuum switch
    reacts to:
    a. Oil temperature
    b. Coolant temperature
    c. Exhaust gases
    d. The vacuum solenoid

PART FOUR

Electronic Engine Management

14

Electronic Fuel Metering Control

The arrival of electronic fuel metering resulted in a gradual modification of the traditional carburetor and how it worked. In more recent years, however, the carburetor has been largely replaced by fuel injection systems that are also electronically controlled.

In this chapter, you will learn about the basic components of an electronic fuel metering system, how the components interact, and how the early systems evolved. We will continue our study of electronic engine management in subsequent chapters dealing with electronic engine controls, fuel injection, supercharging, and turbocharging.

ELECTRONIC CONTROL SYSTEMS

To meet stringent emission control requirements in the early 1970s, automotive engineers began to apply electronic control to basic automotive systems. The use of electronics was first applied to ignition timing and later to fuel metering. Electronic control introduced a degree of precision that electromechanical and vacuum-operated systems could not achieve in matching fuel delivery and ignition timing with engine load and speed requirements. With electronic control came a significant decrease in emission levels, major improvements in driveability, and increased reliability of the systems.

Electronic ignitions appeared first, followed a few years later by electronic fuel metering systems which were quickly integrated with the electronic ignitions to form the early engine management systems. By the early 1980s, many automotive systems were controlled by an onboard computer.

To understand how electronic controls function, you must have an understanding of basic electricity and how a computer works.

Electrical Review

Because electronic fuel metering is based on the simple principles of electricity, we will begin with a review of basic electrical theory. You may have studied these principles in an automotive electrical and electronics class, and you were introduced to some basic electrical terms and ideas in Chapter 7. By reviewing basic electrical theory here, and then moving to a study of electronic engine control, you will see that the most complex computer systems are based on fundamental laws of science and engineering.

Electric current can be described by either the conventional theory or the electron theory, figure 14-1. Either theory can be used with

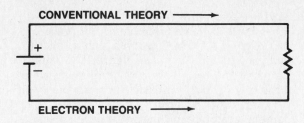

Figure 14-1. Two theories of current flow.

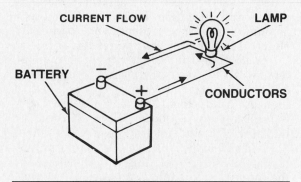

Figure 14-2. A simple circuit.

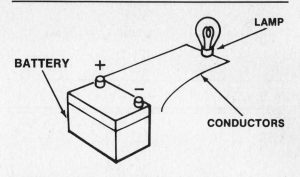

Figure 14-3. An incomplete (open) circuit.

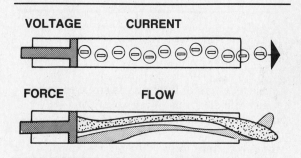

Figure 14-4. Voltage pushes current flow; force pushes water flow.

equal accuracy, as long as it is used consistently. When scientists first began to make discoveries about electricity, they thought it flowed from positive to negative. This became what we call the **conventional theory of current flow**. In the past, the conventional theory always was used to describe automobile electrical systems. It is still the more common method of describing those systems.

The **electron theory of current flow** states that current moves from negative to positive. This theory generally is used in electronic communications, computers, and all other areas of the electronics industry. In recent years, however, the electron flow theory also has been used to describe some automotive electronic control systems. Our review of current, voltage, and resistance in this chapter is based on the conventional current theory, unless stated otherwise.

Current, voltage, and resistance

An electrical current needs a path along which to flow. This path is called a circuit, which means circle. Any break in the circuit prevents current from flowing, since the electrons have nowhere to go.

One of the simplest circuits contains an energy source (battery), conductors (wires), and a load (lamp), figure 14-2. The current flows from the positive side, or terminal, of the battery through the wires meting the lamp, lighting

the lamp, and back to the negative terminal of the battery. If one wire is taken off the battery terminal, figure 14-3, the circuit is incomplete. Current will not flow, and the lamp will not light. Breaking the circuit by removing one wire from its terminal is the same as using a switch to break the circuit.

The rate of electric current flow is measured in amperes. Current through a conductor is comparable to water flowing through a pipe, figure 14-4. Water flow is measured by counting how many gallons or liters flow past a point within a certain time. When measuring electrical charges, electrons are counted instead of gallons or liters. When 6.28-billion electrons pass a point in one second, we say that one ampere, or amp, of current is flowing. Remember that current (amperes) flows *through* a circuit.

Conventional Theory of Current Flow: The current flow theory which says electricity flows from positive to negative. Also called positive current flow theory.

Electron Theory of Current Flow: The current flow theory which says electricity flows from negative to positive.

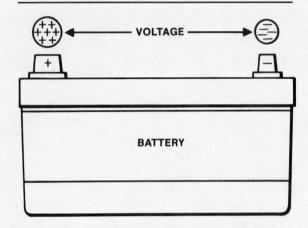

Figure 14-5. Voltage is a potential difference in electromotive force.

Current cannot flow unless some force pushes the electrons in one direction. This push is called electromotive force (emf) and is measured in units called volts. The force that causes a current to flow through a conductor is called voltage. It can be compared to the pressure that moves water through a pipe, figure 14-4. Voltage also is the measurement of a potential difference in force that exists between two points. One point may be negatively charged, and the other may be positively charged, figure 14-5, such as the two terminals of a battery. The strength of the force (voltage) depends on the strength of the charges at each point.

Voltage can exist even when there is no current, such as when one wire is disconnected from its battery terminal in a simple circuit. Voltage is present at the terminals of the battery in figure 14-5, but no current can flow without a complete circuit.

Voltage is required to force current through a conductor. All conductive materials oppose current flow to some extent. This opposition is called resistance. However, the resistance of an electrical device is more important than the resistance of a conductor. The lamp in figure 14-2 is an electrical device that has more resistance than the wire conductors. Other electrical devices, such as motors, radios, solenoids, or ignition coils, also offer resistance.

Resistance can be present in places other than the wires and devices of a circuit. A break in the circuit, such as in figure 14-3, creates infinite resistance. Loose or corroded connections also cause resistance to current. Remember that resistance exists *in* a circuit.

Resistance is measured by a unit called an ohm. There is an important relationship between volts (electromotive force), amperes (current), and ohms (resistance) that must be understood. When a force of *one volt* pushes *one ampere* of current through a circuit, the resistance present is *one ohm*, figure 14-4. This statement is an expression of Ohm's Law, one of the most important basic electrical rules.

Electricity travels through conductors. The filament of a bulb and the windings of a motor are both conductors. The electrical devices in a circuit, such as bulbs and motors, are also called "loads". These are the devices that do work — produce light, heat, or motion. The amount of resistance present in any part of an electrical circuit depends upon five factors:

1. *The atomic structure of the material* — Any material with few free electrons is a poor conductor, since resistance to current flow will be high. All conductors have some resistance, but the resistance of a good conductor is so small that a fraction of a volt will cause current flow.

2. *The length of the conductor* — Electrons in motion are constantly colliding with the atoms of the conductor. The longer a piece of wire, the farther the flow must travel. The more collisions that occur, the greater the resistance of a conductor.

3. *The cross-sectional area of the conductor* — The thinner a piece of wire is, the higher its resistance will be.

4. *The temperature of the conductor* — In most cases, the higher the temperature of the conducting material, the greater its resistance. That is why alternator regulators are tested at normal operating temperature for accurate readings.

5. *The condition of the conductor* — If a wire is partially cut, it will act almost as if the entire wire were of a smaller diameter, offering a high resistance at the damaged point. Loose or corroded connections have the same effect. High resistance at connections is a major cause of electrical problems.

Every electrical load in a circuit offers some resistance. This means that voltage is reduced as it moves the current through each load. Voltage is electrical energy, and as it moves current through a load, some of the electrical energy is changed to another form of energy, such as light, heat, or motion. The amount of voltage used to move current through each load is called the voltage drop across the load. If you measure the voltage drop at every load in a circuit and add the measurements, they will equal the original voltage available. Voltage does not disappear; the resistance of the load just changes it into a different form of energy.

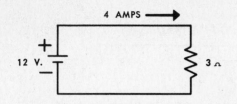

Figure 14-6. A simple series circuit.

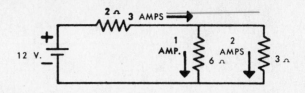

Figure 14-8. A series-parallel circuit. (Delco-Remy)

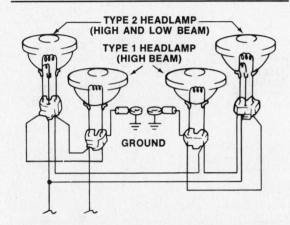

Figure 14-7. The headlamps are wired in parallel with each other in all headlamp circuits.

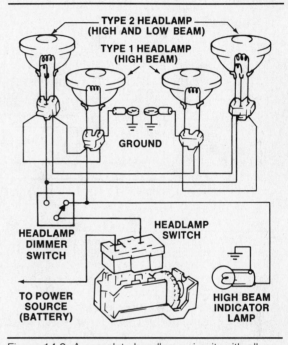

Figure 14-9. A complete headlamp circuit, with all bulbs and switches, is a series-parallel circuit.

The resistance of any electrical part (load or conductor) can be measured in three ways:
1. Direct measurement with an ohmmeter, which measures the ohms of resistance offered by the part.
2. Indirect measurement with a voltmeter, which measures the voltage drop through the part.
3. Indirect measurement with an ammeter, which measures the current through the part.

While voltage, current, and resistance are measured in different units, they are directly related. If you know the voltage drop and the current, the resistance and the current, or the resistance and the voltage drop, you can calculate the other factor using Ohm's Law.

Basic circuits

There are three basic types of circuits:
1. Series
2. Parallel
3. Series-parallel.
In a **series circuit**, the current has only one path to follow. Using conventional current flow theory, you can see that the current in figure 14-6 must flow from the battery, through the resistor, and back to the battery.

The circuit must be continuous (have continuity). If one wire is disconnected from the battery (no continuity), the circuit is broken and no current can flow. If electrical loads are wired in series, they must all be switched on and working, or the circuit will be broken and none of them will work.

In a **parallel circuit**, current can follow more than one path to complete the circuit. The points where current paths split and rejoin are called junction points. The separate paths which split and meet at junction points are called branch circuits or shunt circuits. Figure 14-7 shows a parallel circuit.

Series Circuit: A circuit with only one path for the current to follow.

Parallel Circuit: A circuit with more than one path for the current to follow.

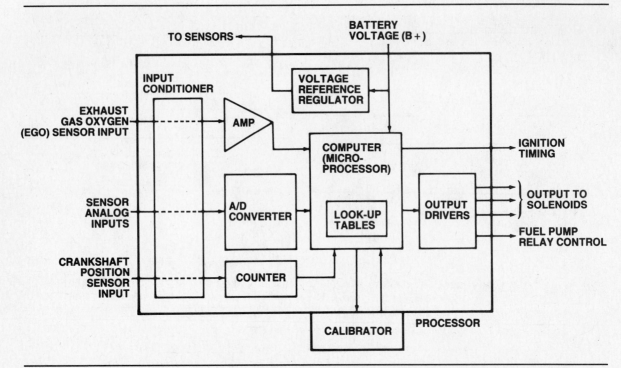

Figure 14-10. The internal components of an engine control computer that do the input, processing, storage, and output functions. (Ford)

As the name suggests, a **series-parallel circuit** combines the two types of circuits already discussed. Some of the loads are wired in series, but there are also some loads wired in parallel, figure 14-8. The entire headlamp circuit of an automobile is a series-parallel circuit, figure 14-9. The headlamps are in parallel with each other, but the switch is in series with the battery and with each lamp. Both lamps are controlled by the switch, but one lamp still will light if the other is burned out. Most of the circuits in an automobile electrical system are series-parallel.

COMPUTER CONTROL

A computer is simply a machine that receives information which it uses to make a series of decisions and then acts as a result of the decisions made. It cannot think on its own but does everything according to a detailed set of instructions called a program.

Computers use voltage to send and receive information. As we have learned, voltage is electrical pressure and does not flow through circuits. It causes current, which does the real work in an electrical circuit. However, voltage can be used as a signal. A computer converts input information or data into voltage signal combinations that represent number combinations. The number combinations can represent a wide variety of information — temperature, speed, or even words and letters. A computer processes the input voltage signals it receives by computing what they represent and delivering the data in computed or processed form.

The Four Basic Computer Functions

Regardless of the size or use to which it is put, the operation of every computer can be divided into four basic functions, figure 14-10:
1. Input
2. Processing
3. Storage
4. Output.
    These basic functions are not unique to computers; they can be found in many non-computerized systems. However, we need to know how the computer handles these functions.
1. The computer receives a voltage signal (*input*) from an input device. The device can be as simple as a button or a switch on an instrument panel, or a sensor on an automotive engine. Typical types of automotive sensors are shown in figure 14-11. The keyboard on your personal computer or the programming keyboard of a video cassette recorder are other examples of an input device.

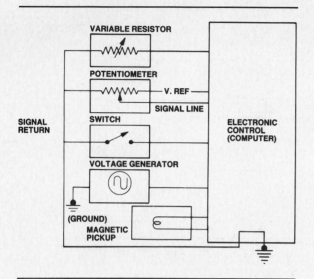

Figure 14-11. Five basic types of sensors send input data to an engine control computer. (Ford)

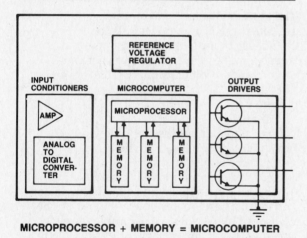

MICROPROCESSOR + MEMORY = MICROCOMPUTER

Figure 14-12. Input conditioners within the computer amplify weak voltage signals and convert analog signals to digital ones. (Ford)

Modern automobiles use various mechanical, electrical, and magnetic sensors to measure factors such as vehicle speed, engine rpm, air pressure, oxygen content of exhaust gas, airflow, and temperature. Each sensor transmits its information in the form of voltage signals. The computer receives these voltage signals, but before it can use them, the signals must undergo a process called **input conditioning**. This process includes amplifying voltage signals that are too small for the computer circuitry to handle. Input conditioners generally are located inside the computer, figure 14-12, but a few sensors have their own input conditioning circuitry.

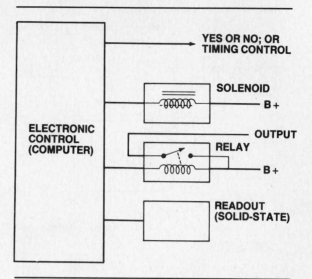

Figure 14-13. When the computer makes a decision, it signals an actuator which translates the voltage signal into mechanical action. (Ford)

2. Input voltage signals received by a computer are *processed* through a series of electronic logic circuits maintained in its programmed instructions. These logic circuits change the input voltage signals, or data, into output voltage signals, or commands.

3. The program instructions for a computer are *stored* in electronic memory. Some programs may require that certain input data be stored for later reference or future processing. In others, output commands may be delayed or stored before they are transmitted to devices elsewhere in the system. Computers use a number of different memory devices which we will look at later in this chapter.

4. After the computer has processed the input signals, it sends *output* voltage signals or commands to other devices in the system, such as a system actuator, figure 14-13. An **actuator** is an electrical or mechanical device that does the desired operation, such as adjusting engine idle speed, altering suspension height, or regulating fuel metering.

Series-Parallel Circuit: A circuit in which some loads are wired in series and some are wired in parallel.

Input Conditioning: The process of amplifying or converting a voltage signal into a form usable by the computer's central processing unit.

Actuator: An electrical or mechanical device that receives an output signal from a computer and does something in response to that signal.

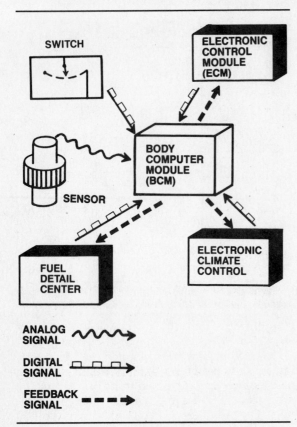

ANALOG SIGNAL

DIGITAL SIGNAL

FEEDBACK SIGNAL

Figure 14-14. Cadillac's BCM accepts inputs from a variety of sources and manages the other onboard computer systems. (General Motors)

Computers also can communicate with, and control, each other through their output and input functions. This means that the output signal from one computer system can be the input signal for another computer system. General Motors introduced a body computer module (BCM) on some 1986 models. This acts as a master control unit by managing a network containing all sensors, switches, and other vehicle computers, figure 14-14.

As an example, let's suppose the BCM sends an output signal to disengage the air conditioning compressor clutch. That same output signal can become an input signal to the electronic control module (ECM) that controls engine operation. Based on the signal from the BCM, the ECM signals an actuator to reduce engine speed to account for the decreased load of the compressor. This in turn affects the fuel metering system.

The four basic functions described above are common to all computers, regardless of size or purpose. They also form an organizational pattern to troubleshoot a malfunctioning system. While most input and output devices can be adjusted or repaired, the processing and storage functions can only be replaced.

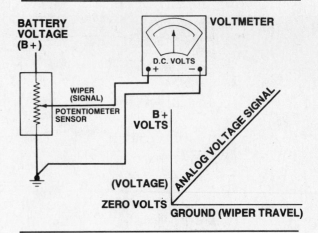

Figure 14-15. An analog signal is continuously variable. (Ford)

Analog and Digital Systems

A computer has to be told how to do its job. The instructions and data necessary to do this are called the program. Since a computer cannot read words, the information must be translated into a form the computer can understand — voltage signals. This can be done in two ways, using an analog or a digital system.

An **analog** computer is one in which the voltage signal or processing function is continuously variable, relative to the function being measured or the adjustment required, figure 14-15. Most operating conditions affecting an automobile, such as engine speed, are analog variables. These operating conditions can be measured by sensors. For example, engine speed does not change abruptly from idle to wide-open throttle. It varies in clearly defined, finite steps — 1,500 rpm, 1,501 rpm, 1,502 rpm, etc. — which can be measured. The same is true for temperature, fuel metering, airflow, vehicle speed, and other factors.

If a computer is to measure engine speed changes from 0 rpm through 6,500 rpm, it can be programmed to respond to an analog voltage that varies from 0 volts at 0 rpm to 6.5 volts at 6,500 rpm. Any analog signal between 0 and 6.5 volts will represent a proportional engine speed between 0 and 6,500 rpm.

Analog computers have several shortcomings, however. They are affected by temperature changes, supply voltage fluctuations, and signal interference. They also are slower in operation, more expensive to manufacture, and more limited in what they can do than digital computers.

In a **digital** computer, the voltage signal or processing function is a simple high/low, yes/

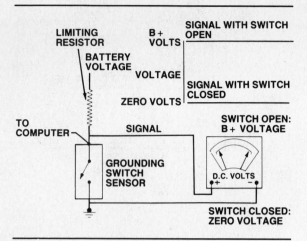

Figure 14-16. A digital signal is a simple on/off, or voltage/no voltage. (Ford)

no, on/off. The digital signal voltage is limited to two voltage levels. One is a positive voltage, the other is no voltage, figure 14-16. Since there is no stepped range of voltage or current in between, a digital binary signal is a square wave, figure 14-17.

Using our engine speed example above, suppose that the computer needs to know that engine speed is either above or below a specific level, say 1,800 rpm. Since it doesn't need to know the exact engine speed, but only whether it is above or below 1,800 rpm, the digital signal can be no voltage below 1,800 rpm and any arbitrary voltage when engine speed is above 1,800 rpm. As you can see, a digital signal acts like a simple switch to open and close a circuit, figure 14-16.

Analog: A voltage signal or processing action that is continuously variable relative to the operation being measured or controlled.

Digital: A 2-level voltage signal or processing function that is either on/off or high/low.

■ Digital Logic

All digital computers handle data bits with three basic logic circuits called logic gates: the NOT, AND, and OR gates. This terminology is used to describe circuit switching functions only — it has nothing to do with their physical construction. Logic gates are called gates because the circuits act as routes or gates for output voltage signals according to different input signal combinations. The thousands of field-effect transistors (FETs) in a microprocessor are logic gates.

A digital computer does its job by switching output voltage on and off according to the input voltage signals. When input voltage enters a logic gate, its transistors can change from a cutoff state (no voltage) to full saturation (voltage). This is equal to an off (low) signal and an on (high) signal. By combining input and output signals in logical combinations, they can be made to equal binary numbers.

The most elementary logic gate is called a NOT gate and inverts the signal. When voltage to its single input terminal is high or on, the output voltage is low or off.

The AND gate has two inputs and one output. Its output is high only if both inputs are high. If one or both inputs are low, output is low.

The OR gate has two or more inputs and one output. It differs from the AND gate in that output is high when one or more outputs are high. OR gate output is low when all inputs are low.

These gates can be combined to produce other logic functions. By placing an inverter or NOT gate after an AND or an OR gate, we can invert the signal and create a NAND (not AND) or a NOR (not OR gate).

NOT GATE		AND GATE			OR GATE		
INPUT A	OUTPUT C	INPUTS A	INPUTS B	OUTPUT C	INPUTS A	INPUTS B	OUTPUT C
1	0	0	0	0	0	0	0
0	1	0	1	0	0	1	1
		1	0	0	1	0	1
		1	1	1	1	1	1

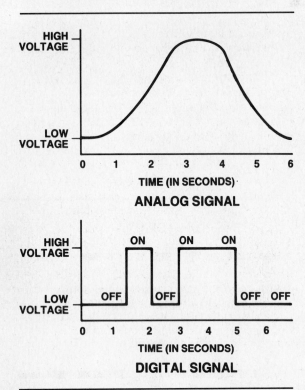

Figure 14-17. An analog signal takes the form of a sine wave; a digital signal is a square wave. (Ford)

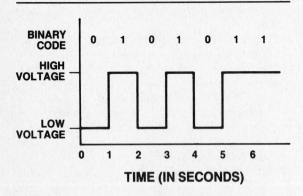

Figure 14-18. Digital computers receive information in a form called binary code. As shown here, a low-voltage signal is represented by 0; a high-voltage signal is 1. (Ford)

An engineer can reverse the switch functions to provide a high input signal below 1,800 rpm and a low (zero voltage) signal above 1,800 rpm. The result at the computer will be the same. The computer will get a simple digital input signal that represents a *change in operating conditions.*

The signal is called "digital" because the on and off signals are processed by the computer as the digits, or numbers, 0 and 1. The number system containing only these two digits is called the **binary** system. Any number or

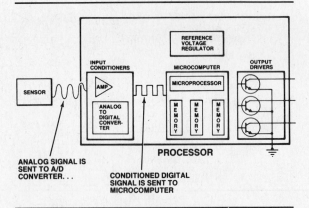

Figure 14-19. An analog signal must be "input conditioned" by a converter in the computer before the computer can deal with it. (Ford)

letter from any number system or language alphabet can be translated into a combination of binary 0s and 1s for the digital computer, figure 14-18.

A digital computer changes the analog input signals (voltage) to digital bits (BInary digiTS) of information through an **analog-to-digital (AD)** converter circuit, figure 14-19. The binary digital number, figure 14-20, is used by the computer in its calculations or logic networks. Output signals usually are digital signals that turn system actuators on and off. A digital signal can be changed to an analog output signal through a **digital-to-analog (DA)** converter. This is the opposite of the AD converter circuit that changes analog input signals. More often, however, a digital output signal is made to approximate an analog signal through a variable duty cycle, which you will learn more about later.

The digital computer can process thousands of digital signals per second because its circuits are able to switch voltage signals on and off in billionths of a second.

Binary Numbers

As we have just seen, digital computer switching circuits are characterized by being either off or on. This state can be represented by a 0 (off) or a 1 (on). For a digital computer to understand a command, it must be stated in a binary form — as zeros or ones. Since a binary number system represents all numbers as sequences of zeros or ones, off and on voltage signals can represent the 0 and 1 of the binary number system, figure 14-18.

Our decimal (base ten) system uses the numbers 0 through 9 written in a single column. When numbers above 9 are used, another column is added to the left — the ten's

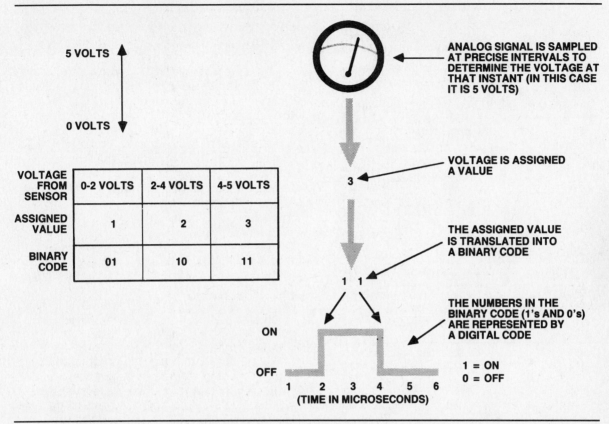

VOLTAGE FROM SENSOR	0-2 VOLTS	2-4 VOLTS	4-5 VOLTS
ASSIGNED VALUE	1	2	3
BINARY CODE	01	10	11

ANALOG SIGNAL IS SAMPLED AT PRECISE INTERVALS TO DETERMINE THE VOLTAGE AT THAT INSTANT (IN THIS CASE IT IS 5 VOLTS)

VOLTAGE IS ASSIGNED A VALUE

THE ASSIGNED VALUE IS TRANSLATED INTO A BINARY CODE

THE NUMBERS IN THE BINARY CODE (1's AND 0's) ARE REPRESENTED BY A DIGITAL CODE

1 = ON
0 = OFF

(TIME IN MICROSECONDS)

Figure 14-20. The process of analog-to-digital conversion performed by the converter section of the computer. (Ford)

position. Therefore, the number 10 is equal to one ten and zero ones. Each additional position to the left multiplies the number by ten, giving us powers of ten:

$$1 = 10^0$$
$$10 = 10^1$$
$$100 = 10^2$$
$$1000 = 10^3$$

Using the binary (base two) system, we group whole numbers from right to left, just as in the decimal system. However, since the system uses only two digits, the first one must equal either 0 or 1. Then to indicate the value of 2, we must use the second position (the *two's* position) and write it as 10, since it equals one two and zero ones. The next position, the hundred's position in base ten, is the *four's* position in base two. Each additional position to the left multiples the number by two, giving us powers of two:

$$1 = 2^0 \text{ (decimal 1)}$$
$$10 = 2^1 \text{ (decimal 2)}$$
$$100 = 2^2 \text{ (decimal 4)}$$
$$1000 = 2^3 \text{ (decimal 8)}$$

In the same way, we can change any decimal number to a binary number:

Decimal	Binary
3	11
4	100
5	101
6	110
7	111
8	1000
9	1001
10	1011

Binary: A mathematical system consisting of only two digits (0 and 1) which allows a digital computer to read and process input voltage signals.

Analog-to-Digital (AD): An electronic conversion process for changing analog voltage signals to digital voltage signals.

Digital-to-Analog (DA): An electronic conversion process for changing digital voltage signals to analog voltage signals.

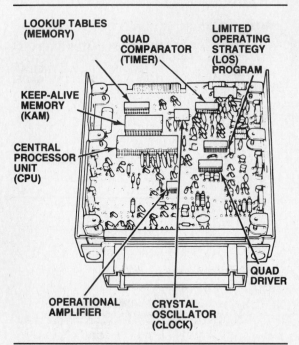

LOOKUP TABLES
(MEMORY)

QUAD
COMPARATOR
(TIMER)

LIMITED
OPERATING
STRATEGY
(LOS)
PROGRAM

KEEP-ALIVE
MEMORY
(KAM)

CENTRAL
PROCESSOR
UNIT
(CPU)

QUAD
DRIVER

OPERATIONAL
AMPLIFIER

CRYSTAL
OSCILLATOR
(CLOCK)

Figure 14-21. Some of the basic components of an engine control computer, housed in a metal box for protection. (Ford)

By translating decimals into their binary equivalents, we can tell the computer exactly what we wish it to do. With several thousand transistor circuits arranged in various series and parallel combinations inside the microprocessor, various combinations can switch on and off to equal any binary number in microseconds. You will never have to do this conversion, but understanding it gives you a better insight into how a digital computer works and how it can handle so much information in very short periods of time.

How does the computer know where one binary number (voltage pulse) ends and another one begins? How does it differentiate between a 01 and a 0011? A clock generator inside the computer provides constant pulses. Each pulse is the length of one bit. The computer monitors these clock pulses while reading or sending data. In this way, it knows how long each voltage pulse should last.

Analog-to-Digital Conversion

We mentioned earlier that most operating conditions which affect an automobile are analog variables. When our computer needs to know whether an operating condition is above or below a specified point, a digital sensor can be used to act as a simple off/on switch. Below the specified point, the switch is open. The computer receives no voltage signal until the

condition reaches the specified point, at which time the switch closes. This is an example of a simple digital off/on circuit: off = 0, on = 1.

Let's use engine coolant temperature as an example and specify that the computer needs to know the exact temperature within one degree. Suppose our sensor measures temperature from 0° to 300° and sends an analog signal that varies from 0 to 6 volts. Each 1-volt change in the sensor signal is the equivalent of a 50-degree change in temperature. If 0 volts equals a temperature of 0° and 6 volts equals 300°:

1.0 volt = 50°
0.5 volt = 25°
0.1 volt = 5°
0.02 volt = 1°

In order for the computer to determine temperature within 1 degree, it must react to sensor voltage changes as small as 0.020 volt or 20 millivolts. For example, if the temperature is 125°, the sensor signal will be 2.50 volts. If the temperature rises to 126°, sensor voltage increases to 2.52 volts. In reality, temperature does not pass directly from one degree to another; it passes through many smaller increments, as does voltage as it changes from 2.50 to 2.52 volts. Our digital computer, however, processes only signals equaling 1-degree changes in temperature. To do so, the computer sends the signal through analog-to-digital (AD) conversion circuits, where the analog sensor voltage is converted to a series of 0.020-volt changes for each degree. This is called "digitizing" an analog signal.

The analog-to-digital conversion process brings us back to binary numbers. Transistors can be designed to switch on and off at different voltage levels or with differing combinations of voltage signals. In the computer we are discussing, transistor groups must switch from off to on at 20-millivolt increments. The input signal is created by varying the transistor combinations that are on or off. Since the computer can read the various voltage signal combinations as binary numbers, it performs its calculations. It does so almost instantly because the current travels through the miniature circuits at almost the speed of light.

PARTS OF A COMPUTER

We have dealt with the functions, logic, and software used by a computer. The software consists of the programs and logic functions stored in the computer's circuitry. The hardware is the mechanical and electronic parts of the computer. Figure 14-21 shows the basic structure of a computer.

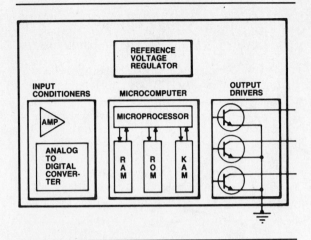

Figure 14-22. Three different types of memory are used by an engine control computer. (Ford)

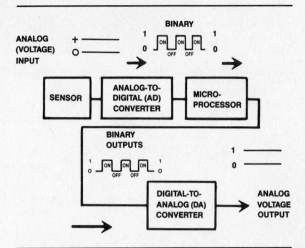

Figure 14-23. A/D and D/A converters interface the microprocessor with its input and output devices. (Chrysler)

Central Processing Unit (CPU)

As mentioned earlier, the microprocessor is the **central processing unit**, or CPU, of a computer. Since it does the essential mathematical operations and logic decisions that make up its processing function, the CPU can be considered the heart of a computer. Some computers use more than one microprocessor, called a coprocessor.

Computer Memory

The computer storage or memory function is provided by other integrated circuit (IC) devices. These simply store the computer operating program, system sensor input data, and system actuator output data for use by the CPU. Automobile computers use three different types of memory for their storage functions, figure 14-22:

• Read-only memory (ROM) or programmable read-only memory (PROM)
• Random-access memory (RAM)
• Keep-alive memory (KAM).

Permanent memory is called **read-only memory (ROM)** because the central computer can read the contents of the memory but cannot change the information contained within it. Data stored in ROM is retained even when power to the computer is turned off. The computer control program and specific vehicle data are stored in ROM so they will not be lost when power to the computer is interrupted. ROM containing the control program is built into the computer. The specific vehicle data is located in a separate ROM chip called a **programmable read-only memory (PROM)**. The PROM is used to individualize a single computer for use in various models.

Temporary memory is called **random-access memory (RAM)** because the central computer can both read information from it and write new information into it as dictated by the computer program. However, data contained in RAM is lost whenever power to the computer is interrupted. Depending upon the computer design, RAM can provide both short- or long-term memory. Short-term memory is lost every time the ignition switch is turned off; long-term memory is retained until the computer power supply is completely disconnected. System trouble codes and diagnostic test results are common items stored in RAM.

Central Processing Unit (CPU): The processing and calculating portion of a computer.

Read-Only Memory (ROM): The permanent part of a computer's memory storage function. ROM can be read but not changed, and is retained when power is shut off to the computer.

Programmable Read-Only Memory (PROM): An integrated circuit chip installed in a computer which contains appropriate operating instructions and database information for a particular application.

Random-Access Memory (RAM): Temporary short-term or long-term computer memory that can be read and changed, but is lost whenever power is shut off to the computer.

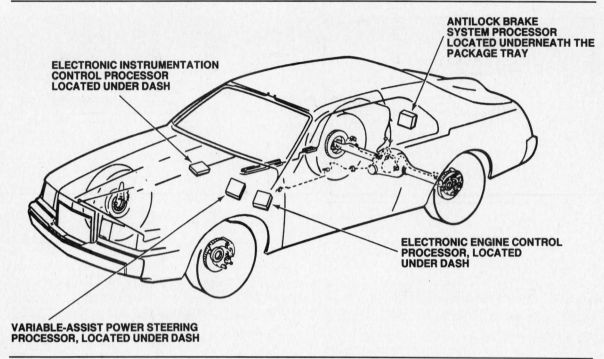

ELECTRONIC INSTRUMENTATION
CONTROL PROCESSOR
LOCATED UNDER DASH

ANTILOCK BRAKE
SYSTEM PROCESSOR
LOCATED UNDERNEATH THE
PACKAGE TRAY

ELECTRONIC ENGINE CONTROL
PROCESSOR, LOCATED
UNDER DASH

VARIABLE-ASSIST POWER STEERING
PROCESSOR, LOCATED UNDER DASH

Figure 14-24. Most onboard computers are located in the passenger compartment. (Ford)

Keep-alive memory (KAM) shares characteristics of ROM and RAM. Like RAM, data can be written into keep-alive memory. It also can be read and erased, but like ROM, it is not lost when the ignition is turned off. However, like long-term memory, KAM is erased whenever the power supply to the computer is disconnected. KAM is used primarily in conjunction with adaptive strategies, which we will study in the next chapter.

Input and Output Circuits

A computer is not directly connected to every input or output device. The signals are received and sent by other IC devices, many of which provide the computer with parallel connections. This allows it to receive several input signals while it is sending several output signals.

Converter Circuits

The computer must have circuits to convert input data into a form with which it can work. The analog signals which we have discussed must be digitized, or changed to digital signals. This conversion is done by separate IC devices called analog-to-digital (AD) converter circuits, figure 14-19.

The computer's output signals also must be converted into a form which the output device

can recognize and upon which it can act. Since some of the output devices are analog, the digital signals must be changed to analog signals. This conversion is done by digital-to-analog (DA) converter circuits. Because the circuits which perform these functions "interface" the CPU with the input and output devices, they are sometimes called the input/output (I/O) interface, figure 14-23.

Control Module Locations

The onboard automotive computer may be called an electronic control unit, module, or assembly, depending upon the carmaker and the computer application. The computer hardware is all mounted on one or more circuit boards and installed in a metal case, figure 14-21, to help shield it from electromagnetic interference (EMI). The wiring harnesses which link the computer to sensors and actuators connect to multipin connectors or edge connectors on the circuit boards.

Onboard computers range from single-function units that control a single operation to multifunction units that manage all of the separate (but linked) electronic systems in the vehicle. They vary in size from a small module to a notebook-sized box. Chrysler's early computers were attached to the air cleaner housing in the engine compartment. The computers used with Chrysler 4-cylinder engines are

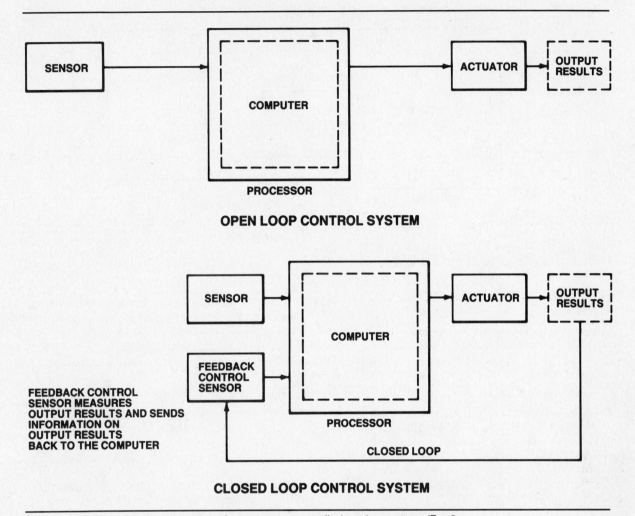

OPEN LOOP CONTROL SYSTEM

**FEEDBACK CONTROL
SENSOR MEASURES
OUTPUT RESULTS AND SENDS
INFORMATION ON
OUTPUT RESULTS
BACK TO THE COMPUTER**

CLOSED LOOP CONTROL SYSTEM

Figure 14-25. The two control modes of a computer-controlled engine system. (Ford)

2-piece units, with the power module installed between the battery and the fenderwell in the engine compartment, and the logic module behind a kick panel in the passenger compartment. Most other computers are installed in the passenger compartment either under the instrument panel or in a side kick panel where they can be shielded from physical damage caused by temperature extremes, dirt and vibration, or from interference from the high currents and voltages of various underhood systems, figure 14-24.

FUEL CONTROL SYSTEM OPERATING MODES

A computer-controlled fuel metering system can be selective; depending upon the computer program, it may have different operating modes. The onboard computer does not have to respond to data from all of its sensors, nor does it have to respond to the data in the same way each time. Under specified conditions, it may ignore sensor input. Or, it may respond in different ways to the same input signal, based on inputs from other sensors. Most current control systems, figure 14-25, have two operating modes: open loop and closed loop. We touched on these briefly in Chapter 8. The most common application of these modes is in fuel-metering feedback control, although there are other open- and closed-loop functions. Air conditioning automatic temperature control is an example. Control logic programmed into the computer determines the choice of operating mode according to engine operating conditions.

Keep-Alive Memory (KAM): A form of long-term RAM used mostly with adaptive strategies. Requires a separate power supply circuit to maintain voltage when the ignition is off.

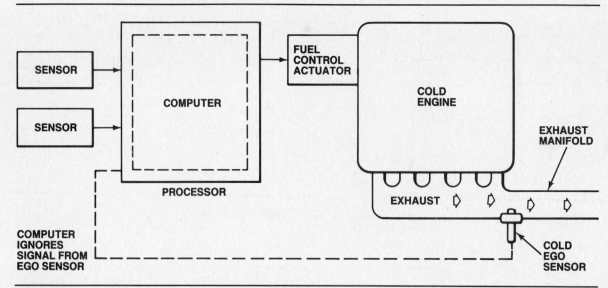

Figure 14-26. In open loop, the computer ignores the EGO sensor signal and operates on a predetermined program. (Ford)

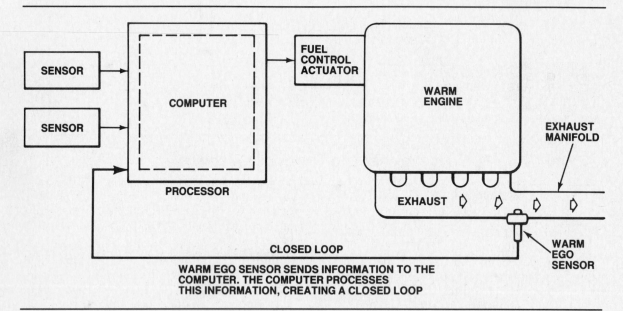

Figure 14-27. In closed loop, the computer accepts the EGO sensor signal and readjusts the air-fuel mixture accordingly. (Ford)

Open-Loop Control

Open-loop control means that the onboard computer works according to established conditions in its program. It gives the orders and the output actuators carry them out. The computer ignores sensor feedback signals as long as the established conditions exist.

For example, the computer is programmed to provide a specific amount of fuel and spark timing when the engine is first started. Since these factors are predetermined in the program (regardless of other factors), the computer will ignore signals (feedback) from the exhaust gas oxygen (EGO) sensor until coolant temperature reaches the predetermined level, figure 14-26.

Closed-Loop Control

Once certain conditions (such as coolant temperature) have been met, the system goes into closed loop. The computer now reads and responds to signals from *all* of its sensors. When the engine is first started (open loop), the computer ignores input from the EGO sensor. As

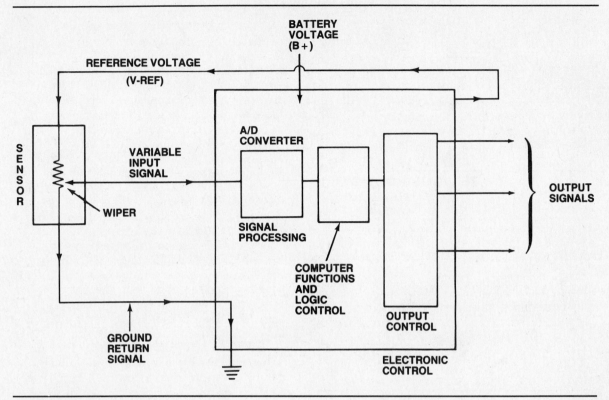

Figure 14-28. The computer reference voltage is sent out to a sensor and returns changed. This tells the computer how to readjust engine operation. (Ford)

soon as the coolant temperature reaches a pre-determined level (specified in the computer program), the computer accepts the sensor input and adjusts the fuel and spark timing accordingly. We say that the computer is responding to a ''feedback'' signal; that is, the sensor is telling the computer that there is an error factor in its operation that must be corrected, figure 14-27.

SENSORS AND ACTUATORS

All sensors and actuators are transducers, or devices which change one form of energy into another:
- Sensors convert light, temperature, motion, pressure, heat and other types of energy into voltage signals.
- Actuators convert voltage signals into mechanical energy or work.

Sensors and actuators used with automobile computer systems often do the same work that mechanical transducers such as vacuum diaphragms do on older vehicles without computer systems.

Sensors
Engine control system sensors fall into several basic categories including switches, timers, resistors, transformers, and generators. Except for generators, all automotive sensors are resistive devices. This means that they cannot create a voltage, but only can modify a voltage applied to them. The voltage applied is controlled by the computer and is called the **reference voltage**.

The computer sends this reference voltage to a sensor, and receives a different voltage back, figure 14-28. The returning signal is determined by the changing sensor resistance.

Reference Voltage: A constant voltage signal (below battery voltage) applied to a sensor by the computer. The sensor alters the voltage according to engine operating conditions and returns it as a variable input signal to the computer, which adjusts system operation accordingly.

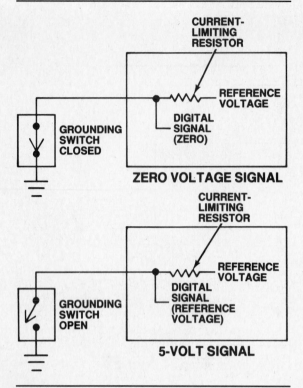

Figure 14-29. How a grounding switch operates. (Ford)

The computer interprets the altered return voltage as a sign of specific changes in the engine operating condition and adjusts engine operation accordingly.

Either a 5-volt or a 9-volt signal generally is used as the reference voltage. It must always be less than minimum battery voltage so that it can be maintained at a constant level at all times (even when battery power is low) to prevent faulty input signals from the sensors.

Characteristics and features
Automotive sensors function in a severe environment. For this reason, they must be designed for long-term, dependable operation while providing reliable signals. A sensor must have certain characteristics, or operating features, for it to operate properly. These characteristics affect the selection of a particular sensor for a given function, and establish the specifications for troubleshooting and service. The important characteristics are:

• *Repeatability* — the sensor must function consistently. For example, a temperature switch must open and close at the design points thousands of times without deviation. If the sensor produces a voltage in proportion to the condition being measured, it must do so throughout its operating range.

• *Accuracy* — the sensor must work within the tolerances or limits designed into it. Our temperature switch may close at 195° ± 1°, or it may close at 195° ± 10°. The tolerances depend on how the sensor is used, but once established, the sensor must work consistently. These tolerances are used to design sensor test specifications for troubleshooting.

• *Operating range* — an operating or dynamic range within which it must function is established for the sensor. A digital sensor has only one or two switching points. Since the operating range of an analog sensor is wider, it must be proportional. Signals outside the operating range are ignored by the computer.

• *Linearity* — this refers to sensor accuracy throughout its dynamic range. Within this range, an analog sensor must be as consistently proportional as possible to the measured value. While sensor linearity is most accurate near the center of its dynamic range, no sensor has perfect linearity and computer programs rely on memory data to compensate for this.

In the following paragraphs, you will learn about the various sensors used in an automobile. These include:
• Switches and timers
• Potentiometers
• Thermistors
• Piezoresistive devices
• Transformers
• Signal generators.

Switches and timers
The simplest form of sensor is a switch. A switch signals either a totally on, or a totally off, condition. A switch can signal the computer in one of two ways: through reference voltage, or by grounding a signal.

In the first way, full reference voltage is returned to the computer when the switch is closed. When the switch is open, no return voltage signal is sent. Not all switches relay reference voltage back to the computer; some send a battery voltage signal directly to the computer when the condition they are monitoring is met.

In the second way, a grounding switch is used in series with a fixed, current-limiting resistor and operates just the opposite of the first way of signalling. When the switch is closed, no voltage signal is sent. When the switch is open, reference voltage returns to the computer, figure 14-29.

A common use for a switch sensor is to signal the computer when a high-load accessory, such as an air conditioning compressor or rear window defogger, is turned on or off. The computer uses the switch signal to adjust the

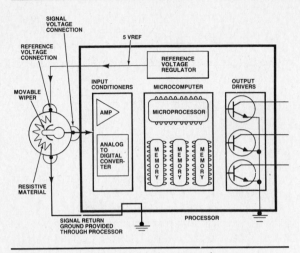

Figure 14-30. The basic components of a potentiometer and how it interacts with the computer. (Ford)

idle speed to compensate for the added or reduced load. Coolant temperature switches that are closed when the engine has reached a certain temperature are also used in some systems.

When combined with a switch, a timer can delay a signal for a specific and predetermined time. Timers prevent the computer from having to compensate for momentary conditions that do not significantly affect engine operation. The timer may be built into the computer, or it can be part of the switch itself.

Potentiometers

A potentiometer is a variable-resistance sensor with three terminals. One end of the resistor receives reference voltage, while the other end is grounded. The third terminal is attached to a movable contact that slides across the resistor to vary its resistance. Depending on whether the contact is near the supply end or the ground end of the resistor, return voltage will be high or low, figure 14-30.

Throttle position sensors are among the most common potentiometer-type sensors. The computer uses their input to determine the amount of throttle opening and the rate of change. Vane-type intake airflow meters use a potentiometer to signal the amount of air entering the engine. EGR valve flow sensors use a potentiometer to signal the valve position which the computer can use to interpret the amount of flow.

Thermistors

A thermistor is a solid-state variable resistor whose resistance changes with temperature.

■ The Rise and Fall of "Gaskets in a Tube"

In the 1970s, carmakers replaced many traditional cork gasket installations with room-temperature-vulcanizing (RTV) silicone sealants. RTV sealants quickly gained an unchallenged reign as "gaskets in a tube" for installing such parts as water pumps, valve covers, oil pans, transmission and differential covers, and other components.

Cork gaskets had been the industry standard for decades in these applications. Cork, however, dries out with age and loses it shape. Parts departments often found themselves with an inventory of unusable, overage gaskets. Moreover, car dealers and garages had to stock a variety of gaskets for different car models. RTV sealant in a tube seemed to be a revolutionary breakthrough.

When properly applied, RTV is an excellent sealer, but mating surfaces must be perfectly clean of oil and grease because oil dissolves the RTV sealant. Additionally, RTV residue in bolt holes can cause a hydraulic effect that affects torque when a bolt is installed. These are minor problems, however, and were easily overcome by professional technicians. However, RTV also has longer-term disadvantages that took time for the service industry to discover. For example, it:
● Has a short shelf life of about one year
● Does not cure properly when the shelf life has expired
● Will spoil if the cap is left off the tube because moisture in the air causes it to cure
● Is expensive to manufacture and stock for long periods.

Despite these disadvantages, carmakers used and specified RTV sealants and created a virtual depression in the cork gasket industry. In the mid-1980s, however, General Motor discovered that RTV sealants can cause long-term problems that had been unforeseen a decade earlier.

Although RTV sealant cures sufficiently to provide a firm seal in 24 to 48 hours, it can require as long as one year after installation to cure *completely*. Final curing time depends on where it is used in a vehicle and how thickly it is applied. During the prolonged curing time, RTV sealant gives off acidic fumes that can corrode electrical connections and sensitive electronic parts.

As solid-state electronic components increased in use during the 1980s, GM found that RTV sealant can contribute to failure of these sensitive devices. As goes GM, so goes the entire auto industry, and carmakers are again providing cork-based gaskets for applications where RTV sealant had been used. The gasket makers, meanwhile, have learned to bond cork to both sides of thin metal to manufacture gaskets that meet the needs of modern vehicles and eliminate the shrinkage and deterioration problems that plagued gaskets of a generation ago.

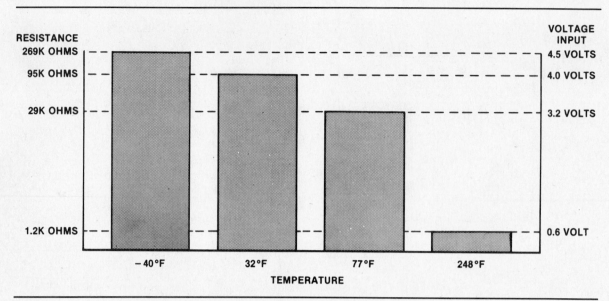

Figure 14-31. A thermistor requires a reference voltage from the computer. (Ford)

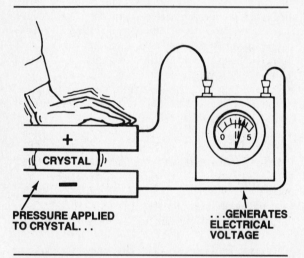

Figure 14-32. Sensors containing a certain type of quartz generate a voltage when pressure or force is applied. (Ford)

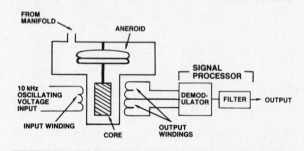

Figure 14-33. A transformer sensor creates a voltage differential between two output windings.

The resistance of any resistor changes as temperature changes, but the resistance variations across the operating range of a thermistor make it very accurate as an analog temperature sensor.

Thermistors are classified in two groups: **positive temperature coefficient (PTC) resistors** and **negative temperature coefficient (NTC) resistors**. These names simply mean that:
• The resistance of a PTC thermistor increases as temperature increases.
• The resistance of an NTC thermistor decreases as temperature increases.

Both kinds are used in automobile systems, but the NTC thermistor is more common. Heat can come from an external source or from current through the resistor. Externally heated NTC thermistors are the most common analog sensors for engine coolant temperature and intake air temperature.

The computer applies the reference voltage to one sensor terminal and receives the input (return) signal from the other, figure 14-31. As the sensor warms up, resistance decreases, and signal voltage increases.

Piezoresistive sensors
A **piezoelectric** crystal develops voltage across its surfaces when pressure is applied to it, figure 14-32. Similar crystals change their resistance when pressure is applied to them. This feature makes **piezoresistive** sensors ideal for analog pressure measurement.

When used as an engine detonation sensor, a piezoresistive device senses vibration and converts the degree of vibration into an electri-

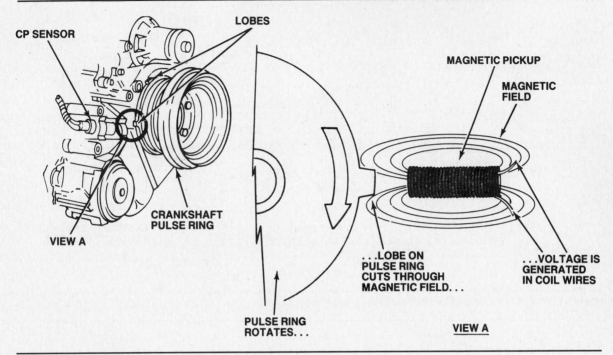

Figure 14-34. A crankshaft position (CP) sensor uses a magnetic pickup similar to those used in breakerless distributors. (Ford)

cal signal that tells the computer the extent of engine knock present.

When used as a barometric or manifold pressure sensor, the piezoelectric device changes the frequency of its output signal rather than the voltage. A pressure-sensing capacitor contains a sealed vacuum reference input on one side of a diaphragm, with barometric or manifold pressure on the other side. Any change in pressure results in a change in capacitance.

Transformers

A transformer sensor has input and output windings with a movable core in between them, figure 14-33. The electric coupling between the two cores varies with the core position. Reference voltage is applied to the input winding. The signal voltage generated in the output winding is the same as that in the input winding when the core is centered. As the core moves away from the center position, the return signal voltage changes. Transformer sensors are used as one type of manifold pressure sensor.

Signal generators

Signal generator sensors do not depend on a reference voltage. They generate an output signal that is sent to the computer. This output signal may be a varying voltage, a varying frequency, or a combination of the two. There are several types of generator sensors, including

magnetic pulse generators, Hall-effect switches, and galvanic batteries.

Magnetic pulse generators operate in a manner similar to the pickup coil and reluctor used in many electronic ignition systems. Hall-effect switches are used in some newer versions. These sensors commonly are used to provide an ignition trigger signal or crankshaft or camshaft position information. They may be located in the distributor or mounted in the block to respond to a tooth or cutout on the crankshaft reluctor, harmonic damper, or flywheel, figure 14-34. Some engines use sepa-

Positive Temperature Coefficient (PTC) Resistor: A thermistor whose resistance decreases as the temperature increases.

Negative Temperature Coefficient (NTC) Resistor: A thermistor whose resistance decreases as the temperature increases.

Piezoelectric: Voltage caused by physical pressure applied to the faces of certain crystals.

Piezoresistive: A sensor whose resistance varies in relation to pressure or force applied to it. A piezoresistive sensor receives a constant reference voltage and returns a variable signal in relation to its varying resistance.

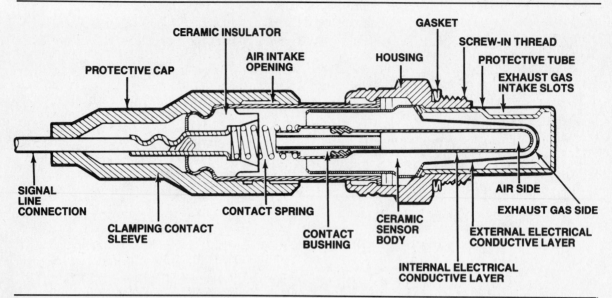

Figure 14-35. The components of a typical EGO sensor. (Ford)

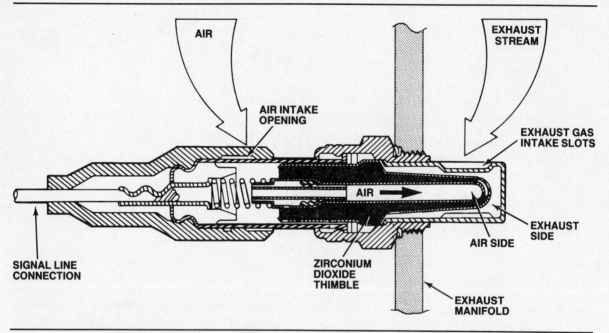

Figure 14-36. How the EGO sensor works. (Ford)

rate sensors to signal crankshaft and camshaft position.

A **galvanic battery** is a generator sensor that produces a voltage by comparing the oxygen level in the ambient air to that in the engine exhaust. The only galvanic battery on modern cars is the EGO sensor, figure 14-35, used to help control the air-fuel mixture.

Exhaust Gas Oxygen Sensors and Fuel Metering Control

The exhaust gas oxygen (EGO) sensor is one of the most important sensors on a car. It is usually installed in the exhaust manifold, although in some vehicles it may be located downstream from the manifold in the headpipe (but before the catalytic converter). This places it directly in the path of the exhaust gas

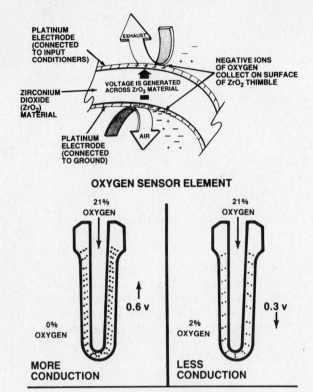

OXYGEN SENSOR ELEMENT

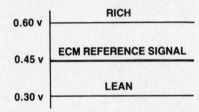

Figure 14-37. The difference in negative ion collection between the outside and inside of the EGO sensor creates a voltage potential. (Ford)

stream where it can monitor both the exhaust gas and ambient air. The sensor tip contains a thimble made of zirconium dioxide (ZrO_2), an electrically conductive material capable of generating a small voltage in the presence of oxygen.

Exhaust gases from the engine pass through the end of the sensor installed in the manifold where they contact the outer side of the thimble. Atmospheric air enters through the other end of the sensor and contacts the inner side of the thimble, figure 14-36. The inner and outer surfaces of the thimble are plated with platinum. The inner surface is a negative electrode; the outer surface is a positive electrode.

The atmosphere contains a relatively constant 21 percent oxygen. Rich exhaust gases contain virtually no oxygen. Exhaust from a lean mixture combustion, or from a misfire, contains more uncombined oxygen (still far less than the atmosphere, however).

Negatively charged oxygen ions are drawn to the thimble, where they collect on both the inner and outer surfaces, figure 14-37. Because the oxygen present in the atmosphere exceeds that in exhaust gases, the air side of the thimble draws more negative oxygen ions than the exhaust side. The difference between the two sides creates an electrical potential. When the concentration of oxygen on the exhaust gas side of the thimble is low, a high voltage (0.60 to 1.00 volt) is generated between the electrodes. As the oxygen concentration on the exhaust side increases, the voltage generated drops (0.00 to 0.40 volt).

This voltage signal is sent to the computer, where it passes through the input conditioner for amplification. The computer interprets the high-voltage signal as a rich air-fuel ratio, and a low-voltage signal as a lean air-fuel ratio. Based on the EGO signal, the computer will either lean or enrich the mixture as required to maintain as close to a 14.7 air-fuel ratio as possible. The EGO sensor is therefore the key sensor of an electronically controlled fuel-metering system.

An EGO sensor does not send a voltage signal until its tip reaches a temperature of about 572°F (300°C). EGO sensors provide their fastest response to mixture changes at about 1,472°F (800°C). This is the primary reason for open-loop fuel control on a cold engine.

Figure 14-38 shows the operating range of an EGO sensor at 1,472°F (800°C). Sensor voltage changes fastest at an air-fuel ratio of 14.7 at this temperature.

Another important point about an EGO sensor is that *it measures oxygen; it does not measure air-fuel ratio*. If the engine misfires, no oxygen is consumed in combustion. There is a large amount of oxygen in the unburned exhaust mixture, and the sensor will deliver a false "lean mixture" signal. This is one reason

Galvanic Battery: A direct current voltage source, generated by the chemical action of an electrolyte.

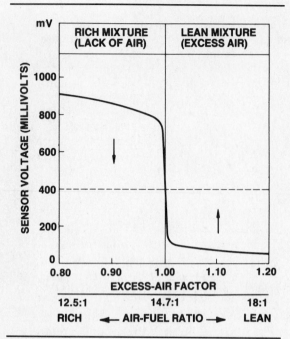

Figure 14-38. The EGO sensor provides its fastest response at the stoichiometric air-fuel ratio of 14.7:1.

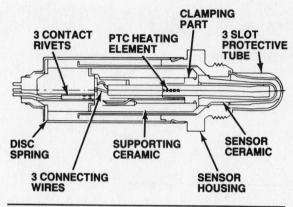

Figure 14-39. The components of a typical HEGO sensor. (Ford)

why computer control of ignition timing and EGR is essential for effective fuel metering control.

Unlike resistive sensors, an EGO sensor (as well as any other generator sensor) does not require a reference voltage. The computer, however, uses an internal reference voltage as a comparison for the sensor signal. Because the EGO sensor signal ranges from 0.1 to 0.3 volt (100 to 300 millivolts) with a lean mixture to 0.6 or 0.9 volt (600 to 900 millivolts) with a rich signal, the computer uses an internal reference of 0.45 volt (450 millivolts) as a reference, figure 14-37. The internal reference voltage also is the basis for fuel-metering signals during open-loop operation.

To make the system more responsive, carmakers went first to the concept of installing a separate EGO sensor in each manifold of a V-type engine. While this arrangement is still used, the heated exhaust gas oxygen (HEGO) sensor, figure 14-39, is the most recent development.

A HEGO sensor is constructed and operates the same as an EGO sensor, but contains a built-in heater powered by the vehicle battery whenever the ignition is in the run position. A third wire to the sensor delivers battery current (1 ampere or less) to the sensor electrode. This helps warm the sensor to operating

temperature more quickly and permits the sensor to operate at a lower exhaust gas temperature (approximately 392°F or 200°C). The heating element also keeps the sensor from cooling off when exhaust temperature drops, such as during prolonged idling in cold weather. HEGO sensors often are used on turbocharged engines where the sensor is installed downstream from the turbocharger, which absorbs much of the heat in the exhaust.

All EGO sensors work on the principles just discussed, but they are not all built the same. They may have one, two, or three wires that connect to the vehicle wiring harness. Early model sensors had two wires and were grounded through the computer or to some point on the chassis or engine. Later sensors have a single wire and ground through their outer shell to the exhaust pipe or manifold. Single- and double-wire EGO sensors are not interchangeable (the three-wire sensor is an HEGO).

Some sensors have a silicone boot to protect the sensor and to provide a vent for ambient air circulation. The positioning of a boot (when used) is important. If the boot is seated too far down on the sensor body, it can block the air vent, resulting in an inaccurate signal to the computer. The silicone boot has been abandoned on some late-model engines because it was thought that the silicone material gives off fumes that corrode electrical connections and terminals.

Actuators
The computer receives the sensor inputs and does the necessary calculations to determine which engine systems must be adjusted to meet the demands of the moment. Then it sends electrical control signals to one or more

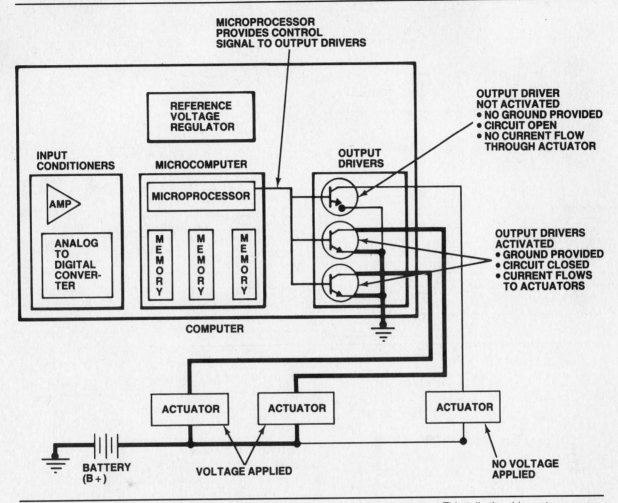

Figure 14-40. The output drivers receive a voltage signal from the microprocessor. This tells the drivers to open or close the ground circuit of the actuators they control. (Ford)

output drivers, which in turn operate the control devices or actuators by completing the actuator ground circuits. This process is illustrated in figure 14-40.

Some of the computer's output signals, such as those that regulate ignition timing, control engine operation directly. However, an actuator is required whenever the output must regulate a mechanical device. An actuator converts the computer's electrical signal into a mechanical action.

Most engine actuators either are solenoids or relays, although stepper motors also are used in some cases.

Solenoids and relays
Solenoids and relays both operate on the principle of electromagnetism. These two simple mechanical devices allow the computer to control almost any automotive system. A solenoid

essentially is a digital actuator; it is either on or off. Battery voltage is applied to one terminal of the solenoid and the computer opens and closes the ground circuit attached to the other terminal. A solenoid contains a coil winding around a spring-loaded metallic plunger, figure 14-41. When the switch is closed and current flows through the windings, the magnetic field of the coil attracts the movable plunger. This pulls it against spring pressure into the center of the coil toward the plate. Once current is shut off, the magnetic field collapses and spring pressure moves the plunger out of the coil.

In most applications, the solenoid is energized for varying periods of time determined by the computer program. When energized, a solenoid may extend a plunger to control engine speed. Other types of solenoids regulate

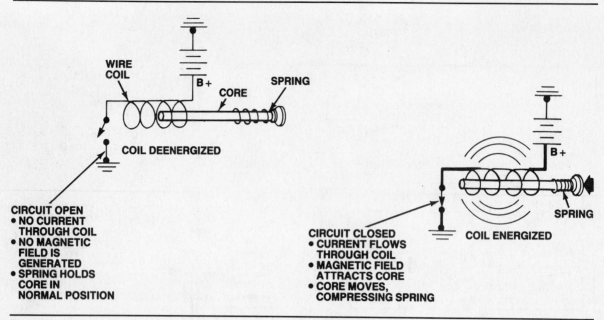

Figure 14-41. How a solenoid works. (Ford)

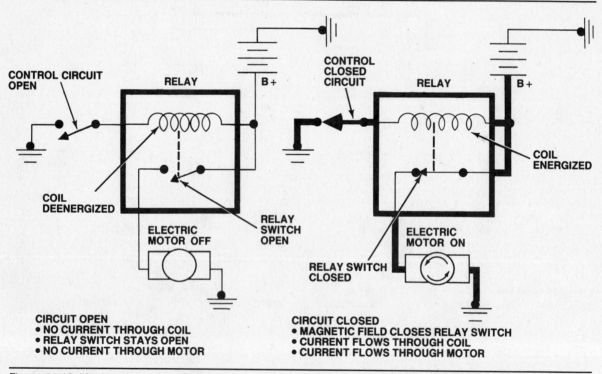

Figure 14-42. How a relay works. (Ford)

vacuum flow to various emission-related systems such as air injection, vapor canister purge, and EGR.

A relay is a switch that uses electromagnetism to move internal contacts, allowing a small electrical current to control a large current. To do this, it contains a control circuit

and a power circuit, figure 14-42. The small flow of current through the relay coil moves an armature to open or close a set of contact points. This is called the control circuit because it controls the flow of a much larger current through a separate circuit called the power circuit. The computer controls the operation of a

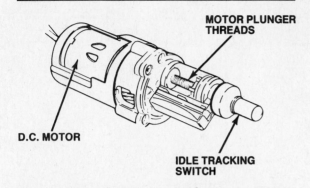

Figure 14-43. The stepper motor is a DC motor which moves in specific increments. (Ford)

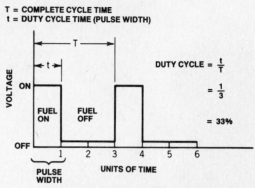

A. SHORT DUTY CYCLE (PULSE WIDTH), MINIMUM FUEL INJECTION

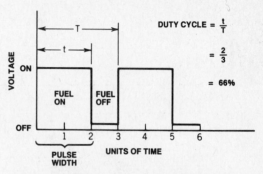

B. LONG DUTY CYCLE (PULSE WIDTH), MAXIMUM FUEL INJECTION

Figure 14-44. The GM electronic fuel control (EFC) system.

relay through its output drivers, which open and close the relay control circuit.

Stepper motors

A stepper motor, figure 14-43, also is a digital actuator. Stepper motors are d.c. motors that move in fixed increments from deenergized (no voltage) to fully energized (full voltage). A stepper motor can have as many as 120 discrete steps of motion which allow it to serve as an analog output operated by a digital signal.

The most common uses for stepper motors are as idle speed controls. On carbureted engines, the motor often acts directly on the throttle linkage, but in most fuel injection systems, it controls an idle air bypass built into the throttle body.

Pulse Width and Duty Cycle

Solenoids are more precisely controlled on some late-model cars with a procedure called pulse width modulation (PWM). This is the same technique used to control carburetor mixture control solenoids, as we learned in Chapter 13. With this technique, the solenoid is continuously cycled on and off a fixed number of times per second. The solenoid is on (energized) for part of each cycle, and off (deenergized) for the remainder of that cycle. The percentage of the total cycle time that the solenoid is energized is called its duty cycle. The duty cycle is determined by a timed voltage pulse from the computer. The computer varies, or modulates, this pulse width to establish the duty cycle and achieve the desired solenoid output.

A solenoid can operate at any number of cycles per second: 10, 20, 30, 60, or whatever the engineer chooses to design. Each complete cycle lasts the same amount of time, but duty cycle can vary as a percentage of each cycle. Pulse width varies along with the duty cycle

because it is the actual *time* that the solenoid is energized. Figure 14-44 shows two different pulse widths and duty cycles for the same complete cycle time. The system computer calculates the necessary pulse width and duty cycle from information provided by system sensors. Modern digital computers operate fast enough to change pulse width in fractions of a second to maintain precise fuel metering.

Pulse width modulation allows a digital output signal to provide varied or analog control of a mechanical device. It also is used to control fuel injectors and carburetor mixture control solenoids.

EARLY FUEL MANAGEMENT SYSTEMS

As you learned at the beginning of this chapter, the first application of electronic control to an automotive system was to control ignition timing. Chrysler Corporation receives historical credit as the first automaker to equip its engines with a breakerless ignition in 1972. However, the first computer-controlled fuel

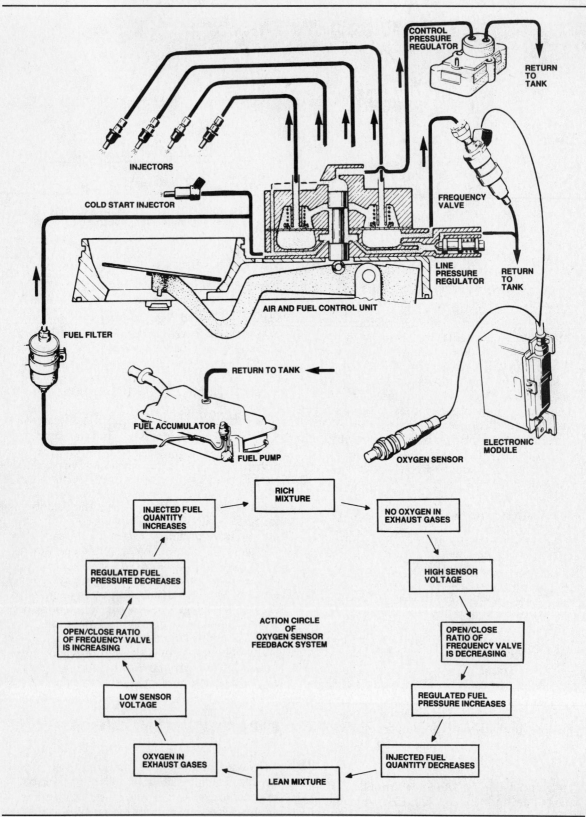

INJECTORS

CONTROL PRESSURE REGULATOR

RETURN TO TANK

COLD START INJECTOR

FREQUENCY VALVE

LINE PRESSURE REGULATOR

RETURN TO TANK

AIR AND FUEL CONTROL UNIT

FUEL FILTER

RETURN TO TANK

FUEL ACCUMULATOR

FUEL PUMP

OXYGEN SENSOR

ELECTRONIC MODULE

RICH MIXTURE

INJECTED FUEL QUANTITY INCREASES

NO OXYGEN IN EXHAUST GASES

REGULATED FUEL PRESSURE DECREASES

HIGH SENSOR VOLTAGE

OPEN/CLOSE RATIO OF FREQUENCY VALVE IS INCREASING

ACTION CIRCLE OF OXYGEN SENSOR FEEDBACK SYSTEM

OPEN/CLOSE RATIO OF FREQUENCY VALVE IS DECREASING

LOW SENSOR VOLTAGE

REGULATED FUEL PRESSURE INCREASES

OXYGEN IN EXHAUST GASES

INJECTED FUEL QUANTITY DECREASES

LEAN MIXTURE

Figure 14-45. The Volvo Lambda-Sond system. (Volvo)

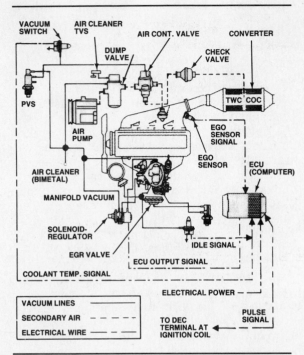

Figure 14-46. Ford's Feedback Electronic Engine Control system.

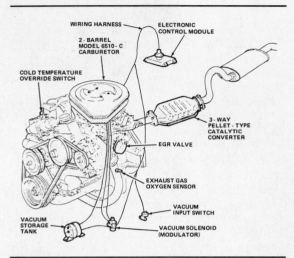

Figure 14-47. The GM electronic fuel control (EFC) system.

metering system made its appearance on European vehicles. In this section, we'll take a brief historical look at the development of electronic fuel management systems.

Bosch Lambda-Sond

Volvo offered the first electronically controlled feedback fuel system on 1977 models sold in the United States. This application was produced by the Robert Bosch company, a pioneer European manufacturer of fuel injection systems and electronic components.

The Volvo system combined the use of a 3-way catalytic converter (TWC) and EGO sensor with K-Jetronic fuel injection, figure 14-45. Sensor input was processed by the electronic control module, which then signaled a timing valve in the K-Jetronic system to vary injection control pressure and regulate the amount of fuel delivered by the continuous injection system. Saab and other European carmakers quickly followed with their own versions.

Ford and GM Feedback Fuel Control Systems

Ford and GM both introduced 3-way catalyst and feedback carburetor systems on some 1978 4-cylinder engines sold in California. Ford's

system was called the "electronic control feedback carburetor with a three-way catalyst and conventional oxidation catalyst (TWC-COC)", figure 14-46. GM's system was called "Phase II" emission control or "Electronic Fuel Control (EFC)", figure 14-47. Both systems controlled only fuel metering.

In both systems, the signal voltage from the EGO sensor was sent to a control module which in turn activated or deactivated a solenoid-operated vacuum valve. The vacuum valve or regulator controlled the flow of engine vacuum to a diaphragm in the carburetor. The diaphragm controlled the position of a fuel metering valve, which effectively varied the air-fuel ratio as desired.

The Ford system used an analog computer which was replaced by a digital computer on 1980 models when the system was redesignated as the microprocessor control unit (MCU) system. It remained unchanged on many Ford engines during the early 1980s. The GM system was replaced on 1980 front-wheel drive vehicles by a fully integrated computer-controlled catalytic converter (C-4) system, which evolved into the computer command control (CCC or C-3) system on 1981 models.

SUMMARY

There are two theories of electric current flow. The conventional current theory says that current flows from positive to negative. The electron current theory says that current flows from negative to positive. Either theory can be used to describe current in a circuit.

A circuit is a complete path from an electrical energy source, through wires and electrical loads, and back to the source. A complete circuit is necessary for current to flow. Current flows *through* a circuit. Voltage is *applied to* or *impressed on* a circuit. Resistance, measured in ohms, opposes current flow and is *contained within* the circuit.

There are three kinds of electrical circuits: series, parallel, and series-parallel. In a series circuit, there is only one current path. In a parallel circuit, there are two or more current paths. A series-parallel circuit has several current paths in parallel with each other, but in series with other parts of the circuit.

Every computer has four main functions: input, processing, storage, and output. Computers can operate on analog or digital signals. An analog signal is infinitely variable. A digital signal is an on/off or high/low signal. In automobile applications, most variable measurements produce analog signals which must be changed to digital signals for computer processing.

Digital computers use the binary system in which on/off or high/low voltage signals are represented by combinations of 0s and 1s.

Onboard computers are used in automotive fuel metering control systems. The control system regulates the operation of the vehicle's fuel system and operates in open loop or closed loop modes. In an open loop mode, the system does not respond to an output feedback signal. In a closed loop mode, the computer responds to the feedback signal and adjusts the output value accordingly.

Computer input is provided by sensors. Sensors can be switches, timers, potentiometers, piezoresistors, transformers, or generators. Computer output is sent to actuators, which transduce, or convert, the electrical signal to mechanical action. Most actuators are solenoids or relays, but some are stepper motors. The first feedback fuel metering system was Volvo's Lambda-Sond system in 1977. Ford and GM followed in 1978 with their own versions, which quickly evolved into integrated engine management systems.

Review Questions

Choose the single most correct answer.
Compare your answers with the correct answers on page 451.

1. The electromotive force that moves electrons from one point to another is called:
   a. Resistance
   b. Voltage
   c. Amperes
   d. Ohms

2. The rate of current flow in a circuit is measured in:
   a. Ohms
   b. Volts
   c. Amperes
   d. Watts

3. Resistance is measured in:
   a. Ohms
   b. Amperes
   c. Watts
   d. Voltage drop

4. Mechanic A says that a parallel circuit contains several current paths.
   Mechanic B says that a series-parallel circuit contains several current paths.
   Who is right?
   a. A only
   b. B only
   c. Both A and B
   d. Neither A nor B

5. Mechanic A says that an engine computer receives input information from its actuators, processes data, stores data, and sends output information to its sensors.
   Mechanic B says that most late-model automotive computers are based on analog microprocessors.
   Who is correct?
   a. A only
   b. B only
   c. Both A and B
   d. Neither A nor B

6. The operational program for a specific engine and vehicle is stored in the computer's:
   a. Logic module
   b. Programmable read-only memory (PROM)
   c. Random-access memory (RAM)
   d. Keep-alive memory (KAM)

7. An exhaust gas oxygen (EGO) sensor is an example of a:
   a. Resistor
   b. Potentiometer
   c. Generator
   d. Solenoid

8. An engine detonation sensor uses a:
   a. Piezoresistive crystal
   b. Voltage divider pickup
   c. Potentiometer
   d. Thermistor

9. The binary system used by a digital computer consists of:
   a. 10 numbers
   b. 5 numbers
   c. 3 numbers
   d. 2 numbers

10. The computer can read but not change the information stored in:
    a. ROM
    b. RAM
    c. KAM
    d. None of these

11. Mechanic A says that analog input data must be digitized by an A/D converter.
    Mechanic B says that output data must be changed to analog signals by a D/A converter.
    Who is right?
    a. A only
    b. B only
    c. Both A and B
    d. Neither A nor B

12. An onboard computer can do all of the following except:
    a. Ignore sensor input under certain conditions
    b. Respond in different ways to the same input
    c. Accept an input signal from another computer
    d. Ignore its program instructions under certain conditions

13. When the onboard computer is in open loop operation, it:
    a. Controls fuel metering to a predetermined value
    b. Ignores the temperature sensor signals
    c. Responds to the EGO sensor signal
    d. All of the above

14. The reference value sent to a sensor by the computer must be:
    a. Above battery voltage
    b. Exactly the same as battery voltage
    c. Less than minimum battery voltage
    d. Either a or c

15. The simplest digital sensor is a:
    a. Solenoid
    b. Switch
    c. Timer
    d. Relay

16. A variable resistance sensor is called a:
    a. Potentiometer
    b. Thermistor
    c. Transformer
    d. Generator

17. The percentage of time a solenoid is energized relative to total cycle time is called the:
    a. Pulse width modulation (PWM)
    b. Frequency
    c. Duty cycle
    d. KAM

18. A stepper motor:
    a. Is either on or off
    b. Is one form of solenoid
    c. Is used to operate the EGR valve
    d. Has discrete steps of movement

19. Most onboard computers work with:
    a. Binary numbers
    b. Voltage signals
    c. Both a and b
    d. Neither a nor b

20. Mechanic A says that throttle position sensors are potentiometers.
    Mechanic B says that throttle position sensors are analog devices.
    Who is right?
    a. A only
    b. B only
    c. Both A and B
    d. Neither A nor B

15

Electronic Engine Control Systems

The computers used to control various electrical systems, including engine operation, may be called modules, assemblies, or electronic control units, as you learned in Chapter 14. Some, like the HEI module we saw in Chapter 11, are single-function devices that control a single system, in this case, ignition. Others are multiple-function devices that regulate more than one system. A few even act as master units, supervising a network of computer-controlled systems. These computers use input signals from various sensors to control a given system through a series of actuators, figure 15-1, and the output signal from one computer can act as an input signal to another computer.

COMPUTER FUNCTIONS — A REVIEW

As you learned in the previous chapter, every computer, regardless of its use, has four basic functions. Electronic engine control systems provide some of the best examples of these functions:

1. *Input* — Variable voltage signals provided by sensors are the computer's input data. After conditioning the signals, the computer compares them to programmed information and makes a decision.

2. *Processing* — Processing begins with the receipt of input signals and continues as the computer evaluates and compares multiple signals and makes decisions for output commands.

3. *Storage* — A computer stores its own program, or operating instructions, in its memory. It also stores a basic set of data about vehicle design, such as weight, engine, transmission, and accessory combinations. The read-only memory (ROM) and random access memory (RAM) allow the computer to store this programmed data, as well as input and output signals for later reference.

4. *Output* — After receiving and processing input data, the computer sends output voltage signals to various actuators in the engine control system. The actuators are electromechanical or electronic devices that control fuel metering, ignition timing, emission control operation, and other engine operations.

Open- and Closed-Loop Operation

Every engine control system has two basic operating modes: open loop and closed loop. In open-loop operation, however, the computer does not respond to a feedback error signal from an actuator or from a sensor that measures output results. The computer simply

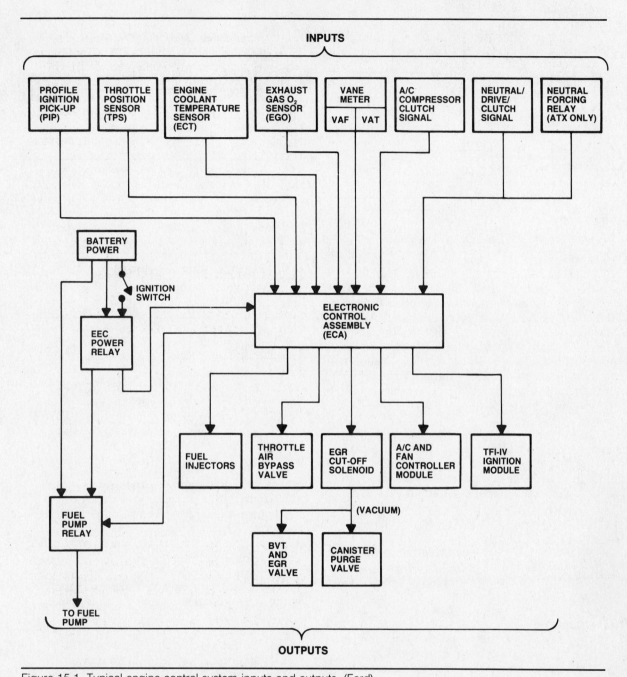

INPUTS

Figure 15-1. Typical engine control system inputs and outputs. (Ford)

assumes that its output signals achieve the desired performance. Nothing tells it differently unless it gets an input signal that is radically out of limits.

In closed-loop operation, a computer receives, and responds to, a signal from a sensor that measures output results. The principal feedback signal in an engine control system is the exhaust gas oxygen (EGO) sensor. The EGO sensor measures oxygen in the exhaust and sends a corresponding voltage signal to

the computer. The computer interprets this signal as a measurement of the air-fuel ratio. The EGO sensor signal closes the loop. The computer no longer has to assume that its output signals achieve the desired results. It measures the results and adjusts the signals if the results are out of the desired limits. Figure 15-2 is a simple block diagram of closed-loop control system operation.

Although the EGO sensor is the principal closed-loop feedback sensor, engine control

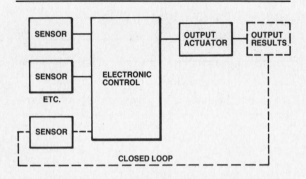

Figure 15-2. Typical open- and closed-loop block diagram. (Ford)

computers receive, or infer, feedback signals from other sensors. A detonation sensor, for example, sends a signal when the combined results of engine temperature, ignition timing, and air-fuel ratio cause engine pinging. Although a detonation sensor signal is not a feedback from a single output, it measures the results of combined output signals and allows the computer to correct its signals accordingly. Exhaust gas recirculation (EGR) sensors provide similar feedback signals that indicate EGR valve position.

Idle speed control is another example of a feedback signal. If idle speed changes from a programmed value, an ignition (tachometer) signal informs the computer. The computer then directs an actuator (a solenoid or a stepper motor) to adjust airflow or throttle position and return the engine to the desired idle speed.

Essentially, a computer operating in closed loop is constantly ''retuning'' the engine to keep it within programmed limits. This retuning compensates for changes in operating factors such as temperature, speed, load, and altitude.

The distinctions between open-loop and closed-loop operation are fundamental to any engine control system. The basic difference is simple: does or does not the computer respond to a feedback error signal. The specific applications can become quite subtle and complex, however. Figure 15-3 is a chart that summarizes seven basic engine operating modes and how the computer responds to each. The following paragraphs summarize open- and closed-loop computer operations.

Open-loop operating mode
When a vehicle is first started, the control system is in an open-loop mode. This means that:
• The sensors provide information to the computer in the form of voltage signals

ENGINE OPERATING MODES

Engine Operating Mode	Air/Fuel Ratio	Engine Temperature	Exhaust Gas Sensor Input	Air/Fuel Temperature
Engine Crank	Fixed 2:1 to 12:1	Cold to cool	None	Cold to cool
Engine Warm-up	Fixed 2:1 to 15:1	Warming	None until engine warm-up	Warming
Open Loop	Fixed 2:1 to 15:1	Cold or warm	May signal, but ignored by processor	Cold or warm
Closed Loop	14.7:1 Depends on exhaust gas sensor input	Warm	Signalling	Warm
Hard Acceleration	Variable rich mixture, depends on driver demands	Warm	Signals, but ignored by processor	Warm
Deceleration	Variable lean mixture	Warm	Signals, but ignored by processor	Warm
Idle	Rich or lean depends on calibration	Warm	Signal, may be ignored (depends on calibration)	Warm

Figure 15-3. Ford computers are programmed for seven different engine operating modes. Sensor input determines the mode selected. (Ford)

• The computer compares the signals to its stored program and makes a decision
• The computer transmits a voltage signal to its output drivers to implement the decision
• The output drivers react to the signal by opening or closing the ground circuit of one or more output actuators
• The actuators operate in a specific manner without providing any feedback to the computer.
This unidirectional operating sequence is shown by the solid lines in figure 15-2.

For an engine computer to determine whether the air-fuel mixture is correct, it requires an EGO sensor feedback signal. If the computer ignores this signal, it relies on its stored program and signals from other sensors to make its decision. In this case, suppose the engine coolant sensor tells the computer that the engine is cold. The throttle position sensor also signals that engine speed is increasing. Based on this information, the computer tells the fuel control actuator to enrich the mixture. It does this under certain specified conditions:
• During a cold start or hot restart
• Under low vacuum conditions

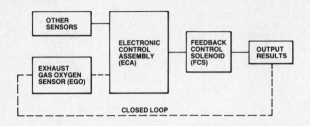

Figure 15-4. Closed-loop fuel metering block diagram. (Ford)

• At wide-open throttle or under full load, regardless of engine speed
• During idle or deceleration conditions (some systems).

Closed-loop operating mode

Once the computer switches system operation into a closed-loop mode, it responds to feedback signals provided by sensors or actuators. These feedback signals tell the computer whether the output is insufficient, optimum, or excessive. In other words, the feedback signals regulate the output control. This cycle is summarized by the dotted line in figure 15-4.

In the fuel metering example above, the computer will respond to the EGO sensor signal. If the sensor measures an excessively rich mixture, it signals the computer. The computer then directs the fuel control actuator to lean the mixture. If the actuator leans the mixture too much, the EGO sensor informs the computer, which then directs the fuel control actuator to again enrich the mixture. This is an on-going process that occurs many times per second.

Fuel metering is not the only use of closed-loop control. Systems that use a detonation sensor retard ignition timing according to the sensor signal until detonation stops, then return the timing to normal. Idle speed control is still another example. If the engine idle speed changes from a preset value, the computer receives a signal from the speed sensor and directs the idle speed control (an actuator) to change the idle airflow until idle speed is brought back into specifications.

In essence, a computer operating in closed loop is constantly ''retuning'' the engine while it is running in order to compensate for changes in various operating factors, such as temperature, speed, load, altitude, among others.

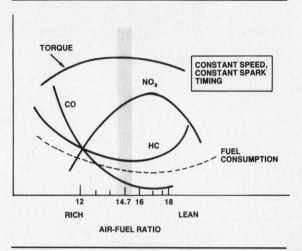

Figure 15-5. Changes in air-fuel ratio produce these fuel consumption, emission, and torque curves.

AIR-FUEL RATIO, TIMING, AND EGR EFFECTS ON OPERATION

This is a good time to consider the effects of air-fuel ratio, timing and exhaust gas recirculation (EGR) operation on overall engine operation. Almost all late-model engine systems recirculate a measured amount of exhaust gas into the intake air-fuel mixture. Exhaust gas recirculation was introduced in the early 1970s to reduce NO_x emissions by diluting the intake air-fuel charge (displacing oxygen) and lowering combustion temperatures. EGR also is an effective detonation control method, which allows spark timing to be maintained at optimum advance for performance and economy. The following explanations will help you to understand why only a computer can control air-fuel ratios, spark timing, and EGR for maximum engine efficiency.

Air-Fuel Ratio — A Review

Assuming fixed timing and engine speed, variations in air-fuel ratio have a dramatic effect on pollutants, figure 15-5. When the ratio is richer than 14.7 to 1, hydrocarbon (HC) and carbon monoxide (CO) emissions are high, as would be expected with the increase in fuel consumption. However, oxides of nitrogen (NO_x) emissions are low. Torque is greatest at ratios between 12 and 16. Above 16, torque decreases, as does NO_x, while HC increases. When the ratio is very lean, HC emissions also increase, as does fuel consumption. This is caused by the engine misfiring from the lean mixture and passing unburned fuel through the cylinders. The result is a reduction in both power and torque.

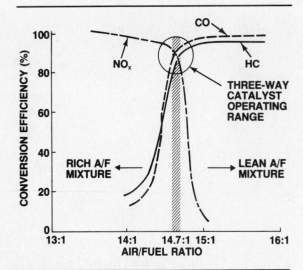

Figure 15-6. Three-way catalysts work properly only in a narrow air-fuel ratio range.

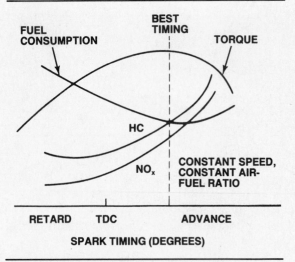

Figure 15-8. Changes in ignition timing produce these fuel consumption, emission, and torque curves.

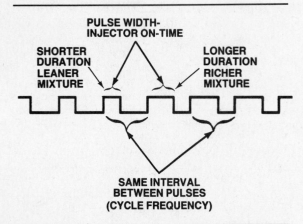

Figure 15-7. Fuel injector pulse width determines the air-fuel ratio.

Stoichiometric ratio

The stoichiometric or ideal air-fuel ratio is 14.7 to 1. This ratio gives the most efficient combination of air and fuel during combustion. This ratio is a compromise between maximum power and economy, and it delivers the optimum combination of performance and mileage.

Emission control also is optimum at this ratio, if a 3-way oxidation-reduction catalytic converter is used, figure 15-6. As the mixture gets richer, HC and CO conversion efficiency falls off. With leaner mixtures, NOx conversion efficiency also falls off. As figure 15-6 shows, the conversion efficiency range is very narrow — between 14.65 and 14.75 to 1. A fuel system without feedback control cannot maintain this narrow range.

Ratio control with carburetors and fuel injection

Two types of fuel control actuators are used with carburetors:
- A solenoid or stepper motor mounted on or in the carburetor to directly control the fuel-metering rods or the air bleeds, or both
- A remote-mounted, solenoid-actuated vacuum valve to regulate vacuum diaphragms that control the fuel-metering rods and air bleeds.

The computer sends a pulsed voltage signal to the control device, varying the ratio of on-time to off-time according to the signals received from the EGO sensor. As the percentage of on-time is increased or decreased, the mixture becomes leaner or richer.

With fuel injection systems, however, the computer controls the ratio by switching one or more fuel injectors on and off. Engine speed determines the switching rate, and the computer varies the length of time the injectors remain open (pulse width) to establish the air-fuel ratio, figure 15-7. As the computer receives data from its inputs, it increases the pulse width to supply more fuel for situations such as cold running, heavy loads, or fast acceleration. In a similar manner, it shortens the pulse width to lean the mixture for situations such as idling, cruising, or decelerating.

Ignition Timing

Assuming a fixed air-fuel ratio and engine speed, variations in ignition timing also have a dramatic effect on fuel consumption and pollutants, figure 15-8. When timing is at top dead

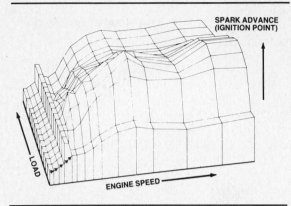

Figure 15-9. A typical spark advance "map" produced by the engine mapping process. (Bosch)

center (tdc) or slightly retarded, emissions are low and fuel consumption is high. As timing is advanced, fuel consumption drops off but emissions increase. Engine computers are programmed to calculate the best timing for any combination of air-fuel ratio and engine speed without detonation problems.

Exhaust Gas Recirculation

Exhaust gas recirculation is the most efficient way to reduce NO_x emissions without adversely affecting fuel economy, driveability, and HC emission control. The recirculation of exhaust gases lowers the combustion temperature, so NO_x emissions drop off sharply when EGR is introduced into the air-fuel mixture. However, excessive reliance on EGR leads to an increase in both HC emissions and fuel consumption. Again, the engine computer is programmed to calculate the percentage of EGR that delivers the best compromise between NO_x control, HC emissions, and fuel economy without detonation problems.

Computer Integration

One of the primary values of a computer is its ability to integrate the operation of two or more individual and relatively uncomplicated systems to form a larger and more complex system. For example, we know that centrifugal and vacuum advance mechanisms can control spark timing relative to engine speed and load. We also know that fuel metering through a carburetor is controlled by airflow, and that manifold or ported vacuum can manage basic EGR flow. Integrating such independent systems through a computer provides faster, more precise regulation of each system, and

allows the computer to calculate the effect of changing several variable factors at the same time.

Engine Mapping

Every computer needs instructions to do its job. These instructions are called a computer program. The program for an engine control computer consists of several elements:
• The mathematical instructions that tell the computer how to process, or "compute", the information it receives.
• The information that pertains to *fixed* vehicle values, such as vehicle weight, the number of cylinders, engine compression ratio, transmission type and gear ratios, firing order, and emission control devices.
• The data that pertains to *variable* vehicle values such as engine rpm, car speed, coolant temperature, intake airflow, fuel flow, ignition timing, and other factors.

Since the mathematical instructions and vehicle valves are constant values, they are fixed and are easily placed into computer memory. To place the variable values into memory, it is necessary to simulate the vehicle and its system in operation. Carmakers use a large mainframe computer to calculate all of the possible variable conditions for any given system. This process of system simulation is called **engine mapping** and provides the control program for the individual onboard computer.

By operating a vehicle on a dynamometer and manually adjusting the variable factors such as speed, load, and spark timing, it is possible to determine the optimum output settings for the best driveability, economy, and emission control. Engine mapping creates a 3-dimensional performance graph, figure 15-9, which applies to a given vehicle and powertrain combination.

The vehicle information mapped in this manner is stored along with the mathematical instructions in a computer chip called a programmable read-only memory (PROM), figure 15-10, which is installed in the central computer for that particular car model. The computer uses the PROM as its memory; it

Engine Mapping: Vehicle operation simulation procedure used to tailor the onboard computer program to a specific engine/powertrain combination. This program is stored in a PROM or calibration assembly.

Figure 15-10. A typical GM PROM.

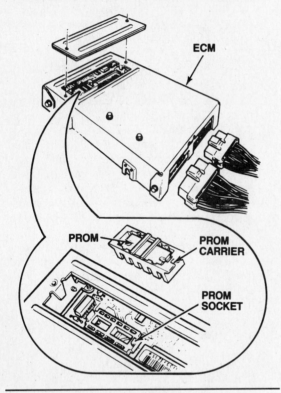

Figure 15-11. A GM engine control module (ECM) with a replaceable PROM. (GM)

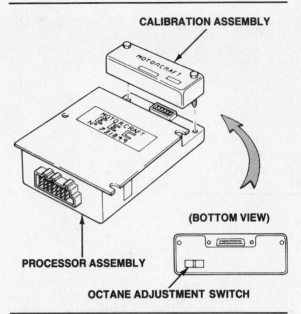

Figure 15-12. A Ford computer with a replaceable calibration assembly. (Ford)

compares the input from various sensors to the data in memory, and adjusts the systems under its control accordingly.

Mapping allows a carmaker to use one basic computer for all models; the unique PROM individualizes the computer for a particular model. Also, if a driveability problem can be resolved by a change in the program, the carmaker can release a revised PROM to supersede the earlier part. Some PROMs are made so that they can be erased when exposed to ultraviolet light and reprogrammed. These are called erasable programmable read-only memories (EPROMs).

Most carmakers use a single PROM which plugs into the computer, figure 15-11. Some Ford computers use a larger "calibration module" that contains the system PROM, figure 15-12. If the onboard computer must be replaced, the PROM or calibration unit is removed from the defective unit and installed in the replacement computer.

Adaptive Memory, Integrator, and Block Learn

Recent engine control systems can be programmed to learn from their own experience. This **adaptive memory** feature allows the computer to adjust its memory for computing open-loop operation. Once the system is operating in closed loop, the computer compares its open-loop calculated air-fuel ratios against the average limit cycle values in closed loop. If there is a substantial difference, the computer corrects its memory so that it can match closed-loop control as closely as possible when it is in open-loop. This data is stored in keep-alive memory (KAM) so that it can be used the next time the vehicle is started, providing more accurate air-fuel ratio control. KAM is a specialized form of random access memory (RAM). It also allows a computer to adapt its program to deal with long-term changes in engine operation resulting from wear.

The ECM used on GM fuel-injected engines contains a pair of functions called **integrator** and **block learn.** These are responsible for making minor adjustments to the air-fuel ratio of a fuel-injected engine, similar to the mixture control solenoid dwell on a carbureted engine. Integrator and block learn represent injector on-time.

The ECM program contains a base fuel calculation. When the EGO sensor tells the ECM to enrich the air-fuel mixture, the ECM adds fuel to the base calculation. If the mixture is to be leaned, the ECM subtracts fuel from the base calculation.

This information can be retrieved from the ECM using a scan tool, or scanner. The tool connects to the ECM serial data transmission line through either the assembly line communication link (ALCL) or the assembly line diagnostic link (ALDL) connector. Acting as a bystander, the SCAN tool monitors the inputs and outputs as received and sent by the ECM.

The scan tool reads the base fuel calculation as the number 128. If the scan tool reads a higher number, the ECM is adding fuel to the mixture. If the number is less than 128, the ECM is subtracting fuel. This corrective action taken by the ECM is the integrator function; it is effective only on a short-term basis. Block learn, or long-term correction, only changes if the integrator sees a condition which remains for a predetermined length of time.

In summary, adaptive memory allows the engine computer to alter its program over the life of the vehicle. The computer can adapt its program to such long-term variables as:
• Engine wear
• Changes in fuel quality
• Changes in regular driving habits
• Changes in environmental conditions.

The integrator capability allows the computer to make short-term — minute-by-minute — corrections in fuel metering. Such corrections may be necessary, for example, when a car is driven from low altitude across a high mountain pass and back to low altitude in an hour or two.

Block learn represents the long-term effects of integrator corrections. As such, it complements adaptive memory. If the computer continually must overcompensate fuel metering to maintain the stoichiometric ratio, it "learns" the correction and adapts its memory to make the correction factor part of its basic program. The period necessary for block learn to become part of basic memory may be 8 hours, 40 hours, 80 hours, or some other period determined by the system engineers.

PARTIAL-FUNCTION CONTROL SYSTEMS

Early electronic engine control systems of the late 1970s were partial-function systems. They regulated fuel metering or ignition timing, but not both. They were, however, the starting point for the full-function systems used on today's vehicles. You were introduced to some of these systems in Chapter 14, and the last section of this chapter provides histories of system development by major domestic and foreign carmakers. We will use some of these same systems as examples of partial-function engine controls in the following paragraphs.

Partial-function systems have one or more of the following features. Late-model, full-function systems all have:
• A 3-way catalytic converter and an EGO sensor for stoichiometric air-fuel ratio control
• Electronic feedback control of fuel metering in the carburetor or fuel injection system
• Open- and closed-loop operating modes
• Electronic spark timing control in place of traditional centrifugal and vacuum spark advance
• Electronic control of air injection switching, EGR, and vapor canister purging
• Electronic control of transmission shifting, torque converter lockup, and accessory operation.

Ignition Timing Control

Chrysler's electronic lean burn (ELB) system, figure 15-13, was introduced in 1976. It was an early example of a partial-function ignition timing control system. Although the name sounds

---

Adaptive Memory: A feature of computer memory that allows the microprocessor to adjust its memory for computing open-loop operation, based on changes in engine operation.

Integrator: The ability of the computer to make short-term — minute-by-minute — corrections in fuel metering.

Block Learn: The long-term effects of integrator corrections. As such, block learn complements adaptive memory. If, for example, the computer continually must overcompensate fuel metering to maintain the stoichiometric ratio, it "learns" the correction and adapts its memory to make the correction factor part of its basic program.

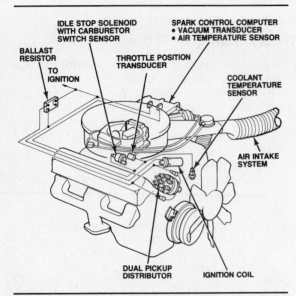

Figure 15-13. A Chrysler Lean-Burn system.

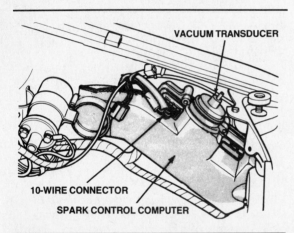

Figure 15-14. The Chrysler 4-cylinder spark control computer.

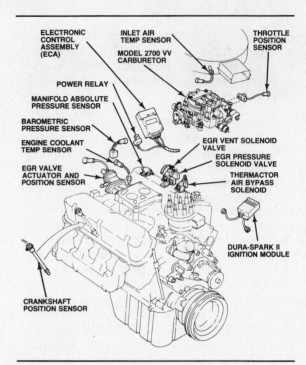

Figure 15-15. Ford's EEC-I engine control system.

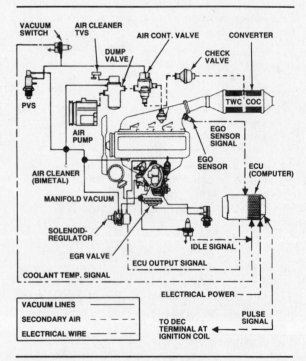

Figure 15-16. Ford's Feedback Electronic Engine Control system.

like it was a fuel control system, ELB simply used a carburetor calibrated for lean air-fuel ratios. No feedback, or variable, fuel control was used. The system computer regulated ignition timing to allow the engine to operate smoothly on lean ratios. The first ELB systems used a distributor with centrifugal advance but no vacuum advance. In 1977, centrifugal advance was eliminated, and timing was under full electronic control. Chrysler's ELB system continued through 1978 on V-8 and 4-cylinder engines, and in 1979 was renamed electronic spark control (ESC), figure 15-14.

Ford's first electronic engine control system (EEC-I), figure 15-15, was introduced in 1978 and controlled spark timing, EGR, and air injection. It did not include feedback fuel meter-

ing control. Ignition timing signals were provided by a crankshaft position sensor. On 1978 models, the sensor was installed in the rear of the engine block; in 1979, it was moved to the front of the crankshaft, behind the vibration damper.

General Motors' first partial-function timing control system was the microprocessor sensing and automatic regulation (MISAR) system used on 1977 Oldsmobile Toronados. The system used a crankshaft position sensor, a standard high energy ignition (HEI) distributor, and an electronic control module (the system computer) to control spark advance. In 1978, the system was renamed electronic spark timing (EST).

Fuel Metering Control Only

In 1979, Chrysler modified its ELB, or electronic spark control system, to work with feedback carburetors and EGO sensors. This system was used on some 6-cylinder engines and was close to a full-function engine control system.

In Chapter 14 you read about Ford's earliest feedback control (FBC) system used on some 1978 2.3-liter 4-cylinder engines, figure 15-16. Used with a 3-way catalytic converter (TWC-COC) and an EGO sensor, this system controlled only fuel metering through the Holley

---

■ Drive by Wire

You have learned that cable-operated throttle linkage is a standard design, used on many vehicles for several decades. It's a pretty obvious design choice when you think about it. Connect the accelerator pedal to the carburetor or fuel injection throttle body with a flexible cable. On many cars, it's a lot simpler than an arrangement of levers, cranks, and springs. Cable-operated throttles are simple and straightforward devices, but they are not what engineers refer to when they talk about "drive-by-wire" systems today.

Current electronic engine control systems use various actuators to control fuel metering, EGR operation, and idle speed. Imagine, for a moment, the possibility of replacing a throttle lever or cable with an electronic control system. Then the driver could control the engine through electrical wires, without a direct mechanical connection to the throttle.

Such systems are not a scientific pipedream. Developmental systems are in operation today. Here is how they generally work:

• The accelerator pedal is connected to a position sensor, usually a potentiometer. This is similar to the airflow sensors or throttle position sensors used with engine control systems.

• The accelerator sensor sends a variable (analog) voltage signal to the engine control computer to indicate pedal position.

• The computer evaluates this signal along with signals from other sensors that indicate engine and vehicle speed, crankshaft position, temperature, ignition timing, air-fuel metering, and other operating variables.

• The computer sends an output signal to a servomotor connected to the throttle valve.

• The servomotor opens and closes the throttle valve in direct relation to the driver's movement of the accelerator pedal.

It's all quite practical, and such a system can be built with the technology available since the late 1970s. Besides applications to cars, drive-by-wire systems have

major advantages for construction equipment and other specialized machinery where the driver is in a remote and mechanically awkward position in relation to the engine. For such equipment, electronic throttle control can be much more precise and economical than a complex arrangement of cables and levers.

Even though drive-by-wire systems can be built with today's technology, one final electronic development is necessary to "fine tune" them for automotive applications. That is the production of an economical and reliable engine torque sensor. Engine torque — pulling power — is one operating condition that a driver's brain and right foot can sense more accurately and more quickly than a simple electronic device can.

Torque sensors exist today, and engineers are working to make them practical, cheap, and reliable for automotive use. When torque sensors are added to engine control systems, driving by wire will be commonplace in the 21st century.

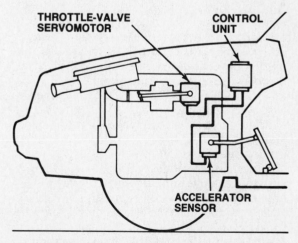

An accelerator sensor, an electronic control unit (computer), and a throttle servomotor are the major parts of a drive-by-wire system.

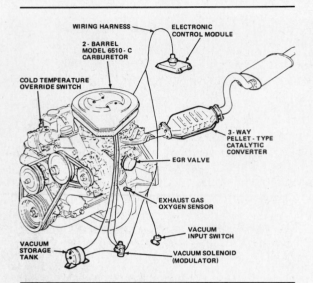

Figure 15-17. The GM electronic fuel control (EFC) system.

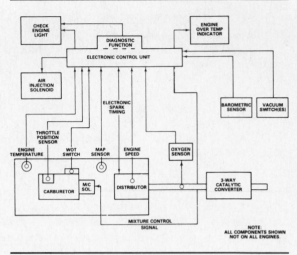

Figure 15-18. The GM C-4 system.

6500 carburetor. It did not control ignition timing or other engine functions.

Ford changed the system computer from an analog to a digital processor on 1980 models and reidentified the system as the microprocessor control unit (MCU) system. The first versions controlled fuel metering in a way similar to the earlier FBC or TWC-COC systems. Later versions in the mid-1980s controlled canister purging, idle speed, and detonation spark timing. Some MCU systems include simple self-diagnostic capabilities.

Ford's EEC-II system appeared on some 1979 V-8s and controlled air injection switching and vapor canister purging, along with feedback fuel metering. Fully electronic spark timing control was not included. Ford's EEC-III, introduced in 1980, also was based on 3-way catalytic converters and EGO sensors. It was used with feedback carburetors and with throttle body fuel injectors (called central fuel injection — CFI — by Ford). EEC-III was the first Ford system to have a self-test program.

Chapter 14 of this manual also introduced you to General Motors' electronic fuel control (EFC) system used on some 1978-79 151-cid (2.5-liter) engines, figure 15-17. The GM EFC system was quite similar to Ford's early FBC system. It used a 3-way converter, an EGO sensor, and a Holley 6510-C feedback carburetor. The early GM and Ford systems both controlled the carburetor through a vacuum solenoid that operated diaphragms to regulate metering rods and air bleeds.

In mid-1979, GM introduced the computer-controlled catalytic converter (C-4) system on the 1980 X-cars and some Buick V-6 engines,

figure 15-18. The first C-4 systems were partial-function systems that controlled fuel metering and provided limited ignition timing control. The C-4 system developed into the GM full-function computer command control (CCC or C-3) system, described later in this chapter.

Limited (Partial) Function Systems

GM introduced a minimum function control system on certain 1982 Chevette and Pontiac T-1000 4-cylinder engines. It differs from the full-function systems in four major ways:
1. It controls fuel metering only.
2. It has only seven trouble codes.
3. A coolant temperature switch closes when a predetermined engine coolant temperature is reached. At this time, the ECM switches system operation from open to closed loop, if the EGO sensor is at operating temperature and a programmed time interval has elapsed after the engine is started. Once the coolant switch closes, there is no effect on system operation if it opens due to a malfunction. The temperature switch was replaced by a coolant sensor on 1983 models.
4. Since the ECM does not provide a fixed dwell during open-loop operation, the range of dwell control is limited. Open-loop time consists of four regions, or areas. Dwell control varies according to which region the ECM is in at that time. For example, the system may be in open loop, but if dwell were measured, it would give a reading as if the system were in closed loop.
5. Memory is short-term, as is the case with some early C-4 systems. Any trouble codes set in memory are lost each time the ignition is

turned off. With short-term memory, trouble codes must be located before shutting the engine off.

FULL-FUNCTION CONTROL SYSTEMS

As we have seen, the earliest control systems affected a single system: ignition timing or fuel metering. Full-function systems control two or more engine functions. In doing so, they share many components and operational principles.

The early full-function control systems had one or more of the following characteristics; late-model systems have all of them.
• The computer controls timing electronically instead of relying on distributor vacuum and centrifugal advance mechanisms.
• The computer controls air-fuel ratio as close as possible to the stoichiometric value (14.7) through an EGO sensor and a 3-way catalytic converter.
• The computer controls fuel metering by operating a carburetor mixture control solenoid or by pulsing fuel injectors according to data received from various sensors.
• Engine operation is divided into open- and closed-loop operational modes. A separate ''limp-in mode'', or ''limited operational strategy'', is provided when a serious system malfunction occurs, allowing the vehicle to be driven in for service.
• The computer can set a number of trouble codes and may have a self-diagnostic capability.

CONTROL SYSTEM DEVELOPMENT

Engine computer control systems have developed considerably since they first appeared a decade ago. Today's systems, however, are undergoing even more rapid development into a highly sophisticated electronic network composed of many microprocessors (computers) that eventually will manage all operational and customer convenience systems in a vehicle. The body computer module (BCM) concept which appeared on some 1986 GM luxury cars is the first generation of these ''total control'' systems, and their development should be more rapid than the progress we've seen with engine control systems.

COMMON COMPONENTS

As we have seen, all engine control systems use a computer, a series of sensors, and various actuators. The sensors feed data to the computer in the form of voltage signals. The computer processes the sensor data according to its internal program and then signals the actuators to exercise the desired control over the subsystems that require adjustment.

System Sensors

As we learned in Chapter 14, a sensor is an input device used to change temperature, motion, light, pressure, and other forms of energy into voltage signals that a computer can read. Input sensors tell the computer what is happening in several areas of vehicle operation at any given moment. Typical sensors used as computer inputs are shown at the top of figure 15-19.

These basic types of sensors were dealt with at length in Chapter 14. For our purposes here, a quick review of their outstanding characteristics should refresh your memory before we look at specific sensor applications.
• *Switch* — the simplest form of sensor, it signals an on or off condition.
• *Timer* — used to delay a signal for a predetermined length of time to prevent the computer from compensating for momentary conditions that do not significantly affect engine operation.
• *Resistive sensors* — may be potentiometers, thermistors, or piezoresistive devices.
• *Transformer* — contains a movable core that varies its position between input and output windings to produce a voltage signal.
• *Generator* — may be a magnetic pulse generator, a Hall-effect switch, or a galvanic battery. These sensors do not require a reference voltage but generate their own signal voltage.

Airflow sensors

Some fuel injection systems use a vane-type airflow sensor, figure 15-20, positioned between the air filter and the intake manifold. The airflow sensor monitors the volume of air entering the intake manifold. A thermistor is used to sense air temperature and is part of the vane. Since the angular position of the vane is proportional to airflow, a potentiometer connected to the vane sends a voltage signal proportional to intake air volume to the computer.

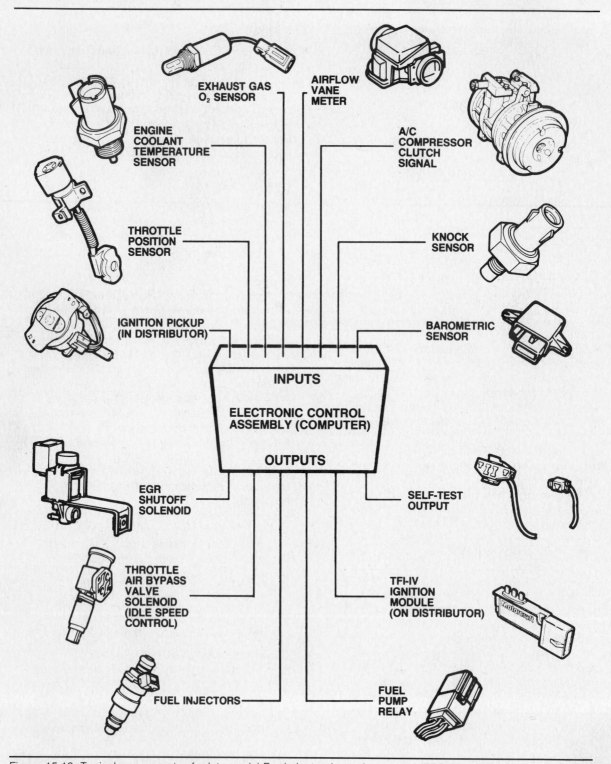

Figure 15-19. Typical components of a late-model Ford electronic engine control (EEC-IV) system.

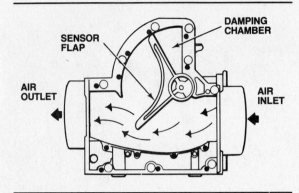

Figure 15-20. A vane-type airflow sensor.

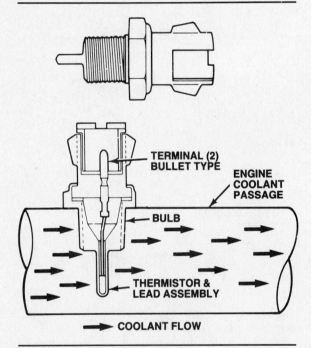

Figure 15-21. An engine coolant temperature sensor is installed in a coolant passage. (Ford)

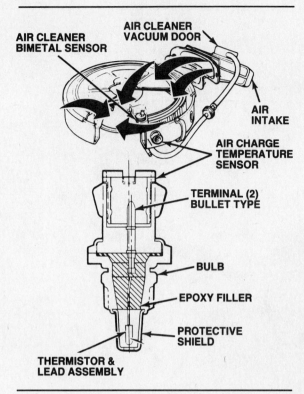

Figure 15-22. An air charge temperature (ACT) sensor may be installed in the air cleaner or intake manifold. (Ford)

Manifold pressure, vacuum, and barometric pressure sensors

These sensors keep the computer informed about air volume and engine load, allowing it to adjust fuel metering accordingly. Their input also is used by the computer to adjust timing and EGR flow relative to load. They may be a piezoresistive device, a transformer, or a potentiometer operated by an aneroid bellows or vacuum diaphragm.

Temperature sensors

Two types of temperature sensors are used: engine coolant and **air charge temperature (ACT).** If the computer is only interested in whether coolant or air temperature is above a stated point, a simple bimetal switch is used.

However, when the computer requires information about a temperature range, a thermistor is used.

The thermistor-type sensor used to track coolant temperature is threaded into a passage where its sensing bulb is immersed in engine coolant, figure 15-21.

An air charge temperature sensor is similar in construction to the coolant temperature sensor, but provides a faster response time to air temperature changes. It may be located in the air cleaner, figure 15-22, to measure only air temperature, or in the intake manifold where it measures the air-fuel mixture temperature.

Throttle position sensors

A throttle position sensor (TPS) may be a simple on/off switch, used to indicate wide-open throttle or idle position with a high or low voltage. The carburetor switch used on some Chrysler carburetors is an example of this type of TPS.

Air Charge Temperature (ACT) Sensor: A thermistor used to measure intake air temperature or air-fuel mixture temperature.

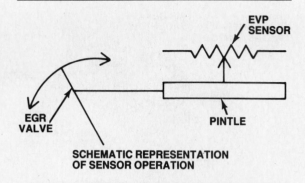

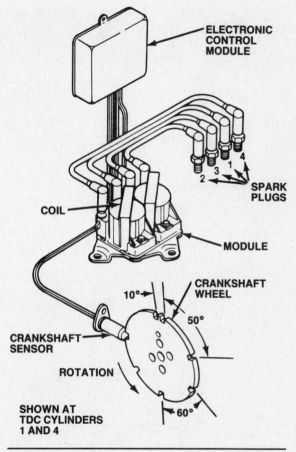

Figure 15-24. Rotation of a crankshaft timing disc through a sensor field tells the computer the cylinder position and provides a triggering signal to fire the proper coil. (GM)

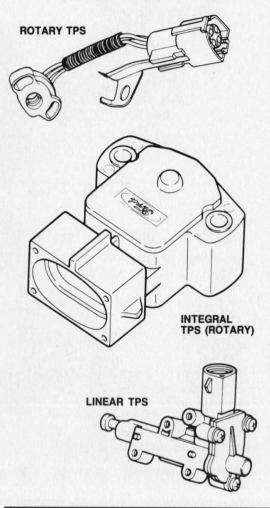

Figure 15-23. Typical throttle position sensors and their operation. (Ford)

A potentiometer also can be used to indicate the exact position and speed of throttle movement. The TPS may be a rotary or a linear potentiometer, figure 15-23, depending upon its application. A rotary throttle position sensor is used on fuel injection assemblies. A linear TPS generally is used with carburetors. The two types differ primarily in how they work, but both send the computer an analog signal proportional to the angle of the throttle plate opening. The rotary potentiometer moves on an axis with the throttle shaft; the linear potentiometer uses a plunger that rides on a throttle shaft cam.

Ignition timing, crankshaft position, and engine speed sensors

These sensors send analog and digital signals which the computer uses to control timing, fuel metering, and EGR. A Hall-effect switch is mounted on or in the engine block. A timing disc mounted on the harmonic balancer or cast as part of the crankshaft, figure 15-24, passes through the Hall-effect switch field. This is used as a signal to inform the computer of cylinder position and firing order.

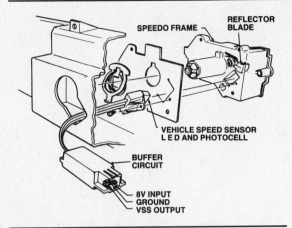

Figure 15-25. An LED and a photocell in the speedometer act as a speed sensor. (GM)

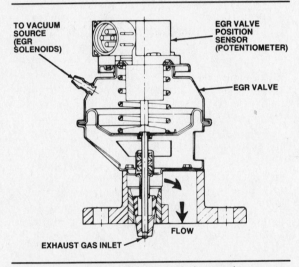

Figure 15-26. A potentiometer may be used to sense EGR flow. (Ford)

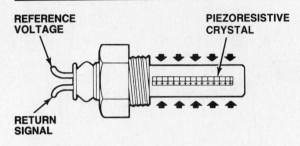

NO DETONATION—EQUAL PRESSURE

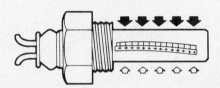

DETONATION—UNEQUAL PRESSURE

Figure 15-27. A piezoresistive crystal changes its resistance when pressure is applied. (Ford)

Vehicle speed sensors
Vehicle speed information necessary to control torque converter lockup is provided to the computer by a pulse generator or optical sensor. The most common type now in use has a reflective blade attached to the speedometer assembly, figure 15-25. As the blade spins, it passes through a light emitting diode (LED) beam. Each time the blade cuts through the LED beam, it reflects light back to a phototransistor. This creates a low-power signal which is amplified and sent to the ECM.

EGR sensors
A sliding-contact potentiometer may be connected to the top of the EGR valve stem to inform the computer of EGR flow rate, figure 15-26. This information is used by the computer to control timing, fuel metering and EGR valve operation.

Air conditioning sensors
An air conditioning compressor adds to the engine load when the compressor clutch is engaged. To allow the computer to make the necessary adjustments to compensate for the increased load, a simple on/off switch is used to tell the computer whether the compressor clutch is engaged or disengaged.

Detonation sensors
Detonation sensors generally use a piezoresistive crystal which changes resistance whenever pressure is applied to it, figure 15-27. A reference voltage from the computer is applied to one terminal. The return signal voltage from the other terminal remains at its programmed value as long as there is no detonation and as long as pressure on the crystal is uniform. However, if detonation occurs, the unequal pressure on the crystal changes the sensor's resistance and the return voltage signal changes.

SYSTEM ACTUATORS

In Chapter 14, we learned that an actuator is an output device that changes the computer's voltage signal into a mechanical action. Most engine control actuators are solenoids, although stepper motors are used in some applications.

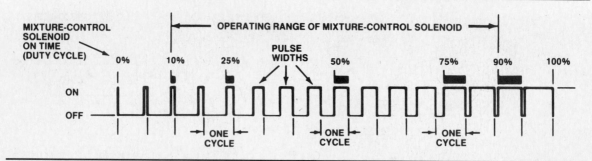

Figure 15-28. Duty cycle, or the percentage of solenoid on-time, can be altered to control fuel metering. While total cycle time remains constant, duty cycle and pulse width may vary. (GM)

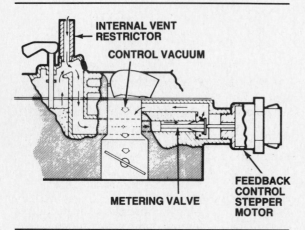

Figure 15-29. A stepper motor is used in early Ford 7200 VV carburetors to vary air pressure on the fuel bowl. (Ford)

A solenoid is an electromechanical device that operates much like a simple switch: voltage is applied to energize it and removed to deenergize it. For this reason, it can be considered a digital actuator. Solenoids typically are used to control a vacuum signal or to control fuel flow and air bleeds.

A stepper motor is a d.c. motor that moves in approximately 100 to 120 incremental steps as it goes from a deenergized state (no voltage) to a fully energized state (full voltage). The stepper motor functions as an analog actuator with digital signals. Stepper motors are primarily used for idle speed and mixture control.

Solenoid Operation

Most solenoids used in a computer control system are grounded through the computer. This allows the computer to control voltage to the solenoid without having to switch system voltage. The solenoid can be energized for any length of time the computer desires, or it can pulse on and off at a given rate per second.

You learned about pulse width modulation and duty cycle in Chapter 14 and also in this chapter when you studied fuel injector solenoids. Pulse width, or the length of time that a solenoid remains energized, is not a concern with solenoids that are energized indefinitely. However, if a solenoid is required to pulse on and off rapidly, pulse width and duty cycle become factors. Figure 15-28 illustrates the relationship between pulse width, variable duty cycle, and fixed cycle time for a mixture control solenoid used in a feedback carburetor.

As we saw earlier, a computer-controlled fuel system operating in open-loop ignores the EGO sensor. It sends a predetermined, fixed duty cycle to the fuel solenoid. When the system switches into closed-loop operation, the fuel solenoid duty cycle is varied by the computer according to sensor input to maintain the 14.7 air-fuel ratio as closely as possible.

Fuel Metering Actuators

A mixture control solenoid or a stepper motor is designed to produce a 14.7 air-fuel ratio at the midpoint of its operational range (or at a 50-percent duty cycle). Such actuators usually have a leeway of ± 2, making them capable of producing air-fuel ratios from 12.7 to 16.7:1.

Stepper motors

This type of actuator is used in some Motorcraft and Carter carburetors. The motor can control the air-fuel ratio by moving the metering pins into the main circuit air bleeds to reduce air and thus enrich the mixture, or moving them outward to allow more air to enter and lean the mixture. The stepper motor used in the Motorcraft 7200 VV carburetor controls the air-fuel ratio by moving a metering valve inside the carburetor. In early models of this carburetor, the metering valve opened a passage, figure 15-29. This allows control vacuum to enter the fuel bowl, lowering the air pressure on the fuel and leaning the air-fuel

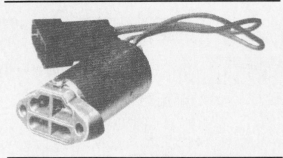

Figure 15-32. A pulse solenoid controls variable air bleeds in some Carter carburetors. (Carter)

The idle speed control (ISC) and idle air control (IAC) motors used on some Ford and General Motors fuel systems are other examples of stepper motors, figure 15-30.

Mixture control solenoids

All mixture control solenoids work on the variable duty cycle principle, but they can manage air-fuel ratios in different ways. The mixture control solenoid used in Rochester carburetors, figure 15-31, is an integral part of the carburetor. It operates both a metering rod in the main jet and a rod that controls an idle air bleed passage. Other systems use a solenoid that controls vacuum to a diaphragm installed in the carburetor. The vacuum diaphragm controls the operation of the metering rods and air bleeds.

Some Carter carburetors use a pulse solenoid with a variable duty cycle to control the air bleeds, figure 15-32.

EGR Actuators

Engine control computer systems that manage EGR flow use solenoids to regulate the amount of vacuum applied to the EGR valve. Although system designs differ, figure 15-33 shows a typical system, as used in Ford's EEC-II.

Other System Actuators

In addition to controlling ignition timing and fuel metering, the newer integrated electronic engine systems control several other functions:
• Torque converter lockup or engine shifting: solenoid valves in the transmission or transaxle hydraulic circuits respond to computer signals based on vehicle speed and engine load sensors

Figure 15-30. GM uses a stepper motor as an idle speed control for a carburetor (top) or to control airflow in a fuel injection throttle body (bottom).

Figure 15-31. A mixture control solenoid used in Rochester carburetors.

ratio. Later models of the 7200 VV worked differently. The valve opens air bleeds to let more air into the air-fuel mixture at the discharge jets.

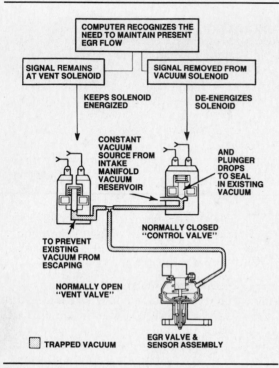

Figure 15-33. A typical computer-controlled EGR system. (Ford)

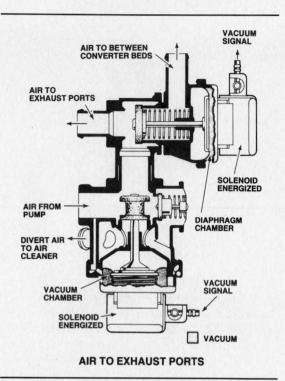

Figure 15-34. The Delco air switching valve uses two solenoids. (Delco-Remy)

• Air injection switching: one or more solenoids operate a valve in the vacuum line to the air switching or air control valve, figure 15-34
• Vapor canister purge: a solenoid installed in the canister-to-carburetor or manifold valve line opens and closes as directed by the computer.

HISTORY OF ENGINE CONTROL SYSTEMS

Electronic engine controls appeared on the automotive scene with the 1977 models. The early control systems regulated only a single function: either ignition timing or fuel metering. However, they were rapidly expanded to control both systems, as well as numerous other engine functions. Most late-model engine control systems have a self-diagnostic capability, and display trouble codes for troubleshooting, and do the following:
• Open- and closed-loop operation
• Electronic ignition timing control
• Fuel metering control
• Stoichiometric air-fuel ratio control
• EGR flow control
• Air injection switching
• Vapor canister purging
• Automatic transmission or transaxle torque converter lockup.

Bosch Lambda and Motronic Systems

The Robert Bosch Company pioneered fuel injection and electronic controls used in European vehicles. The Volvo Lambda-Sond system (manufactured by Bosch) was combined with K-Jetronic fuel injection on 1977 Volvo models sold in the U.S. This was the first electronically controlled fuel metering system using a 3-way catalytic converter and EGO sensor. (This system was also described in Chapter 14 and illustrated in figure 14-45.)

An input signal from the EGO sensor results in an output signal to the K-Jetronic timing valve. This valve varies the injection control pressure and regulates the fuel supplied by the continuous injection nozzles. The original Lambda-Sond system controls only fuel metering.

The Bosch Motronic or digital motor electronics (DME) system added ignition timing and electronic spark control to the fuel metering control of the Lambda-Sond system. In addition to the 3-way converter and EGO sensor, the DME system receives input signals from crankshaft speed and position sensors, a magnetic pulse generator in the distributor, and the L-Jetronic sensors. This allows the computer to:
• Adjust injector pulse width for air-fuel ratio control

• Adjust ignition timing for combined speed and load conditions
• Shut off injection completely during closed-throttle deceleration.

Chrysler

Chrysler introduced its electronic lean-burn (ELB) spark timing control system in 1976 on some 6.6L (400-cid) V-8 engines, figure 15-13. The system is based on a special carburetor that provides air-fuel ratios as lean as 18:1 and a modified electronic ignition controlled by an analog spark control computer attached to the air cleaner housing. Two printed circuit boards inside the computer contain the spark control circuitry. The program schedule module receives the sensor inputs and interprets them for the ignition control module, which directs the spark timing output. The 1976 ELB distributor has dual ignition pickups and a centrifugal advance mechanism. The distributor secondary components are similar to those used with the basic Chrysler electronic ignition. A dual ballast resistor controls primary current and protects the spark control computer from voltage spikes.

In 1977, ELB became available on all Chrysler V-8 engines and the centrifugal advance mechanism was eliminated. A second-generation ELB design was used on 5.2L (318-cid) V-8s. The start pickup in the distributor was dropped, and the computer was redesigned so all the circuitry fit on a single board.

The second-generation system was adopted on all V-8s in 1978, and a new ELB version was introduced on the Omni and Horizon 4-cylinder engine. The 4-cylinder system uses a Hall-effect distributor instead of a magnetic pickup. It has variable dwell to control primary current and does not use a ballast resistor. The 4-cylinder spark control computer is mounted on the left front fender, figure 15-14.

With the introduction of 3-way converters, the ELB system was modified in 1979 to work with revised carburetors that provided air-fuel ratios closer to 14.7. The protection circuitry was integrated into the computer, and the dual ballast resistor was replaced by a single 1.2-ohm resistor to control primary current only. This third-generation system was renamed electronic spark control (ESC) and appeared on some 6-cylinder inline engines with an EGO sensor and a feedback carburetor.

The 1980 model year was a transitional one for Chrysler. All California engines received ESC with feedback fuel control. The 5.9L (360-cid) V-8 and Canadian 5.2L (318-cid) 4-barrel V-8s continued to use ESC without the feedback system. All other engines reverted to basic electronic ignition with mechanical and vacuum advance mechanisms. Detonation sensors were introduced on some 1980 ESC systems, but the biggest change was the switch from an analog to a digital computer. Models with the digital computer in 1980 can be identified by their return to dual ignition pickups in the distributor. Systems with digital computers also eliminate the ballast resistor completely. Since 1981, all of Chrysler's domestic, carbureted, 4-cylinder engines and all 6-cylinder and V-8 powerplants have feedback fuel control and digital ESC systems without ballast resistors.

Chrysler introduced the modular control system (MCS), figure 15-35, in late 1983 on throttle-body fuel-injected 4-cylinder engines. In 1984, its use was expanded to turbocharged port-injected engines as well. The modular control system regulates vehicle functions using two separate modules whose functions are similar to the two circuit boards in the original ELB computer. The logic module handles all of the low-current tasks within the system, including receiving the inputs and making control decisions. A replaceable PROM is mounted in the logic module housing, and a self-test program is provided to aid in system diagnosis. The logic module is mounted inside the car to avoid underhood electrical interference.

The power module handles the high-current tasks and is located in the left front fender. It looks similar to the spark control computer used in 4-cylinder ESC systems. The power module contains the regulated power supply for the entire control system, along with the switching controls for the ignition coil, fuel injectors, and auto-shutdown relay (ASD). The ASD supplies power to the coil, the fuel pump relay, and the power module when it detects a distributor cranking signal.

All of these Chrysler computer control systems are designed with an emergency "limp-in" mode. In case of a system failure, the computer reverts to a fixed set of operating values. This allows the vehicle to be driven to a shop for repair. If the failure is in the start pickup or the coil triggering circuitry, however, the engine will not start.

Ford

Ford introduced its feedback electronic engine control system, figure 15-16, on some 1978 2.3-liter, 4-cylinder engines. The system contains a

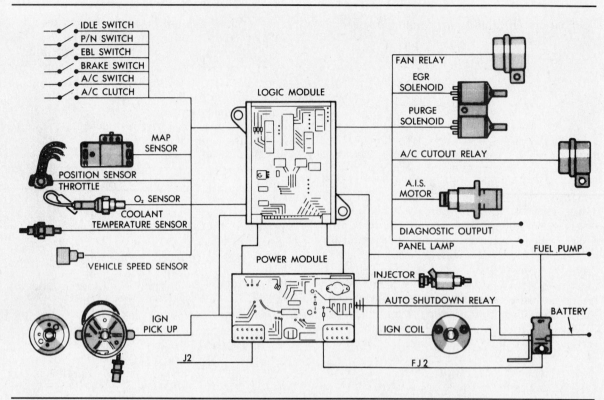

Figure 15-35. Chrysler's modular engine control system (single-point injection version shown).

3-way catalyst and conventional oxidation catalyst (TWC-COC) converter, an EGO sensor, a vacuum control solenoid, and an analog computer. Its control was limited to fuel metering. In 1980, a digital computer replaced the analog unit and the system was renamed the microprocessor control unit (MCU) fuel feedback system. The major change in early applications is the addition of self-diagnostics, but later designs have expanded capabilities including control over idle speedup, canister purge, and detonation spark control. They might be considered complete engine control systems except that they lack continuous spark timing control.

Ford also introduced its first generation electronic engine control (EEC-I) system, figure 15-15, on the 1978 Lincoln Versailles. This system controls spark timing, EGR flow, and air injection. A digital microprocessor electronic control assembly (ECA) installed in the passenger compartment receives signals from various sensors. It then determines the best spark timing, EGR flow rate, and air injection operation and sends signals to the appropriate control devices.

All 1978-79 California EEC-I systems use a variation of the blue-grommet Dura-Spark II

ignition. The 1979 Federal EEC-I system has a yellow-grommet dual-mode Dura-Spark II module. Although these modules appear similar to their non-EEC counterparts, they are controlled through the ECA and cannot be tested with the same procedures.

The ignition switching signal on 1978 EEC-I systems is provided by a sensor at the rear of the engine block that detects four raised ridges on a magnetic pulse ring mounted to the end of the crankshaft. In 1979, the pickup and pulse ring were moved to the front of the engine immediately behind the vibration damper. This design is used on the later EEC-II and EEC-III systems as well.

Late in 1979, Ford's second generation EEC-II system appeared on some 5.8L (351-cid) V-8 engines. EEC-II added electronic controls for vapor canister purging and air injection switching. In addition, dual 3-way converters are used with a feedback carburetor for precise air-fuel mixture control.

Ford's third generation EEC-III system appeared in 1980 and is available in two versions through 1984. EEC-III/FBC incorporates a feedback carburetor similar to the EEC-II system; EEC-III/CFI, figure 15-36, has a throttle-body-type central fuel injection system. All EEC-III

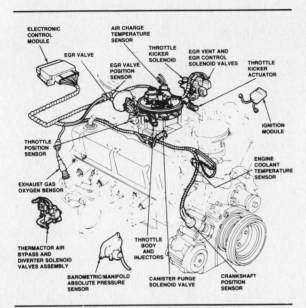

Figure 15-36. EEC-III/CFI system components.

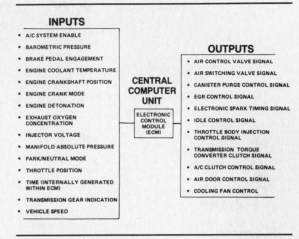

INPUTS

- A/C SYSTEM ENABLE
- BAROMETRIC PRESSURE
- BRAKE PEDAL ENGAGEMENT
- ENGINE COOLANT TEMPERATURE
- ENGINE CRANKSHAFT POSITION
- ENGINE CRANK MODE
- ENGINE DETONATION
- EXHAUST OXYGEN CONCENTRATION
- INJECTOR VOLTAGE
- MANIFOLD ABSOLUTE PRESSURE
- PARK/NEUTRAL MODE
- THROTTLE POSITION
- TIME (INTERNALLY GENERATED WITHIN ECM)
- TRANSMISSION GEAR INDICATION
- VEHICLE SPEED

CENTRAL COMPUTER UNIT

ELECTRONIC CONTROL MODULE (ECM)

OUTPUTS

- AIR CONTROL VALVE SIGNAL
- AIR SWITCHING VALVE SIGNAL
- CANISTER PURGE CONTROL SIGNAL
- EGR CONTROL SIGNAL
- ELECTRONIC SPARK TIMING SIGNAL
- IDLE CONTROL SIGNAL
- THROTTLE BODY INJECTION CONTROL SIGNAL
- TRANSMISSION TORQUE CONVERTER CLUTCH SIGNAL
- A/C CLUTCH CONTROL SIGNAL
- AIR DOOR CONTROL SIGNAL
- COOLING FAN CONTROL

Figure 15-37. Typical CCC system sensors (inputs) and controls (outputs).

systems use the Dura-Spark III ignition module. EEC-III is the first Ford computer engine control system to have a self-test program.

Ford's EEC-IV, figure 15-19, was introduced in 1983 and incorporates the thick-film integrated (TFI) ignition system. The 2-microchip EEC-IV microprocessor is much more powerful than the 4- or 5-microchip ECAs used with earlier EEC systems. EEC-IV has both increased memory and the ability to handle almost one million computations per second. Unlike earlier EEC systems, however, the EEC-IVs calibration assembly is located inside the ECA and cannot be replaced separately. All EEC-IV systems have an improved self-test capability with trouble codes that are stored for readout at a later date.

All Ford EEC systems have a limited operating strategy (LOS) mode in case of a failure within the system. The exact nature of the LOS varies from one system to another, but generally, the timing is fixed at 10 degrees, and other ECA outputs are rendered inoperable.

General Motors

The first GM spark timing control was offered on 1977-78 Oldsmobile Toronados. The 1977 system was called microprocessed sensing and automatic regulation (MISAR). MISAR is a basic spark timing system only. A rotating disc and stationary sensor on the front of the engine replace the pickup coil and trigger wheel of the distributor. Except for this change, the 1977 MISAR system uses a standard HEI distributor with a basic 4-terminal ignition module.

The MISAR system was modified in 1978 and renamed electronic spark timing (EST). The crankshaft-mounted disc and stationary sensor were dropped, and a conventional pickup coil and trigger wheel were again fitted in the HEI distributor. The ignition module, however, is a special 3-terminal design that is not interchangeable with any other HEI system.

In mid-1979, GM introduced the computer-controlled catalytic converter (C-4) system, figure 15-18. At first, the C-4 system was purely a fuel control system used with 3-way converters. But in 1980, Buick V-6 engines with C-4 were also fitted with an electronic spark timing (EST) system. Although this is the same name applied to the MISAR system just discussed, the two systems are not the same. C-4 with EST has a single electronic control module (ECM) that regulates both fuel delivery and spark timing. It was GM's first complete computer engine control system. The C-4 system was further upgraded in 1981 with EST in almost all applications, and additional control capabilities were added. The expanded system, figure 15-37, was renamed computer command control (CCC or C-3).

In 1986, GM began to update the CCC system through the introduction of a new ECM on certain vehicles. The new ECM is smaller than previous models, but has more functional capabilities. It operates at twice the speed of previous ECMs, and has fewer IC chips and internal connections. The new ECM draws less current with the ignition off, provides more diagnostic functions, and operates reliably on battery voltage as low as 6.3 volts.

BASIC COMPONENT LOCATIONS

1 INJECTOR	13 ELECTRONIC CONTROL UNIT (ECU)
2 THROTTLE POSITION SENSOR	14 SOLENOID-TO-EVAP CANISTER CONTROL
3 PRESSURE REGULATOR	15 STARTER MOTOR RELAY
4 IDLE SPEED CONTROL MOTOR	16 FUEL PUMP RELAY
5 SOLENOID-TO-EGR VALVE	17 FUEL PUMP
6 EGR VALVE	18 IGNITION CONTROL MODULE
7 MANIFOLD AIR/FUEL TEMPERATURE SENSOR	19 IN-LINE FUEL FILTER
8 O$_2$ - SENSOR	20 AIR CONDITIONER ON
9 SPEED SENSOR	21 TRANSAXLE NEUTRAL/PARK SWITCH
10 IGNITION SWITCH	22 CLOSED-THROTTLE (IDLE) SWITCH
11 POWER RELAY	23 WIDE-OPEN THROTTLE (WOT) SWITCH
12 MAP SENSOR	24 TEMPERATURE SENSOR (COOLANT)

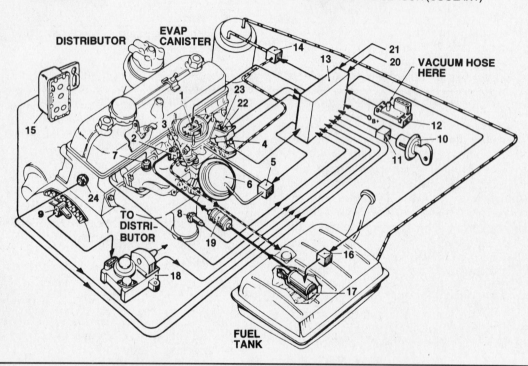

Figure 15-38. This AMC-Renault system is used to control fuel metering, ignition timing, emission devices, and transmission shift points. (AMC-Renault)

Service procedures for the new ECM allow repair and reprogramming by replacing several different integrated circuits in the computer. All C-4 and C-3 systems have self-diagnostic capabilities. The newer the system, the more comprehensive the diagnostic capabilities are. Several GM cars provide diagnostic readouts accessible through instrument panel displays.

American Motors

AMC uses the GM C-4 and C-3 systems on its Pontiac-built, 4-cylinder engines and its Chevrolet-built V-6s. AMC also has used a computerized emission control (CEC) system on 4- and 6-cylinder engines of its own manufacture since 1980.

AMC-Renault uses a fully integrated electronic engine control system made by Renix, a partnership between Renault and Bendix. The Renix system, figure 15-38, uses an array of sensors to control fuel metering, ignition timing, automatic transmission shifting, and emission controls.

Control System Development

As you have learned in this chapter, engine systems have developed considerably since they first appeared a decade ago. Today's computer control systems, however, are undergoing an even more rapid development into a highly sophisticated electronic system composed of many microprocessors (computers) that will eventually manage all operational and convenience systems in a vehicle. The body computer module (BCM) concept which appeared on some 1986 GM luxury cars is the first generation of these "total control" systems, and their development should be more rapid than the progress we've seen with engine control systems.

When a particular vehicle arrives for service, you will have to know the system's components, understand its operation, and use the correct procedures and specifications. As described in Chapter 6 of the *Shop Manual*, this information is available in service manuals available from the carmaker or independent publishers such as Chek-Chart. It is impossible for the individual technicians to carry all of this information in their heads.

However, you should not forget that the laws of electricity, physics, and chemistry have no manufacturer's trademark on them. They remain the same, and all of the systems we have studied operate on the same principles.

SUMMARY

All computers must perform four basic functions: input, processing, storage, and output. Engine control computers use various sensors to receive input data. This data is compared to lookup tables in the computer's memory. Some data may be stored in memory for future use. The computer output takes the form of voltage signals to its actuators.

A control system operates in an open loop-mode until the EGO sensor is warm enough, then the computer switches into the closed-loop mode. In open loop, the computer ignores feedback signals and functions with a predetermined set of values. Once the system switches into closed loop, the computer acts on the feedback signals and is constantly "re-tuning" the engine while it is running. The most recent computers have the ability to adapt their operating strategies to account for a number of conditional changes, including the wear that results from engine operation.

System sensors generally measure analog variables. Their voltage signals are digitized by the computer, which compares the signals to its program and sends an output signal to the actuators. Actuators change the computer voltage signal into electromechanical motion. Sensors are generally switches, resistors, transformers, or generators. Actuators are usually solenoids and stepper motors.

Computer-controlled engine systems began as a way of managing fuel metering for better mileage and emission control. Manufacturers used electronic ignitions with the fuel metering systems to form the basis for an engine management system. Chrysler's lean-burn, the Bosch DME system, Ford's EEC-I, and GM's C-4 system are examples of early engine control systems. The most recent systems, such as GM's CCC and Ford's EEC-IV systems, have self-diagnostic capabilities, control many more functions, and are far more efficient and powerful than their predecessors.

Review Questions

Choose the single most correct answer.
Compare your answers with the correct answers on page 451.

1. The first domestic engine control system was Chrysler's Electronic Lean-Burn. It controls:
   a. Ignition timing
   b. Fuel metering
   c. Both a and b
   d. Neither a nor b

2. A recent Ford engine control system is called:
   a. Electronic Feedback Fuel Control (EFC)
   b. Microprocessor Control Unit (MCU)
   c. Electronic Engine Control-IV (EEC-IV)
   d. Computerized Emission Control (CEC)

3. NO_x emissions may be reduced by:
   a. Enriching the fuel mixture
   b. Lowering the engine's compression ratio
   c. Recirculating exhaust gases
   d. Retarding spark timing

4. An engine coolant temperature sensor:
   a. Receives reference voltage from the computer
   b. Is a potentiometer
   c. Provides the computer with a digital signal
   d. Contains a piezoelectric crystal

5. Mechanic A says that an exhaust gas oxygen (EGO) sensor with two wires is grounded to the exhaust manifold.
   Mechanic B says that the computer ignores an EGO sensor in closed-loop operation.
   Who is right?
   a. A only
   b. B only
   c. Both A and B
   d. Neither A nor B

6. Mechanic A says that a throttle position sensor (TPS) may be either a rotary or a linear potentiometer.
   Mechanic B says that a TPS can be a simple on/off switch.
   Who is right?
   a. A only
   b. B only
   c. Both A and B
   d. Neither A nor B

7. Mechanic A says that the output signal from one computer can act as an input signal for another computer.
   Mechanic B says that late-model computers have self-diagnostic capabilities and can display trouble codes.
   Who is right?
   a. A only
   b. B only
   c. Both A and B
   d. Neither A nor B

8. Mechanic A says that excessive exhaust gas recirculation will increase HC emissions and fuel consumption.
   Mechanic B says that emissions are low and fuel consumption is high when timing is advanced.
   Who is right?
   a. A only
   b. B only
   c. Both A and B
   d. Neither A nor B

9. The first electrically controlled fuel metering system with a 3-way converter and EGO sensor was the:
   a. C-4 system
   b. Lambda-Sond system
   c. Ford FEEC system
   d. None of these

10. A GM "minimum function" system:
   a. May use a coolant temperature switch
   b. Has long-term memory
   c. Provides fixed dwell
   d. Controls only ignition timing

11. Which of the following is *not* true of a fuel-injected engine?
   a. The computer controls the air-fuel ratio by switching injectors on or off
   b. The pulse width is increased to supply more fuel
   c. To lean the mixture, the computer opens the air bleeds
   d. Engine speed determines the injector switching rate

12. What is the most efficient way to reduce NO_x without adversely affecting fuel economy, driveability, and HC emissions?
   a. Engine mapping
   b. Adaptive memory
   c. Spark timing delay
   d. Exhaust gas recirculation

13. The first GM ignition timing control was called:
   a. MISAR
   b. HEI
   c. EST
   d. TWC

14. Ford's EEC-II added what element to the earlier spark timing, EGR flow, and Thermactor air injection?
   a. Feedback carburetor
   b. Electronic controls for vapor canister purging
   c. Central fuel injection with TBI
   d. Electronic fault codes

15. A self-test program was part of which version of Ford's electronic engine controls?
   a. EEC-I
   b. EEC-II
   c. EEC-III
   d. EEC-IV

16. Which of the following is *not* true of a late-model full-function control system?
   a. The computer controls timing electronically
   b. The computer changes the air-fuel ratio within the range of 14:1 to 17:1
   c. Fuel metering is controlled with a carburetor MC solenoid or by pulsing fuel injectors
   d. The car can be driven in a limited operational strategy

16

Gasoline Fuel Injection Systems

A carburetor is a mechanical device that is neither totally accurate nor particularly fast in responding to changing engine requirements. Adding electronic feedback mixture control improves a carburetor's fuel metering capabilities under some circumstances, but most of the work is still done mechanically by the many jets, passages, and air bleeds. Adding feedback controls and other emission-related devices in recent years has resulted in very complex carburetors that are extremely expensive to repair or replace.

The intake manifold also is a mechanical device that, when teamed with a carburetor, results in less than ideal air-fuel control. Because of a carburetor's limitations, the manifold must locate it centrally over (V-engines), or next to (inline engines), the intake ports while remaining within the space limitations under the hood. The manifold runners have to be kept as short as possible to minimize fuel delivery lag, and there cannot be any low points where fuel might puddle. These restrictions severely limit the amount of manifold tuning possible, and even the best designs still have problems with fuel condensing on cold manifold walls.

The solution to the problems posed by a carbureted fuel system is **electronic fuel injection (EFI)**. EFI provides precise mixture control over all speed ranges and under all operating conditions. Its fuel delivery components are simpler and often less expensive than a feedback carburetor. Some designs allow a wider range of manifold designs. Equally important is that EFI offers the potential of highly reliable electronic control.

In this chapter, we will discuss:
• The advantages of fuel injection over carburetion
• The differences among various fuel injection systems
• The fundamentals of electronic fuel injection
• The subsystems and components of typical fuel injection systems now in use.

FUEL INJECTION OPERATING REQUIREMENTS

The major difference between a carbureted and an injected fuel system is the method of fuel

---

Electronic Fuel Injection (EFI): A computer-controlled fuel injection system which gives precise mixture control and almost instant response to all operating conditions at all speed ranges.

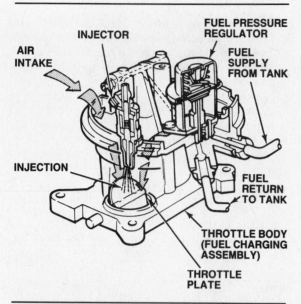

Figure 16-1. Air and fuel combine in a TBI unit at about the same point as in a carburetor. (Ford)

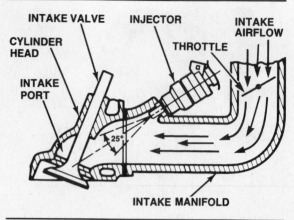

Figure 16-2. In a multipoint system, the air and fuel combine at the intake valve. (GM)

delivery. In a carbureted system, the carburetor mixes air and fuel. In a fuel injection system, one or more injectors meter the fuel into the intake air stream.

An electronic fuel injection system uses the same principle of pressure differential used in a carbureted system, but in a slightly different way. As you learned in Chapter 13, it is the difference in pressure between the inside and the outside of the engine that forces fuel out of the carburetor fuel bowl. In EFI systems, the airflow or air pressure sensor determines the pressure difference and informs the computer. The computer evaluates the air sensor's input along with that of other sensors to decide how much fuel is required for engine operation, then controls injector operation to provide the correct fuel quantity. The computer makes it possible for the fuel injectors to do all the functions of the main systems used in a carburetor. However, throttle response in an injected system is more rapid than in a carbureted system because the fuel is under pressure at all times. The computer calculates the changing pressure and opens the injector much quicker than a carburetor can react under similar conditions.

Carburetors must break up liquid gasoline into a fine mist, change the liquid into a vapor, and distribute the vapor evenly to the cylinders. Fuel injectors do the same. A fuel injector delivers atomized fuel into the air stream where it is instantly vaporized. In **throttle body injection (TBI)** systems, this occurs

above the throttle at about the same point as in a carbureted system, figure 16-1. With **multipoint injection** systems, the injectors are mounted in the intake manifold near the cylinder head and injection occurs as close as possible to the intake valve, figure 16-2. We will look at both systems in greater detail later in the chapter.

To review basic engine air-fuel requirements:
1. When an engine starts, low airflow and manifold vacuum, combined with a cold engine and poor fuel vaporization, require a rich air-fuel ratio.
2. At idle, low airflow and high manifold vacuum, combined with low carburetor vacuum and poor vaporization, still require a slightly rich air-fuel ratio.
3. At low speed, the air-fuel ratio becomes progressively leaner as engine speed, airflow, and carburetor vacuum increase.
4. At cruising speed, air-fuel ratios become the leanest for best economy with light load and high, constant vacuum and airflow.
5. For extra power such as acceleration or heavy load operation, the engine needs a richer air-fuel ratio. This requirement is combined with low vacuum and airflow on acceleration or with low vacuum and high airflow at wide-open throttle.

A carburetor satisfies all of these requirements as its systems respond to changes in air pressure and airflow. A fuel injection system does exactly the same things. All of the sensors and other devices in an injection system respond to the same operating conditions that a carburetor does, but an injection system responds faster and more precisely for a better combination of performance, economy, and emission control.

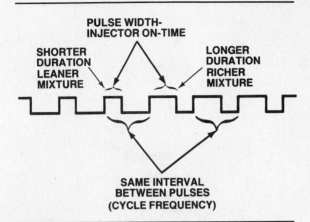

PULSE WIDTH-
INJECTOR ON-TIME

SHORTER
DURATION
LEANER
MIXTURE

LONGER
DURATION
RICHER
MIXTURE

SAME INTERVAL
BETWEEN PULSES
(CYCLE FREQUENCY)

Figure 16-3. Fuel injector pulse width determines the air-fuel ratio.

ADVANTAGES OF FUEL INJECTION

Fuel injection is not a new development. The first gasoline fuel injection systems were developed in 1912 by the Robert Bosch Company in Germany. Bosch's early work in fuel injection was restricted to aircraft applications, but the technology was transferred to automotive use in the 1930s. A decade later, two Americans named Hilborn and Enderle developed injection systems for use on racing engines. Chevrolet, Pontiac, and Chrysler offered mechanical fuel injection systems during the late 1950s and early 1960s. Some imported vehicles have had fuel injection since 1968. Among domestic manufacturers, Cadillac made electronic fuel injection standard on its 1976 Seville model, and other automakers soon followed suit.

What really made fuel injection a practical alternative to the carburetor was the development of reliable solid-state components during the 1970s. Automakers were quick to apply these advances in electronics to fuel injection. The result was a more efficient and dependable system of fuel delivery.

Electronic fuel injection systems offer several major advantages over carburetors:
• Injectors can precisely match fuel delivery to engine requirements under all load and speed conditions. This reduces fuel consumption with no loss of engine performance.
• Since intake air and fuel are mixed at the engine port, keeping a uniform mixture temperature is not as difficult with multipoint fuel injection systems as it is with carburetors. There is no need for manifold heat valves.
• The manifold in a multipoint injection system carries only air, so there is no problem of the air and fuel separating.

• Exhaust emissions are lowered by maintaining a precise air-fuel ratio according to engine requirements. The improved air-fuel flow in an injection system also helps to reduce emissions.
• Continuing improvements in electronic fuel injection design have allowed some automakers to eliminate other emission control systems such as heated intake air and air pumps.

AIR-FUEL MIXTURE CONTROL

Almost all of the electronic fuel injection systems used on domestic vehicles in recent years are integrated into complete electronic engine control systems with exhaust gas oxygen (EGO) feedback mixture control. The electronic controls of a fuel-injected engine are similar to those of an engine with a feedback carburetor. The main difference is that instead of regulating a vacuum solenoid, a stepper motor, or a mixture control solenoid, the computer switches one or more solenoid-operated fuel injectors on and off. Engine rpm determines the rate of switching, and the computer varies the length of time the injectors remain open (pulse width) to establish the air-fuel ratio, figure 16-3. Injector pulse width and duty cycle are explained in more detail later in this chapter.

This variable pulse width takes the place of all the different carburetor metering circuits. As the computer receives data from its inputs, it can lengthen the pulse width to supply additional fuel for cold running (choke), heavy loads (power enrichment), fast acceleration (accelerator pump), or several other situations. Similarly, it can shorten the pulse width to lean the mixture at idle (idle circuit), under cruise (main circuit), or during deceleration. On such systems, the EGO sensor provides fine tuning of the mixture under most operating conditions.

Throttle Body Injection (TBI): A fuel injection system in which one or two injectors are installed in a carburetor-like throttle body mounted on a conventional intake manifold. Fuel is sprayed at a constant pressure above the throttle plate to mix with the incoming air charge.

Multipoint (Port) Injection: A fuel injection system in which individual injectors are installed in the intake manifold at a point close to the intake valve. Air passing through the manifold mixes with the injector spray just as the intake valve opens.

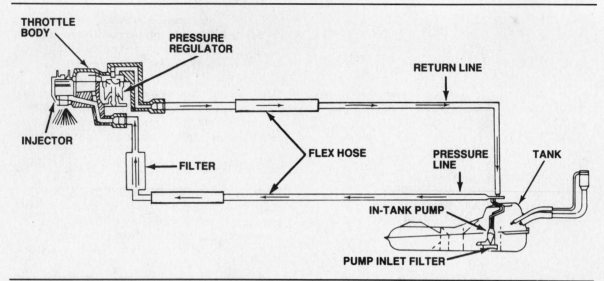

Figure 16-4. A typical throttle body injection system. (GM)

By weight, fuel makes up only about one-fifteenth of the air-fuel mixture. The computer is mainly concerned with regulating the fuel delivery, but to do this accurately, it must know the amount of air entering the engine. Because airflow and air pressure cannot act directly on the fuel as occurs in a carburetor, fuel injection systems use one of three basic kinds of intake air sensors:

1. A manifold pressure sensor
2. An airflow sensor
3. An air mass sensor.

Manifold pressure, airflow velocity, and the molecular mass of the intake air are all directly related to the weight of intake air. (Remember that air-fuel ratios are expressions of air and fuel weights by volume.) The computer has a set of values (similar to a graph) stored in memory. These values relate manifold pressure, airflow, or air mass to engine speed and the required fuel entering for any combination of conditions. Once the computer knows the amount of air entering the engine, as well as other conditions, it adjusts injector pulse width to achieve the required air-fuel ratio.

Some injection systems use combinations of the three basic kinds of sensors listed above. You will learn more about these sensors later in this chapter's section on air control systems.

TYPES OF FUEL INJECTION SYSTEMS

There are three general ways to categorize modern fuel injection systems:
• Mechanical or electronic injection

• Throttle body or multipoint (port or manifold) injection
• Continuous or intermittent injection.

However, the distinctions between the various types of fuel injection systems are not simple and clear-cut. All mechanical systems make use of some electronic components, and electronic systems may share some of the features of multipoint and TBI in a single system. One example is Chrysler's continuous-flow TBI system introduced in 1981 and used exclusively on V-8 engines in the Imperial. Although a technological dead end, this system breaks the rules of operation we're about to discuss. It has two injectors, mounted in the throttle body, which respond to varying pressure from a control pump and deliver fuel continuously. A unique airflow sensor in the air cleaner inlet measures the volume of air passing into the system. The entire operation is controlled electronically.

Mechanical or Electronic Injection

A mechanical fuel injection system delivers gasoline by using its pressure to open the injector valve. Mechanical injection systems generally are continuously operating. In other words, they inject fuel constantly while the engine is operating. The Bosch K-Jetronic is a typical example of a mechanical injection system.

An electronic fuel injection EFI system generally uses one or more solenoid-operated injectors to spray fuel in timed pulses, either into the intake manifold or near the intake

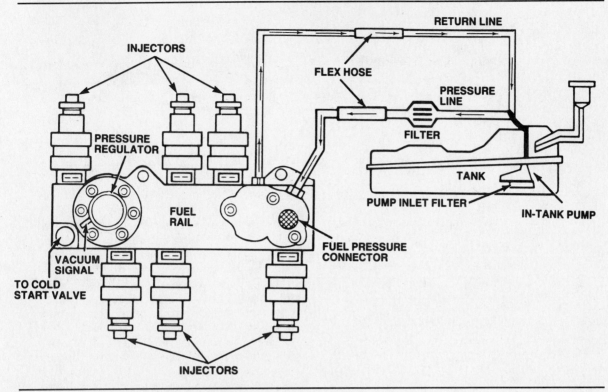

Figure 16-5. A typical 6-cylinder multipoint injection system. (GM)

port. EFI systems are operated intermittently. All domestic manufacturers use some form of EFI.

Throttle Body or Multipoint Injection

The most common type of EFI system is throttle body injection (TBI), figure 16-4. This design is something of a halfway measure between feedback carburetion and multipoint injection. It generally is classified as a single-point, pulse-time, modulated injection system. TBI injection, as its name implies, has one or two injectors in a carburetor-like TBI assembly that mounts on a traditional intake manifold. Fuel is kept at a constant pressure by a regulator built into the throttle body, figure 16-1.

The computer controls injector pulsing in one of two ways: synchronized or nonsynchronized. If the system uses a synchronized mode, the injector pulses once for each distributor reference pulse. When dual injectors are used in a synchronized system, the injectors pulse alternately. In a nonsynchronized system, the injectors are pulsed once during a

given period (which varies according to calibration) completely independent of distributor reference pulses.

A TBI system has certain advantages: it provides improved fuel metering over a carburetor, it is easier to service, and it is less expensive to manufacture. Its disadvantages are primarily related to the manifold: fuel distribution is unequal and a cold manifold still causes fuel to condense and puddle. To compensate for this placement, some systems use two differently calibrated injectors. This results in a different amount of fuel being sprayed by each injector. Also, a TBI unit, like a carburetor, must be mounted above the combustion chamber level. This generally prevents the use of tuned intake manifold designs.

Multipoint, or port, injection, figure 16-5, is older than TBI and because of its many advantages, will probably be the system of choice for all but economy-class vehicles in the future. Multipoint systems have one injector for each engine cylinder. The injectors are mounted in the intake manifold near the cylinder head where they can inject fuel as close as possible to the intake valve, figure 16-2.

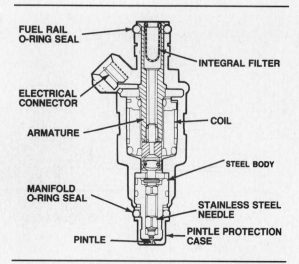

Figure 16-6. A multipoint (port) electronic fuel injector.

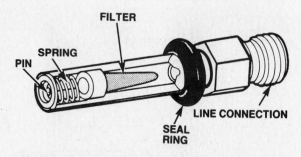

Figure 16-7. A Bosch K-Jetronic mechanical fuel injector. (Bosch)

The advantages of this design also are related to characteristics of intake manifolds:
• Fuel distribution is equal to all cylinders because each cylinder has its own injector, figure 16-6.
• The fuel is injected almost directly into the combustion chamber, so there is no chance for it to condense on the walls of a cold intake manifold.
• Because the manifold does not have to carry fuel or properly position a carburetor or TBI unit, it can be shaped and sized to tune the intake airflow to achieve specific engine performance characteristics.

The primary disadvantage of multipoint injection is the higher cost of individual injectors and other parts, as well as the computer software to control their operation.

Continuous or Intermittent Injection

A **continuous injection system** constantly injects fuel whenever the engine is running. The most common example used on production vehicles is the Bosch K-Jetronic mechanical continuous injection system. (Many carmakers refer to K-Jetronic simply as CIS.)

The individual injectors, figure 16-7, operate on the opposing forces of fuel pressure and the spring-loaded valve in the injector tip. When inlet fuel pressure reaches about 45 psi (310 kPa), it overcomes spring pressure and forces the injector open. Each injector then delivers fuel continuously to the port near the intake valve. Fuel collects or "waits" at the valve to mix with incoming air. When the intake valve opens, the air-fuel mixture enters the cylinder.

In the K-Jetronic system, fuel pressure controls injector opening and the amount of fuel that is injected. Fuel pressure varies continually during different engine operating conditions. Under heavy load, for example, fuel pressure may reach 70 psi (483 kPa). This forces the injector farther open to admit more fuel.

The main fuel distributor and regulator controls fuel pressure in response to airflow and preset regulator pressure. Injector spring force and fuel pressure cause the injector valve to vibrate. This constantly varies the amount of fuel in relation to engine requirements and helps to atomize the fuel as it is injected.

When the engine is shut off, fuel pressure drops below injector tip spring pressure, and the injectors close. Residual fuel pressure is retained in the lines to ensure a ready fuel supply when the engine is restarted.

Electronic Injection Nozzle

To understand fuel injection as part of a complete engine control system, you must understand the operation and control of electronic injection nozzles. An electronic injection nozzle is simply a specialized solenoid, figure 16-8. It has an armature and a needle or ball valve. A spring holds the needle or ball closed against the valve seat, and the armature opens the valve when it receives a current pulse from the system computer. When the solenoid is energized, it unseats the valve to inject fuel.

The injector always opens the same distance, and the fuel pressure is maintained at a constant value by the pressure regulator. The amount of fuel delivered by the injector depends on the amount of time that the nozzle is open. This is the injector pulse width: the time in milliseconds that the nozzle is open.

The system computer varies pulse width to supply the amount of fuel that an engine needs at a specific moment. A long pulse

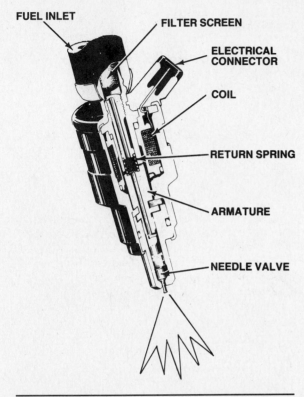

Figure 16-8. Solenoid actions intermittently open the EFI nozzles. (Volvo)

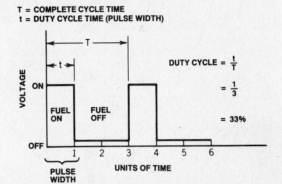

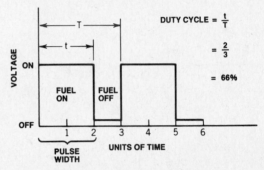

A. SHORT DUTY CYCLE (PULSE WIDTH), MINIMUM FUEL INJECTION

B. LONG DUTY CYCLE (PULSE WIDTH), MAXIMUM FUEL INJECTION

Figure 16-9. Comparison of pulse width and duty cycle for the same cycle time.

width delivers more fuel; a short pulse width delivers less fuel.

Injector pulse width relates to another important concept that you will use to test injection systems. This is the injector duty cycle. The duty cycle relates to any intermittently operating device. Ignition dwell, for example, is really the ignition duty cycle. The complete operating cycle of any solenoid-operated device is the entire time from *on* to *off* to *back on* again. The duty cycle is the percentage of on-time to total cycle time.

A solenoid can operate at any number of cycles per second: 10, 20, 30, 60, or whatever the engineer chooses to design. Each complete cycle lasts the same amount of time, but duty cycle can vary as a percentage of each cycle. Pulse width varies along with the duty cycle because it is the actual *time* that the solenoid is energized. Figure 16-9 shows two different pulse widths and duty cycles for the same complete cycle time. The system computer calculates the necessary pulse width and duty cycle from information provided by system sensors. Modern digital computers operate fast enough to change injector pulse width in fractions of a second to maintain precise fuel metering.

Various Sequence Combinations

Electronic fuel injection systems use a solenoid-operated injector, figure 16-6, to spray atomized fuel in timed pulses (intermittently) into the manifold or near the intake valve. Injectors may be sequenced and fired in one of several ways, as we will see shortly, but their duty cycle and pulse width are determined and controlled by the engine computer.

Multipoint systems contain an injector for each cylinder but they do not all fire the injectors in the same way. Domestic systems use one of four ways to trigger the injectors:
• Grouped single-fire
• Grouped double-fire
• Simultaneous double-fire
• Sequential.

Continuous Injection System: A fuel injection system in which fuel is injected constantly whenever the engine is running. Bosch K-Jetronic and CIS systems are typical examples.

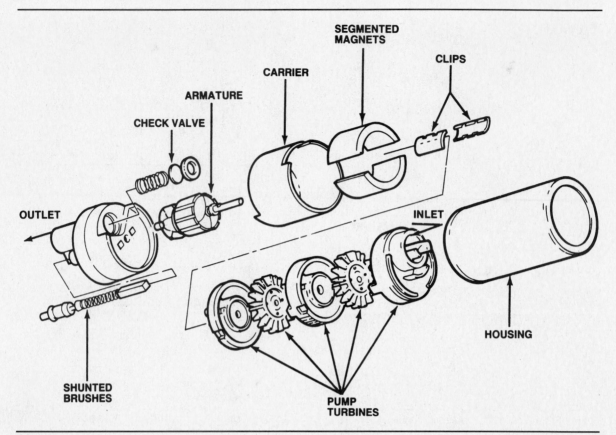

Figure 16-10. An in-tank turbine-type electric pump provides continuous low pressure (above 9 psi or 62 kPa). (GM)

In the first three of these word combinations, the first words refer to the way in which the injectors are connected electrically within the system. Some systems fire, or trigger, the injectors in groups; others fire them all together. The second words (hyphenated) in each combination refer to how many firings of each injector are used to make up the fuel charge for one combustion stroke.

Grouped single-fire
Injectors in this system are split into two groups. The groups are fired alternately with one group firing each engine revolution. Only one injector pulse is used for each combustion stroke. Early Cadillac V-8 systems use this design and while it works reasonably well, it is not as precise as newer designs. Since only two injectors can be fired relatively close to the point where the intake valve is about to open, the fuel charge for the remaining six cylinders must stand in the intake manifold for varying times. Since a new charge is released only once every two crankshaft revolutions, it is necessary to wait this long before any change can be made in the air-fuel mixture.

Grouped double-fire
This system again splits the injectors into two equal-sized groups. The groups fire alternately, but each group fires once each revolution. Two injector pulses make up each intake charge, which means that the air-fuel mixture remains in the manifold for a shorter time and that mixture changes can be made sooner than with a single-fire system.

Simultaneous double-fire
This design fires all of the injectors at the same time once every engine revolution. Many multipoint injection systems on 4-cylinder engines use this pattern of injector firing. It is easier for engineers to program and it can make relatively quick adjustments in the air-fuel ratio, but it still requires the intake charge to wait in the manifold for varying lengths of time.

Sequential
Sequential firing of the injectors according to engine firing order is the most accurate and desirable method of regulating multipoint injection. However, it is also the most complex and expensive to design and manufacture. In

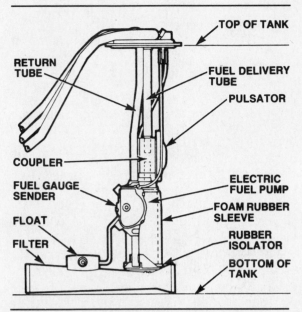

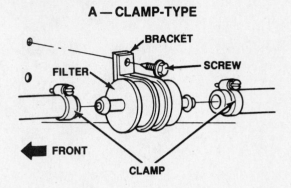

Figure 16-11. This in-tank roller vane fuel pump is combined with the fuel gauge sender unit. (GM)

this system, the injectors are controlled individually. Each cylinder receives one charge every two revolutions just before the intake valve opens. This means that the mixture is never static in the intake manifold and mixture adjustments can be made almost instantaneously between the firing of one injector and the next. A camshaft sensor signal or a special distributor reference pulse informs the computer when the No. 1 cylinder is on the compression stroke. If the sensor fails or the distributor reference pulse is interrupted, some injection systems shut down, while others revert to pulsing the injectors simultaneously.

COMMON SUBSYSTEMS AND COMPONENTS

Regardless of the type, all fuel injection systems have three basic subsystems:
- Fuel delivery
- Air control
- Electronic control with auxiliary sensors or actuators.

Fuel Delivery System

The fuel delivery system consists of an electric fuel pump, a filter, a pressure regulator, one or more injectors, and the necessary connecting fuel distribution lines.

Fuel pump
An electric fuel pump provides constant and uniform fuel pressure at the injectors. Most

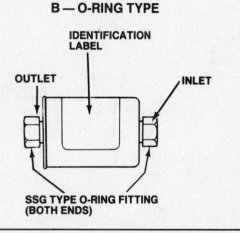

Figure 16-12. Fuel injection systems use large disposable filter canisters to ensure proper filtration. When threaded connections are used instead of clamps, O-ring seals are required. (GM)

systems use a positive-displacement vane, turbine, or roller pump, figure 16-10. Fuel-injected vehicles generally use one of the following pump applications:
- High pressure, in-tank
- Low pressure, in-tank
- Low pressure, in-tank and high pressure, inline.

In-tank fuel pumps may be separate units, but often are combined with the fuel gauge sender assembly, figure 16-11. The pump supplies more fuel than the system requires through an inline filter to the TBI unit or fuel rail, with the pressure regulator controlling volume and pressure. An internal relief valve protects the pump from excessive pressure if the filter or fuel lines become restricted.

Fuel filter
Clean fuel is extremely important in a fuel injection system because of the small orifice in the injector tip through which fuel must pass.

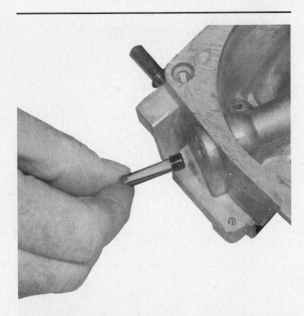

Figure 16-13. A filter screen may be installed in the fuel inlet of some throttle bodies.

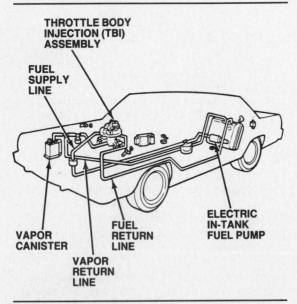

THROTTLE BODY
INJECTION (TBI)
ASSEMBLY

FUEL
SUPPLY
LINE

VAPOR
CANISTER

FUEL
RETURN
LINE

VAPOR
RETURN
LINE

ELECTRIC
IN-TANK
FUEL PUMP

Figure 16-14. A typical fuel injection system showing fuel line routing. (Ford)

Most injection systems use three forms of filters. The first is a fuel strainer or filter of woven plastic attached to the fuel pump inlet, figure 16-11. This prevents contamination from entering the fuel line and separates water from the fuel. The filter is self-cleaning and requires no maintenance. If a fuel restriction occurs at this point, the tank contains too much sediment or moisture and should be removed and cleaned.

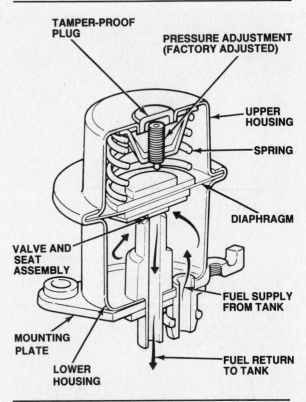

TAMPER-PROOF
PLUG

PRESSURE ADJUSTMENT
(FACTORY ADJUSTED)

UPPER
HOUSING

SPRING

DIAPHRAGM

VALVE AND
SEAT
ASSEMBLY

FUEL SUPPLY
FROM TANK

MOUNTING
PLATE

LOWER
HOUSING

FUEL RETURN
TO TANK

Figure 16-15. The pressure regulator commonly used with a TBI system functions by fuel pressure alone. (Ford)

Additional filtration is provided by a high-capacity inline filter, figure 16-12, to remove contamination larger than 10 to 20 microns (0.0025 to 0.0050 inch). This filter generally is mounted on a frame rail under the vehicle, but sometimes it may be mounted in the engine compartment.

The final line of defense against fuel contamination is in the fuel injector or TBI unit itself. Each injector contains its own inlet filter screen, figure 16-6, to prevent contamination from reaching the tip. Some TBI units have a similar filter screen installed in the fuel inlet fitting, figure 16-13.

Fuel lines
A supply line carries fuel from the pump through the filter to the TBI unit or fuel rail. A return line carries excess fuel back to the tank. This allows fuel to be continuously circulated from the tank to the injectors and back to the tank, figure 16-14. The system maintains constant fuel pressure and volume while minimizing fuel heating and vapor lock. Most injection system fuel lines are made of steel tubing, although Ford vehicles use nylon fuel line tubing. Flexible hose may be used in some low-pressure return lines.

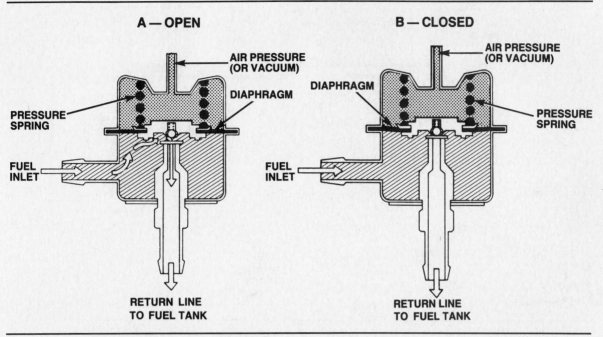

Figure 16-16. The pressure regulator commonly used with a multipoint system works on a combination of fuel pressure and manifold vacuum or air pressure. (GM)

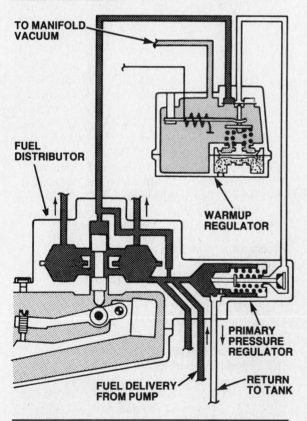

Figure 16-17. Injection pressure is controlled in a Bosch K-Jetronic system by a main pressure regulator and a separate warmup regulator. (Bosch)

Pressure regulator

The pressure regulator and fuel pump work together to maintain the required constant pressure at the injector tips. The regulator consists of a spring-loaded diaphragm-operated valve in a metal housing. Two types of pressure regulators are used in injection systems.

All fuel pressure regulators on current EFI systems are installed on the return (downstream) side of the injectors. Downstream regulation minimizes fuel pressure pulsations caused by pressure drop across the injectors as the nozzles open. It also ensures positive fuel pressure at the injectors at all times and holds residual pressure in the lines when the engine is off.

The pressure regulator used with a TBI system is built into or on the TBI unit. With this type, figure 16-15, fuel pressure must overcome spring pressure on the spring-loaded diaphragm to uncover the return line to the tank. This happens when system pressure exceeds operating requirements. The spring side of the diaphragm is exposed to inlet air pressure, or manifold vacuum, inside the TBI unit. Because it is close to the injector tip, the regulator senses essentially the same air pressure as the injector.

The pressure regulator used in a multipoint injection system, figure 16-16, has an intake manifold connection on the regulator vacuum

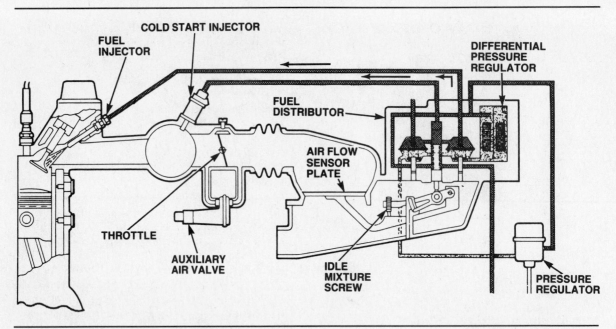

Figure 16-18. A differential pressure regulator is used instead of a control pressure regulator on some CIS late-model electronic systems. (Volkswagen)

chamber. This allows fuel pressure to be modulated by a combination of spring pressure and manifold vacuum acting on the diaphragm.

In both systems, the regulator shuts off the return line when the fuel pump is not running. This maintains pressure at the injectors for easy restarting and reduced vapor lock.

Mechanical injection systems without electronic control operate on the differential between fuel pump pressure and the control pressure developed by the fuel distributor. The pressure regulator is located on the control pressure side of the fuel distributor and connected to the fuel return line, figure 16-17. Spring force and control pressure operate on one side of the regulator with pump pressure on the other side to modulate the return line opening. Bosch K-Jetronic systems vary control pressure for different operation requirements with a primary regulator and a warmup regulator.

In later mechanical injection system designs, such as the CIS electronic system used on the Volkswagen Golf, a differential pressure regulator replaces the control pressure regulator. This device is a part of the fuel distributor, figure 16-18, and is operated by the computer. A separate spring-loaded, diaphragm-operated pressure regulator governs system pressure. This eliminates the need for a pressure relief valve in the fuel distributor.

Multipoint injection systems generally operate with pressures at the injector of about 30 to 55 psi (207 to 379 kPa), while TBI systems work with injector pressures of about 10 to 20 psi (69 to 138 kPa). The difference in system pressures results from the difference in the systems operation. Remember that an injection system requires only enough pressure to move the fuel through the injector and help in atomizing it. Since injectors in a TBI system inject the fuel into the airflow at the manifold inlet (above the throttle), there is more time for atomization in the manifold before the air-fuel charge reaches the intake valve. This allows TBI injectors to work at lower pressures than injectors used in a multipoint system.

Mechanical injection nozzles

The most common type of mechanical injection is the Bosch K-Jetronic system. Two types of injectors are used. Non-electronic systems use an injector with a spring-loaded tip to seal the nozzle against fuel pressure, figure 16-7. When pressure is greater than a specified level, it forces the nozzle open. The amount of fuel that enters the manifold is controlled by the nozzle opening, which in turn depends on fuel pressure. The mixture control unit controls injection pressure by a combination of control pressure and pump pressure. K-Jetronic nozzles inject fuel constantly as long as the pump

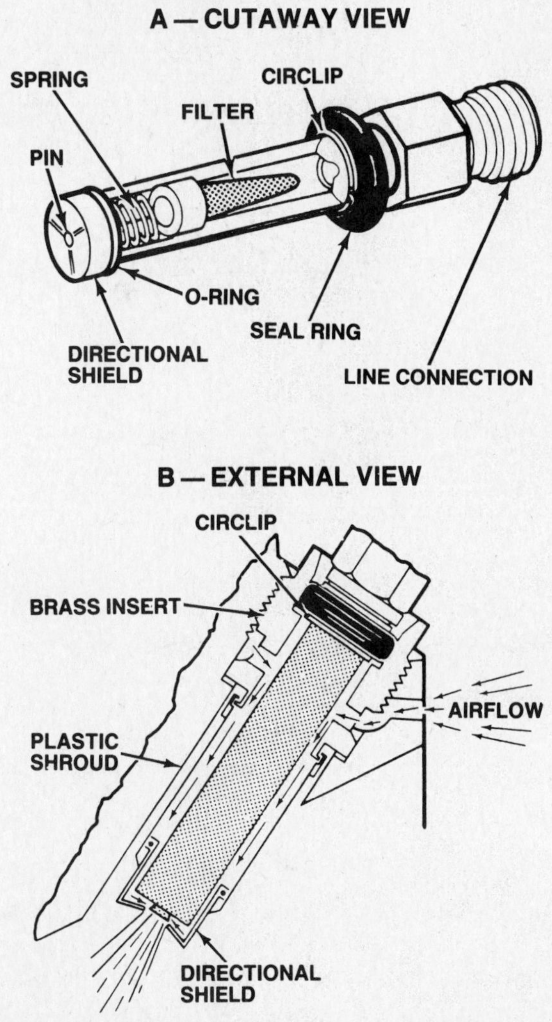

A — CUTAWAY VIEW

SPRING

CIRCLIP

FILTER

PIN

O-RING

SEAL RING

DIRECTIONAL
SHIELD

LINE CONNECTION

B — EXTERNAL VIEW

CIRCLIP

BRASS INSERT

AIRFLOW

PLASTIC
SHROUD

DIRECTIONAL
SHIELD

Figure 16-19. Air-shrouded injectors are similar to the K-Jetronic design, but flow air past the nozzle to improve atomization. (Volkswagen)

is operating. Bosch K-Jetronic nozzles are described in detail in the Continuous Injection section, earlier in this chapter.

Electronically controlled K-Jetronic systems use an air-shrouded injector. These injectors work in the same way as those used with non-electronic systems, but design changes have made them more efficient. Air flows in through a cylinder head passage, passes between the injector and plastic shroud surrounding it, and exits close to the injector tip. This improves atomization of the fuel as it leaves the injector, which reduces fuel condensation in the manifold. A second-generation air-shrouded injector, figure 16-19, uses a circlip to retain the seal ring. A separate plastic injector shroud and fluted air directional shield

on the injector tip improve airflow around the injector tip. These changes further improve fuel atomization.

Electronic injection nozzles

EFI systems use a solenoid-operated injector. Figure 16-20 shows typical TBI injectors; figure 16-21 shows the two types of multipoint injectors now in use. This electromagnetic device contains an armature and a spring-loaded needle valve or ball valve assembly. When the computer energizes the solenoid, voltage is applied to the solenoid coil until the current reaches a specified reference level (usually about 4 amperes). This permits a quick pull-in of the armature during turn-on. The armature is pulled off its seat against spring force, allowing fuel to flow through a 10-micron screen to the spray nozzle, where it is sprayed in a conical pattern. When current reaches the reference level, it is regulated at a specified value (usually about 1 ampere) until the injector is turned off. The low energy level during the holding state prevents overheating of the solenoid coil. The injector opens the same amount each time it is energized, so the amount of fuel injected depends on the length of time the injector remains open. The injector duty cycle and the operating pulse width are explained earlier in this chapter.

Most injectors are manufactured by Bosch (or made under Bosch license) and use a needle valve or pintle design, figure 16-21. This design allows deposits to gather on the sides of the pintle, causing the injector to malfunction. To overcome this problem, Rochester Products introduced the Multec injector for both TBI and multipoint systems on some 1987 automobiles. The Multec injector design uses a stainless steel ball and seat valve with a director plate for fuel control. The director plate gives a more precise spray pattern. Coupled with the near-mirror finish on the ball and seat assembly, Multec injectors are not as prone to clogging as the pintle valve design.

Air Control System

As you learned in Chapter 8, the difference between fuel bowl air pressure and carburetor barrel air pressure controls fuel metering in a carbureted system. A fuel injection system needs the same kind of control. However, since the fuel is not introduced to the airflow until it passes through the injectors, there must be some way to measure intake air volume and meter the fuel accordingly. All fuel injection systems use a throttle to control the

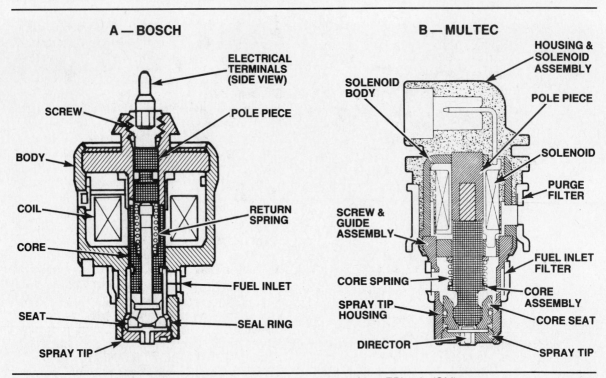

Figure 16-20. Bosch (left) and Rochester Multec (right) injectors used in a TBI unit. (GM)

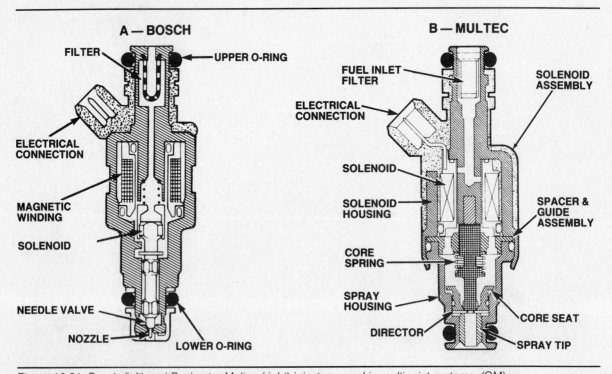

Figure 16-21. Bosch (left) and Rochester Multec (right) injectors used in multipoint systems. (GM)

volume of air. They also must measure air volume with one of the following:
- An airflow meter or sensor
- A manifold or barometric pressure sensor
- An air mass sensor.

Throttle
The throttle works exactly the same in both a carbureted and a fuel-injected system. It is connected to the accelerator linkage, and regulates the amount of air taken into the engine.

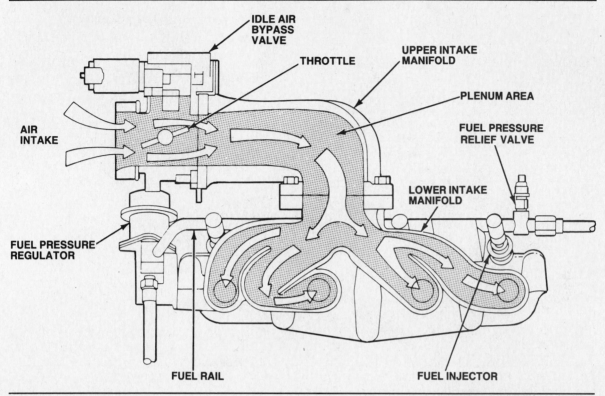

Figure 16-22. The horizontal throttle used in a multipoint system controls airflow only. (Ford)

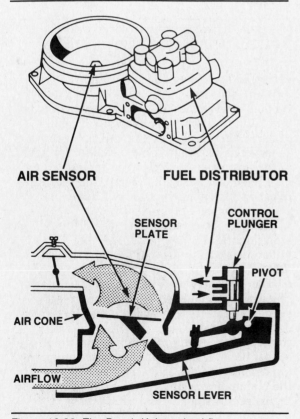

Figure 16-23. The Bosch K-Jetronic airflow sensor. (Bosch)

With a TBI system, the throttle is mounted between the injectors and the manifold, figure 16-1. Since the fuel is introduced to the air above the throttle plate, the throttle regulates the amount of air-fuel mixture that enters the manifold. On multipoint systems, the throttle is mounted horizontally in the air intake throttle body on the air inlet side of the injectors and controls only airflow, figure 16-22. A sensor determines the intake air volume. It can do this in one of three ways: by measuring airflow speed, manifold pressure, or the molecular mass of the air drawn into the engine. All of these methods directly relates to the amount of fuel required from the injectors.

Airflow sensors

Multipoint injection systems that use mass airflow for fuel adjustment have a movable plate or vane called an airflow sensor which is deflected by intake airflow, figure 16-23. In a Bosch K-Jetronic system, the movement of the sensor plate moves two counterweighted levers which operate the fuel distributor control plunger. The sensor plate deflects the control plunger proportionate to the amount of air flowing through the system. This causes the control plunger to regulate fuel pump pressure to each cylinder's differential pressure valve.

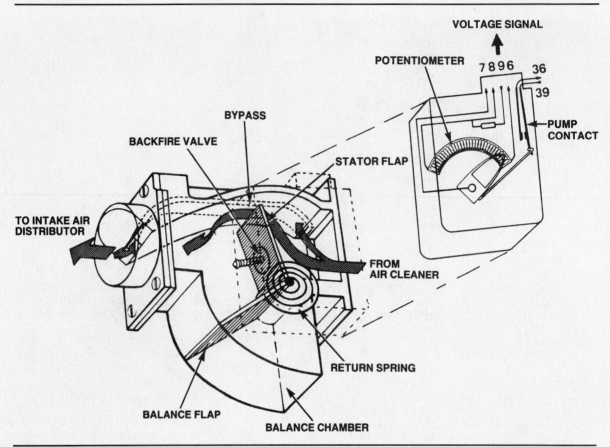

Figure 16-24. The Bosch L-Jetronic and many other airflow systems use a movable vane sensor connected to a potentiometer. (Bosch)

Control pressure exerted by the fuel on the opposite end of the plunger acts to balance airflow sensor force. The combined pressures found at the differential pressure valve will control injection relative to airflow.

The airflow sensor used in Bosch L-Jetronic, Ford, and most Japanese electronic multipoint systems is a movable vane connected to a potentiometer, figure 16-24. The vane is mounted on a pivot pin and is deflected by intake airflow proportionate to air velocity. As the vane moves, it also moves the potentiometer. This causes a change in the reference voltage applied to it by the computer. For example, if the reference voltage is 5 volts, the potentiometer's return signal to the computer will vary from a zero voltage signal (no airflow) to almost a 5-volt signal (maximum airflow), figure 16-25. In this way, the potentiometer provides the information the computer needs to vary the injector pulse width proportionate to airflow.

Manifold and barometric (absolute) pressure sensors

As you have already learned, oxygen content and barometric pressure change with differences in altitude. Because of this, the computer must be able to compensate for changes in the flow of fuel entering the engine. To provide the computer with this information, a fuel injection system may use one of three kinds of pressure sensors:

- Manifold absolute pressure (MAP)
- Barometric absolute pressure (BAP)
- Barometric and manifold absolute pressure (BMAP)

The MAP sensor may be a ceramic capacitor diaphragm, an aneroid bellows, or a piezoresistive crystal. It has a sealed vacuum reference input on one side; the other side is connected (vented) to the intake manifold. The sensor housing also contains signal conditioning circuitry, figure 16-26. Pressure changes in the manifold cause the sensor to deflect, varying its return signal to the computer.

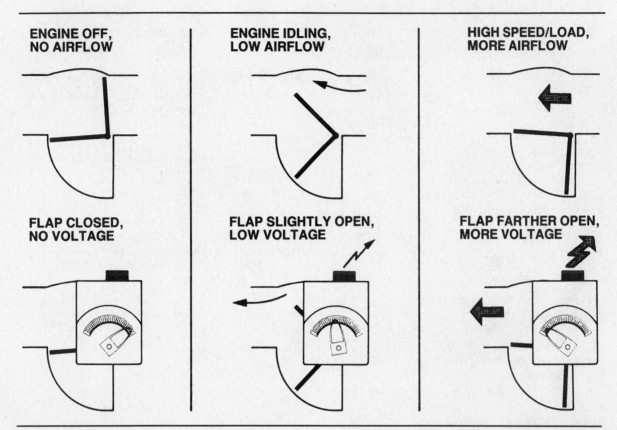

ENGINE OFF, NO AIRFLOW

ENGINE IDLING, LOW AIRFLOW

HIGH SPEED/LOAD, MORE AIRFLOW

FLAP CLOSED, NO VOLTAGE

FLAP SLIGHTLY OPEN, LOW VOLTAGE

FLAP FARTHER OPEN, MORE VOLTAGE

Figure 16-25. Operational cycle of a vane-type airflow sensor. (Bosch)

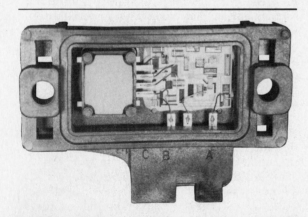

Figure 16-26. The signal conditioning circuitry of a GM MAP sensor.

Figure 16-27. Many GM MAP sensors are mounted on the side of the air cleaner housing. They also may be mounted on the cowl or fenderwell.

A BAP sensor is similar in design, but senses changes in barometric absolute pressure (atmospheric air pressure). It is vented directly to the atmosphere. The BMAP sensor is actually a combination of a BAP and MAP sensor in the same housing. The BMAP sensor has individual circuits to measure barometric and manifold pressure. It sends separate signals to the computer for comparison to determine the operating manifold pressure and required amount of fuel. Pressure sensors generally are remotely mounted, figure 16-27, and connected to the intake manifold by tubing.

Air mass sensor
There are two types of air mass sensors. One contains a platinum wire; the other uses a metal foil sensing element, figure 16-28. Both sensors operate in essentially the same way. A resistor wire or screen is installed in the path of intake airflow and is heated to a constant

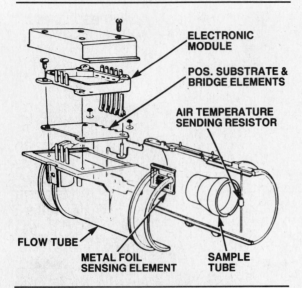

Figure 16-28. Components of a metal foil air mass sensor. (GM)

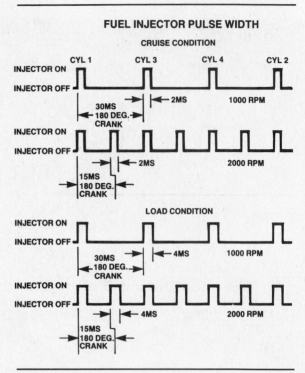

Figure 16-29. Fuel flow timing and pulse width. (Chrysler)

temperature by electric current provided by the computer. Air flowing past the wire or screen cools it. The degree of cooling varies with air velocity and temperature. These factors combine to indicate the mass volume of air entering the engine. As the wire or screen cools, more current is required to maintain the specified temperature. As the wire or screen heats up, less current is required.

The operating principles can be summarized as follows:
• More intake air volume = cooler sensor, more current
• Less intake air volume = warmer sensor, less current

The computer constantly monitors the change in current and translates it into a voltage signal which is used to determine injector pulse width.

Electronic Control System with Auxiliary Sensors and Actuators

You may have noticed that to this point, we have not mentioned chokes, power valves, accelerator pumps, or idle speed and mixture controls in our discussion of fuel injection. Earlier in this chapter, however, you learned that a fuel injection system does the same jobs that a carburetor does. The enrichment and mixture control functions of a carburetor are done by the devices just mentioned. Now you'll learn how a fuel injection system does the same thing.

Computer control
An electronic fuel injection system uses engine sensors and auxiliary metering devices to perform the required enrichment and mixture control functions. Sensors provide input data to the engine computer. After processing the data, the computer sends output signals to actuators. In an EFI system, the actuators are solenoid-operated fuel injectors.

You should remember from the section on electronic fuel injectors that the injector opens the same amount each time it is energized, so the amount of fuel injected depends on the length of time the injector is energized. As you learned earlier this time duration is called pulse width, and is measured in milliseconds. The computer varies the injector pulse width according to the amount of fuel required under any operating condition, figure 16-29. Pulse width also may be called duty cycle. Each on/off sequence of an injector is a *full* cycle. The pulse width, or duty cycle, is a variable portion, or percentage, of that full cycle.

Cold starting
A cold engine requires a richer air-fuel mixture for starting. Multipoint systems often use a separate cold-start injector to provide additional fuel during the crank mode. During engine cranking, the individual injectors send fuel into the cylinder ports. At the same time, the

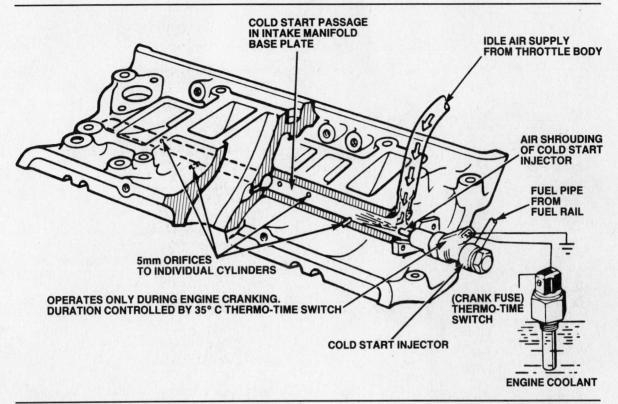

COLD START PASSAGE
IN INTAKE MANIFOLD
BASE PLATE

IDLE AIR SUPPLY
FROM THROTTLE BODY

AIR SHROUDING
OF COLD START
INJECTOR

FUEL PIPE
FROM
FUEL RAIL

5mm ORIFICES
TO INDIVIDUAL CYLINDERS

OPERATES ONLY DURING ENGINE CRANKING.
DURATION CONTROLLED BY 35° C THERMO-TIME SWITCH

(CRANK FUSE)
THERMO-TIME
SWITCH

COLD START INJECTOR

ENGINE COOLANT

Figure 16-30. A cold-start injector provides extra fuel during cranking. In this design, it mixes with air and flows through small orifices into individual cylinders. (GM)

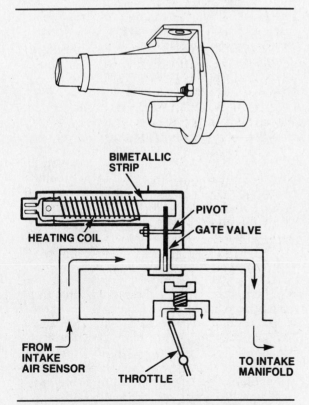

BIMETALLIC
STRIP

PIVOT

GATE VALVE

HEATING COIL

FROM
INTAKE
AIR SENSOR

THROTTLE

TO INTAKE
MANIFOLD

Figure 16-31. The auxiliary air regulator controls the air intake through a gate valve operated by a heated bimetallic strip. (Bosch)

cold-start injector provides the additional fuel by injecting it into a central area of the manifold or into a separate passage in the manifold, figure 16-30. In either location, the extra fuel is distributed more or less equally to all cylinders. The colder the engine, the longer the cold-start injector remains on.

Cold-start injector duration is regulated by a thermal-time switch in the thermostat housing. This switch grounds the cold-start injector circuit when the engine is cranked at a coolant temperature below a specified value. A heating element inside the switch also is activated during cranking and starts to heat a bimetallic strip in the ground circuit. Once the bimetallic strip reaches the specified temperature, it opens the ground circuit and shuts off power to the cold-start injector.

Idle control

Multipoint injection systems use an auxiliary air bypass, figure 16-22, or auxiliary air regulator, figure 16-31, to do the same job as the air bypass circuit in a carburetor. This air bypass or regulator provides needed additional airflow by opening an intake air passage to let more air into the engine. The system is calibrated to maintain engine idle speed at a specified value regardless of engine temperature.

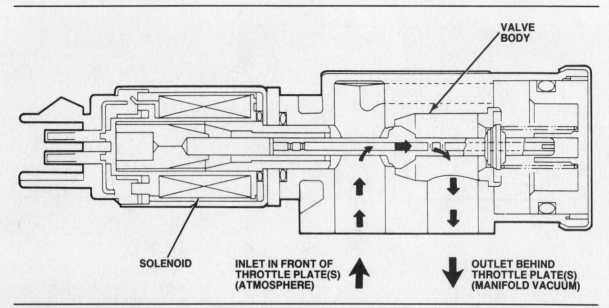

Figure 16-32. A solenoid-operated air bypass valve is used with most domestic multipoint systems to provide idle air flow around the throttle plate. (Ford)

Most domestic multipoint injection systems use a computer-controlled, solenoid-operated valve, figure 16-32, to regulate the airflow. The Bosch auxiliary air regulator used in several kinds of systems, figure 16-31, contains a heated bimetallic strip. When the engine is first started, air passes through the gate valve and current is applied to the bimetallic strip. As the engine warms up, the bimetallic strip starts to deflect and gradually closes off the gate valve passage to shut off the additional airflow. By the time the engine has fully warmed up, the gate valve is completely closed and the idle bypass in the throttle chamber determines engine speed.

Idle airflow in a TBI system travels through a passage around the throttle and is controlled by a stepper motor. Idle fuel metering on a Bosch K-Jetronic system is controlled by a mechanical adjustment. Electronic fuel injection systems may control idle fuel metering either by a predetermined program in the computer or from signals provided by a manifold pressure sensor.

Acceleration and load enrichment

Airflow and manifold pressure change rapidly when an engine needs more fuel for additional power. With a mechanical injection system, these changes affect fuel pressure, causing the metering assembly to increase the volume of fuel flow. In an electronic injection system, signals from the airflow or pressure sensors to the computer result in an increase in injector pulse width.

Engine speed and crankshaft position

Engine speed is used by mechanical injection systems to operate the cold-start and cranking-enrichment subsystems. Electronic injection systems use engine speed and crankshaft position to time the injection pulses and determine the pulse width. Speed and position signals can be provided either by a magnetic sensor in the engine or by Hall-effect switches or pulse generators in the distributor.

Engine-mounted sensors generally are positioned in the bell housing. They react to the changes in magnetic reluctance caused by flywheel grooves or teeth, figure 16-33. On GM engines with a distributorless ignition system, the sensor is in the engine block and uses a special reluctor or wheel on the crankshaft to generate the signal, figure 16-34. Distributor signals generally are provided by the magnetic pulse generator or Hall-effect switch, figure 16-35, although a separate signal generator or switching device can be used.

As mentioned previously, sequential multipoint systems require a number 1 cylinder signal to time the injector firing order. This signal can be provided by the same sensor that indicates crankshaft position or engine speed. Some engines use a separate sensor for the sequential timing signal, but it works on the same principles as other position or speed sensors. Without the number 1 cylinder signal, a sequential injection system will not run; or it will revert to a programmed pulsed firing sequence that allows the car to be driven in for repair.

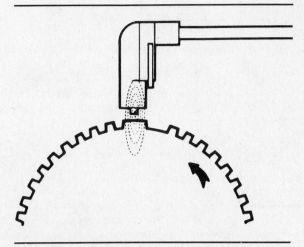

Figure 16-33. A typical crankshaft sensor which reads crankshaft position from the flywheel teeth. (AMC/Renault)

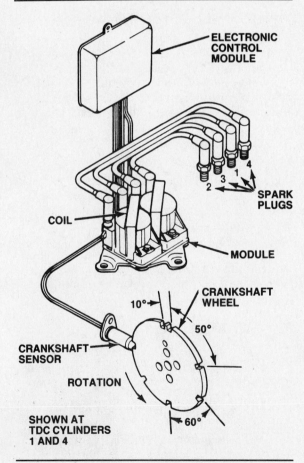

ELECTRONIC CONTROL MODULE

SPARK PLUGS

COIL

MODULE

CRANKSHAFT WHEEL

CRANKSHAFT SENSOR

ROTATION

10°

50°

60°

SHOWN AT TDC CYLINDERS 1 AND 4

Figure 16-34. Distributorless ignitions use a sensor and notched wheel or reluctor on the crankshaft to inform the computer of crankshaft position. (GM)

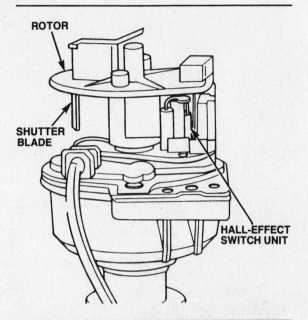

ROTOR

SHUTTER BLADE

HALL-EFFECT SWITCH UNIT

Figure 16-35. A Hall-effect switch in the distributor also can be used to determine crankshaft position. (Chrysler)

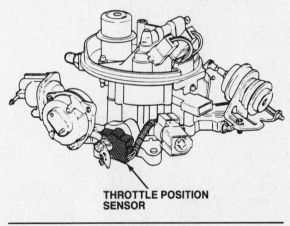

THROTTLE POSITION SENSOR

Figure 16-36. A typical throttle position sensor. (Ford)

Throttle position

A sensor monitors throttle position for the computer. Throttle position sensors (TPS) may be a simple on/off switch, or a potentiometer that sends a variable resistance signal to the computer, figure 16-36. By interpreting the signal, the computer determines when the engine is at:

• Closed throttle (during idle and deceleration)
• Part throttle (normal operation)
• Wide-open throttle (acceleration and full-power operation).

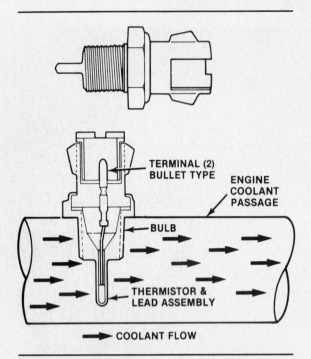

TERMINAL (2)
BULLET TYPE

ENGINE
COOLANT
PASSAGE

BULB

THERMISTOR &
LEAD ASSEMBLY

→ COOLANT FLOW

Figure 16-37. Thermistors are used to measure engine coolant or intake air temperatures. (Ford)

Proper TPS adjustment is critical to ensure that fuel enrichment and shutoff occur at the appropriate times. Otherwise, driveability problems such as stalling, surging, and hesitation will occur. Some throttle position sensors can be adjusted; others are nonadjustable and must be replaced if they are not set to specifications.

Air and coolant temperature
The computer must be kept aware of intake air temperature and engine coolant temperature. Intake air temperature is used as a density corrector for calculating fuel flow and proportioning cold enrichment fuel flow. Coolant temperature is used to determine the correct air-fuel ratio according to the engine's operating temperature. This information is provided to the computer by coolant and air temperature sensors.

Most temperature sensors are thermistors or variable resistors, figure 16-37. With this type of sensor, resistance decreases as the sensor is heated. The reference voltage applied by the computer is thus altered according to temperature, resulting in a varying return voltage to the computer from the sensor. This data is integrated with data from other sensors by the computer, and used to change the injector pulse width or fuel pressure.

SPECIFIC SYSTEMS
Fuel injection systems have almost replaced the carburetor. The summary descriptions that follow provide the basic features of these systems and can help you to recognize the different devices, and how they do similar tasks.

Bosch K-Jetronic System
The Bosch K-Jetronic system was used on many European vehicles in the early 1970s and now is the most common example of a production mechanical (continuous) port injection system, figure 16-38. The system also is a continuous injection system (CIS). Air volume is measured by sensing airflow; fuel pressure is regulated relative to air volume. Fuel pressure also activates the individual injectors.

Bosch D-Jetronic System
This electronically controlled injection system, figure 16-39, was used on 1968-73 Volkswagens and other European vehicles. It uses solenoid-operated injectors which operate in intermittent pulses; fuel is measured relative to engine speed and manifold air pressure.

Bosch L-Jetronic System
This system was introduced in 1974 and uses individual solenoid-operated injectors that operate intermittently. It is similar to the mechanical K-Jetronic system in that fuel metering is controlled relative to airflow, but the airflow sensor is connected to an electronic module which also regulates fuel metering relative to temperature and engine speed, figure 16-40. The L-Jetronic system sometimes is called airflow-controlled (AFC) injection.

Cadillac EFI System
This EFI system by Bendix, figure 16-41, was used on the 1976 through 1979 Cadillac Seville. It was the first electronically controlled multipoint injection system to be used on domestic vehicles. Fuel is supplied to individual injectors in the intake manifold through a fuel rail, with air intake controlled by a throttle body which looks much like a carburetor, figure 16-42. An electronic control unit (ECU) controls fuel delivery according to the various sensor inputs shown in figure 16-41. The injectors were pulsed intermittently in two banks. Feedback control of fuel metering with an EGO sensor was used in later versions of this system.

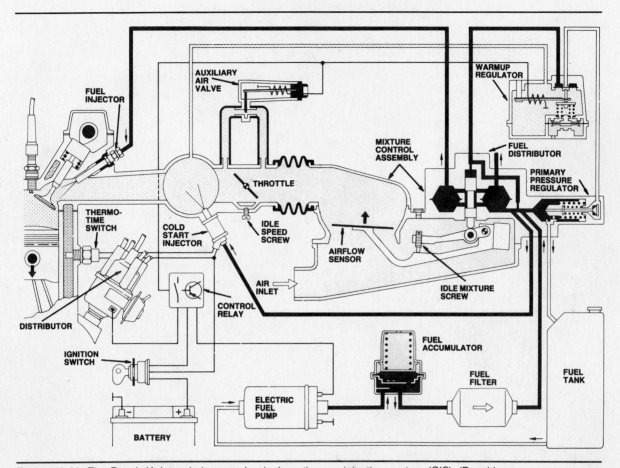

Figure 16-38. The Bosch K-Jetronic is a mechanical continuous injection system (CIS). (Bosch)

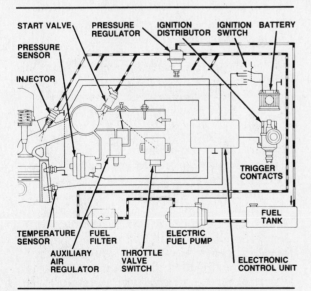

Figure 16-39. An electronic intermittent injection system, the Bosch D-Jetronic is controlled by manifold pressure. (Bosch)

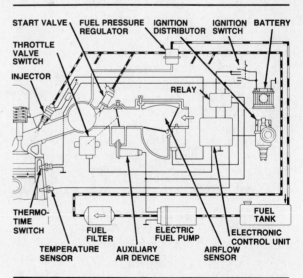

Figure 16-40. The Bosch L-Jetronic is controlled by engine speed and airflow measurement. (Bosch)

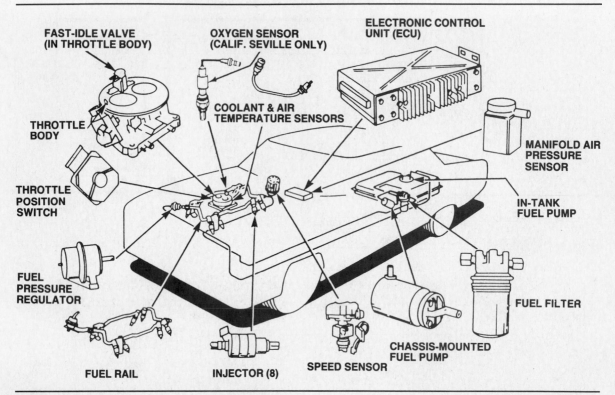

Figure 16-41. The Bendix EFI system was the first modern multi-point injection system used on domestic vehicles. (Cadillac)

Figure 16-42. The Bendix EFI system on Cadillac Sevilles used a carburetor-like throttle body for air intake and a fuel rail with individual injectors.

Late-Model Multipoint Injection Systems

The multipoint injection systems used on domestic and many Japanese vehicles are based on Bosch designs and contain many components manufactured by or under license from Bosch. All have individual injectors installed in some form of fuel rail and mounted in the intake manifold.

General Motors

GM has used three multipoint injection systems since 1984:

1. *Port fuel injection (PFI)* is a simultaneous double-fire system in which all injectors fire once during each engine revolution. In other words, two injections of fuel are mixed with incoming air for each combustion cycle. PFI systems are used on 4-cylinder and small V-6 engines *without* the distributorless ignition system. On some 1984-85 engines, this system was called multipoint fuel injection (MFI).

2. *Sequential fuel injection (SFI)* is a port injection system like PFI and TPI, but the injectors operate in firing order sequence. SFI systems are used on all GM engines with a distributorless ignition system. This type of ignition system requires sequential fuel injection so that the ''waste-spark'' that fires in the cylinder on an exhaust stroke does not ignite any air-fuel mixture.

Most GM multipoint fuel injection systems use a heated-film, mass-airflow sensor, figure 16-28. This consists of a screen to break up the

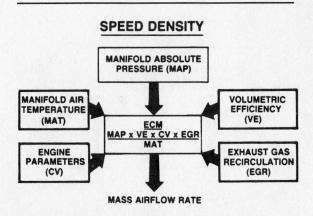

Figure 16-43. A GM speed-density fuel injection system takes several inputs into consideration to determine mass airflow rate. (GM)

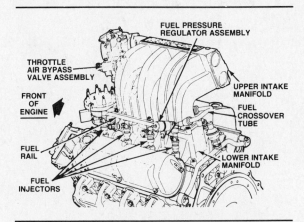

Figure 16-44. A typical Ford SEFI system. (Ford)

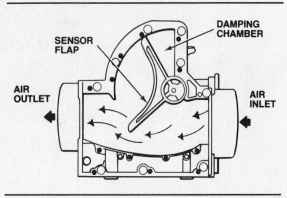

Figure 16-45. A vane-type airflow sensor. (Ford)

airflow, a ceramic resistor which measures the incoming air temperature, the heated film, and an electronic module. The sensor is mounted in the intake air duct between the air cleaner and air intake throttle body. The ECM of the CCC system heat the sensor to a constant 167°F (75°C) above ambient air temperature. As incoming air cools the sensor, the ECM provides additional current to maintain the sensor temperature. As the intake airflow changes for different driving conditions, the ECM translates the varying current requirements into measurements of intake air mass. The ECM then regulates injector pulse width to provide the required air-fuel ratio.

Some GM multipoint fuel injection systems use a speed-density air measurement system instead of the mass airflow. A speed-density system uses manifold absolute pressure and temperature along with an engine mapping program in the computer to calculate mass airflow rate, figure 16-43. This type of system is sensitive to engine and EGR variations.

Many 1987 and later GM multiport systems on V-6 and V-8 engines have dual, or "split," fuel rails. The injectors for each bank of the engine have their own fuel distribution rail. As a further refinement, some of these split-rail systems have "biased" injectors. The computer controls each bank differently, and the injectors for right and left banks may have different flow rates for identical duty cycles and pulse widths. For example, with a pulse width of 5 milliseconds, the left bank injectors may flow 1.5 cc, and the right bank injectors may flow 1.6 cc. Biased injectors are color coded for identification. Most engines with split-rail injection also have two EGO sensors so that the engine computer can control fuel metering independently for each bank of the engine.

Ford

Ford refers to its multipoint injection systems as Electronic Fuel Injection (EFI). Based on the Bosch L-Jetronic design, Ford EFI systems for 4-cylinder engine use simultaneous double-fire injector control. Ford introduced its first multipoint EFI system on 1.6-liter engines in 1983 Escort, Lynx, and EXP/LN7 models. The same basic system continues in use on some later 1.6- and 1.9-liter engines. Ford uses a similar multipoint EFI system on 1984 and later turbocharged 1.6- and 2.3-liter engines.

Two new EFI systems were introduced in 1986. Taurus and Sable models with 3.0-liter V-6 engines use a multipoint simultaneous injection system similar to the ones on 4-cylinder engines. All 1986 5.0-liter V-8 engines use a new sequential electronic fuel injection (SEFI) system, figure 16-44. In the SEFI system, the EEC-IV computer operates the injectors in firing order sequence. Each injector fires once every two crankshaft revolutions as the intake valve opens.

Ford EFI systems on 4-cylinder engines use a vane-type airflow meter, figure 16-45, to

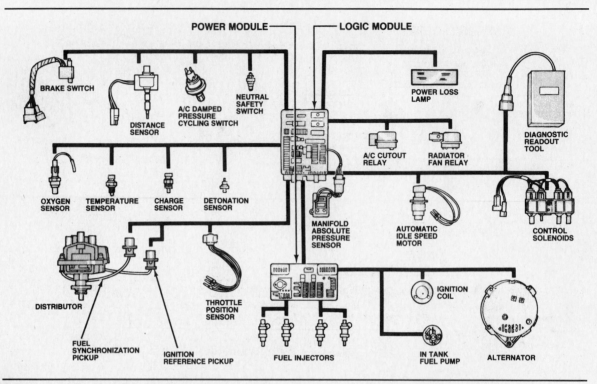

Figure 16-46. The Chrysler grouped double-fire injection system used on 2.2-liter engines. (Chrysler)

measure intake airflow. Similar to the Bosch L-Jetronic design, the airflow meter is installed ahead of the throttle body in the air intake system. The vane moves a potentiometer sensor that sends a voltage signal to the EEC computer in proportion to intake airflow.

Chrysler

A grouped double-fire multipoint injection system, figure 16-46, is used on some 1984 and later 2.2-liter 4-cylinder engines. This system is similar to a Bosch D-Jetronic system and uses Bosch-designed fuel injectors in combination with Chrysler-engineered electronics. The pressure regulator on the fuel rail maintains a nominal 55 psi (379 kPa) of fuel pressure at the injector nozzles.

AMC-Renault

The multipoint injection system used on AMC-Renault vehicles manufactured in the United States is a variation on the Bosch L-Jetronic system, figure 16-47. This is an electronic intermittent injection system controlled by airflow measurement and engine speed.

Imports

The major Japanese automakers use multipoint injection systems derived from the Bosch L-Jetronic or AFC system. Figure 16-48 shows common components used in both Nissan and Toyota EFI systems. Nissan introduced its system in 1975, with Toyota following in 1979. These early Japanese systems control only injector duration. Systems introduced in 1981 (Nissan) and 1983 (Toyota) are fully integrated into the engine management system, controlling idle speed, EGR, and ignition timing in relation to fuel injection.

Late-Model Throttle Body Injection Systems

TBI systems made their first appearance on domestic engines in the early 1980s and now account for about half of the EFI systems in use, although multiport injection seems to be gaining in the number of applications.

With the exception of the Chrysler V-8 system introduced on 1981 Imperials, all TBI systems use similar components. Single or dual solenoid-operated injectors are positioned in a

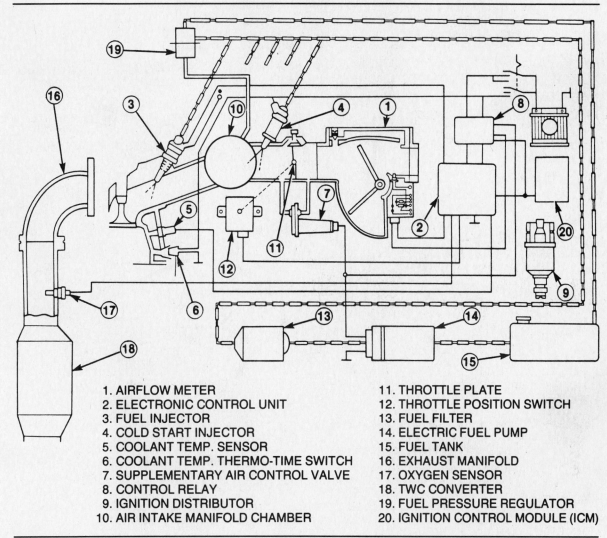

1. AIRFLOW METER
2. ELECTRONIC CONTROL UNIT
3. FUEL INJECTOR
4. COLD START INJECTOR
5. COOLANT TEMP. SENSOR
6. COOLANT TEMP. THERMO-TIME SWITCH
7. SUPPLEMENTARY AIR CONTROL VALVE
8. CONTROL RELAY
9. IGNITION DISTRIBUTOR
10. AIR INTAKE MANIFOLD CHAMBER

11. THROTTLE PLATE
12. THROTTLE POSITION SWITCH
13. FUEL FILTER
14. ELECTRIC FUEL PUMP
15. FUEL TANK
16. EXHAUST MANIFOLD
17. OXYGEN SENSOR
18. TWC CONVERTER
19. FUEL PRESSURE REGULATOR
20. IGNITION CONTROL MODULE (ICM)

Figure 16-47. A variation of the Bosch D-Jetronic system is used on American-built AMC-Renault vehicles. (AMC-Renault)

throttle body assembly that looks much like a carburetor base, figure 16-49. A MAP sensor measures intake air volume and the computer controls injection volume proportionately.

General Motors

All GM TBI systems since 1980 are manufactured by Rochester and have one or two injectors on the throttle body. There are several basic models:
● Models 100, 200 and 220 are 2-barrel, 2-injector assemblies. Cadillac has used these types of systems since 1980, although Cadillac has not used a Rochester model number for the system. In 1980, the system was called digital electronic fuel injection (DEFI). In 1981, the

name was shortened to digital fuel injection (DFI). The Model 220 was introduced in 1985. Some Model 220 TBI units use injectors which are calibrated to flow fuel at a different rate in each throttle bore.
● Models 300, 500 and 700 are 1-barrel, 1-injector systems. The Model 300 was used on 1.8- and 2.5-liter 4-cylinder engines, and the Model 500 was used on 2.0-liter 4-cylinder engines. With the exception of minor fuel and airflow differences, these two units are the same. The Model 700 was introduced on 1987 4-cylinder engines as a replacement for both the 300 and 500. It uses a Multec low-pressure injector, and has a redesigned pressure regulator that permits replacement of the diaphragm assembly instead of the entire regulator unit.

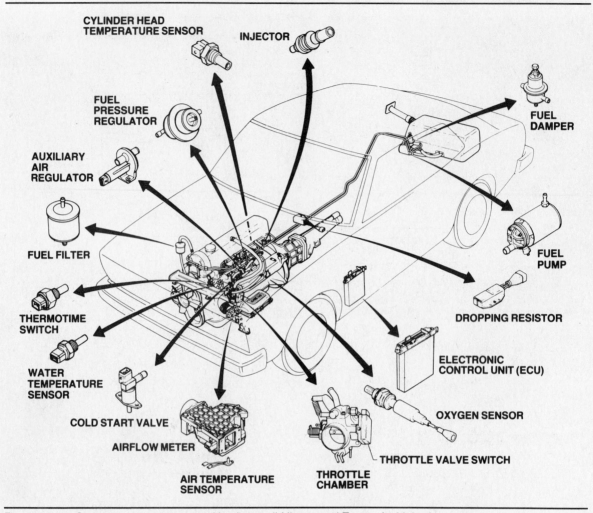

CYLINDER HEAD
TEMPERATURE SENSOR

INJECTOR

FUEL DAMPER

FUEL
PRESSURE
REGULATOR

AUXILIARY
AIR
REGULATOR

FUEL FILTER

FUEL
PUMP

THERMOTIME
SWITCH

DROPPING RESISTOR

WATER
TEMPERATURE
SENSOR

ELECTRONIC
CONTROL UNIT (ECU)

COLD START VALVE

OXYGEN SENSOR

AIRFLOW METER

THROTTLE VALVE SWITCH

AIR TEMPERATURE
SENSOR

THROTTLE
CHAMBER

Figure 16-48. Common components used in almost all Nissan and Toyota fuel injection systems.

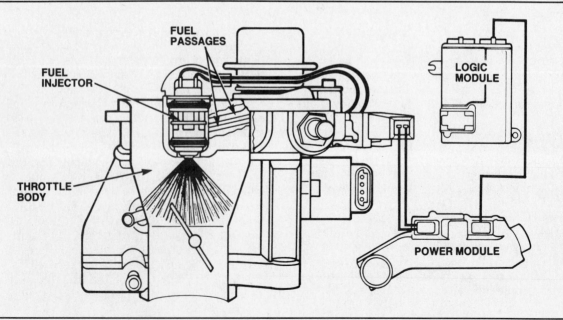

FUEL
PASSAGES

FUEL
INJECTOR

LOGIC
MODULE

THROTTLE
BODY

POWER MODULE

Figure 16-49. The throttle body assembly in a TBI system looks much like a carburetor, but contains only an injector, idle air motor, and pressure regulator. (Chrysler)

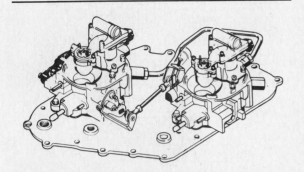

Figure 16-50. The Model 400 cross-fire injection (CFI) assembly consists of two TBI units mounted on a common manifold. (Chevrolet)

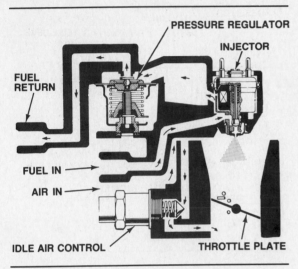

Figure 16-51. Throttle body injection fuel pressure regulation. (GM)

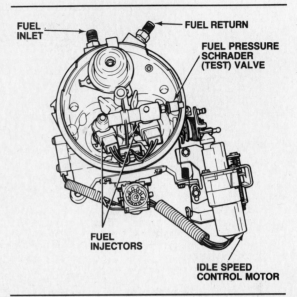

Figure 16-52. A Ford CFI fuel charging (throttle body) assembly. (Ford)

• Model 400 is the unique crossfire assembly of two 1-barrel, 1-injector throttle bodies mounted on a single intake manifold, figure 16-50. This system is used on some 1982-83 5.0-liter V-8 engines in Camaros and Firebirds, as well as 1982-84 5.7-liter V-8 Corvette engines. The ECM of the CCC system is reprogrammed to handle the two units, but operation is otherwise the same as other GM TBI systems. Like the Chrysler V-8 TBI system, the GM crossfire fuel injection (CFI) system proved to be a technological dead end.

All GM TBI systems have a fuel pressure regulator built into the throttle body, figure 16-51. The regulator senses intake manifold vacuum (or air pressure drop across the injector)

at the same point as the injector nozzle tip. The regulator controls fuel pressure by opening and closing the fuel return line. All regulators are serviced as an assembly except for the Model 700, which has a replaceable diaphragm.

Ford

Ford calls all of its throttle body injection systems central fuel injection (CFI) because the fuel is injected at a central point. The first such system was a twin-injector design, figure 16-52, introduced in 1980 and used on some 5.0-liter V-8 engines through 1985. The twin CFI system was adapted to the 3.8-liter V-6 in 1984. Fuel pressure in this system is regulated between 35 and 45 psi (241 and 310 kPa). All 1980-83 and 1984 California V-8 twin CFI systems are controlled by the EEC-III system. Later V-8 and all V-6 CFI systems are regulated by the newer EEC-IV system.

A single injector CFI system was introduced in 1985 for the 2.3-liter 4-cylinder engine used in Tempo and Topaz models. This same design is used on the 2.5-liter engine in Taurus and Sable models. Unlike the twin CFI system, the single injector version operated at a lower fuel pressure of approximately 14.5 psi (100 kPa).

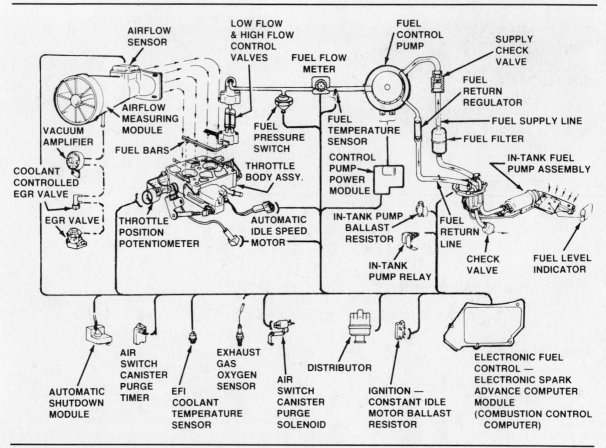

Figure 16-53. The Chrysler continuous-flow TBI system. (Chrysler)

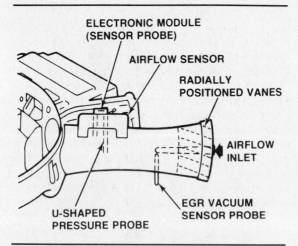

Figure 16-54. Chrysler's continuous-flow TBI airflow sensor. (Chrysler)

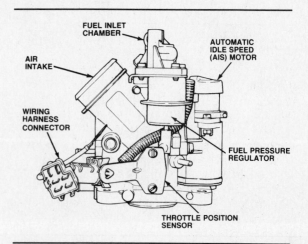

Figure 16-55. The Chrysler-Holly-Bendix high-pressure TBI unit. (Chrysler)

Chrysler

Chrysler's first TBI system was a continuous flow system used on its V-8 engine in 1981-83 Imperials, figure 16-53. A special sensor in the air cleaner snorkel measures air intake volume,

figure 16-54. Radial vanes swirl the air and a U-shaped pressure probe in the vortex of the swirling air determines the amount of air entering the engine.

Most 1981 and later nonturbocharged Chrysler-built 4-cylinder engines use a single injector TBI system. The original system used

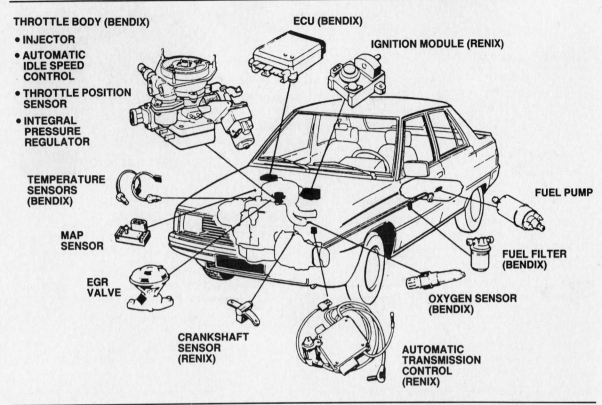

THROTTLE BODY (BENDIX)
• INJECTOR
• AUTOMATIC IDLE SPEED CONTROL
• THROTTLE POSITION SENSOR
• INTEGRAL PRESSURE REGULATOR

ECU (BENDIX)

IGNITION MODULE (RENIX)

TEMPERATURE SENSORS (BENDIX)

MAP SENSOR

EGR VALVE

CRANKSHAFT SENSOR (RENIX)

FUEL PUMP

FUEL FILTER (BENDIX)

OXYGEN SENSOR (BENDIX)

AUTOMATIC TRANSMISSION CONTROL (RENIX)

Figure 16-56. The major components of AMC-Renault's TBI and electronic engine management system. (AMC-Renault)

through 1985 had a Holley-designed throttle body, figure 16-55, with an injector supplied by Bendix. A pressure regulator on the throttle body maintains a nominal 36 psi (248 kPa) of fuel pressure at the injector nozzle. Chrysler refers to this system as a ''high-pressure'' EFI system, but in the context of other injection systems, it is a medium-pressure system.

The TBI system was revised in 1986, with the newer design using a low-pressure injector designed by Bosch, figure 16-49. The throttle body includes a pressure regulator that maintains fuel pressure at 14.5 to 15 psi (100 to 103 kPa).

AMC-Renault

The TBI system used on AMC-Renault vehicles manufactured in the United States is a combination of Bendix and Renix components, figure 16-56, which work about the same as the domestic TBI systems described earlier. The injection system is fully integrated into the engine management system.

Imports

Most import vehicles equipped with TBI use systems that are quite similar in design and function to those used on domestic vehicles. The AMC/Renault design is a typical example.

Turbocharged Japanese vehicles sold by Mitsubishi and Chrysler Corporation in the United States use a TBI system which measures intake airflow rate based on Karman's vortex theory (a well-known theory dealing with aerodynamics and ultrasound waves), figure 16-57. This system is considerably more complex than the other TBI systems which we have seen.

The airflow sensor and intake air temperature sensor are located inside the filter element in the air cleaner housing, figure 16-58. Filtered air passes through the airflow sensor, which contains a stabilizer plate and generating rod. The plate and rod vibrate according to the rate of airflow, setting up ultrasonic wave patterns which are transformed into a voltage signal by the sensor and sent to the computer indicating flow rate. At the same time, the air temperature sensor signals the computer concerning the temperature of the airflow.

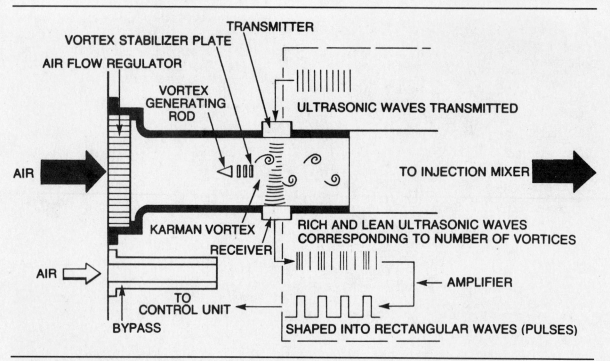

Figure 16-57. Operation of the Mitsubishi-Chrysler TBI system which measures airflow rate according to Karman's vortex theory. (Chrysler)

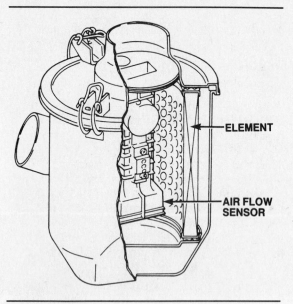

Figure 16-58. The airflow sensor is mounted inside the air cleaner filter element. (Chrysler)

Two injectors installed in the inlet port of the injection mixer or air intake throttle body operate in an alternating sequence. Injector operation is similar to that of other solenoid-operated injectors, but a swirl nozzle design is used to atomize the fuel and "jiggle" the fuel spray, figure 16-59. A schematic of the complete system is shown in figure 16-60.

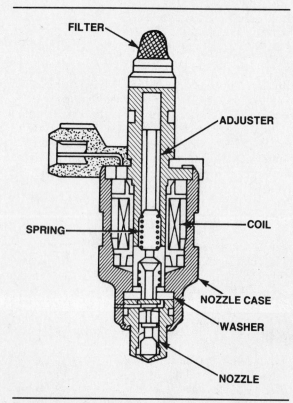

Figure 16-59. The Mitsubishi-Chrysler TBI injector uses a swirl nozzle for better fuel atomization, but operates like any other solenoid-actuated injector. (Chrysler)

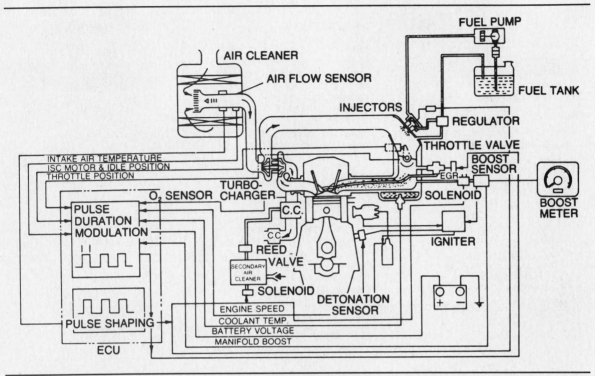

Figure 16-60. The Mitsubishi-Chrysler ECI system components. (Chrysler)

SUMMARY

Fuel injection systems must do the same tasks as carburetors. However, they do so in a slightly different way. Two types of injection systems are used: throttle body injection (TBI) or multipoint (port) injection.

The TBI system uses a carburetor-like throttle body containing one or two injectors. This throttle body is mounted on the intake manifold in the same position as a carburetor. Fuel is injected above the throttle plate and mixed with incoming air.

In a multipoint system, individual injectors are installed in the intake manifold at a point close to the intake valve where they inject the fuel to mix with the air as the valve opens. Intake air passes through an air intake throttle body containing a butterfly valve or throttle plate and travels through the intake manifold where it meets the incoming fuel charge at the intake valve. The difference in injector location permits more advance manifold designs in multipoint systems to aid in fuel distribution.

Fuel injection has numerous advantages over carburetion. It can match fuel delivery to engine requirements under all load and speed conditions, maintain an even mixture temperature, provide more efficient fuel distribution, and reduce emissions while improving driveability.

Electronic fuel injection (EFI) is far more common than the earlier mechanical injection represented by the Bosch K-Jetronic. EFI integrates the injection system into a complete engine management system which includes control of EGR, ignition timing, canister purging, and various other functions.

The EFI computer uses various sensors to gather data on engine operation. Intake air volume is determined by measuring airflow speed, manifold pressure, or the mass of the air drawn into the engine. This data is added to information about throttle position, idle speed, engine coolant and air temperature, crankshaft position, and other operating conditions. After processing the data, the computer signals the solenoid-operated injectors when to open and close. Injectors may be fired in various combinations, but all use the principle of pulse width modulation, in which the computer varies the percentage of on-time in each full on/off cycle according to engine requirements. In this way, the amount of fuel injected can be varied instantly to accommodate changing conditions.

Review Questions

Choose the single most correct answer. Compare your answers with the correct answers on page 451.

1. Fuel injection systems can lower emissions:
   a. By matching the air-fuel ratio to engine requirements
   b. Only at high speeds
   c. By using the intake manifold to vaporize fuel
   d. By matching engine speed to load conditions

2. All of the following are common kinds of gasoline fuel injection systems *except*:
   a. Multipoint injection
   b. Throttle body injection
   c. Direct cylinder injection
   d. Continuous injection

3. Mechanic A says that Bosch K-Jetronic systems are mechanical injection systems that operate on differential fuel pressure.
   Mechanic B says that Bosch K-Jetronic systems are intermittent injection systems.
   Who is right?
   a. A only
   b. B only
   c. Both A and B
   d. Neither A nor B

4. Bosch L-Jetronic and similar systems measure airflow with a:
   a. BMAP sensor
   b. Hot-wire air mass sensor
   c. Vane-type airflow sensor
   d. Air charge temperature sensor

5. Mechanic A says that TBI systems are electronic, intermittent injection systems.
   Mechanic B says that TBI systems require fuel pressure regulators.
   Who is right?
   a. A only
   b. B only
   c. Both A and B
   d. Neither A nor B

6. Mechanic A says that most TBI systems measure airflow and volume manifold absolute pressure, barometric absolute pressure or barometric and manifold absolute pressure.
   Mechanic B says that most Ford multipoint injection systems use a heated-film air mass sensor.
   Who is right?
   a. A only
   b. B only
   c. Both A and B
   d. Neither A nor B

7. Mechanic A says that fuel pressure regulators always are on the upstream (inlet) side of the injectors in an EFI system.
   Mechanic B says that mechanical injection systems do not require a pressure regulator.
   Who is right?
   a. A only
   b. B only
   c. Both A and B
   d. Neither A nor B

8. Mechanic A says that the throttle in a multipoint system is located between the injectors and the manifold.
   Mechanic B says that the throttle in an EFI system operates the same as a throttle on a carbureted engine.
   Who is right?
   a. A only
   b. B only
   c. Both A and B
   d. Neither A nor B

9. Mechanical fuel injectors are operated:
   a. Continuously by fuel pressure
   b. Intermittently by the computer
   c. Alternately by air pressure
   d. Sequentially by firing order

10. Modern fuel injection systems are based on work begun by:
    a. Rochester Products Division of GM
    b. Ford Motor Company
    c. Hitachi
    d. Robert Bosch GmbH

11. A cold-start injector is a:
    a. Temperature-controlled detonation device
    b. Solenoid-operated auxiliary injector
    c. Mechanical intermittent injector
    d. None of the above

12. Multec injectors used in a multipoint injection system differ from those produced by Robert Bosch in that they use a:
    a. Pintle valve
    b. Swirl nozzle
    c. Pin and spring
    d. Ball-seat valve with director plate

13. All of the following are filter locations in a fuel injection system *except*:
    a. In the pressure regulator
    b. At the fuel pump
    c. In the fuel line
    d. In the fuel injectors

14. Mechanic A says that an EFI system can use an on/off throttle position switch.
    Mechanic B says that a throttle position sensor is a variable resistor.
    Who is right?
    a. A only
    b. B only
    c. Both A and B
    d. Neither A nor B

15. A hot-wire, or heated-film, air mass sensor measures:
    a. Airflow velocity entering the engine
    b. Barometric absolute pressure
    c. Air temperature in a turbocharged system
    d. Molecular mass of air entering the engine

Chapter

17

Supercharging and Turbocharging

Engines with carburetors rely on atmospheric pressure to push an air-fuel mixture into the combustion chamber vacuum created by the downstroke of a piston. The mixture is then compressed before ignition to increase the force of the burning, expanding gases. The greater the mixture compression, the greater the power resulting from combustion. In this chapter, we will study ways to increase mixture compression.

ENGINE COMPRESSION VS. SUPERCHARGING

A high compression ratio is one way in which mixture compression can be increased. In the late 1960s, compression ratios on high-performance car engines reached more than 11 to 1. During the 1970s, emission control requirements brought compression ratios down to the range of 8 or 8.5 to 1. This was necessary because higher-compression engines tend to emit too much NO_x. Lower compression ratios also were required due to the greatly reduced lead content in the gasoline. However, the use of electronic engine management systems in the 1980s has allowed compression ratios in the 9 to 10 range.

High compression ratios have two major benefits:
• Volumetric efficiency is improved because the piston displaces a larger percentage of the total cylinder volume on each intake stroke.
• Since temperature increases as pressure increases, combustion is more complete and so thermal efficiency is higher with a high-compression engine.

There are, however, major disadvantages with high compression ratios:
• Since the compression ratio remains the same throughout the engine's operating range, temperature and pressure also are high and cause increased emissions during deceleration, idle, and part-throttle operation.
• A high compression ratio causes increased NO_x emissions.
• High compression ratios require the use of effective antiknock additives. While lead is the most effective additive, it produces harmful emissions and destroys catalytic converters.

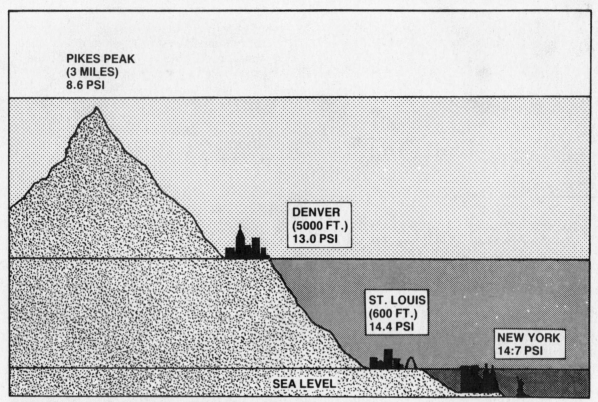

Figure 17-1. Air is a substance and has weight, which causes atmospheric pressure. Atmospheric pressure decreases as altitude increases. (Ford)

Another way to achieve this increase in mixture compression is called **supercharging**. This is a method by which a denser air-fuel charge can be packed into the engine's cylinders. Since the density of the air-fuel charge is greater, so is its weight — and power is directly related to the weight of an air-fuel charge consumed within a given time period. The result is much the same as a higher compression ratio, but the effect can be controlled during idle and deceleration to avoid high emissions.

Supercharging Principles

To this point, we have dealt with what we call **normally aspirated** engines. This term describes how an automotive engine breathes, which you studied in Part 1 of this manual. As you recall, air is drawn into a normally aspirated engine by atmospheric pressure forcing it into the low-pressure area of the intake manifold. The low pressure or vacuum in the manifold is created by the reciprocating motion of the pistons and is controlled by the action of the valves and throttle. Basically, this works well, but the engine's volumetric efficiency is considerably less than 100 percent. Volumetric efficiency, as we have seen, is a percentage measurement of the volume of air drawn into

a running engine compared to the maximum amount this engine could draw in (total displacement volume). While a stock engine averages approximately 70 to 80 percent volumetric efficiency, racing engines with the proper intake and exhaust tuning can exceed 100 percent volumetric efficiency at their power curve peak.

The volumetric efficiency of any normally aspirated engine is related to the density of the air drawn into it. Since atmospheric pressure and air density are greatest at (or below) sea level, both pressure and density normally decrease as altitude above sea level increases. For example, atmospheric pressure at sea level is about 14.7 psi (101 kPa); at higher elevations, atmospheric pressure may be only 8 or 9 psi (55 or 62 kPa), figure 17-1. Therefore, the volumetric efficiency of any engine will be greater at sea level than at an altitude above sea level.

By increasing the pressure on the air drawn into the engine above that of atmospheric pressure, it is possible to force more air into a cylinder during the intake stroke. Increasing the engine's air intake in this manner means that more fuel can be mixed with the air while still maintaining the same air-fuel ratio. The combination of more air and fuel entering an engine during its intake stroke means greater

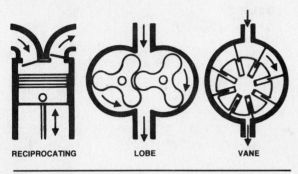

Figure 17-2. Three common positive-displacement pump designs.

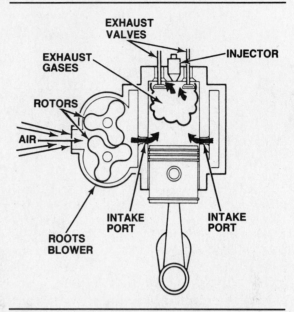

Figure 17-3. The Roots blower is the most common positive displacement pump supercharger. (Ford)

potential energy during combustion and more power as a result of combustion.

A supercharger pressurizes air to greater than atmospheric pressure. This amount of pressurization above atmospheric pressure is called **boost**. Boost can be measured in the same way as atmospheric pressure, which we studied in Chapter 8. Normal sea-level atmospheric pressure is 14.7 psi (101 kPa). Some superchargers can almost double that pressure, providing about 12 psi (83 kPa) boost *above* atmospheric pressure. At sea level, that would make a total intake pressure of 26.7 psi (184 kPa).

Atmospheric pressure drops as altitude increases, but boost pressure remains the same. For example, in Denver, where the atmospheric pressure is 13 psi (90 kPa), figure 17-1, our supercharger described above would provide a boost of 12 psi (83 kPa). This equals a total intake pressure of 25 psi (172 kPa). Superchargers also can be designed to provide increased boost at higher altitudes to make up for the loss of atmospheric pressure. When used on racing engines, superchargers can be designed to double or even triple the horsepower of a normally aspirated engine.

One of the major advantages of using a supercharger with a normally aspirated engine is that it can increase the air-fuel charge density to provide high-compression pressure when power is required, but it allows the engine to run on lower pressures when the additional power is not required.

Superchargers

In basic concept, a supercharger is nothing more than an air pump mechanically driven by the engine itself. Gears, shafts, chains, or belts from the crankshaft turn the pump. This means that the air pump or supercharger pumps air in direct relation to engine speed.

There are two general types of supercharger pumps:
- Positive displacement
- Centrifugal.

Positive displacement pumps include the reciprocating, the lobe (Roots), and the vane designs, figure 17-2. These are called positive displacement pumps because every revolution pumps the same volume of air. They operate by taking in a large column of air, compressing it into a small area and then forcing it through an outlet at high pressure. Some of these designs are very inefficient, and the efficient designs have been too expensive for passenger car use in the past. They are more often found on diesel trucks or racing engines.

The lobe-type, or Roots blower, figure 17-3, is the most common positive displacement supercharger in use. It was first developed in 1864 as a device to separate wheat from chaff

---

Supercharging: Use of an air pump to deliver an air-fuel mixture to the engine cylinders at a pressure greater than atmospheric pressure.

Normally Aspirated: An engine that uses normal vacuum to draw in its air-fuel mixture. Not supercharged.

Boost: A measure of the amount of air pressurization, above atmospheric, that a supercharger can deliver.

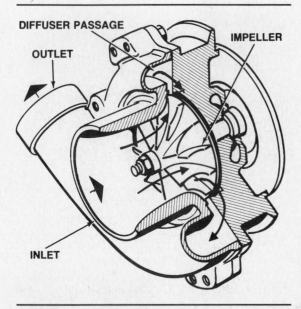

DIFFUSER PASSAGE

IMPELLER

OUTLET

INLET

Figure 17-4. The centrifugal pump design accelerates and then slows the air in order to compress it.

ROOTS SUPERCHARGER

MASS
AIRFLOW
SENSOR   AIR CLEANER

THROTTLE

BYPASS
VALVE

INTER-
COOLER

ENGINE

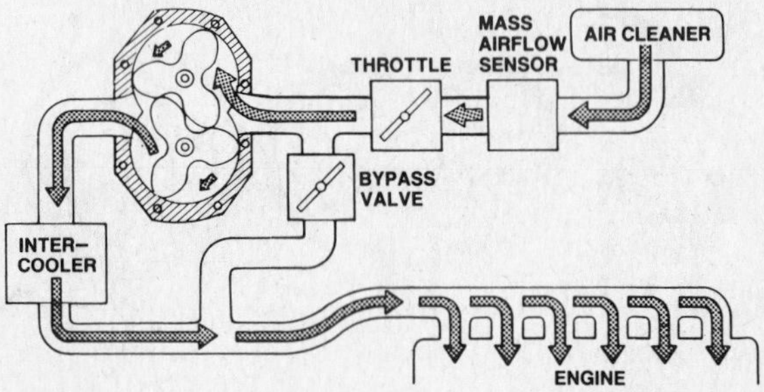

Figure 17-5. The Ford-Eaton supercharger system integrates a Roots blower with fuel injection and an engine management system.

but was applied to automotive engines around the turn of the century. Roots blowers are used on many high-performance and racing engines, but also are found on 2-stroke diesel engines, where they improve air intake and exhaust scavenging instead of acting as primary superchargers. The vane-type and axial-flow (Latham) superchargers are not commonly used.

The centrifugal pump, figure 17-4, is the most commonly used and most efficient variable-displacement supercharger. As the impeller turns at high speed, air pulled into the center of the impeller is speeded up and then thrown outward from the blades by centrifugal force. Air moved to the perimeter of the pump housing is forced through an outlet. Since centrifugal force increases as speed increases, a centrifugal supercharger will draw in more air and create a higher boost pressure as its speed increases.

Specific Supercharger Designs

The mechanical drive methods that operate a supercharger all have inherent limitations. They require up to 20 percent of the engine's power even when the supercharger is not in use. They also need a high overdrive ratio to obtain a speed great enough to provide the desired boost. Since the drive belt or gear speed must be quite high, the mechanical components are subjected to heavy wear.

However, the advent of small 4- and 6-cylinder engines has led automotive engi-

neers to take a second look at the supercharger as a viable means of improving low-speed torque while raising power output. Ford, Volkswagen, and Toyota are manufacturing supercharged engines.

Ford

For the 1989 model year, the Ford Thunderbird Super Coupe and Mercury XR7 were fitted with an intercooled supercharger manufactured by the Eaton Corporation. Its design is based on the traditional Roots-type and is integrated into an engine management system with fuel injection, figure 17-5. Intake airflow is the same as in any mass airflow injection system until it travels past the throttle plate. Instead of being sent directly to the manifold, the airflow is directed into the bottom of the supercharger, where the air is trapped and compressed by the spinning rotors. The air exits the top of the supercharger, then it passes through an intercooler to lower the heat from the turbulence created by the lobes (increasing air density). It is then directed into the intake manifold, where it is mixed with the fuel charge from the injectors. A bypass valve routes intake air directly to the manifold when supercharging is not required. The entire system is controlled by the engine computer, which turns the boost on and off as required by operating conditions.

Since it operates on pressure pulses instead of a constant flow of air, the Roots blower has a characteristic high-pitched whine which some find objectionable. This problem is minimized on the Ford-Eaton supercharger by acoustically tuning the entire intake system, and using helical-lobe rotors rather than the more common straight-lobe design. The helical-lobe rotors help even out the pressure pulses and reduce noise.

VOLKSWAGEN G-LADER

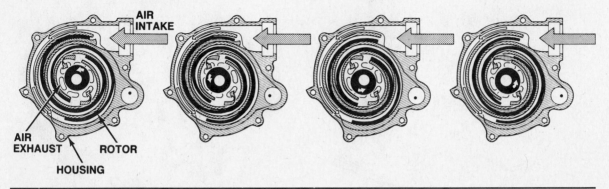

Figure 17-6. The G-Lader supercharger design compresses air by squeezing it through a spiral, then forcing it through outlets in the center of the unit.

Toyota

Toyota has equipped a 1.6-liter 4-valve, 4-cylinder engine used in its MR2 sports car with a 2-lobe Roots-type supercharger and intercooler. The Toyota application uses an electromagnetic clutch (like that used on an air conditioning compressor) to provide computer control over engagement and disengagement according to engine requirements. While the Ford-Eaton supercharger spins freely when it is not on boost, Toyota's computer control reduces any loss of engine efficiency during partial load.

Volkswagen

The supercharger used on some European Volkswagen models is based on a less-traditional design. Called the **G-Lader**, this spiral-channel unit is derived from a French design patented in 1905, figure 17-6. Concentric spiral ramps in both sides of a rotor mesh with similar ramps cast in the split casing. The rotor moves around an eccentric shaft instead of spinning on its axis, as in most other supercharger designs. Air drawn into the casing is squeezed through the spiral. This squeezing action compresses the air, which is then forced through a cluster of ports in the center of the casing and into the engine. The G-Lader supercharger is claimed to have several advantages over a Roots-type blower:
• Intake noise is lower because airflow is fairly constant instead of intermittent
• Wear is minimal because contact between the spiral and housing is slight
• It is considerably more efficient.

G-Lader: A type of supercharger pump which compresses air by squeezing it through an internal spiral, then forcing it through ports into the engine.

■ **Switching the Emphasis on Turbos**

Some drivers may think of turbochargers as exotic trappings for souped-up street cars and racers. That's natural when you consider that automotive engineers normally bring a turbo into play high up on the engine's performance curve to deliver maximum power at top rpm. The result is additional peak power that has won many races, and further convinced the general driving public that turbine-operated superchargers are not for them.

The reappearance of turbocharging as a factory option approached the subject from the opposite viewpoint. Engineers wanted 4-cylinder fuel economy with V-8 performance, and the turbocharger was the way to get it. Since its appearance on 1978 domestic engines, the turbocharger has been used for low- and medium-speed passing, and acceleration from about 1,200 rpm up. As engine speed climbs, the wastegate begins to open, preventing engine overload. This means that the turbocharger will be used for only about five percent of the time the engine is operating.

The performance-oriented 1980s have brought turbocharging into favor with consumers. When used with today's 4-cylinder engines, turbochargers provide the power to make them perform like V-6 and small V-8 engines, while retaining good fuel economy. By the mid-1980s, seven percent of the 4-cylinder engines produced by domestic manufacturers were turbocharged. With the upswing in turbocharger popularity, it faces a challenge from the supercharger, which is gaining popularity on the domestic scene.

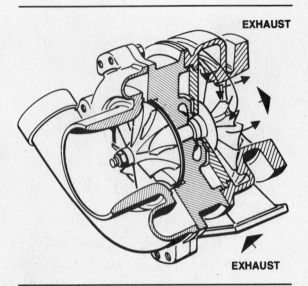

Figure 17-7. A turbine wheel is turned by the expansion of gases against its blades.

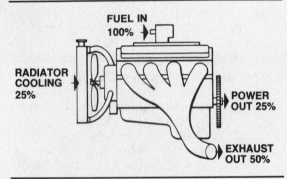

Figure 17-8. A turbine uses some of the heat energy that normally would be wasted.

Aftermarket applications

Superchargers on domestic vehicles date from the 1906 Chadwick and were popular on various American and European luxury cars during the 1920s and 1930s, as well as on pre-WWII race cars. They started to lose popularity after the war and, in recent years, were found primarily on street machines built by enthusiasts. The majority of superchargers or "blowers" in use are variations on the Roots design.

TURBOCHARGERS

The major disadvantage of a supercharger is its reliance on engine power to drive the unit. In some installations, as much as 20 percent of the engine's power is used by a mechanical supercharger. However, by connecting a centrifugal supercharger to a turbine drive wheel and installing it in the exhaust path, that engine horsepower is regained to perform other work

Figure 17-9. This cutaway of a typical turbocharger used by Ford shows how simple it is.

and the combustion heat energy lost in the engine exhaust (as much as 40 to 50 percent) can be harnessed to do useful work. That is the concept of a **turbocharger**.

A turbocharger turbine, figure 17-7, looks much like the centrifugal pump shown in figure 17-4. Hot exhaust gases flow from the combustion chamber to the turbine wheel. The gases are heated and expanded as they leave the engine. It is not the speed or force of the exhaust gases that forces the turbine wheel to turn, as is commonly thought, but the expansion of the hot gases against the turbine wheel's blades.

The turbine's main advantage over a mechanically driven supercharger is that the turbine does not drain power from the engine. In a normally aspirated engine, about half of the heat energy contained in the fuel goes out the exhaust system, figure 17-8. Another 25 percent is lost through radiator cooling. Only about 25 percent is actually converted to mechanical power. A mechanically driven pump uses some of this mechanical output, but a turbine gets its energy from the exhaust gases, converting more of the fuel's heat energy into mechanical energy.

Turbocharger Design

Most automotive turbocharger designs use a centrifugal pump because of cost, size, reliability, and efficiency. The modern turbocharger, figure 17-9, is both simple and compact, with few moving parts. But since those moving parts work at very high speeds and under extreme heat, the turbocharger must be manufactured to very exacting and precise tolerances. A turbocharger consists of two chambers connected by a center housing. The two chambers contain a turbine wheel and a compressor wheel connected by a shaft which passes through the center housing, figure 17-10.

To take full advantage of the exhaust heat which provides the rotating force, a turbocharger must be positioned as close as possible to the exhaust manifold. This allows the hot exhaust to pass directly into the unit with a minimum of heat loss. As exhaust gas enters the turbocharger, it rotates the turbine wheel blades, figure 17-11. The turbine wheel and compressor wheel are on the same shaft so that they turn at the same speed. Rotation of the compressor wheel draws air in through a central inlet and centrifugal force pumps it through an outlet at the edge of the housing.

A pair of bearings in the center housing supports the turbine and compressor wheel shaft, figure 17-11, and are lubricated by engine oil.

To minimize possible leakage around their blades, both wheels must operate with extremely close clearances. Leakage around the turbine blades causes a dissipation of the heat energy required for compressor rotation. Leakage around the compressor blades prevents the turbocharger from developing its full boost pressure.

At low engine speeds, both exhaust heat and pressure are low and the turbine runs at a low speed (approximately 1,000 rpm). Since the compressor does not turn fast enough to

Turbocharger: A supercharging device that uses exhaust gases to turn a turbine that forces extra air-fuel mixture into the cylinders.

■ Turbochargers: The Next Generation

Integrating the turbocharger into electronic engine management systems has brought it a well-deserved reputation for reliability and performance. Up to this point, all production turbocharger applications have been based on the centrifugal pump. The next generation of turbochargers will see numerous design variations, the first of which is Nissan's N2-VN or variable nozzle (scroll) turbo.

A movable curved flap in the turbo housing changes the throat area to vary its output according to engine requirements. The flap can move 27 degrees in stepless increments. Flap position is determined by a vacuum-operated diaphragm controlled by a pressure-controlled modulator and the engine computer.

With the flap closed, the flow of exhaust gas which enters the turbine housing is speeded up, increasing its pressure and rotating the turbine rapidly at low-speed, low-load conditions. At high-speed operation, the flap opens fully and the reduction in exhaust resistance aids in filling the cylinders.

The design provides a normal boost up to 15 psi (103 kPa). However, if operating conditions will permit it without engine damage, the computer will allow boost up to 17 psi (117 kPa) for short periods, such as when overtaking another vehicle.

VARIABLE NOZZLE TURBOCHARGER

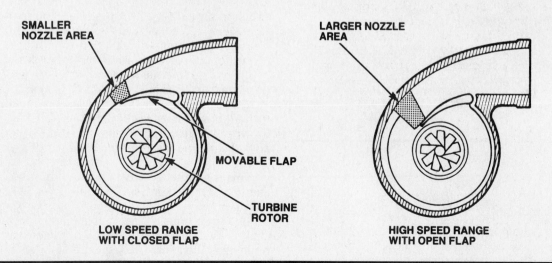

SMALLER NOZZLE AREA

LARGER NOZZLE AREA

MOVABLE FLAP

TURBINE ROTOR

LOW SPEED RANGE WITH CLOSED FLAP

HIGH SPEED RANGE WITH OPEN FLAP

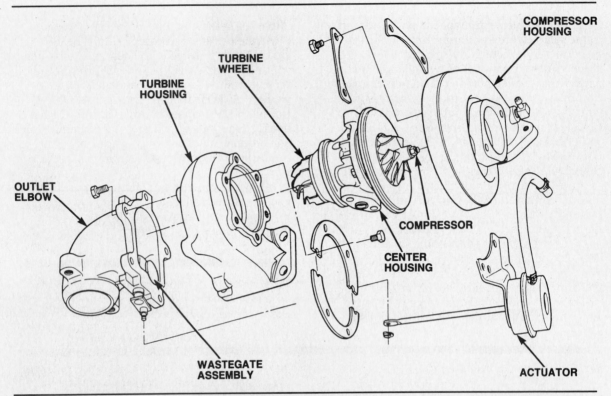

Figure 17-10. The components of a typical turbocharger. (Ford)

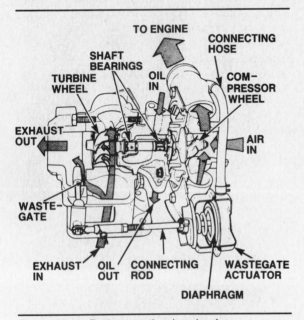

Figure 17-11. Basic operational cycle of a turbocharger. (Ford)

develop any boost pressure, air simply passes through it and the engine works like any normally aspirated engine. As engine speed or load increases, both exhaust heat and flow increase, causing the turbine and compressor

wheels to rotate faster. Since there is little rotating resistance on the turbocharger shaft, the turbine and compressor wheels will accelerate as the exhaust heat energy increases. With an engine running at full power, the typical turbocharger will rotate at speeds between 100,000 and 150,000 rpm.

At this point, you can recognize one of the turbocharger's main disadvantages — there is a time lag between increasing engine speed and the turbocharger's ability to overcome inertia and spin up to speed as the exhaust gas flow increases. This is called **turbo lag**.

Similarly, engine deceleration from full power to idle requires only a second or two because of its internal friction, pumping resistance and drive train load. But the turbocharger has no such load on its shaft, and is already turning many times faster than the engine at top speed. Thus, it may take a minute or more after the engine has returned to idle speed before the turbocharger also has returned to idle.

This is another disadvantage of the turbocharger. If the engine is decelerated to idle and then shut off, engine lubrication stops flowing to the center housing bearings while the turbocharger is still spinning. The oil in the center housing is then subjected to extreme heat and will gradually "coke" or oxidize.

Figure 17-12. Water-cooled turbochargers induct engine coolant into passages in the center housing (arrow) to cool the center bearings.

All clearances within a turbocharger are extremely close and the bearings are no exception. Radial clearance is generally kept between 0.003" and 0.006" (0.08 mm and 0.15 mm) and axial clearance is maintained between 0.001" and 0.003" (0.025 mm and 0.08 mm). Since the bearings must maintain these very critical clearances at extreme speeds, constant lubrication with clean oil is very important. Even a small particle of contamination entering the intake or exhaust housing can damage the turbocharger.

Liquid-cooled turbochargers

As we have seen, the turbocharger is a simple but extremely precise device in which heat plays a critical role. When properly maintained, a turbocharger also is a trouble-free device. To prevent problems with the turbocharger, three conditions must be met:

1. There must be constant and proper lubrication of the turbocharger shaft and bearings with clean engine oil.
2. Dirt particles and other contamination must be kept out of the intake and exhaust housings.
3. Whenever a basic engine bearing has been damaged, the turbocharger must be flushed with clean engine oil. Conversely, if the turbocharger is damaged, the engine oil should be flushed and the oil filter replaced as part of the repair procedure.

Many automakers have turned to liquid cooling to prevent the turbocharger center

bearings from being damaged by too much heat. In a liquid-cooled turbo design, figure 17-12, engine coolant is circulated through passages provided in the center housing to draw off the excess heat. This allows the bearings to run cooler and minimizes the probability of oil coking when the engine is shut down.

Turbocharger size and response time

We have already mentioned turbo lag as one of the main disadvantages of a turbocharger. Turbo lag is caused by the inertia inherent in the turbocharger's motive power. Like any material, moving exhaust gas has inertia. When full power is applied to an engine, there is a brief delay before the flow of exhaust gas develops enough energy to rapidly accelerate the turbine wheel. Inertia also is present in the turbine and compressor wheels, as well as the intake airflow. Since the turbocharger is a variable-displacement pump, it cannot supply an adequate amount of boost at low speed.

Turbocharger response time is directly related to the size of the turbine and compressor wheels. Small wheels accelerate rapidly; large wheels accelerate slowly. While the small wheels would seem to have an advantage over larger ones, they may not have enough airflow capacity for an engine. To minimize turbo lag, the intake and exhaust breathing capacities of an engine must be matched to the exhaust and intake airflow capabilities of the turbocharger.

Another factor influencing turbocharger response time is the location of the turbocharger on the engine. The most efficient setup is to place the turbine close to the exhaust manifold and the compressor outlet close to the intake manifold. Figure 17-13 shows this placement, as well as the operation cycle of a typical turbocharger used with a carbureted engine.

Turbocharger Installation

Turbochargers can be installed either on the air intake side (upstream) or on the exhaust side (downstream) of the carburetor or injectors. In an upstream installation, the turbocharger compresses and delivers a denser air charge to the carburetor or injectors. When installed

Turbo Lag: The time interval required for a turbocharger to overcome inertia and spin up to speed.

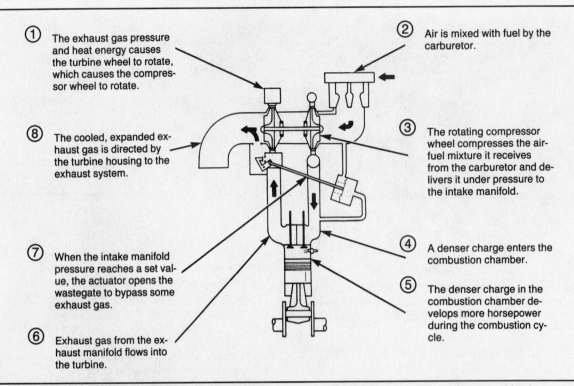

① The exhaust gas pressure and heat energy causes the turbine wheel to rotate, which causes the compressor wheel to rotate.

② Air is mixed with fuel by the carburetor.

⑧ The cooled, expanded exhaust gas is directed by the turbine housing to the exhaust system.

③ The rotating compressor wheel compresses the air-fuel mixture it receives from the carburetor and delivers it under pressure to the intake manifold.

⑦ When the intake manifold pressure reaches a set value, the actuator opens the wastegate to bypass some exhaust gas.

④ A denser charge enters the combustion chamber.

⑤ The denser charge in the combustion chamber develops more horsepower during the combustion cycle.

⑥ Exhaust gas from the exhaust manifold flows into the turbine.

Figure 17-13. Turbo lag is reduced by locating the turbine and compressor close to the exhaust and intake manifolds respectively. This is the operational cycle of a turbocharger used with a carbureted system. (Ford)

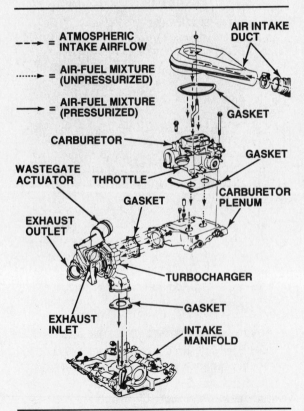

- - -→ = ATMOSPHERIC INTAKE AIRFLOW

········► = AIR-FUEL MIXTURE (UNPRESSURIZED)

———► = AIR-FUEL MIXTURE (PRESSURIZED)

AIR INTAKE DUCT

GASKET

CARBURETOR

GASKET

WASTEGATE ACTUATOR

THROTTLE

CARBURETOR PLENUM

GASKET

EXHAUST OUTLET

TURBOCHARGER

GASKET

EXHAUST INLET

INTAKE MANIFOLD

Figure 17-14. The turbocharger compresses the air-fuel mixture when the carburetor is installed at the compressor inlet. (Buick)

downstream, the air-fuel mixture is compressed and delivered to the cylinders. Both types of installations are used with modern turbocharger applications.

Downstream installations

Turbochargers are usually installed downstream with carbureted engines (this is called a draw-through turbocharger). The carburetor generally is located on the intake side of the turbocharger, although it is occasionally positioned on the outlet side. Positioning the carburetor at the compressor inlet allows the turbocharger to increase airflow and pressure drop through the carburetor. This provides the required air-fuel mixture, which is compressed and sent to the cylinders through the manifold, figure 17-14.

There is a distinct advantage to positioning the carburetor at the compressor inlet. In this location, the carburetor does not have to be modified to accept and withstand boost pressure. This position of the carburetor simplifies air-fuel ratio control. Locating the carburetor at the turbocharger outlet, on the other hand, means that it must be calibrated to meter fuel correctly under both atmospheric and above-atmospheric conditions. In addition, a carburetor positioned at the turbocharger outlet must

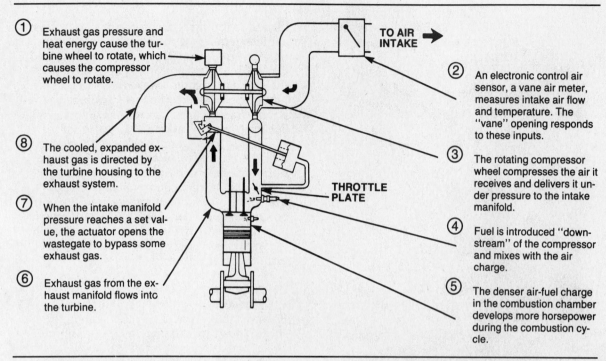

① Exhaust gas pressure and heat energy cause the turbine wheel to rotate, which causes the compressor wheel to rotate.

⑧ The cooled, expanded exhaust gas is directed by the turbine housing to the exhaust system.

⑦ When the intake manifold pressure reaches a set value, the actuator opens the wastegate to bypass some exhaust gas.

⑥ Exhaust gas from the exhaust manifold flows into the turbine.

TO AIR INTAKE

② An electronic control air sensor, a vane air meter, measures intake air flow and temperature. The "vane" opening responds to these inputs.

③ The rotating compressor wheel compresses the air it receives and delivers it under pressure to the intake manifold.

THROTTLE PLATE

④ Fuel is introduced "downstream" of the compressor and mixes with the air charge.

⑤ The denser air-fuel charge in the combustion chamber develops more horsepower during the combustion cycle.

Figure 17-15. The operational cycle of a turbocharger used with a fuel-injected system. (Ford)

also be pressurized to withstand boost pressure without leaking fuel. The fuel system must also move the fuel at a higher pressure to overcome the boost pressure present at the carburetor. These factors all make air-fuel ratio control difficult when the carburetor is located at the turbocharger outlet.

At the same time, there are some minor drawbacks that must be overcome with carburetor placement at the compressor inlet:
• The carburetor is positioned away from the intake manifold, which may cause a slight amount of hesitation when the throttle is opened rapidly.
• Throttle and choke linkages are more complex.
• Preheating the air-fuel mixture on a cold engine is more difficult.
• A special seal must be installed between the center housing and compressor to prevent the air-fuel mixture from entering the engine lubrication system.
• Fuel separation from the compressed mixture may occur before it reaches the manifold. These disadvantages are not as difficult to deal with as the problems inherent with a pressurized carburetor. The drawbacks of carburetor placement at the compressor inlet can be overcome with careful manifold design and the proper choice of carburetor and turbocharger.

Upstream installations
Turbochargers are installed upstream with fuel-injected engines (this is called a blow-through turbocharger). The unit is positioned at the manifold air intake and compresses only intake air, figure 17-15. This reduces fuel delivery time and increases the amount of turbine energy available. Most turbocharged engines with fuel injection use a multipoint system, with an individual injector at each cylinder. Just before the compressed air charge enters the cylinder, fuel is injected into it, as shown in step 4, figure 17-15. The throttle plate installed between the turbocharger and injectors regulates airflow.

Mitsubishi uses a throttle body injection (TBI) system on some engines in which the turbocharger delivers compressed air to the injectors in the TBI unit. The throttle plate, however, is located between the injectors and the intake manifold, figure 17-16. In this system, the throttle plate regulates the intake volume of compressed air-fuel mixture.

Engine Emissions

Turbochargers have just about the same effect as an increased compression ratio. Why, then, can turbochargers be used on emission-controlled engines when increased compression ratios cannot be used?

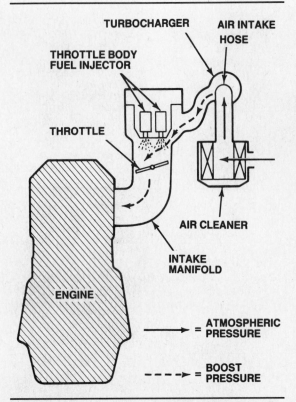

TURBOCHARGER
AIR INTAKE
HOSE
THROTTLE BODY
FUEL INJECTOR
THROTTLE
AIR CLEANER
INTAKE
MANIFOLD
ENGINE
→ = ATMOSPHERIC
PRESSURE
---→ = BOOST
PRESSURE

Figure 17-16. The throttle is placed downstream of the turbocharger and fuel injectors in this Mitsubishi TBI system. (Mitsubishi)

The advantage of a turbocharger is the way in which it controls compression. An engine built with a certain compression ratio always will have that ratio. As mentioned earlier, high-compression engines tend to create high exhaust emissions during idle, deceleration, and choked operation. Turbocharger boost can be controlled so that the engine runs as a normally aspirated unit during these operating modes. Under acceleration or heavy load conditions, turbocharger boost is applied to the intake manifold. The resulting increase in compression improves the engine's volumetric efficiency because the percentage of the total cylinder volume which the piston displaces on the intake stroke increases.

Most turbocharged engines now in production use essentially the same emission control devices as do non-turbocharged versions of the same engines.

TURBOCHARGER CONTROLS

You cannot simply bolt a turbocharger onto an engine and automatically pick up free power. As we have seen, a turbocharger increases both compression pressures and loads on the moving parts of an engine. When automakers

turned to the turbocharger in the late 1970s, engines required stronger pistons, new piston ring designs, strengthened crankshafts, and other internal modifications in order to survive the stress of greater loads and pressures. Current engine designs, however, generally are strong enough to withstand these forces without major modifications.

Even so, the operation of a turbocharger must be controlled to avoid high exhaust emissions and detonation. The maximum boost pressure of a turbocharger also must be controlled, or the higher compression and power potential could damage the engine. Three factors, then, must be controlled because of the high pressures and temperatures created by a turbocharger. These are:

1. Boost pressure
2. Air-fuel mixture temperature
3. Detonation.

These factors are interrelated. Higher pressures (boost) increase the temperature of the air-fuel mixture, which raises combustion temperatures. Higher combustion temperatures and pressures may combine to cause detonation. The following paragraphs explain how carmakers control these factors and what effects the controls have on turbocharger operation.

Boost Control

Boost increases as turbocharger rotation increases. Boost must be held below the maximum that a given engine can withstand without causing detonation or serious engine damage. Boost control systems either can limit the amount of exhaust gas reaching the turbine, or vent off some of the compressed air mixture before it reaches the combustion chamber. The mechanisms involved are wastegates and blowoff valves.

Wastegates

Turbochargers installed on production engines during the 1970s were limited to 6 or 8 psi (41 or 55 kPa) boost. However, steady advances in electronic engine management systems, turbochargers and engine design now allow many turbocharged engines to operate at boost pressures ranging between 10 and 14 psi (69 and 97 kPa). The most efficient way of controlling boost pressure is with a **wastegate** to control the flow of exhaust gas to the turbine. This is a bypass valve at the exhaust inlet to the turbine, figure 17-17. The wastegate can allow all of the exhaust into the turbine, or it can route the exhaust directly to the exhaust system, figure 17-18.

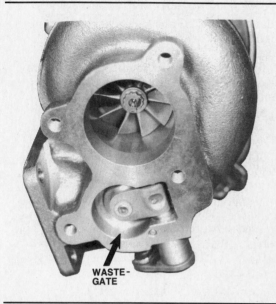

Figure 17-17. A typical wastegate assembly in a turbocharger turbine housing.

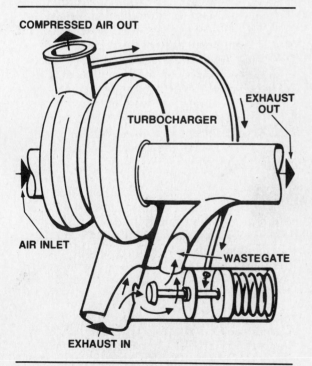

Figure 17-18. The wastegate reacts to intake manifold pressure and controls the amount of exhaust gas reaching the turbine wheel.

Wastegates generally are controlled by an actuator diaphragm linkage, figure 17-19. The diaphragm is exposed to intake manifold pressure. When this pressure reaches a certain level, the diaphragm moves far enough to open the wastegate, which routes exhaust gases directly to the muffler, bypassing the turbine.

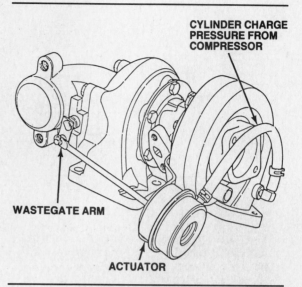

Figure 17-19. Wastegate operation is controlled by linkage connected to a vacuum diaphragm. (Ford)

Since wastegates are constantly exposed to corrosive exhaust gases, they must be made of corrosion resistant alloys.

By bleeding off exhaust gases from the turbine, the wastegate limits the speed of the exhaust turbine and thus controls maximum boost pressure. It also controls detonation to the extent that it holds down boost pressure.

A pressure line connects the actuator to the compressor outlet, figure 17-19. Pressure rises at this point during deceleration because the compressor is working against the closed throttle of an engine that requires little airflow. This causes the actuator to open the wastegate and eliminate overboost during a closed-throttle condition.

Wastegate boost control operates the same on all turbochargers using the system, but the operation of some wastegates can be adapted to adjust the boost level for either low-octane or high-octane fuel. Ford does this on its high-performance engines through a boost control module which interfaces with the engine management computer. The driver indicates the type of fuel being used with an octane switch on the instrument panel. The switch automatically recalibrates the EEC-IV microprocessor for the fuel selected. The microprocessor then

Wastegate: A diaphragm-actuated bypass valve used to limit turbocharger boost pressure by limiting the speed of the exhaust turbine.

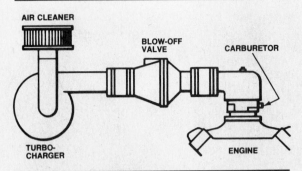

Figure 17-20. A blowoff valve can open to relieve intake manifold pressure.

controls a solenoid which routes pressure between the actuator line and the compressor inlet. This allows the wastegate to maintain a lower boost level with low-octane fuel or a higher boost level with high-octane fuel.

Blowoff valve

A **blowoff valve**, or pressure control valve, affects the flow of compressed air between the turbocharger and the engine, figure 17-20. The valve can be operated in different ways depending on the function that it is meant to control.

If the valve is to control the maximum boost pressure, then it is a simple spring-loaded unit. When boost pressure reaches a certain level, the spring tension is overcome and some of the boost pressure is allowed to escape. If the turbocharger is compressing only air, as shown in figure 17-20, then the air can be vented to the atmosphere. If the turbocharger is compressing the combustible air-fuel mixture, then the mixture must be vented back into the turbocharger inlet.

If the blowoff valve is meant to control exhaust emissions, it is operated by intake manifold vacuum. During idle, closed-throttle deceleration, and choked operation, vacuum in the intake manifold causes a diaphragm to move and open the valve. The engine operates as a normally-aspirated unit, avoiding the excessive emissions that the turbocharger compression would cause. Some blowoff valves are operated by vacuum routed to one side of the diaphragm and boost pressure routed to the other.

Mixture Cooling

You have learned that a turbocharger increases the pressure of intake air. As the pressure of air increases, its temperature also increases. This means that the temperature of the air-fuel mixture provided in a turbocharged engine is higher than that of a normally-aspirated engine.

This higher air-fuel mixture temperature has two unwanted effects: the air-fuel charge density is reduced and it tends to detonate more easily. Detonation is a serious problem with any engine, but even more so with one that is turbocharged. Detonation combined with the high pressures involved in a turbocharged engine can bend a piston rod, burn pistons, or quickly cause other internal damage.

Two methods are used to cool the compressed mixture before it reaches the combustion chamber: water injection systems and intercoolers. The major purpose of each system is to control detonation.

Water injection

The use of **water injection** to cool the intake mixture of a turbocharged engine has been confined mainly to aftermarket or add-on turbochargers, rather than production installations available from carmakers. Water injection can be used most easily on carbureted engines when the turbocharger is located downstream from the carburetor. At maximum boost, a fine spray of water is injected into the carburetor inlet by an electric or vacuum-operated pump. The water has no effect on the combustion process, but since it vaporizes with the gasoline, it tends to cool the intake charge and leaves the engine as water vapor in the exhaust.

Water injection can be highly effective, but it requires the use of precision pumps and valves. Also, water injection requires that the driver maintain a supply of water, something that many drivers would likely forget. Since it is not a driver-proof system, carmakers generally have selected intercooling as a better alternative.

Intercoolers

An **intercooler** is nothing more than a heat exchanger, figure 17-21. By passing the compressed air from the turbo through an intercooler on its way to the manifold, up to 60 percent of the heat can be removed by air-to-air transfer. Since the cooler air charge is much denser, it contains more oxygen, which results in greater combustion efficiency. Air-to-liquid heat exchangers have also been used as intercoolers, but they are heavier and more complicated than the air-to-air type.

Intercoolers work best on fuel-injected systems or with carbureted systems in which the

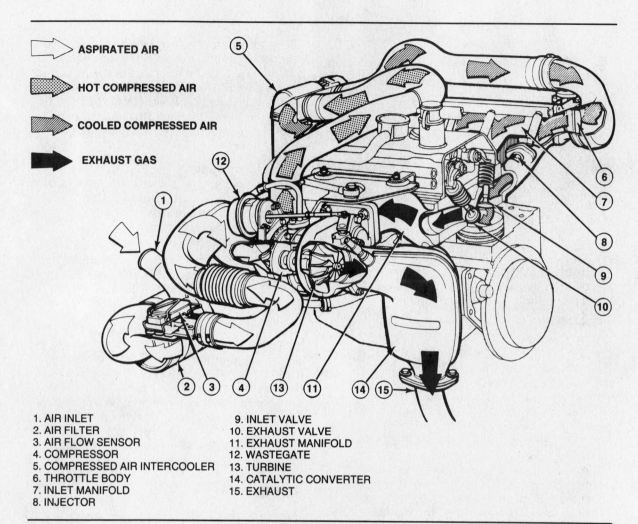

ASPIRATED AIR

HOT COMPRESSED AIR

COOLED COMPRESSED AIR

EXHAUST GAS

1. AIR INLET
2. AIR FILTER
3. AIR FLOW SENSOR
4. COMPRESSOR
5. COMPRESSED AIR INTERCOOLER
6. THROTTLE BODY
7. INLET MANIFOLD
8. INJECTOR

9. INLET VALVE
10. EXHAUST VALVE
11. EXHAUST MANIFOLD
12. WASTEGATE
13. TURBINE
14. CATALYTIC CONVERTER
15. EXHAUST

Figure 17-21. The Renault version of an air-to-air intercooler. (Renault)

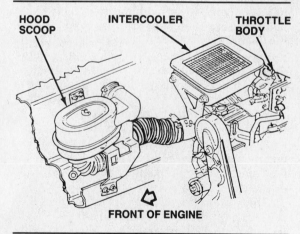

HOOD SCOOP   INTERCOOLER   THROTTLE BODY

FRONT OF ENGINE

Figure 17-22. Ford's high-performance engines use an air-to-air intercooler that draws air from a hood scoop. (Ford)

carburetor is downstream from the turbocharger. With only air passing through the intercooler, there is no possibility of fuel separation from the mixture as it cools.

Among domestic manufacturers, Ford has led the way in air-to-air intercooler use. For maximum efficiency, Ford mounts the intercooler on top of the engine, figure 17-22. The

Blowoff Valve: A spring-loaded valve that opens when boost pressure overcomes the spring tension.

Water Injection: A method of lowering the air-fuel mixture temperature by injecting a fine spray of water which evaporates as it cools the intake charge.

Intercooler: An air-to-air or air-to-liquid heat exchanger used to lower the temperature of the air-fuel mixture by removing heat from the intake air charge.

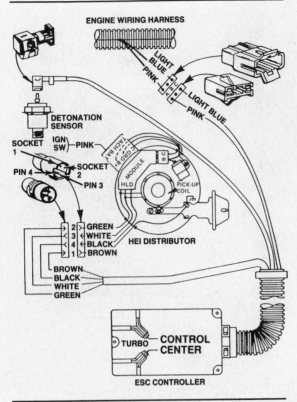

Figure 17-23. A detonation sensor signals the electronic module to retard timing when engine vibration or knocking occurs. (Buick)

intercooler inlet connects directly to the turbocharger; its outlet connects to the air intake throttle body. The top of the intercooler connects to a hood scoop. This scoop gathers ambient air from outside the engine and directs it into the intercooler, whose air fins remove the heat from the air compressed by the turbocharger.

Spark Timing and Detonation

Excessive heating of the air-fuel mixture can cause an explosion in the combustion chamber known as detonation. This wastes power and can damage the engine, as we learned in Chapter 2. Since a turbocharger compresses and therefore heats the air-fuel mixture, detonation is a common problem. Various control methods are used to minimize or prevent detonation.

Retarding the spark timing can control detonation by lowering the peak temperature of combustion. Spark control systems can be mechanically or electronically operated.

Mechanical operation

Turbocharged engines with breaker-point ignitions use a distributor vacuum advance unit where manifold pressure acts on a diaphragm to retard ignition timing under high boost conditions. The retard diaphragm is connected to the breaker plate to move it in the opposite direction. This method is similar to the use of a dual-diaphragm distributor to retard timing with high manifold vacuum during idle and deceleration.

Electronic operation

Electronic detonation sensing offers the precise control lacking in a mechanical system. A detonation sensor (piezoelectric crystal) mounted in the engine block or intake manifold senses vibration caused by detonation or engine knock. The detonation sensor works in different ways depending on the system design. When vibration is sensed, the sensor either independently generates a voltage signal to the computer, or voltage signals constantly sent out by the computer are altered by the sensor and then returned to the computer, figure 17-23. The computer retards ignition timing in increments of 2- or 4-degrees until either a maximum retard setting is reached or the detonation stops. When the sensor no longer picks up knocking vibrations, its signal notifies the computer, which gradually restores spark advance to the amount required for optimum engine operation.

SUMMARY

Supercharging and turbocharging are both proven ways in which mixture compression can be achieved to increase the power resulting from combustion without increasing exhaust emissions. A supercharger is an air pump mechanically driven by the engine in direct relationship to engine speed. Supercharger pumps generally are a positive displacement design in which every revolution pumps the same volume of air. The most common positive displacement supercharger is the lobe-type, or Roots blower. Mechanically driven superchargers may use up to 20 percent of the engine's power even when not in use. The mechanical components involved also are subject to excessive wear.

The Ford-Eaton and Toyota superchargers are based on the traditional Roots-type design in which lobes or rotors literally fling air into the intake manifold. Volkswagen uses a spiral-channel design called the G-Lader in which concentric spiral ramps in both sides of a rotor mesh with similar ramps cast in the split casing. The rotor moves around an eccentric shaft instead of spinning on its axis, compressing the air by squeezing it through the spiral.

A turbocharger is an exhaust turbine-drive centrifugal pump that also increases intake air above atmospheric pressure. Except for its motive power, it does essentially the same job as a supercharger in increasing the volumetric efficiency of an engine and developing more power from the air-fuel mixture.

While a turbocharger is a simple device, its clearances are extremely close. Turbochargers operate at speeds up to 150,000 rpm. One major disadvantage of a turbocharger is "turbo lag," the time interval between increasing engine speed and the turbocharger's ability to overcome inertia and spin up to speed. Turbocharger life can be extended by circulating engine coolant through passages provided in the center housing to draw off the excess heat.

Turbochargers can be installed either on the air intake side (upstream) or on the exhaust side (downstream) of the carburetor or injectors. In an upstream installation, the turbocharger compresses and delivers a denser charge of air to the carburetor or injectors. When installed downstream, the air-fuel mixture is compressed and delivered to the cylinders.

Boost pressure, air-fuel mixture temperature, and detonation must be controlled to prevent high exhaust emissions and possible engine damage. Boost pressure is controlled by a wastegate or bypass valve in the exhaust inlet to the turbine. This limits the speed of the exhaust turbine and controls maximum boost pressure. A blowoff valve also can be used. This is a simple spring-loaded unit. When boost pressure reaches a certain level, the spring tension is overcome and some of the boost pressure is allowed to escape.

Mixture temperature can be controlled by injecting a fine spray of water into the intake charge or by use of an intercooler. This is a heat exchanger which removes heat from the air charge before it mixes with the fuel.

Detonation can be controlled mechanically or electronically. Current systems all use electronic control to retard spark timing and lower the peak temperature of combustion. Electronic control is precise. A detonation sensor mounted in the engine block or intake manifold signals the computer whenever it senses vibration caused by detonation or engine knock. The computer gradually retards ignition timing until detonation disappears, then advances timing to its most efficient point.

Review Questions

Choose the single most correct answer.
Compare your answers with the correct answers on page 451.

1. Supercharging delivers the air-fuel mixture to the cylinder at:
   a. Lower than atmospheric pressure
   b. Atmospheric pressure
   c. Higher than atmospheric pressure
   d. Three times the atmospheric pressure

2. Which is *not* true of superchargers?
   a. They can operate at very low rpm
   b. They are mechanically driven
   c. There are two types
   d. Mechanical superchargers consume a lot of engine power

3. Positive displacement pumps:
   a. Contain impellers
   b. Pump the same volume of air each revolution
   c. Increase air pressure by decelerating it
   d. Are highly efficient

4. A turbine wheel turns because of:
   a. Centrifugal force
   b. Exhaust gas speed
   c. Manifold vacuum
   d. Expansion of hot exhaust gases

5. Of the heat energy contained in gasoline:
   a. 50 percent is converted to mechanical power
   b. 50 percent is lost to cooling
   c. 25 percent is converted to engine power
   d. 50 percent goes out the exhaust system

6. Despite high compression pressures achieved, turbochargers can be used on emission-controlled engines because:
   a. They have fixed compression ratios
   b. Turbocharger boost can be varied to meet engine needs
   c. They are placed between the air cleaner and the carburetor
   d. They are placed between the carburetor and the engine

7. Which is *not* a method of controlling a turbocharger system?
   a. Changing the amount of boost
   b. Cooling the compressed mixture
   c. Readjusting the carburetor idle
   d. Altering spark timing

8. The wastegate controls boost by:
   a. Controlling flow of exhaust gas
   b. Controlling compressed air
   c. Controlling the air-fuel mixture
   d. Controlling exhaust emissions

9. Retarding spark time will control detonation by:
   a. Cooling the compressed mixture
   b. Cooling the exhaust manifold
   c. Reducing compression pressure
   d. Lowering peak temperature of combustion

10. Mechanic A says that turbochargers are constant-displacement pumps.
    Mechanic B says that Roots blowers are variable-displacement pumps.
    Who is right?
    a. A only
    b. B only
    c. Both A and B
    d. Neither A nor B

11. Boost control can be limited by a wastegate or by:
    a. An intercooler
    b. A blowoff valve
    c. A detonation sensor
    d. Manifold vacuum

12. Engine exhaust is used to drive a turbocharger:
    a. Turbine
    b. Wastegate
    c. Compressor
    d. Intercooler

13. The momentary hesitation between throttle opening and boost delivery by the turbocharger is called:
    a. Underboost lag
    b. Turbo lag
    c. Ignition lag
    d. Compression lag

14. Mechanic A says that a turbocharger installed upstream from the fuel source compresses only air.
    Mechanic B says that a turbocharger installed downstream from the fuel source compresses air and fuel.
    Who is right?
    a. A only
    b. B only
    c. Both A and B
    d. Neither A nor B

PART FIVE

Emission Control Systems

18

Positive Crankcase Ventilation

The problem of crankcase ventilation has existed since the beginning of the automobile. No piston ring, new or old, can provide a perfect seal between the piston and the cylinder wall. When an engine is running, the pressure of combustion forces the piston downward. This same pressure also forces gases and unburned fuel from the combustion chamber past the piston rings and into the crankcase. These gases are called crankcase vapors, or blowby, as you learned in Chapter 12.

Under perfect conditions, combustion of an engine's air-fuel mixture would completely consume all of the air and the fuel. It would leave only harmless byproducts, such as water vapor and carbon dioxide. However, combustion seldom is perfect and usually is incomplete. The byproducts of incomplete combustion include carbon monoxide (CO), hydrocarbons (HC) and oxides of nitrogen (NO_x).

These combustion byproducts, particularly unburned hydrocarbons, form blowby, figure 18-1. The crankcase must be ventilated to remove these vapors and gases. However, the crankcase on modern engines cannot be ventilated directly to the atmosphere, because the hydrocarbon vapors add to air pollution. Positive crankcase ventilation (PCV) systems were developed to ventilate the crankcase and recirculate the vapors to the engine's induction system.

In this chapter, you will learn:
• The reasons for crankcase ventilation
• The difference between open and closed ventilation systems
• The components of the modern PCV system
• How the PCV system ventilates the crankcase without polluting the air
• What happens when the PCV system does not work correctly.

DRAFT TUBE VENTILATION

Blowby has three undesirable features:
1. It destroys the lubricating qualities of engine oil.
2. It causes sludge and varnish to form.
3. It helps cause formation of corrosive acids, which can damage engine parts.

After trying various methods of ventilating the engine crankcase, carmakers at first settled on the road draft tube, figure 18-2. This is nothing more than a tube connected to the engine crankcase that allows vapors to pass into the air. Fresh air to ventilate the crankcase enters through a vented oil filler cap. This air passes into the crankcase where it mixes with the vapors. When the car is moving, a vacuum

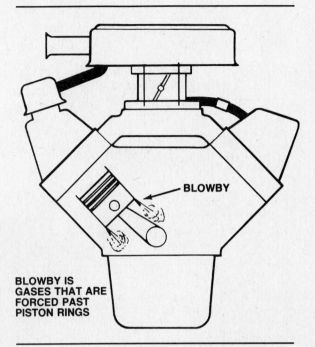

BLOWBY

BLOWBY IS
GASES THAT ARE
FORCED PAST
PISTON RINGS

Figure 18-1. Piston rings do not provide a perfect seal. Combustion gases blow by the rings into the crankcase.

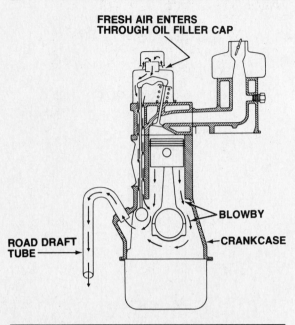

FRESH AIR ENTERS
THROUGH OIL FILLER CAP

BLOWBY

CRANKCASE

ROAD DRAFT
TUBE

Figure 18-2. The road draft tube ventilates the crankcase to the atmosphere when the car is moving.

is created by the air flowing past the road draft tube. This vacuum draws the crankcase vapors out into the atmosphere.

The road draft tube has three major shortcomings:
1. It works best only when there is a pressure difference between the oil filler cap and the draft tube. Since this pressure depends upon car movement, when the car is moving slower than about 25 mph (40 kph), there is not enough vacuum to remove the vapors from the crankcase.
2. It passes the crankcase vapors directly into the atmosphere causing air pollution.
3. At higher vehicle speeds, too much crankcase ventilation will increase engine oil consumption because oil droplets are drawn out through the road draft tube.

POSITIVE CRANKCASE VENTILATION SYSTEMS

The drawbacks of the road draft tube were eliminated when the controlled crankcase ventilation system was introduced. Controlled, or positive, crankcase ventilation relies on intake manifold vacuum to draw the vapors from the crankcase up into the intake manifold. This results in a positive movement of the air through the crankcase whenever the engine is running. The vapors are then returned to the

■ It Wasn't Always As Simple

The early PCV systems caused a good deal of grief and engine troubles for automakers. Many garages, even franchised dealers, ignored the PCV systems on 1963-64 cars. They required a lot of care and cleaning, and they clogged quickly when ignored. Contaminants remained in the crankcase, and sludge and moisture formed, clogging oil lines and preventing adequate engine lubrication. The result was disaster for the engine, and major overhauls on engines still under warranty were often required.

The situation reached a crisis point for one major manufacturer, who stopped using PCV on its cars from the spring of 1964 until early in 1965. Auto engineers were frustrated by the problems PCV systems were creating. The systems had been designed to be simple and require only a minimum amount of service. But mechanics in the field completely ignored the emission control device, and engines began to fail.

These problems resulted in a crash project by the automakers. While engineers worked overtime developing a "better" PCV system, manufacturers started a program to educate dealers, servicemen, and car owners. The so-called "self-cleaning" PCV valve was developed and began appearing on mid-1965 models. This second-generation PCV system is practically the same one in use today.

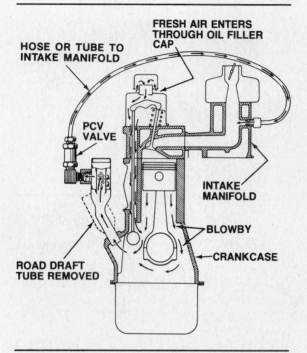

Figure 18-3. In a Type 1 open PCV system, fresh air enters through the oil filler cap. Crankcase vapors are returned to the intake manifold through a PCV valve and hose or tube.

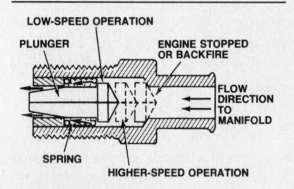

Figure 18-4. The PCV valve plunger responds to spring force and manifold vacuum to regulate the airflow rate.

combustion chambers, where they are burned. These systems may be classified as open or closed PCV systems, depending upon their design.

Open PCV Systems

Positive crankcase ventilation, as we know it today, received its first major use on 1961 California cars. Open systems were installed on many 1963 models nationwide. Open crankcase ventilation systems can be divided into three types.

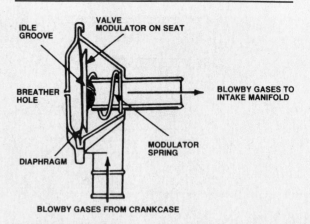

Figure 18-5. When the engine is at idle, the Type 2 PCV valve is closed by crankcase vacuum. Vapors flow through the idle groove at about 3 cubic feet (85 liters) per minute.

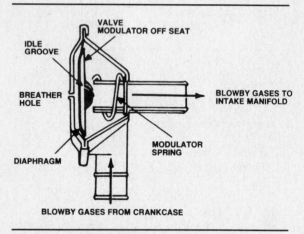

Figure 18-6. When the engine is at cruising speed, the Type 2 PCV valve is opened by crankcase pressure. The flow rate depends on the amount of blowby created by the engine.

Type 1 system operation

A hose connects the crankcase with the intake manifold, figure 18-3. When the engine is running, fresh air is drawn into the crankcase through the vented oil filler cap. This air mixes with the crankcase vapors, then travels to the intake manifold where it is drawn into the engine cylinders. Airflow from the crankcase is metered through a PCV valve, figure 18-4, that contains a spring-oriented plunger to control the rate of airflow through the engine.

Type 1 open PCV systems were used as original equipment on many domestic passenger car engines through the mid-1960s.

Type 2 system operation

A Type 2 system is similar to a Type 1 system, but uses a special PCV valve and oil filler cap.

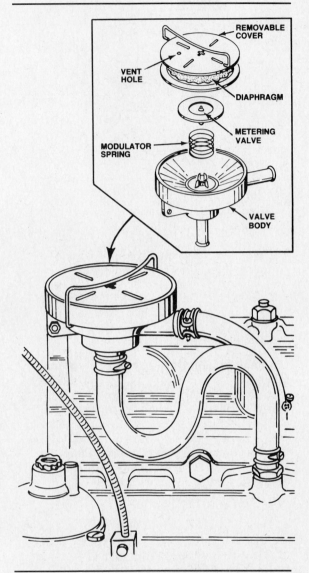

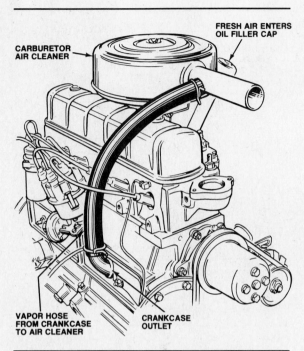

Figure 18-8. A Type 3 open PCV system has no PCV valve.

Type 3 system operation

In a Type 3 system, the crankcase is connected to the air cleaner by a hose, figure 18-8. Vapors are drawn from the crankcase by a slight suction in the air cleaner. No control valve is used. Fresh air enters through the oil filler cap, mixes with the crankcase vapors, and is drawn to the air cleaner. From the air cleaner, the vapors are then drawn through the carburetor and into the cylinders.

■ Check PCV Valve for Fuel Dilution

Winter driving, with its short trips and cold starts, can cause fuel dilution of the engine oil. This will not only thin out the oil, but the gasoline vapors fed to the intake manifold through the PCV system will produce a rich idle mixture. If you are working on a car with a rich idle mixture and you suspect fuel dilution of the oil, you can check it quickly.

Remove the PCV valve from the valve cover and let it draw in fresh air with the engine running. If the idle mixture becomes normal or leaner than normal, the engine oil probably has too much fuel dilution. Drive the car at highway speeds for up to half an hour to purge fuel vapors from the crankcase. Then readjust the idle mixture. As an alternative, drain the crankcase and refill with fresh oil.

Figure 18-7. The Type 2 PCV valve used on some imported cars could be disassembled for cleaning.

The diaphragm-type PCV valve regulates the airflow according to crankcase vacuum. When a vacuum exists in the crankcase, the valve is closed, figure 18-5. When the crankcase is under pressure, figure 18-6, the valve opens. The oil filler cap has an orifice large enough to allow the right amount of air to enter but small enough to maintain crankcase vacuum. The orifice must remain open at all times for the system to work correctly.

Some imported cars, particularly British models in the mid-1960s, had Type 2 PCV systems as original equipment. These were called Smith's PCV valves, figure 18-7. They worked like the one we just described and could be opened for cleaning.

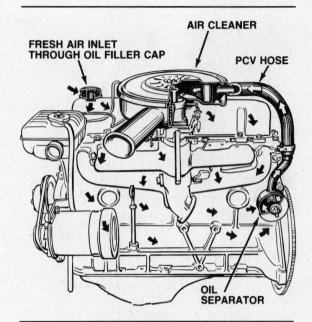

FRESH AIR INLET
THROUGH OIL FILLER CAP

AIR CLEANER

PCV HOSE

OIL
SEPARATOR

Figure 18-9. Ford Type 3 PCV systems had oil separators at the crankcase outlet.

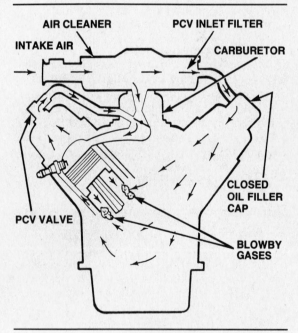

AIR CLEANER

PCV INLET FILTER

INTAKE AIR

CARBURETOR

PCV VALVE

CLOSED
OIL FILLER
CAP

BLOWBY
GASES

Figure 18-10. Type 4 sealed PCV system operation.

Because blowby reaches the carburetor *before* the rich air-fuel vaporization, this system tends to enrich the air-fuel mixture. Carburetors used with a Type 3 system must be adjusted to make up for this richer mixture. Some imported cars use a "sealed" Type 3 system in which the oil filler cap is not vented.

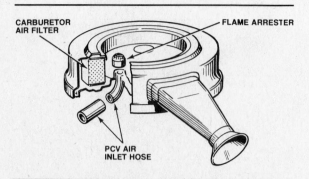

CARBURETOR
AIR FILTER

FLAME ARRESTER

PCV AIR
INLET HOSE

Figure 18-11. When PCV inlet air is drawn from the clean side of the air cleaner, a flame arrester is required in case of a backfire.

Type 3 PCV systems were used as original equipment on some Ford and American Motors cars in the early 1960s. The systems used on Ford 6-cylinder engines had oil separators at the crankcase outlets to minimize the amount of oil drawn through the PCV hose to the air cleaner, figure 18-9.

Limited efficiency of the open PCV system

Open PCV systems only partly control crankcase emissions. Manifold vacuum decreases considerably under heavy load or acceleration, causing crankcase pressures to build. This forces some of the vapors into the atmosphere through the vented oil filler cap. Crankcase vapors also pass through the vented cap into the air if the system becomes clogged.

Open PCV systems do provide some benefits:
1. They promote longer engine life by removing most harmful vapors from the crankcase.
2. They reduce the amount of crankcase vapors which pollute the air.

Closed PCV Systems

Closed, or Type 4, PCV systems were required on all new California cars in 1964. They were standard nationwide by 1968 and are still used today on all new domestically built cars, and all cars imported into the United States.

In a closed PCV system, figure 18-10, the oil filler cap is not vented to the atmosphere. Air for the crankcase is drawn through a hose from the air cleaner to one of the valve covers or to a crankcase inlet below the intake manifold. The dipstick also is sealed to prevent air from leaking into the crankcase.

Crankcase ventilation air may come from either the clean side (inside) or the dirty side (outside) of the carburetor air filter. When air is drawn from the clean side (using the air cleaner filter as a PCV filter), a flame arrester, figure 18-11, is used. This wire screen is in the

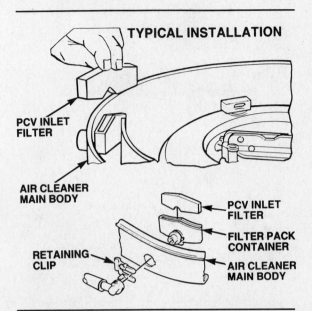

TYPICAL INSTALLATION

PCV INLET FILTER

AIR CLEANER MAIN BODY

PCV INLET FILTER

FILTER PACK CONTAINER

RETAINING CLIP

AIR CLEANER MAIN BODY

Figure 18-12. The PCV inlet filter on many vehicles is located in the air cleaner housing and is serviced as shown.

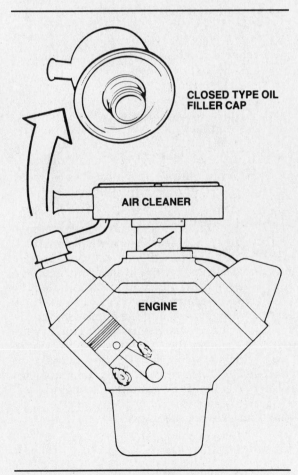

CLOSED TYPE OIL FILLER CAP

AIR CLEANER

ENGINE

Figure 18-13. On other engines, the PCV inlet filter may be located in the oil filler cap.

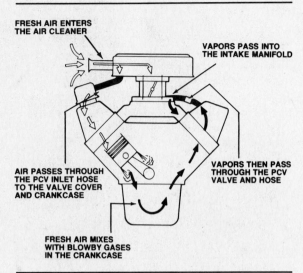

FRESH AIR ENTERS THE AIR CLEANER

VAPORS PASS INTO THE INTAKE MANIFOLD

AIR PASSES THROUGH THE PCV INLET HOSE TO THE VALVE COVER AND CRANKCASE

VAPORS THEN PASS THROUGH THE PCV VALVE AND HOSE

FRESH AIR MIXES WITH BLOWBY GASES IN THE CRANKCASE

Figure 18-14. Closed PCV system operation under normal conditions.

PCV air intake line, either at the air cleaner or at the valve cover. Its purpose is to prevent a crankcase explosion if the engine backfires.

When air is drawn from the dirty side of the air cleaner, a separate PCV air filter, or crankcase ventilation filter, is used. This can be located in the air cleaner, figure 18-12, in the oil filler cap, figure 18-13, or in the inlet air hose where it connects to the valve cover. A flame arrester is not required in this case, since the air cleaner filter does that.

■ PCV System Service

When a PCV system becomes restricted or clogged, the cause is usually an engine problem or the lack of proper maintenance. For example, scored cylinder walls or badly worn rings and pistons will allow too much blow-by. Start-and-stop driving requires more frequent maintenance and causes PCV problems more quickly than highway driving, as will any condition allowing raw fuel to reach the crankcase. Using the wrong grade of oil, or not changing the crankcase oil at periodic intervals will also cause the ventilation system to clog.

When a PCV system begins to clog, the engine tends to stall, idle roughly, or overheat. As ventilation becomes more restricted, burned plugs or valves, bearing failure, or scuffed pistons can result. Also look for an oil-soaked distributor or points, or leaking out around valve covers or other gaskets. Do not overlook the PCV system while troubleshooting. A partly or completely clogged PCV valve, or one of the incorrect capacity, may well be the cause of poor engine performance.

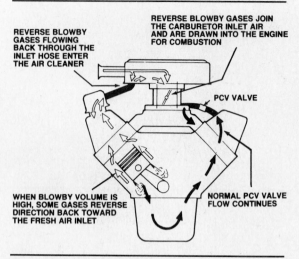

Figure 18-15. Closed PCV system operation under heavy load.

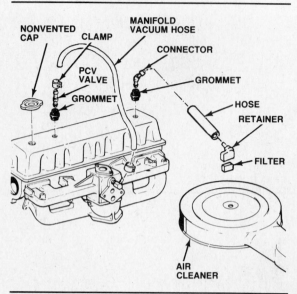

Figure 18-16. Late-model closed PCV systems generally share these common components. (AMC)

Type 4 system operation

Under normal conditions, fresh air from the air cleaner passes through the inlet hose to the crankcase, figure 18-14. The fresh air mixes with the crankcase vapors and passes through a PCV valve before being drawn into the intake manifold. Vapors that back up under certain conditions cannot escape from the closed system. If manifold vacuum drops or if the system becomes clogged, extra crankcase vapors will reverse their direction. In the closed crankcase ventilation system, these excess vapors flow back to the air cleaner, figure 18-15, instead of passing out of the engine and into the atmosphere. Once in the air cleaner, they mix with incoming air and pass through the carburetor, throttle body, or intake manifold (port injection) to be burned in the combustion chamber. This makes the closed system almost 100 percent effective in controlling crankcase emissions.

Closed PCV system efficiency

Closed crankcase ventilation provides three benefits:
1. It promotes longer engine life by removing harmful vapors from the crankcase.
2. It eliminates crankcase vapors that pollute the air.
3. It increases fuel economy by recirculating all unburned blowback to the intake manifold.

When air flows freely, the PCV system will function properly, as long as the PCV valve is not clogged. Modern engine design includes the air and vapor flow as a calibrated portion of the air-fuel mixture. In fact, some engines receive as much as 30 percent of their idle air through the PCV system. For this reason, a

flow problem in the PCV system will result in driveability problems.

A PCV system that is not properly vented, or scavenged, will result in oil dilution, formation of sludge, and oil deposits collecting in the air cleaner. Unlike driveability problems, these are not immediately noticed and their effect is long-term, resulting in premature engine wear and inefficient air cleaner operation.

ORIGINAL EQUIPMENT CLOSED PCV SYSTEMS

All new cars sold in the United States since 1968 have a Type 4 closed PCV system, figure 18-16. The design of closed PCV systems is essentially the same, regardless of manufacturer. All use a PCV valve or calibrated orifice, an air inlet filter, and connecting hoses. An oil/vapor or oil/water separator is used in some systems. The oil/vapor separator lets oil vapors condense and drain back into the crankcase, figure 18-17. The oil/water separator accumulates moisture and prevents it from freezing during cold engine starts, figure 18-18. Separators generally are used with turbocharged and fuel-injected engines. The location of each of these components may vary from one engine to another, but all work the same.

Air Inlet Filter

PCV air inlet filters are usually installed in a retainer inside the air cleaner, figure 18-12, in

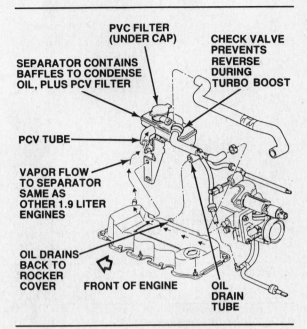

Figure 18-17. Turbocharger pressure increases blowby and creates a large quantity of oil vapor. The oil/vapor separator allows the vapors to condense and drain back into the crankcase. (Ford)

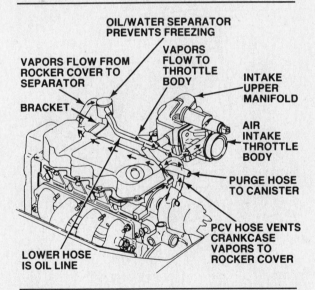

Figure 18-18. An oil/water separator may be used on some fuel-injected engines to accumulate moisture and prevent it from freezing during cold engine starts. (Ford)

the oil filter cap, figure 18-13, or in the oil/vapor separator, figure 18-17. They are made of wire gauze, wire mesh, or polyurethane foam. Some wire gauze or wire mesh filters can be cleaned and reused. Others must be replaced, and like the polyurethane foam type, are usually replaced at the same time as the air cleaner filter element.

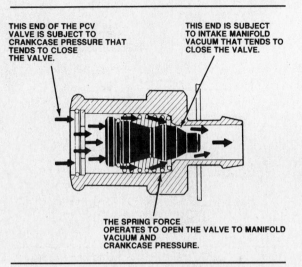

Figure 18-19. Spring force, crankcase pressure, and manifold vacuum work together in regulating PCV valve flow rate.

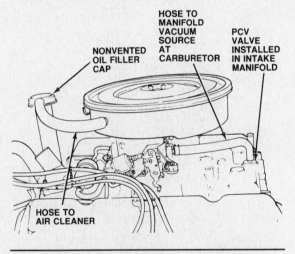

Figure 18-20. The components of a typical V-8 PCV system. (AMC)

Connecting Hoses

The closed PCV system uses two connecting hoses. Fresh air travels from the air cleaner to the engine through the air inlet hose. Crankcase vapors travel from the engine to the intake manifold through the manifold vacuum hose. PCV hoses are made of special materials that resist oil vapors. Heater or fuel line hose should *not* be used as a substitute.

PCV Valve

This one-way valve has a spring-operated plunger, figure 18-19, to control valve flow rate. Flow rate is set for each engine and a

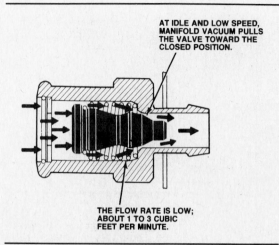

AT IDLE AND LOW SPEED, MANIFOLD VACUUM PULLS THE VALVE TOWARD THE CLOSED POSITION.

THE FLOW RATE IS LOW; ABOUT 1 TO 3 CUBIC FEET PER MINUTE.

Figure 18-21. PCV valve airflow during cruising and light-load operation.

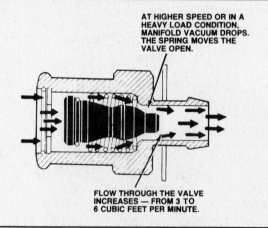

AT HIGHER SPEED OR IN A HEAVY LOAD CONDITION, MANIFOLD VACUUM DROPS. THE SPRING MOVES THE VALVE OPEN.

FLOW THROUGH THE VALVE INCREASES — FROM 3 TO 6 CUBIC FEET PER MINUTE.

Figure 18-22. PCV valve airflow during acceleration and heavy-load operation.

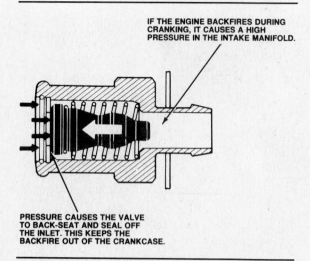

IF THE ENGINE BACKFIRES DURING CRANKING, IT CAUSES A HIGH PRESSURE IN THE INTAKE MANIFOLD.

PRESSURE CAUSES THE VALVE TO BACK-SEAT AND SEAL OFF THE INLET. THIS KEEPS THE BACKFIRE OUT OF THE CRANKCASE.

Figure 18-23. PCV valve operation in case of a backfire.

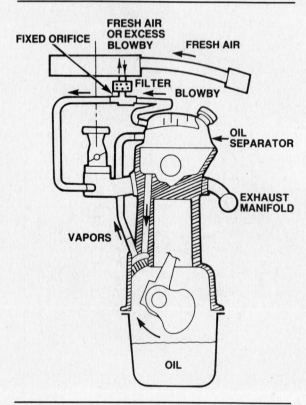

Figure 18-24. The orifice flow control system used on 1981-85 Ford 1.6L/1.9L Escort engines does not use fresh air scavenging of the crankcase.

valve for a different engine should not be substituted. This setting is determined by the size of the plunger and the holes inside the valve. PCV valves usually are located in the valve cover, figure 18-16, or in the intake manifold, figure 18-20.

The PCV valve regulates the airflow through the crankcase under all driving conditions and speeds. When manifold vacuum is high (cruising and light-load operation), the PCV valve restricts the airflow, figure 18-21, to maintain a balanced air-fuel ratio. It also prevents high intake manifold vacuum from pulling oil out of the crankcase and into the intake manifold.

Under high speed or heavy loads, the valve opens and allows maximum airflow, figure 18-22. If the engine backfires, the valve will close instantly, figure 18-23, to prevent a crankcase explosion.

Orifice-Controlled Systems

The closed PCV system used on 4-cylinder engines in some domestic and imported cars contains a calibrated orifice instead of a PCV valve. This often is called an orifice-controlled system. The orifice may be located in the valve

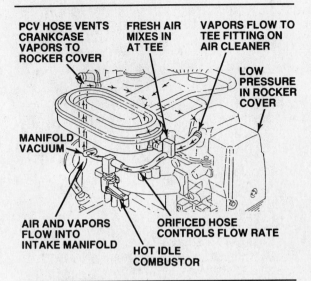

PCV HOSE VENTS CRANKCASE VAPORS TO ROCKER COVER

FRESH AIR MIXES IN AT TEE

VAPORS FLOW TO TEE FITTING ON AIR CLEANER

LOW PRESSURE IN ROCKER COVER

MANIFOLD VACUUM

AIR AND VAPORS FLOW INTO INTAKE MANIFOLD

ORIFICED HOSE CONTROLS FLOW RATE

HOT IDLE COMBUSTOR

Figure 18-25. Normal operation of the 1981-85 Ford 1.6L/1.9L Escort orifice flow control system.

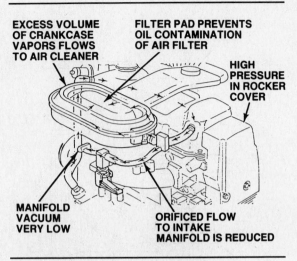

EXCESS VOLUME OF CRANKCASE VAPORS FLOWS TO AIR CLEANER

FILTER PAD PREVENTS OIL CONTAMINATION OF AIR FILTER

HIGH PRESSURE IN ROCKER COVER

MANIFOLD VACUUM VERY LOW

ORIFICED FLOW TO INTAKE MANIFOLD IS REDUCED

Figure 18-26. Operation of the 1981-85 Ford 1.6L/1.9L Escort orifice flow control system under heavy acceleration or high speed conditions.

cover or intake manifold, or in a hose connected between the valve cover, air cleaner, and intake manifold.

While most orifice flow control systems work the same as a PCV valve system, they may not use fresh air scavenging of the crankcase. The carbureted 1981-85 Ford 1.6L/1.9L Escort engine is a good example of this design, figure 18-24. Crankcase vapors are drawn into the intake manifold in calibrated amounts depending on manifold pressure and the orifice size. If vapor availability is low, as during idle, air is drawn in with the vapors. During off-idle operation, excess vapors are sent to the air cleaner. Normal operation of this particular orifice flow control system is shown in figure 18-25; figure 18-26 shows the system under heavy acceleration or high-speed operation.

A dual orifice valve is used on carbureted 1986 and later Ford 1.9L Escort engines to increase PCV flow during off-idle engine operation. At idle, PCV flow is controlled by a 0.050-inch (1.3-mm) orifice. As the engine moves off-idle, spark port vacuum pulls a spring-loaded valve off its seat, allowing PCV flow to pass through a 0.090-inch (2.3-mm) orifice.

■ Retrofit PCV Systems

Several retrofit devices are made and sold to convert an open-type PCV system to the closed-type. These devices are about the same as the factory-installed closed PCV systems, and are offered in two versions: one for the crankcase and one for the air cleaner. The kit components are used to install a PCV system on older engines that did not have them.

Why would anyone want to install a retrofit PCV device? The State of California provides one answer to the question. Used cars sold in California must have a PCV system approved by the state. Those 1955-67 cars originally sold outside California with open PCV systems can be legally driven by their original owner. However, when ownership is transferred within the state (sold as used cars), their open PCV system must be converted to a closed-type system to meet state requirements before they can be properly registered and licensed.

Retrofit kits are made for specific engines and each kit contains detailed instructions for installation and service. Once installed, these kits are serviced the same way as the factory-installed, closed PCV systems.

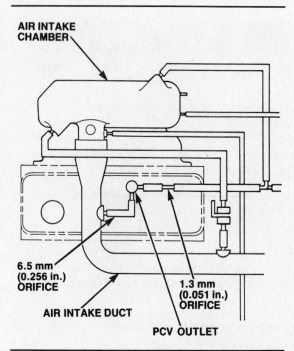

Figure 18-27. The AMC/Renault dual-orifice PCV system used with multiport injection. (AMC/Renault)

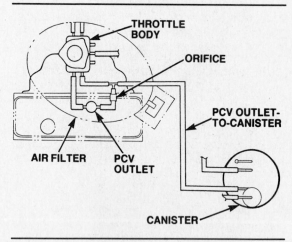

Figure 18-28. The AMC/Renault single orifice PCV system used with throttle body injection. (AMC/Renault)

Other variations of the orifice flow control system have been used over the years, primarily by foreign manufacturers. AMC/Renault 4-cylinder engines with multipoint fuel injection use a 2-orifice system, figure 18-27. One orifice is installed in the air intake chamber circuit; the other orifice is located in the air intake duct circuit. PCV flow passes through one or the other of these orifices according to engine operating conditions.

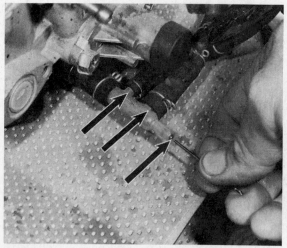

Figure 18-29. The dual-return crankcase ventilation system on Honda CVCC engines connects to the carburetor with a joint containing orifices at the points shown. They can be cleaned with an appropriate size drill bit.

Figure 18-30. The breather hose should be removed from Honda CVCC condensation chambers to drain accumulated fluids.

On AMC/Renault 4-cylinder engines with throttle body fuel injection, a single orifice is located in a vacuum line that tees into the canister purge-to-throttle body line and connects to the valve cover, figure 18-28.

Another common example is the "dual-return" crankcase ventilation system found on Honda CVCC engines. In this system, blowby travels up through the engine, where it passes through a liquid/vapor separator in the top of the valve cover. The vapors then are directed through a breather hose into a plastic condensation chamber installed on the underside of the air cleaner housing. Separation occurs

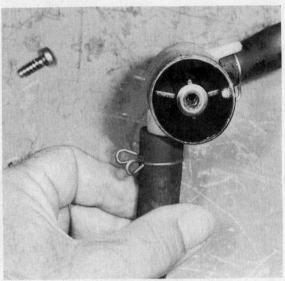

Figure 18-31. Combustion by-products which form harmful sludge and varnish are trapped in the "dual-return" condensation chamber.

again inside the chamber. The lighter vapors are directed into the carburetor through a series of fixed orifices, figure 18-29, according to the amount of manifold vacuum present.

Condensation settles in the chamber, with solids remaining at the bottom and liquids passing into a drain tube. Early models had a slit in the tube that allowed accumulated oil and water to drain when the tube was squeezed enough to open the slit. Later models have a regular hose which must be removed from the chamber and inverted to drain accumulated fluid, figure 18-30. The condensation chamber also must be removed from the air cleaner housing periodically and cleaned in solvent to remove sludge and varnish, figure 18-31.

SUMMARY

Pressure in the engine cylinders forces combustion gases past the pistons. These gases, called blowby, settle in the engine crankcase where they contaminate the lubricating oil and create harmful acids. Ventilation is necessary to remove the vapors from the crankcase. The draft tube system which was used until the 1960s doesn't work well at low speeds, and also allows the vapors to pollute the air.

The recirculation of crankcase vapors to the intake manifold is called positive crankcase ventilation (PCV). Four types of PCV systems have been used. Types 1, 2, and 3 are called open systems because vapors are forced into the atmosphere whenever manifold vacuum is low, or if the system is clogged. Type 4 is called a closed system because vapors cannot escape into the air under any conditions.

A malfunctioning PCV system can cause driveability problems and create harmful acids and sludge that affect engine lubrication and result in premature wear.

PCV systems use either a fixed or a variable metering device to regulate airflow. The variable metering device, or PCV valve, is standard on most modern PCV systems. It contains a spring-operated plunger and reacts to manifold vacuum. Installation of the correct PCV valve in an engine is important. Differences in PCV valve idle airflow can greatly influence idle smoothness and vehicle driveability when incorrect valves are used.

The fixed metering device, or orifice, is used on some domestic and foreign 4-cylinder engines. Honda's dual-return system is a variation of this design.

Review Questions

Choose the single most correct answer.
Compare your answers with the correct answers on page 451.

1. In a PCV system, crankcase vapors are recycled to the:
   a. Exhaust system
   b. Road draft tube
   c. Oil-filler breather cap
   d. Intake manifold

2. Which of these effects of blowby is not harmful to the engine?
   a. It destroys lubricating qualities of the engine oil
   b. It causes air pollution
   c. It causes sludge and varnish to form
   d. It causes formation of corrosive acids

3. Road draft tubes:
   a. Draw fresh air from the carburetor
   b. Work off intake manifold vacuum
   c. Are efficient at low speeds
   d. None of the above

4. Controlled crankcase ventilation was introduced in California in:
   a. 1959
   b. 1960
   c. 1961
   d. 1962

5. The illustration shows a:
   a. Type 1 PCV system
   b. Type 2 PCV system
   c. Type 3 PCV system
   d. Type 4 PCV system

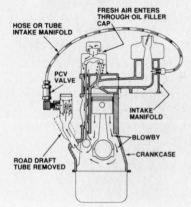

6. Type 2 PCV systems have:
   a. A closed oil filler cap
   b. An open oil filler cap
   c. An oil filler cap with a preset orifice
   d. None of the above

7. In Type 3 PCV systems:
   a. The crankcase is connected to the intake manifold
   b. The PCV valve is a plunger type
   c. The PCV valve is a diaphragm type
   d. There is no PCV valve

8. The Type 3 PCV system:
   a. Is vented to the intake manifold
   b. Tends to make the air fuel mixture leaner
   c. Has no effect on fuel mixture
   d. Tends to make the fuel mixture richer

9. Closed (Type 4) PCV systems became standard nationwide in which year?
   a. 1964
   b. 1966
   c. 1967
   d. 1968

10. A separate flame arrester is used in a closed PCV system when inlet air is drawn from the:
    a. Clean side of the carburetor filter
    b. Dirty side of the carburetor filter
    c. The intake manifold
    d. The oil filler cap on a valve cover

11. The advantages of a closed PCV system are:
    a. It promotes longer engine life
    b. It eliminates crankcase vapors almost entirely
    c. It increases fuel economy
    d. All of the above

12. Which is not part of a Type 4 PCV system?
    a. A PCV valve
    b. A vented oil filler cap
    c. An air inlet filter
    d. A manifold vacuum hose

13. PCV system hoses are made from:
    a. Heater hose material
    b. Low-temperature-resistant nylon
    c. Oil-resistant rubber material
    d. Fuel-resistant neoprene

14. The PCV valve operates in which of the following ways?
    a. Restricts airflow when intake manifold vacuum is high
    b. Increases airflow when intake manifold vacuum is low
    c. Acts as a check valve in case of carburetor backfire
    d. All of the above

15. Most orifice-controlled systems work the same as PCV valve *except*:
    a. They are open systems
    b. They may not use fresh air scavenging of the crankcase
    c. They cannot be used with fuel-injected engines
    d. All of the above

19

Air Injection

Carmakers have various names for their air injection systems, but all do about the same job. They provide additional air to the exhaust manifold where it mixes with the hot exhaust leaving the engine. This helps the oxidation, or burning reaction, necessary to lower HC and CO emissions.

In this chapter, you will learn:
• The reasons for, and principles of, air injection
• The components used in a typical pump air injection or pulse air injection system
• The changes which created second-generation systems used with catalytic converters.

THE NEED FOR AIR INJECTION

During the early days of emission control, **air injection** was an easy way to meet the required standards. Also known as the air pump system, figure 19-1, air injection was one of the first add-on devices used to help oxidize HC and CO exhaust emissions. By 1966, Chrysler was the only domestic automaker not using an air pump system on at least some cars. Early air injection systems contained many hoses and tubes placed across the engine. The external connecting lines made it difficult to work on the engine, and hose failure due to engine heat was common.

While the air injection system was an add-on device, it actually modified the basic process of combustion in the engine. Combustion, as you know, is an oxidation reaction, but usually an incomplete reaction. By providing air to the exhaust system as soon as the hot exhaust gases leave the cylinder, the injection system makes possible the continued oxidation of any HC and CO remaining in the exhaust. As a result, the HC and CO combine with O_2 to form H_2O vapor and CO_2.

Chrysler, however, chose to modify the design of its engines instead of adding air injection. The results proved that emission standards could be met without the add-on pump system. The other automakers profited from Chrysler's experience, and so domestic cars of the later 1960s relied more on engine modifications and less on air injection. The use of air

Air Injection: A way of reducing exhaust emissions by injecting air into each of the exhaust ports of an engine. The air mixes with the hot exhaust and oxidizes the HC and CO to form H_2O and CO_2.

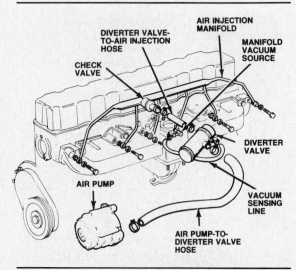

Figure 19-1. The basic components of an air injection system.

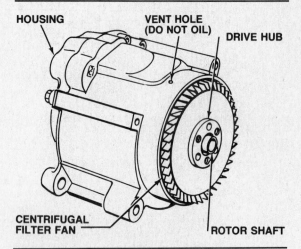

Figure 19-2. Late-model 2-vane air pumps have an external centrifugal filter fan mounted on the front of the housing.

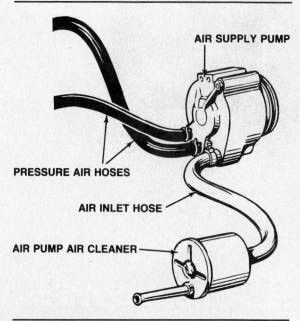

Figure 19-3. Older 3-vane pumps had separate inlet air cleaners.

injection decreased on most engines until 1972. To meet the more stringent emission standards that year, even Chrysler was forced to install an air injection system on some engines.

As emission standards became even more strict during the 1970s, automakers became more dependent on air injection. When the catalytic converter was introduced in 1975, it was hoped that the air pump system could be abandoned for good. However, the additional air provided by the injection system was necessary to increase the catalytic action on many engines. With these changes, the air injection system seemed a permanent part of emission control for many engines.

However, the development of sophisticated electronic fuel management and engine control systems may have turned the tide again. A number of the new and smaller engines equipped with electronic fuel injection now can meet emission standards without air injection. If the trend continues, air injection systems may become less important in the future.

BASIC SYSTEM DESIGN AND OPERATION

Manufacturers use the following names for their air injection systems:
- American Motors — Air Guard
- Chrysler — Air Injection System
- Ford — Thermactor or Managed Thermactor Air System
- General Motors — Air Injection Reactor (AIR).

Regardless of its name, the basic air injection system is a relatively simple system, generally consisting of:
1. A belt-driven air pump with inlet air filter
2. One or more air distribution manifolds and nozzles
3. Antibackfire valve
4. One or more check valves
5. Connecting hoses.

Air Injection Pump

The air pump, figure 19-2, is normally mounted at the front of the engine and is driven by a

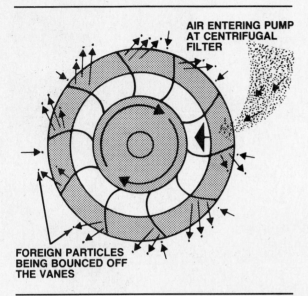

Figure 19-4. Dust and dirt are removed from the inlet air by centrifugal force.

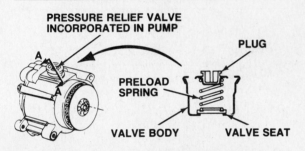

Figure 19-5. Some air pumps have built-in pressure relief valves. (AC-Delco)

belt from the crankshaft pulley. The pump pulls fresh air in through an external filter and pumps it under slight pressure to each exhaust port through connecting hoses. Adding this extra air to the hot HC and CO emissions in the exhaust manifold causes oxidation to take place. This helps change the HC and CO into H_2O and CO_2.

The Saginaw Division of General Motors makes most air pumps used on domestic cars. Early Saginaw pumps (1966-67) were a 3-vane design, figure 19-3, and could be rebuilt if necessary. A Saginaw 2-vane design replaced the 3-vane pump on 1968 and later models. The 2-vane pumps cannot be rebuilt but must be replaced if they fail. Older 3-vane pumps still in use usually are replaced with new 2-vane pumps if they fail.

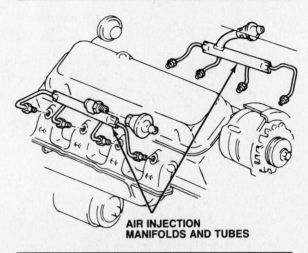

Figure 19-6. External air manifolds are used with many air injection systems. (Chevrolet)

The main difference between the two pumps is the way they filter the intake air. The 3-vane pump draws its fresh air supply through a separate air filter or from the clean side of the air cleaner. The 2-vane pump uses an impeller-type, centrifugal air filter fan mounted on the air pump rotor shaft. This is not a true filter, but cleans the air entering the pump by centrifugal force, figure 19-4. The relatively heavy dust particles in the air are forced in the opposite direction to the inlet air flow. The lighter air is then drawn into the pump by the impeller-type fan.

To prevent pump pressure from becoming too high, many pumps use a pressure relief valve, figure 19-5, which opens at high engine speed. Some late-model pumps use a replaceable plastic plug to control the pressure setting of the relief valve. This pressure setting can be changed by putting in a plug with a different pressure setting. Pumps without a pressure relief valve use a diverter valve, explained later in this section.

Air Distribution Manifolds and Nozzles

In early air injection systems, air is delivered to the engine's exhaust system in one of two ways:
1. An external air manifold, figure 19-6, distributes the air through injection tubes to the exhaust port near each exhaust valve. This method is used primarily on smaller engines.

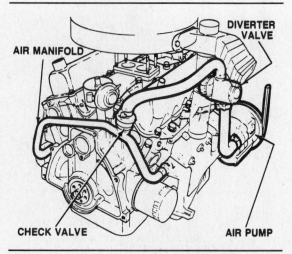

Figure 19-7. Some engines have air distributor passages built into the cylinder heads. (Ford)

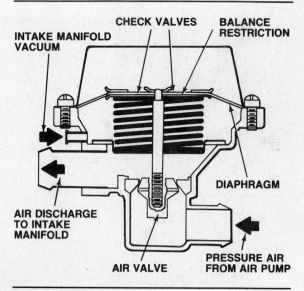

Figure 19-9. The gulp valve was used on early air injection systems and still can be found on some late-model vehicles.

NORMAL FLOW SHOWN BY BLACK ARROWS; BYPASS CONDITIONS SHOWN BY CROSS HATCHED ARROWS

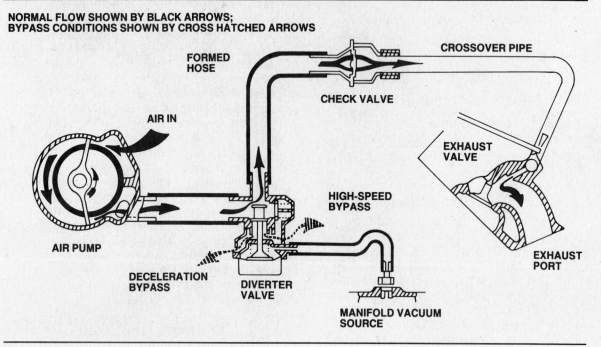

Figure 19-8. Air distribution in a typical air injection system. (AC-Delco)

2. An internal air manifold, figure 19-7, distributes the air to the exhaust port near each exhaust valve through passages cast in the cylinder head or the exhaust manifold. This method is used mainly with larger engines.

The fresh air from the pump passes through the air injector tubes or the manifold to nozzles in the exhaust port. These are made of stainless steel to resist the high exhaust temperatures. This design injects the air in the exhaust at a time when, and at a point where, the gases are the hottest. It also ensures that each cylinder will receive equal air injection for the exhaust. Figure 19-8 shows how air is distributed by a typical air injection system.

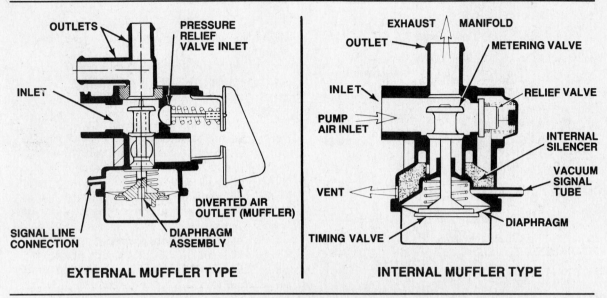

OUTLETS
PRESSURE RELIEF VALVE INLET
INLET
SIGNAL LINE CONNECTION
DIAPHRAGM ASSEMBLY
DIVERTED AIR OUTLET (MUFFLER)

EXTERNAL MUFFLER TYPE

EXHAUST MANIFOLD
OUTLET
METERING VALVE
INLET
RELIEF VALVE
PUMP AIR INLET
INTERNAL SILENCER
VACUUM SIGNAL TUBE
VENT
TIMING VALVE
DIAPHRAGM

INTERNAL MUFFLER TYPE

Figure 19-10. Two types of diverter valves. They differ mainly in placement of the air silencer. (AC-Delco)

Antibackfire Valve

During engine deceleration, high intake manifold vacuum enriches the air-fuel mixture. If air is allowed to flow into the exhaust manifold during deceleration, it will combine with excess unburned fuel in the exhaust. The result is engine **backfire** — a rapid combustion of the unburned gases that can destroy a muffler. To prevent engine backfire, the air pump flow must be shut off during deceleration. This task is done by a diaphragm-operated antibackfire, or backfire suppression, valve. Two kinds of valves have been used: the gulp valve and the diverter valve. They differ in the direction in which they redirect the airflow.

Gulp valve

Early air injection systems used a **gulp valve**, figure 19-9. When intake manifold vacuum is applied to the valve diaphragm, it causes the air valve to move. This motion redirects the pump air to the intake manifold to lean out the enriched air-fuel mixture during deceleration.

The gulp valve is connected to the intake manifold by two hoses. The large hose is the air discharge hose. The small hose is the sensing hose that sends manifold vacuum to the gulp valve to operate the diaphragm. There are balance restrictions or bleed holes inside the valve that equalize pressure on both sides of the diaphragm after a few seconds. Even if manifold vacuum is high, the gulp valve only stays open for a few seconds until pressure equalizes.

Any sudden change in vacuum will operate the gulp valve. This is one of the undesirable

features that led to its replacement. For example, the gulp valve will open when the engine starts. This can cause hard starting and a rough idle. Another problem with the gulp valve is that when the throttle is closed at high speeds while manifold vacuum is low, the valve may not open for a few seconds. During this time, an engine backfire can occur. The gulp valve largely has been replaced by the diverter valve on late-model cars.

Diverter valve

The **diverter valve**, figure 19-10, is also known as a dump or bypass valve. Like the gulp valve, the diverter valve uses a diaphragm operated by manifold vacuum to redirect the airflow from the air pump. However, the pump air passes through the diverter valve continuously on its way to the air injection manifold. During deceleration, manifold vacuum operates the valve diaphragm to divert, or dump,

---

Backfire: The accidental combustion of gases in an engine's intake or exhaust system.

Gulp Valve: A valve used in an air injection system to prevent backfire. During deceleration it redirects air from the air pump to the intake manifold where the air leans out the rich air-fuel mixture.

Diverter Valve: Also called a dump valve. A valve used in an air injection system to prevent backfire. During deceleration it "dumps" the air from the air pump into the atmosphere.

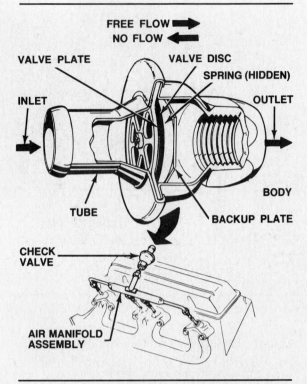

FREE FLOW ➡
NO FLOW ⬅

VALVE PLATE   VALVE DISC
                SPRING (HIDDEN)
INLET   OUTLET
                              BODY
TUBE
                BACKUP PLATE
CHECK
VALVE
AIR MANIFOLD
ASSEMBLY

Figure 19-11. The check valve protects the system against reverse flow of exhaust gases. (AC-Delco)

the air directly to the atmosphere, not to the intake manifold.

Some diverter valves vent the air to the engine air cleaner for muffling. Others vent it through a muffler and filter built into the valve. Diverter valves are used with vacuum solenoids, vacuum differential valves, vacuum vent valves, and idle valves to fine tune air injection. Because diverter valves do not affect the air-fuel mixture in the intake manifold, they are more trouble free than the gulp valves.

Diverter valves also may have a pressure relief valve to keep the pump from building up too much pressure in the system. This kind of diverter valve is used with an air pump that does not have a built-in relief valve.

Check Valves

All injection systems use one or more 1-way check valves, figure 19-11, to protect the air pump from harmful reverse flow of exhaust gases from the engine. A check valve contains a spring-type metallic disc or reed that closes the air line under exhaust backpressure. Check valves are located between the air manifold and the diverter or gulp valve. If exhaust pressure is higher than air injection pressure, or

if the air pump fails, the check valve spring closes the valve to prevent the reverse flow of exhaust.

SECOND-GENERATION AIR INJECTION SYSTEMS

Air injection systems used with catalytic converters do the same thing as the basic air injection system just described. They help to oxidize the HC and CO in the exhaust gases by adding fresh air into the exhaust system. These newer, second-generation systems use many of the same components as the noncatalytic systems.

However, adding the catalytic converter changed the air distribution needs of the engine. The role of the air injection system shifted. It is no longer mainly an oxidation device; now it has become an assist device for the converter. Air injection on late-model cars is used to improve converter efficiency and to accelerate catalyst warmup.

Air Injection and Catalytic Converters

Air can be injected near each exhaust port, into the exhaust manifold outlet, into the exhaust pipe ahead (upstream) of the converter, or directly into the converter (downstream). Air flowing into these points mixes with the exhaust gases and continues the oxidation process inside the converter. During the early stages of engine operation, this injected air increases the exhaust temperature. This brings the converter to operating temperature more quickly and increases its efficiency, because catalysts work best at temperatures of about 400° to 500°F (204° to 260°C).

However, too much HC and CO in the exhaust of an engine that is cold (choke closed) or idling for a long time can damage the catalysts or overheat the converter. Switching the injected air from the upstream exhaust ports to a downstream point near or at the converter helps to dilute the HC and CO concentration in the exhaust. Electronic engine control microprocessors monitor the duration of injection as well as engine temperature to prevent catalyst overheating.

Engines with electronic engine control systems also use one or more exhaust oxygen (O_2) sensors. These devices must reach a certain temperature before they start to function. Air injection in the exhaust stream during engine warmup helps the sensor reach operating temperature more rapidly.

With the introduction of NO_x reduction converters (also called dual-bed, TWC, or

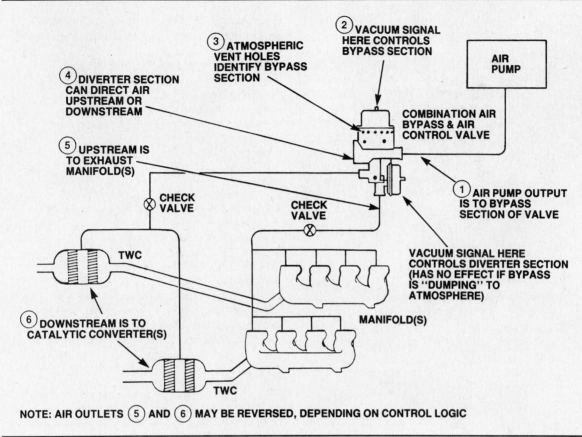

③ **ATMOSPHERIC VENT HOLES IDENTIFY BYPASS SECTION**

② **VACUUM SIGNAL HERE CONTROLS BYPASS SECTION**

AIR PUMP

④ **DIVERTER SECTION CAN DIRECT AIR UPSTREAM OR DOWNSTREAM**

COMBINATION AIR BYPASS & AIR CONTROL VALVE

⑤ **UPSTREAM IS TO EXHAUST MANIFOLD(S)**

① **AIR PUMP OUTPUT IS TO BYPASS SECTION OF VALVE**

CHECK VALVE

CHECK VALVE

VACUUM SIGNAL HERE CONTROLS DIVERTER SECTION (HAS NO EFFECT IF BYPASS IS "DUMPING" TO ATMOSPHERE)

TWC

MANIFOLD(S)

⑥ **DOWNSTREAM IS TO CATALYTIC CONVERTER(S)**

TWC

NOTE: AIR OUTLETS ⑤ AND ⑥ MAY BE REVERSED, DEPENDING ON CONTROL LOGIC

Figure 19-12. Operation of Ford's managed thermactor air (MTA) system using a combination bypass-diverter valve. (Ford)

3-way converters) in 1977, the problem of air distribution became even more complex. The oxidation process *adds* O_2 to HC and CO, but the reduction process *removes* O_2 from NO_x compounds. Therefore, a reduction converter requires more air in the exhaust to bring it to operating temperature. When it reaches operating temperature, however, it works most efficiently with *less* air in the exhaust. This seeming paradox, along with the problems of catalyst damage and converter overheating, led to the development and use of air switching systems.

Figure 19-12 shows the operation of Ford's managed thermactor air (MTA) system used with a 3-way converter. The system is typical of current air-switching systems and controls airflow in three ways:

1. It dumps pump air to the atmosphere during periods of rich exhaust, such as deceleration, extended high-speed, or high-load operation. This prevents backfiring or catalyst damage and removes the pump load from the engine.

2. It directs pump airflow upstream to the exhaust manifold during cold engine start-up when the converter also is cold.

3. When the engine and converter reach operating temperature, it redirects pump airflow

■ Don't Oil the Air Pump!

No air injection system is completely quiet. Usually pump noise increases in pitch as engine speed increases. If the drive belt is removed and the pump shaft turned by hand, it will squeak or chirp. Many who work on their own cars and even some mechanics are not aware that air injection pumps are permanently lubricated, and require no periodic maintenance.

Suppose you pinpoint the air pump as the source of the noise. It would seem that a few squirts of oil would silence it. See those three small holes in the housing? While it is easy to mistake them for oiling points, these are actually vents. Don't oil them. More than a few pumps have failed because someone assumed that taking "good" care of the pump would make it last longer!

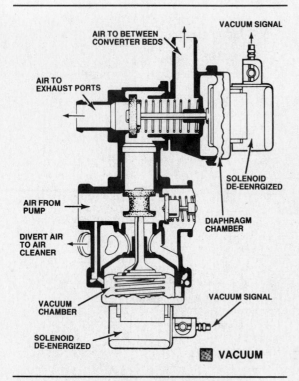

Figure 19-13. GM uses this electrically signaled diverter valve for switching and diverting tasks on air injection systems used with CCC engines.

downstream to a point between the reduction and oxidation catalysts.

The downstream point of entry for air injection is usually the mid-bed of the catalyst in a 3-way converter system, figure 19-12. If separate reduction and oxidation converters are used, an air inlet tube connects to the pipe between them. Air switching is necessary because the air injection requirements have changed. Once the system has reached operating temperature, additional air added to the exhaust will cause the O_2 sensor to send false signals to the engine control computer and reduce the efficiency of the NO_x reduction converter.

Air Management Valves

Air switching is done by air management valves. This term is used to describe the large variety of diverter, bypass, and air control or switching valves that have been used by domestic carmakers in their air injection systems since 1975. For example, GM currently uses more than 16 variations of air management valves with its computer command control

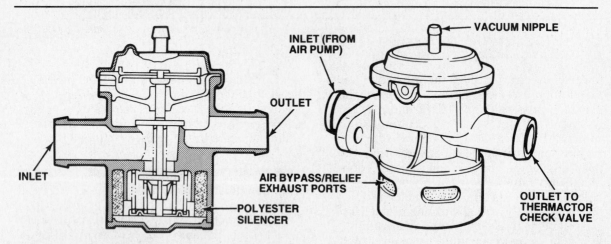

Figure 19-14. A typical normally closed air bypass valve. (Ford)

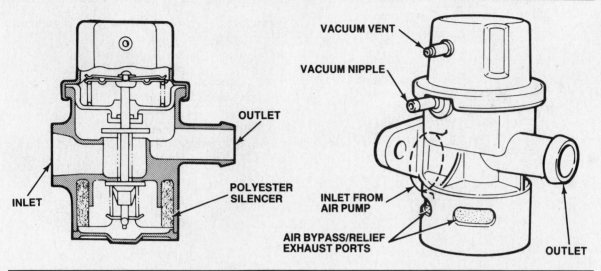

Figure 19-15. A typical normally open air bypass valve. (Ford)

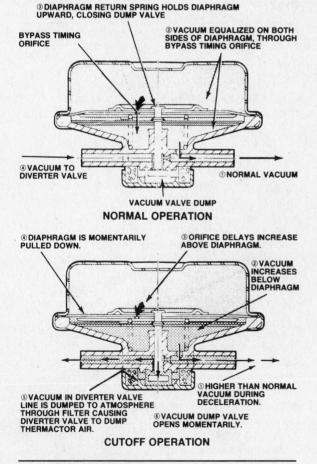

Figure 19-16. This vacuum differential valve dumps the vacuum from the diverter valve whenever vacuum increases suddenly. (Ford)

(CCC) systems. Figure 19-13 shows one such valve used by GM.

Ford also uses many types of valves. These valves are divided into two general groups: normally closed or normally open. Normally closed valves, figure 19-14, provide air to the exhaust system during normal engine operation, brief idle periods, and some acceleration conditions. When vacuum is low or nonexistent, pump air is dumped through the valve silencer ports.

Normally open valves with a vacuum vent, figure 19-15, provide a timed air dump during deceleration. They also dump air when the signal port vacuum is less than 1.5 psi (10 kPa) more than the vent port vacuum. This mode protects the catalyst from overheating.

Various vacuum differential valves, vacuum delay valves, and bleed valves are used to control the vacuum to Ford diverter valves. The vacuum differential valve, figure 19-16, is in the vacuum line to the diverter valve. Sudden changes in vacuum cause the differential valve to dump the vacuum that goes to the diverter valve. This causes the diverter valve to cut off the air injection and dump the air pump output to the atmosphere.

Some Ford diverter valves, figure 19-17, have a built-in vacuum differential valve. The top of the valve also has a vacuum vent. When the vent is closed, the valve acts as a normal diverter valve. When the vacuum vent is open, any manifold vacuum above 2 psi (13.5 kPa) causes the diverter valve to dump the air pump output. An air temperature electric switch and an electric solenoid open the vent line at cold temperatures.

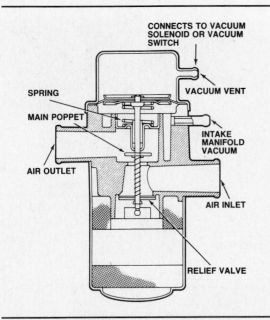

Figure 19-17. This Ford diverter valve has a vacuum vent that allows air to be dumped during cold engine operation. (Ford)

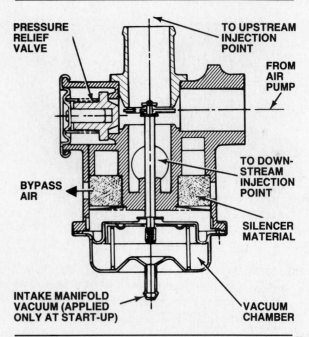

Figure 19-19. Cutaway of Chrysler's air switch/relief valve. (Chrysler)

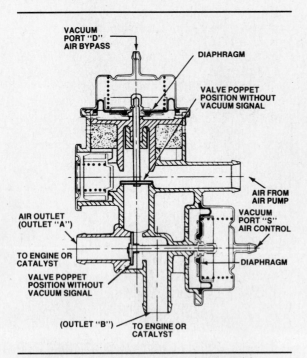

Figure 19-18. Ford's combination air bypass/air control valve handles air switching and diverting tasks. (Ford)

Ford's combination air bypass/air control valve, figure 19-18, and the GM electric divert/electric air switching (EDES) valve, figure 19-13, combine the divert and switching functions in one valve. The divert, or air control, section of the valve protects the converter during

open-throttle operation and high temperatures. The air switching section sends air to the exhaust ports during open-loop operation. When the engine control system moves into the closed-loop mode, the valve switches airflow to a point between the converter beds.

Chrysler uses a combination switch/relief valve, figure 19-19, controlled by a coolant vacuum switch cold open (CVSCO) or a vacuum solenoid. On a cold start, air is injected as close as possible to the exhaust valves. When engine coolant temperature reaches the point where exhaust gas recirculation (EGR) begins, the CVSCO or vacuum solenoid shuts off the vacuum signal to the valve. This causes the valve to send most of the pump air downstream to the catalytic converter. The rest of the pump air continues to reach the exhaust ports by passing through slots in the upstream valve seat.

Regardless of manufacturer or system, most air control valves operate with:
• Manifold vacuum or ported vacuum working on a vacuum diaphragm in the valve
• Output pressure of the air pump working against vacuum or a spring in the vacuum chamber
• Opening or closing of the vacuum supply to the diaphragm by one or more solenoids in the vacuum line.

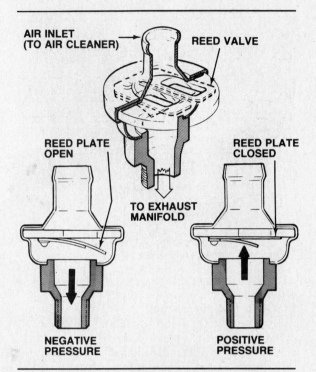

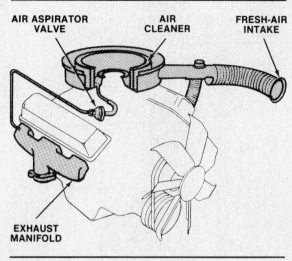

Figure 19-22. Chrysler's air aspirator system has remained unchanged on carbureted models since its introduction in 1977.

Figure 19-20. A pulse air injection valve opens when negative pressure occurs in the exhaust manifold. (Ford)

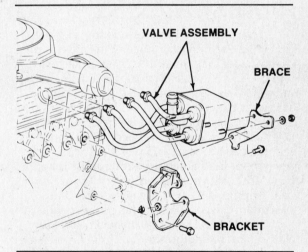

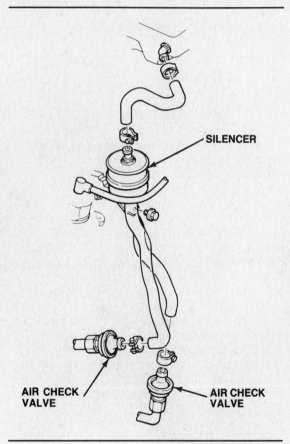

Figure 19-21. GM's pulse air injection system is called PAIR and was first used on the 1975 Cosworth Vega. (Chevrolet)

PULSE AIR INJECTION

The use of pulse air injection has increased on domestic vehicles since 1975. Pulse air systems use a pulse air valve, figure 19-20, instead of an air pump. This device is similar to (but not interchangeable with) the check valve used in an air pump system. The pulse air valve is a spring-loaded diaphragm or reed valve that is connected to the exhaust system.

Figure 19-23. Ford's Thermactor II (pulse air) system uses an external silencer. (Ford)

Pulse air valves can be connected with tubing to each exhaust port, figure 19-21, or to the exhaust manifold, figure 19-22. Some systems use two pulse air valves. One is connected to

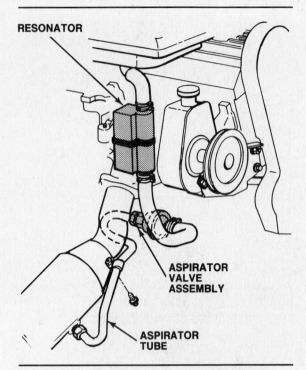

Figure 19-24. Chrysler's turbocharged 4-cylinder engines use a resonator in the line between the air cleaner and the aspirator valve. (Chrysler)

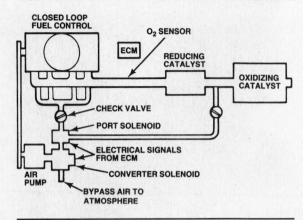

Figure 19-25. A typical General Motors computer-controlled AIR system. (GM)

the exhaust manifold and the other sends air to the converter. An external silencer, figure 19-23, or resonator, figure 19-24, may be installed between the valve and air cleaner to reduce airflow noise.

Each time an exhaust valve closes, there is a period when manifold pressure drops below atmospheric pressure. During these low pressure (slight vacuum) pulses, the air injection valve opens to admit fresh air to the exhaust, figure 19-20. When exhaust pressure rises above atmospheric pressure, the valve acts as a check valve and closes.

Since the pulse air injection system draws its air from the air cleaner, it eliminates the power-consuming air pump. This makes the system useful with small 4- and 6-cylinder engines with no power to waste. However, it works best at low engine speeds when extra air is needed most by the catalytic converter. At high engine speeds, the vacuum pulses occur too rapidly for the valve to follow, and the internal spring simply keeps the valve closed.

Pulse air systems have other disadvantages. They must be connected upstream in the exhaust system where negative pressure pulses are strong. This means that pulse air cannot be switched downstream for use in the converter. The system works best on vehicles equipped

with only an HC-CO oxidation catalyst, although a few models with 3-way converters use pulse air to provide additional air in the exhaust when the engine is cold. Such systems contain valves in the supply line between the air cleaner and pulse air valve to shut off air supply once the engine warms up.

COMPUTER-CONTROLLED AIR SWITCHING

A recent trend in air injection is to put the control of the system in the engine control microprocessor. Figure 19-25 shows a typical system used by General Motors. Air management in the GM system is provided by a combined air control and air switching valve, figure 19-26. Each function of the valve has a vacuum solenoid controlled by the electronic control module (ECM). When the CCC system is in open-loop, both solenoids are grounded by the ECM. This allows airflow from the pump to pass through the control valve to the air switching valve, which routes it to the exhaust ports. Once the CCC system switches to closed-loop operation, the ECM de-energizes the air switching solenoid. This redirects the airflow from the exhaust ports to a point between the catalysts for as long as the system remains in closed-loop. However, if the ECM recognizes the need to divert air, it de-energizes the air control solenoid, causing the valve to switch airflow to the air cleaner. This may be done under the following circumstances:
- Excessively rich operation
- Deceleration
- High engine rpm operation (when air pressure exceeds the internal relief valve setting)

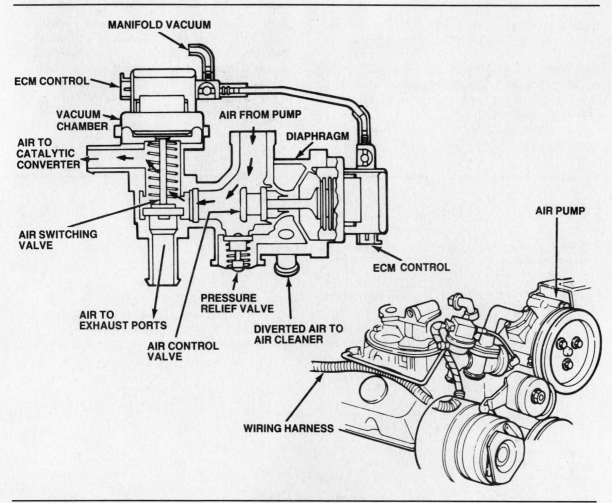

Figure 19-26. The GM computer-controlled AIR system control valve combines the divert and air switching functions in a single housing. Solenoids at both ends of the valve activate the functions on command from the ECM. (GM)

• The ECM sees a problem or failure in the system and turns on the "CHECK ENGINE" light.

The Ford MTA system, figure 19-12, is similar in operation to the GM system just described, but uses separate solenoids which connect to the combination air bypass/air control valve with vacuum lines.

Pulse air systems also may be computer-controlled. For example, the GM PAIR system contains a shut-off valve to control the air supply to the valve assembly. During a cold engine start, and whenever the CCC system is in the open-loop mode, the ECM energizes the shut-off valve. This opens the fresh air line at a time when the engine needs it most. When the CCC system goes into the closed-loop mode, the ECM de-energizes the shutoff valve, closing off the fresh air line.

SUMMARY

Air injection is one of the oldest methods used to control HC and CO exhaust emissions. The injected air mixes with hot exhaust gas as it leaves the combustion chambers to further oxidize HC and CO emissions. All air injection systems used on domestic cars operate in essentially the same way, regardless of manufacturer.

With the advent of the catalytic converter, the role of the air injection system changed from primary oxidation device to that of an assist device for the converter. Oxidation converters that reduce HC and CO emissions require more air; reduction converters that minimize NO_x emissions require less air. Since these two functions are incompatible with the basic air injection system, air switching or control valves are used with converter applications. These valves send pump air upstream near the exhaust port or manifold when the engine is started, and downstream near or to the converter once the engine reaches normal operating temperature.

The pulse air injection system relies on exhaust pulses instead of an air pump to draw fresh air from the air cleaner into the exhaust. Pulse air systems work best with oxidation converters and are most efficient at low engine speeds. Some engine control systems now use the microprocessor to control the air injection or pulse air systems. This provides a quicker response to changing engine requirements.

Review Questions
Choose the single most correct answer.
Compare your answers with the correct answers on page 451.

1. The American Motors air injection system is called:
   a. Air Injection System
   b. Air Guard
   c. Thermactor Air Injection System
   d. Air Injection Reactor

2. The main reason for an air injection system is to:
   a. Oxidize HC and CO exhaust emissions
   b. Reduce NO_x exhaust emissions
   c. Eliminate crankcase emissions
   d. Eliminate evaporative HC emissions

3. Oxidation of HC and CO emissions produces:
   a. HCO and CO_2
   b. H_2CO_3 and CO_2
   c. H_2O and CO_2
   d. All of the above

4. Which of the following is true?
   a. All air pumps can be rebuilt
   b. Two-vane pumps can be rebuilt
   c. No air pumps can be rebuilt
   d. Three-vane pumps can be rebuilt

5. Two-vane pumps have:
   a. An impeller-type fan for filter
   b. An integral wire mesh filter
   c. A hose to the clean side of the air cleaner
   d. A separate air filter

6. Air injection nozzles are made of:
   a. Copper
   b. Stainless steel
   c. Aluminum
   d. Vanadium

7. The two types of air injection backfire suppressor valves are:
   a. The check valve and the gulp valve
   b. The gulp valve and the diverter valve
   c. The diverter valve and the relief valve
   d. The diverter valve and the check valve

8. The Chrysler air switching valve is controlled by:
   a. A vacuum solenoid
   b. A reed valve
   c. A bypass timing orifice
   d. A coolant vacuum switch

9. This illustration shows:
   a. A relief valve
   b. A solenoid operated vacuum valve
   c. A gulp valve
   d. A diverter valve

INTAKE MANIFOLD VACUUM — CHECK VALVES — BALANCE RESTRICTION — DIAPHRAGM — AIR DISCHARGE TO INTAKE MANIFOLD — AIR VALVE — PRESSURE AIR FROM AIR PUMP

10. Pulsed air injection works best at:
    a. Low speeds
    b. High speeds
    c. Idle
    d. Deceleration

11. Mechanic A says that a gulp valve diverts air to the atmosphere.
    Mechanic B says that a diverter valve diverts air to the intake manifold.
    Who is right?
    a. A only
    b. B only
    c. Both A and B
    d. Neither A nor B

12. Mechanic A says that air injection helps an exhaust catalyst reach its operating temperature faster.
    Mechanic B says that a catalyst is most efficient when cooled by air injection.
    Who is right?
    a. A only
    b. B only
    c. Both A and B
    d. Neither A nor B

20

Exhaust Gas Recirculation

When oxides of nitrogen (NO_x) are present in the atmosphere and acted upon by sunlight, they combine with hydrocarbons to form photochemical smog, the prime air pollutant. Even though the elements of photochemical smog had been identified many years earlier, it was not until 1973 that the U.S. Federal Government told the nation's carmakers to drastically reduce the amount of NO_x in car exhaust. In order to meet these new standards, the manufacturers developed an emission control system called **exhaust gas recirculation**, or **EGR**.

Since 1973, various valves and vacuum routings have been used on EGR systems by the carmakers. While these system parts may look different, they all work pretty much alike. Since the EGR system is important to good driveability, it is also an important part of a tune-up or troubleshooting procedure.

In this chapter, you will learn:
- The principles of EGR systems
- How a basic EGR system reduces NO_x formation and prevents engine detonation
- EGR system variations used by domestic automakers.

NO_x FORMATION

Under normal circumstances, nitrogen and oxygen do not combine unless temperatures exceed 2,500°F (1,371°C). When ignition timing is correct, maximum heat and pressure are created in an engine's combustion chambers. Whenever combustion chamber temperatures exceed 2,500°F (1371°C), nitrogen and oxygen combine rapidly to form large amounts of NO_x.

Since peak combustion chamber temperature is controlled by ignition timing, the spark timing control systems discussed in Chapter 10 were the first attempts to meet NO_x control requirements. By retarding spark timing slightly, less pressure and heat are produced, keeping combustion chamber temperatures below the level at which NO_x forms rapidly. Spark timing control systems were used to control NO_x formation until 1972, when Federal test procedures to determine NO_x levels were changed. As a result, a more effective way of controlling NO_x was needed.

Exhaust Gas Recirculation (EGR): A way of reducing NO_x emissions by directing unburned exhaust back through an engine's intake.

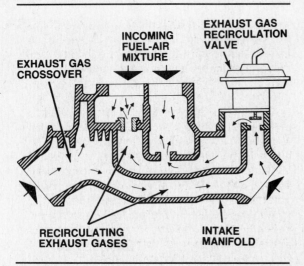

EXHAUST GAS CROSSOVER

INCOMING FUEL-AIR MIXTURE

EXHAUST GAS RECIRCULATION VALVE

RECIRCULATING EXHAUST GASES

INTAKE MANIFOLD

Figure 20-1. Basic exhaust gas recirculation methods.

EGR Function

Although small amounts of NO$_x$ are formed at temperatures below 2,500°F (1,371°C), these quantities can be easily controlled. But once combustion chamber temperatures reach 2,500°F (1371°C) or more, NO$_x$ formation increases rapidly.

There are four basic ways to reduce NO$_x$ formation:
1. Enrich the air-fuel mixture. This allows the engine to run cooler but increases HC and CO emissions, as well as reducing fuel economy.
2. Lower the compression ratio. This has been done to allow engines to burn unleaded gasoline, but is a limited means of controlling NO$_x$. Too low a ratio results in inefficient combustion and increased HC and CO emissions.
3. Retard spark timing slightly. This method was used until 1972, but could not provide enough control to meet the more stringent emission standards after that date.
4. Dilute the incoming air-fuel mixture with a small amount of **inert gas** to lower combustion temperatures. Since exhaust gases are relatively inert, a portion of them can be recirculated to dilute the mixture. This is the most efficient method of lowering combustion temperatures and reducing NO$_x$ emissions without affecting engine performance, fuel economy, and other exhaust emissions.

Exhaust gas recirculation is accomplished by routing small quantities (6 to 10 percent) of exhaust gas from the engine's exhaust ports to the intake manifold, figure 20-1. This exhaust gas dilutes the incoming air-fuel mixture in the cylinder. Since exhaust gas contains no oxygen, the resulting air-fuel-exhaust gas mixture is not as powerful when ignited. This means that it will not create as much heat as an undiluted air-fuel mixture would produce.

EGR Effects on Combustion

Since it does not require much exhaust gas to cool down peak combustion temperatures, recirculation must be held to very low levels. Even when the EGR valve used to reroute the exhaust gas is wide open, the orifice through which the gas passes is very small.

Because the amount of NO$_x$ produced at low engine speeds is very small, exhaust gas recirculation is neither required nor desirable at idle. It also is undesirable during high-speed driving at wide-open throttle, since it adversely affects efficient operation and good driveability. Maximum recirculation is required only during cruising and acceleration at speeds between 30 to 70 mph, (48 to 113 kph), when NO$_x$ formation is greatest. Engine temperature also is a determining factor in recirculation. When engine temperature is low, NO$_x$ formation is also low, and recirculation is eliminated to produce fast warmup and better driveability.

The dilution of the air-fuel mixture with EGR reduces the energy involved in combustion. This in turn reduces the amount of heat created in the combustion chamber, as well as the peak combustion pressure. The power output of early engines equipped with EGR systems was less than that of the same engine without EGR, giving rise to the idea that exhaust gas recirculation automatically meant a reduction in power output. During the early years of EGR, many drivers were convinced that they could increase the performance of their engine by disconnecting the EGR system, a popular myth that still exists today. For many years now, EGR dilution of the air-fuel charge has been calculated into the fuel system calibration and it is required for maximum performance.

EGR and Engine Detonation

A secondary effect of EGR is that it helps to control engine detonation. Detonation (engine ping) is an explosion or uneven burning of the air-fuel charge which generally takes place near the end of the combustion burn time because of the high pressure and temperature created. Detonation reduces engine power and efficiency. In some situations, detonation can severely damage the engine.

In the days when tetraethyl lead was added to gasoline, detonation was not a great problem, but it has become one for the engines

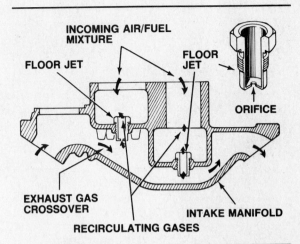

Figure 20-2. Chrysler's floor jet EGR system.

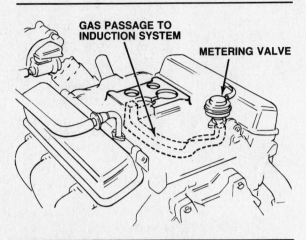

Figure 20-4. EGR metering valve mounted on the intake manifold.

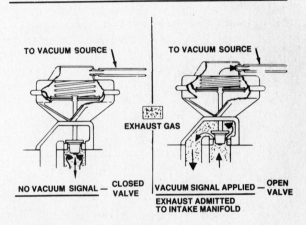

Figure 20-3. Typical single-diaphragm EGR valve. (AC-Delco)

operating on the unleaded gasoline required with catalytic converters. Diluting the air-fuel charge with exhaust gas helps reduce the temperature and pressure that cause detonation.

The use of EGR with electronically-controlled late-model engines permits split-second changes in ignition timing that further minimize the problem of detonation. In essence, this incorporates the timing retard provided by the older spark timing control systems, but more efficiently. You can prove this by simply disconnecting the EGR system on such an engine and listen to the pinging that results. Reconnect the system and the pinging disappears.

SYSTEM COMPONENTS AND OPERATING PRINCIPLES

The devices used to recirculate exhaust gas are described in the following paragraphs. Since

system designs and controls differ from one manufacturer to another, we will discuss each of the carmakers later in this chapter.

EGR Floor Jets

The floor jet system, figure 20-2, is a historical curiosity used only on some 1972-73 Chrysler-built engines. On V-8 engines, stainless steel jets are threaded into the floor of the intake manifold under the carburetor. With 6-cylinder engines, the jet is in the intake manifold hot spot beneath the carburetor. The jets provide an opening between the exhaust passage and the intake manifold. In this way, manifold vacuum controls how much exhaust is drawn into the intake system through the preset jet orifice. Floor jets are the simplest of all EGR system designs. However, they are also unsatisfactory because they allow exhaust gas to enter the intake manifold at all times. This causes rough engine operation when the engine is idling or when warming up.

EGR Valves

Introduced on 1972 Buicks, the EGR valve is a spring-loaded, vacuum-operated, poppet-type valve, figure 20-3. Modulating valves and tapered-stem valves also are used, and they operate about the same as the poppet type. This valve meters the exhaust gas entering the intake system. The EGR valve is mounted on the intake manifold, figure 20-4, or on a plate

Inert Gas: A gas that will not undergo chemical reaction.

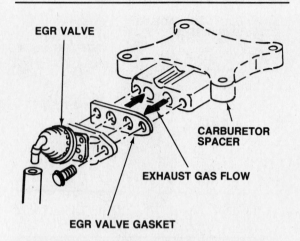

Figure 20-5. This EGR valve is mounted on a spacer installed between the carburetor and the intake manifold.

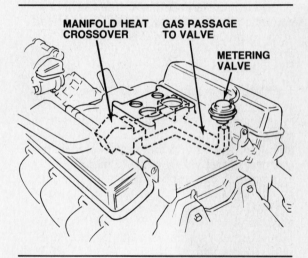

Figure 20-6. Exhaust gas passages to the EGR valve.

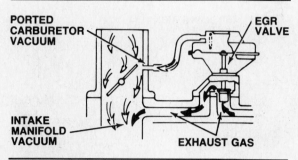

Figure 20-7. This EGR valve is operated by ported vacuum.

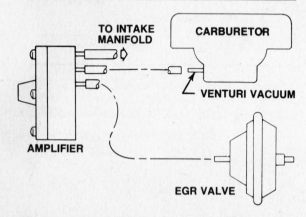

Figure 20-8. EGR systems controlled by venturi vacuum require a vacuum amplifier. (Ford)

under the carburetor, figure 20-5. The valve may be connected to the intake and exhaust systems by internal passages in the intake manifold, figures 20-4 and 20-6, or in some cases by external steel tubing. The EGR valve is held in the closed position by the spring. The valve is opened by ported or venturi vacuum from the carburetor, depending on the system design.

Ported Vacuum Systems

EGR systems controlled by ported vacuum use a slot-type port in the carburetor throttle body above the throttle plate, figure 20-7. This port is connected to the EGR valve by a vacuum line. With the throttle plate closed, no vacuum is transmitted. As the throttle plate opens, the port is exposed to increasing manifold vacuum. The amount of exhaust gas flow depends on manifold vacuum, throttle position, and exhaust gas backpressure. Because ported vacuum cannot be greater than intake manifold vacuum, recirculation at wide-open throttle is prevented. The valve opens at a point greater than the relatively weak manifold vacuum produced during wide-open throttle operation.

Venturi Vacuum Systems

EGR systems controlled by venturi vacuum use a vacuum port at the throat of the carburetor venturi to provide a control vacuum, figure 20-8. Since this control vacuum is very weak, a vacuum amplifier boosts it enough to operate the EGR valve. The amount of exhaust gas flow depends mainly on engine intake airflow. It is also affected by intake vacuum and exhaust gas backpressure.

Recirculation at wide-open throttle is prevented by a relief valve, or dump diaphragm, that compares venturi and manifold vacuum. When the diaphragm senses that the throttle is

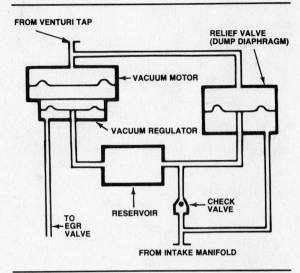

Figure 20-9. A vacuum amplifier is controlled by venturi vacuum and uses manifold vacuum to operate the EGR valve. (Ford)

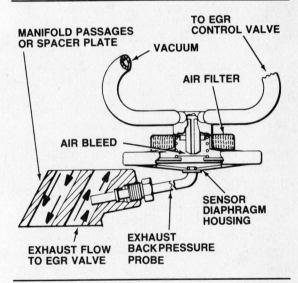

Figure 20-10. Typical EGR backpressure transducer.

wide open, the stored vacuum in the amplifier is vented to the atmosphere. This limits the vacuum output reaching the EGR valve to that provided by manifold vacuum. Since the EGR valve opens at a point greater than the relatively weak manifold vacuum, the valve remains closed at wide-open throttle.

Vacuum amplifiers

The vacuum amplifier, figure 20-9, converts the weak venturi control vacuum into one that is strong enough to operate the EGR valve. It

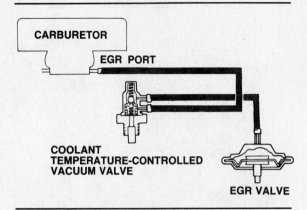

Figure 20-11. The coolant-temperature-controlled vacuum valve cuts off vacuum to the EGR valve when the engine is cold. (Ford)

does this by storing manifold vacuum in a reservoir inside the amplifier unit. This guarantees enough vacuum, regardless of variations in manifold vacuum. Whenever the venturi is equal to, or greater than, manifold vacuum, a relief valve (dump diaphragm) vents the reservoir, cancelling the output EGR signal.

A vacuum amplifier working perfectly would produce an accurate, repeatable, and precise proportion between venturi air flow and EGR flow. However, vacuum amplifiers are no longer used on late-model EGR systems because storage reservoirs tend to leak in actual use.

Backpressure Transducer

This diaphragm-operated sensor unit, figure 20-10, has a tube that extends into an exhaust gas passage. When high exhaust backpressure is sensed through the tube, the diaphragm closes an air bleed hole in the EGR vacuum line. This provides maximum EGR during acceleration, when backpressure is high. As backpressure drops, a spring moves the sensor diaphragm to reopen the vacuum line bleed. Since this decreases the vacuum at the EGR valve, the amount of exhaust gas recirculated also is reduced.

Modulating Devices

Engineers have developed various methods of modulating, or adjusting, EGR valve operation in relation to engine operating conditions. High and low ambient temperature vacuum modulators weaken the vacuum signal to the EGR valve. A coolant temperature override switch or valve, figure 20-11, may be used to eliminate EGR vacuum below certain engine

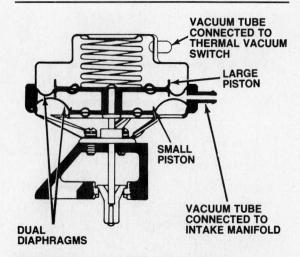

Figure 20-12. The dual-diaphragm EGR valve modulates the exhaust gas flow.

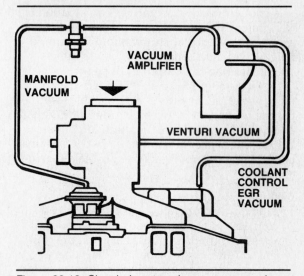

Figure 20-13. Chrysler's external vacuum reservoir.

operating temperatures. Some venturi-vacuum-controlled systems use a time delay solenoid to shut off vacuum to the EGR valve for about half a minute after the ignition is turned on.

A vacuum-bias valve is used to bleed off part of the EGR vacuum signal under high-manifold-vacuum conditions to eliminate **high-speed surge**. A dual-diaphragm EGR valve, figure 20-12, sometimes is used. This uses manifold vacuum to help the valve spring offset the carburetor vacuum under certain cruising conditions.

Closed-Loop Electronic Control

When the EGR system is part of a closed-loop electronic control system, it contains a sensor

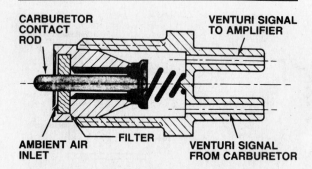

Figure 20-14. Wide-open-throttle EGR dump valve. (Chrysler)

that informs the microprocessor of how the system is working. It may do this by sending a position signal indicating how far the valve is open, or a pressure signal indicating the EGR gas flow rate. The microprocessor compares the sensor data with its program to determine whether the flow rate should be increased, maintained, or decreased. It then signals a solenoid in the EGR system.

The solenoid operation can be precisely controlled through pulse width modulation (PWM). This means that the solenoid is continuously cycled on and off a fixed number of times per second. The solenoid is on (energized) for part of each cycle, and off for the rest of that cycle. The percentage of the total cycle time that the solenoid is energized is called its duty cycle. The duty cycle is calculated by the input from various other sensors to the microprocessor and determined by a timed voltage pulse to the solenoid from the microprocessor. The microprocessor varies, or modulates, this pulse width to establish the duty cycle and achieve the desired solenoid output.

CHRYSLER EGR SYSTEMS

Chrysler used the floor jet system, figure 20-2, described earlier, on some 1972-73 models. The system was supplemented in 1973 with both the ported and venturi vacuum systems, and discontinued at the end of the 1973 model year.

Venturi Vacuum System

The venturi vacuum system was changed on some 1975 and later engines to include an external vacuum reservoir mounted on a bracket and attached to the vacuum amplifier, figure 20-13. After the internal vacuum reservoir has

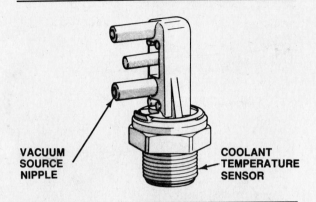

VACUUM SOURCE NIPPLE

COOLANT TEMPERATURE SENSOR

Figure 20-15. The CCEGR and CVSCC valves are combined as a coolant temperature sensor. (Chrysler)

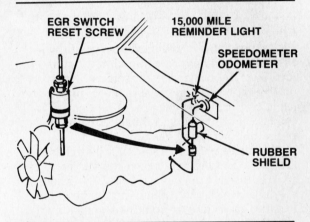

EGR SWITCH RESET SCREW

15,000 MILE REMINDER LIGHT

SPEEDOMETER ODOMETER

RUBBER SHIELD

Figure 20-16. Chrysler's EGR maintenance reminder system.

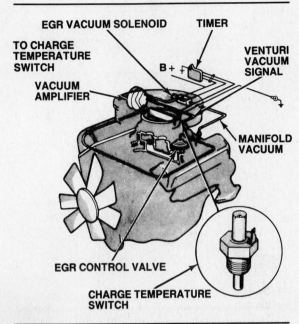

EGR VACUUM SOLENOID

TIMER

TO CHARGE TEMPERATURE SWITCH

VENTURI VACUUM SIGNAL

B +

VACUUM AMPLIFIER

MANIFOLD VACUUM

EGR CONTROL VALVE

CHARGE TEMPERATURE SWITCH

Figure 20-17. Chrysler's EGR system with charge temperature switch and timer. (Chrysler)

been vented, or dumped, the external reservoir supplies manifold vacuum for exhaust recirculation until the internal reservoir can be refilled.

Wide-Open-Throttle Dump Valve

A wide-open-throttle dump valve, figure 20-14, was added to some engines in March 1976. These engines use a delay-dump amplifier, which can hold the EGR valve open too long at wide-open throttle. Mounted on the carburetor, the wide-open throttle EGR dump valve overrides the delay-dump amplifier at wide-open or near wide-open throttle by mechanically bleeding the vacuum to the amplifier. This closes the EGR valve immediately.

Coolant Control Valves

Chrysler has used both a coolant control EGR valve (CCEGR) and a coolant vacuum switch cold closed (CVSCC). These devices are combined as a coolant temperature sensor with a

molded vacuum port connector, figure 20-15. The sensor was first added to 1974 systems to block vacuum flow to the EGR valve whenever coolant temperature is less than specified for the particular engine. Some 1974 and later engines use an EGR delay timer. This electric timer mounted on the firewall operates an engine-mounted vacuum solenoid to prevent exhaust gas recirculation for about half a minute after the ignition is turned on.

EGR Maintenance Reminder System

An EGR maintenance reminder system, figure 20-16, was used on 1975 engines only. This mileage counting device signals the driver every 15,000 miles (24,000 kilometers) to have the EGR system inspected. An instrument panel reminder light comes on at 15,000-mile (24,000-kilometer) intervals and remains lighted until the switch attached to the speedometer cable is manually reset.

Charge Temperature Switch

The charge temperature switch, figure 20-17, used on some 6-and 8-cylinder Chrysler engines, measures air-fuel mixture temperature

High-Speed Surge: A sudden increase in engine speed caused by high manifold vacuum pulling in an excess air-fuel mixture.

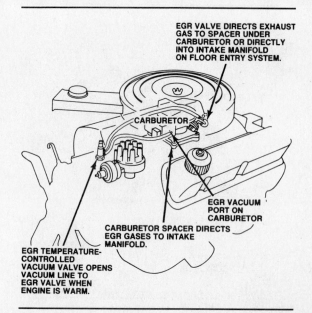

EGR VALVE DIRECTS EXHAUST GAS TO SPACER UNDER CARBURETOR OR DIRECTLY INTO INTAKE MANIFOLD ON FLOOR ENTRY SYSTEM.

CARBURETOR

EGR VACUUM PORT ON CARBURETOR

CARBURETOR SPACER DIRECTS EGR GASES TO INTAKE MANIFOLD.

EGR TEMPERATURE-CONTROLLED VACUUM VALVE OPENS VACUUM LINE TO EGR VALVE WHEN ENGINE IS WARM.

Figure 20-18. Basic Ford EGR system. (Ford)

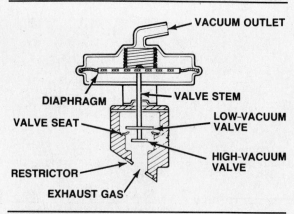

VACUUM OUTLET

DIAPHRAGM

VALVE STEM

VALVE SEAT

LOW-VACUUM VALVE

HIGH-VACUUM VALVE

RESTRICTOR

EXHAUST GAS

Figure 20-19. Ford modulating EGR valve. (Ford)

in the intake manifold and prevents EGR flow unless the temperature is above the switch specification. When the intake charge temperature reaches about 60°F (16°C), the charge temperature switch opens, allowing the charge temperature timer (EGR delay timer) to time out. At the end of the timer cycle, vacuum flows to the EGR valve and it opens to pass exhaust gas into the intake manifold.

FORD EGR SYSTEMS

The basic Ford EGR system, figure 20-18, was introduced on all Ford-built cars in 1973, except those using the 1,600-cc and 2,000-cc engines. The basic system has three main components: an EGR valve, a temperature-controlled vacuum valve, and a carburetor or throttle body spacer. Some later-model Ford engines have been certified by the Environmental Protection Agency (EPA) for use without an EGR system.

EGR Valve

Three types of EGR valves are used: poppet, modulating, and tapered stem. The poppet valve contains a spring-loaded diaphragm, a valve and valve stem, and a flow restrictor. Ported carburetor vacuum opens the valve at a specific vacuum level and allows exhaust gas to enter the valve. Exhaust gas flow to the combustion chambers is controlled by the flow restrictor in the valve body inlet port.

The modulating valve, figure 20-19, has an extra disc valve on the stem below the main

valve, and it operates much like a poppet valve. However, at a specific vacuum level, the lower disc valve restricts exhaust gas flow to the valve chamber. This modulating action improves the driveability of some engines.

The tapered-stem valve operates in the same way. Exhaust gas flow is modulated by the tapered stem as it gradually unseats to permit an increasing gas flow.

The three valve types are not interchangeable between engine types or model years.

Ford uses various ways to deliver exhaust gas to the EGR valve. On many inline engines, exhaust gas is drawn from the exhaust manifold through an external stainless steel tube. Most V-6 and V-8 engines use a passage in the exhaust crossover of the intake manifold. This routes the gas through the carburetor or throttle body spacer to the EGR valve. The EGR valve then meters the gas back through a separate passage in the spacer to the carburetor primary venturis or throttle body, where it is mixed with the air-fuel mixture.

Some 1974 engines use a floor-entry system, figure 20-20. The intake manifold has two runners cast in the floor under the intake runners. One connects the exhaust crossover to the EGR valve. The other connects the valve with two holes in the manifold floor directly under the carburetor primary venturis. This allows exhaust gas to mix with the air-fuel mixture before entering the combustion chambers. This is a valve-controlled system and is not the same as Chrysler's floor jet EGR system, which does not use a valve.

Temperature-Controlled Vacuum Valve

A temperature-controlled vacuum valve in the engine cooling system cuts off vacuum to the

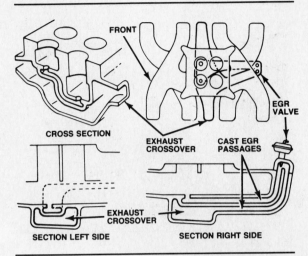

Figure 20-20. Ford 1974 floor entry EGR system. (Ford)

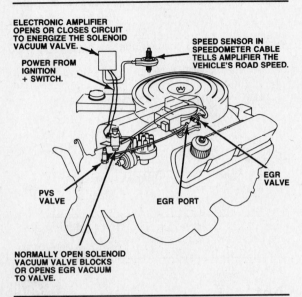

Figure 20-21. Ford high-speed EGR modulator subsystem. (Ford)

EGR valve when the engine is cold, figure 20-18. Ford calls this valve a ported vacuum switch (PVS). It works the same as American Motors' coolant temperature switch (CTO) and Chrysler's coolant-controlled EGR switches (CCEGR or CVSCC). The valve may be installed in a heater hose or in the intake manifold water jacket. Different temperature settings are used for different Ford engines. The valves are color coded for identification.

Spacer Plate

Ford's spacer plate contains separate inlet and outlet passages to the EGR valve. The valve is mounted at one end of the plate with a gasket. In some engines, an EGR cooler is installed between the valve and plate to improve EGR flow and valve durability. The spacer is installed between the carburetor or throttle body and the intake manifold with top and bottom gaskets to prevent leaks. Spacer plates are not interchangeable between engine types.

System Modifications

Basic EGR system operation is modified by the following subsystems.

High-speed EGR modulator subsystem

Some Ford V-8 engines have this subsystem, figure 20-21, to improve durability at speeds above 64 mph (103 kph). This subsystem shuts off carburetor vacuum to the EGR valve to prevent recirculation. A speed sensor driven by the speedometer cable signals an electronic module. When road speed exceeds 64 mph (103 kph), the module closes the open solenoid

valve. This, in turn, closes the EGR vacuum port and vents the vacuum outside the valve. As road speed drops below 64 mph (103 kph), the module deenergizes the solenoid valve. This closes the vent and opens the EGR vacuum line.

■ Engine Modifications Can't Do the Whole Job

Since the automobile was discovered to produce significant amounts of air pollution, many changes in engine design have been made to "clean it up". These engine modifications, such as EGR systems, have reduced exhaust emissions, but it is impossible to eliminate the major cause of HC emissions simply by changing the engine design. This is because the major cause of HC emissions is the effect of the "quench area" on combustion.

The quench area is the inner surface of the combustion chamber. When the ignition flame front passes through the combustion chamber, it burns the fuel charge as it goes until the quench area is reached. This is a thin layer between .002" and .010" (.05-mm and .25-mm) thick at the edge of the combustion chamber. When the flame front reaches the quench area, it is snuffed out because the quench area is so close to the cylinder head water jacket that the temperature there is too low for combustion to continue. Consequently, hydrocarbons within the quench area do not burn. They are ejected from the cylinder on every exhaust stroke along with the exhaust gases formed by combustion, and enter the atmosphere as pollutants.

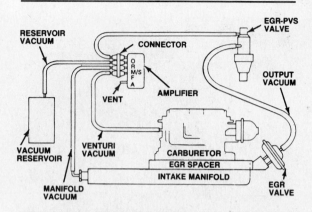

Figure 20-22. Ford venturi vacuum control subsystem with single connector amplifier. (Ford)

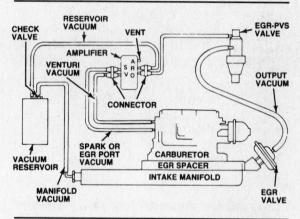

Figure 20-23. Ford venturi vacuum control subsystem with dual-connector amplifier. (Ford)

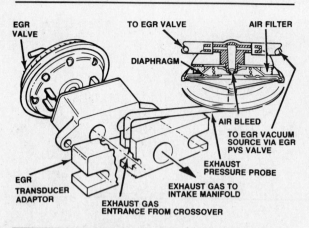

Figure 20-24. EGR backpressure transducer (sensor). (Ford)

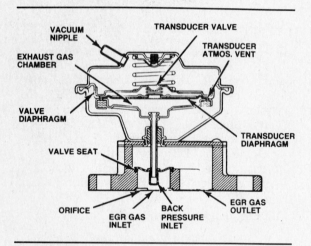

Figure 20-25. This Ford EGR valve has a built-in exhaust backpressure transducer. (Ford)

Venturi vacuum control

Some 1974 6-cylinder engines use venturi vacuum rather than ported vacuum. A vacuum amplifier, figure 20-22, is connected between the EGR valve and intake manifold vacuum. When air flow through the venturi is high enough, venturi vacuum opens the amplifier, allowing manifold vacuum to open the EGR valve.

The EGR valve remains closed at idle, since there is no venturi vacuum produced at idle. Whenever venturi vacuum is equal to or greater than manifold vacuum (such as under wide-open throttle), the vacuum amplifier dumps the output vacuum to the EGR valve, causing the valve to close. Some of the amplifiers contain an output bias, a bleed designed for quicker EGR valve opening.

A single-connector amplifier with all ports on one side is used with 1974-75 systems, figure 20-22. A dual-connector amplifier with ports on both sides is used with 1975 and later systems, figure 20-23.

Backpressure transducer

Late 1975 and most later engines use a backpressure sensor, or transducer, figure 20-24. This is connected between the EGR valve and the intake manifold. It modulates exhaust gas flow by varying the vacuum to the EGR valve, according to exhaust backpressure.

On some 1977 models, the backpressure transducer is within the EGR valve, figure 20-25. This combination unit has an internal exhaust gas chamber and a transducer diaphragm to sense exhaust backpressure through a hollow valve stem. This combination EGR valve-transducer constantly meters exhaust flow according to exhaust backpressure.

Many late-model 4-cylinder Ford engines use a remote backpressure variable transducer (BVT) to modulate EGR vacuum relative to two different sources of backpressure.

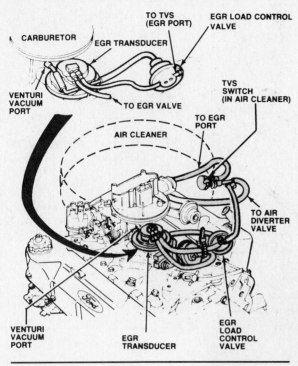

Figure 20-26. Ford air temperature vacuum switch and EGR load control valve installation on a 6.6L/400-cid V-8. (Ford)

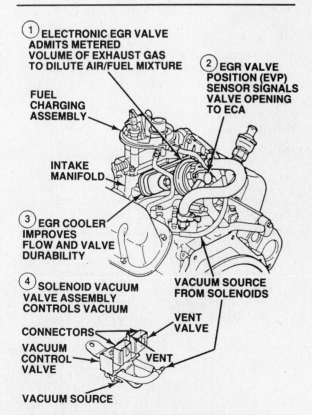

Figure 20-27. Ford closed-loop electronic control EGR system with solenoid vacuum valve control. (Ford)

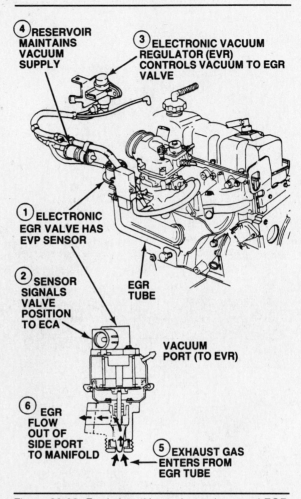

Figure 20-28. Ford closed-loop electronic control EGR system with solenoid vacuum valve control. (Ford)

Temperature control

Some 1976 and later V-8 engines use an air-temperature vacuum switch (TVS) mounted in the air cleaner, figure 20-26, instead of the coolant PVS. The TVS also controls the vacuum flow to the diverter valve in the Thermactor air injection system. Since the switch is closed at temperatures below about 60°F (16°C), exhaust gas does not recirculate on a cold engine.

Computer Control and Pulse Width Modulation

Ford uses two slightly different types of control for its EGR systems that are part of the electronic engine control (EEC) system. One type uses solenoid vacuum valve control, figure 20-27. The other type uses an electronic vacuum regulator, figure 20-28. The sensor in each system sends a position signal which tells the microprocessor how far the valve is open.

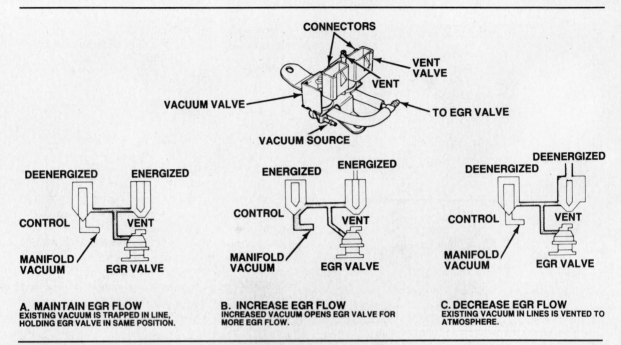

CONNECTORS

VENT VALVE

VENT

VACUUM VALVE

TO EGR VALVE

VACUUM SOURCE

DEENERGIZED   ENERGIZED

CONTROL   VENT

MANIFOLD VACUUM   EGR VALVE

A. MAINTAIN EGR FLOW
EXISTING VACUUM IS TRAPPED IN LINE, HOLDING EGR VALVE IN SAME POSITION.

ENERGIZED   ENERGIZED

CONTROL   VENT

MANIFOLD VACUUM   EGR VALVE

B. INCREASE EGR FLOW
INCREASED VACUUM OPENS EGR VALVE FOR MORE EGR FLOW.

DEENERGIZED   DEENERGIZED

CONTROL   VENT

MANIFOLD VACUUM   EGR VALVE

C. DECREASE EGR FLOW
EXISTING VACUUM IN LINES IS VENTED TO ATMOSPHERE.

Figure 20-29. Ford's EGR solenoid vacuum valve assembly. (Ford)

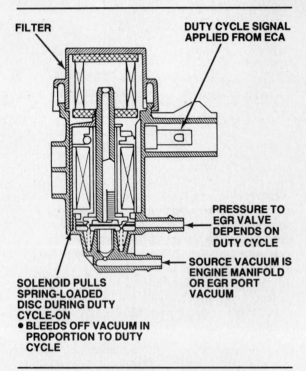

FILTER

DUTY CYCLE SIGNAL APPLIED FROM ECA

PRESSURE TO EGR VALVE DEPENDS ON DUTY CYCLE

SOURCE VACUUM IS ENGINE MANIFOLD OR EGR PORT VACUUM

SOLENOID PULLS SPRING-LOADED DISC DURING DUTY CYCLE-ON
● BLEEDS OFF VACUUM IN PROPORTION TO DUTY CYCLE

Figure 20-30. Ford's electronic vacuum regulator. (Ford)

In each case, the EEC microprocessor compares the sensor data with its program to determine whether the flow rate should be increased, maintained, or decreased. It then signals the solenoid vacuum valve assembly,

figure 20-27, or the electronic vacuum regulator, figure 20-28, to maintain or change the vacuum on the EGR diaphragm as required. The EGR valve used in both systems is essentially a ported vacuum valve with a position sensor (potentiometer) attached to the top of the EGR valve stem, figure 20-28.

In a system using the solenoid assembly, figure 20-29, the two solenoids "dither", that is, they open and close rapidly to modulate the valve opening. The vacuum valve solenoid provides vacuum to the EGR valve when energized. The vent valve solenoid vents the EGR valve to the atmosphere when deenergized. The vacuum valve solenoid contains an inlet port restrictor to reduce its flow rate compared to the vent valve solenoid. This allows the vent valve solenoid to vent vacuum flow immediately if the vacuum valve solenoid sticks open.

The electronic vacuum regulator, figure 20-30, is a spring-loaded solenoid that responds to the duty cycle established by the EEC microprocessor by applying, trapping, or bleeding off vacuum to the EGR valve as required.

GENERAL MOTORS EGR SYSTEMS

Exhaust gas recirculation was introduced by Buick on 1972 models with manual transmissions and all 1972 vehicles sold in California.

POSITIVE BACKPRESSURE

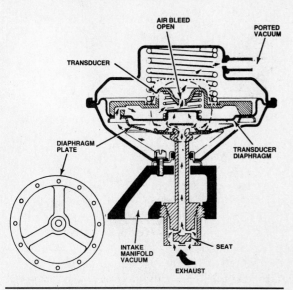

Figure 20-31. General Motors' positive backpressure EGR valve has a built-in transducer. (Buick)

The EGR system used on a General Motors vehicle is one of four types:
- Ported vacuum
- Positive backpressure
- Negative backpressure
- Pulse width modulation (PWM).

System Components

You must accurately identify the type of system you are working on because test procedures differ according to the design. Most systems include a coolant temperature override switch or a thermal vacuum switch (TVS) to prevent EGR operation when the engine is cold.

The ported vacuum EGR valve is a conventional design that meters exhaust gas into the intake manifold during part-throttle operation. Some of these systems have a remote-mounted backpressure transducer that allows the EGR valve to supply additional flow under load when ported vacuum is low. The transducer is installed in the vacuum line to the EGR valve and contains an air bleed that is normally open. When exhaust system backpressure to the transducer exceeds a preset level, the air bleed is sealed off and full vacuum is applied to the EGR valve diaphragm.

Single-diaphragm EGR valve
The single diaphragm valve, figure 20-3, contains a single spring-loaded diaphragm connected to the valve by a shaft. As the throttle valve opens, vacuum is applied to the diaphragm from a carburetor EGR port. The vacuum pulls the diaphragm up to open the valve and permit EGR flow. Variations in the strength of the vacuum signal control the quantity of exhaust gas that is recirculated.

Dual-diaphragm EGR valve
The dual-diaphragm EGR valve, figure 20-12, was an early attempt to modulate EGR flow. It contains two diaphragms with differing effective areas and two vacuum ports. The upper diaphragm receives a ported signal from the carburetor; the lower diaphragm is rigidly attached to the shaft, forming a vacuum chamber connected to manifold vacuum. High manifold vacuum (during cruising) pulls the valve partially closed, decreasing EGR flow. Low manifold vacuum (acceleration) allows the ported vacuum signal to open the valve and increase EGR flow.

Positive backpressure EGR valve
Before the introduction of the positive backpressure EGR valve, a separate backpressure transducer or backpressure valve (BPV) was used with single-diaphragm EGR valves to regulate the vacuum signal according to engine load.

Building the transducer into the valve resulted in the positive backpressure EGR valve, figure 20-31, which first appeared in 1977. This valve uses both engine vacuum and exhaust backpressure to control EGR flow. Exhaust system backpressure travels up the inside of the EGR valve stem and moves a diaphragm to seal off the air bleed when pressure exceeds a preset level. It provides a greater amount of recirculation during heavy engine loads than the single-diaphragm valve. EGR systems using this valve regulate the timed vacuum to the EGR valve according to exhaust backpressure level.

Negative backpressure EGR valve
This valve, figure 20-32, was introduced in 1979 for use on engines that have relatively little exhaust backpressure. In a negative-backpressure system, the transducer air bleed is normally closed. As ported vacuum opens the EGR valve, a negative pressure signal from the vacuum in the intake manifold is buffered by the exhaust system pressure and travels up the inside of the EGR valve stem to the backside of the transducer diaphragm. If the pressure signal is low enough (high vacuum), it will open the air bleed and reduce the amount

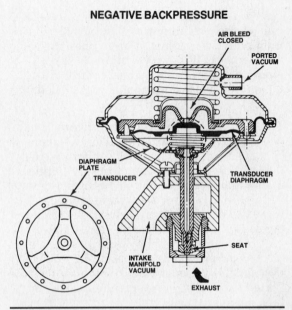

Figure 20-32. General Motors' negative backpressure EGR valve. (AC-Delco)

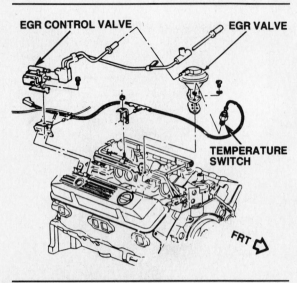

Figure 20-33. The GM PWM EGR system used on 5.0L and 5.7L engines. (GM)

of EGR. This modulating process goes on constantly and has the advantage of supplying a consistent percentage of EGR under most operating conditions.

Other EGR system controls

EGR flow is blocked on many GM engines when the engine is cold. You can easily determine if a temperature control device is used, because it will be found in the EGR vacuum line. If no temperature control is used, the EGR vacuum line will run directly between the valve and the carburetor EGR port. EGR systems with temperature control may use one of three different methods to control the EGR flow:

1. A coolant temperature sensor located in the thermostat housing, intake manifold, or engine coolant passage
2. A temperature-sensitive vacuum switch in the intake manifold to sense intake mixture temperature
3. A temperature-sensitive valve near the thermostat housing or strapped to the engine to sense radiated heat from the engine.

Some engines may use a combination of these methods. For example, the system may be designed to keep EGR off until both the coolant temperature and mixture temperature or radiated heat reach specified values.

In addition to these controls, GM EGR systems may use a delay valve or restrictor in the EGR vacuum line to delay valve closing under specified conditions.

EGR with Computer Command Control (CCC)

The first GM EGR systems to be computer-controlled were on Cadillacs with electronic fuel injection. When the engine reached a specified temperature, the electronic control module turned on an electric solenoid. This passed vacuum to the EGR valve and allowed exhaust gas flow. This same concept has been further refined with current PWM systems which first appeared on 1983 models.

Pulse-width-modulated EGR systems

The typical pulse-width-modulated system, figure 20-33, uses a PWM solenoid and works much the same as the Ford system previously described. In this design, the computer operates the solenoid continuously at a fixed frequency of 32 Hz. This is similar to the operation of a carburetor mixture control solenoid but at a faster rate. To regulate the amount of vacuum applied to the EGR valve, the computer varies the solenoid duty cycle (modulates the pulse width), the ratio of on-time to off-time. The duty cycle is calculated by the ECM according to data from various sensors which measure factors such as engine coolant temperature, throttle position, mass airflow, manifold air temperature, engine rpm, and transmission gear.

For most driving conditions, the duty cycle ranges from 10 to 90 percent. A low duty cycle provides less vacuum to the EGR valve while a high duty cycle provides more. The solenoid operates at zero duty cycle only when the transmission or transaxle is in Park or Neutral.

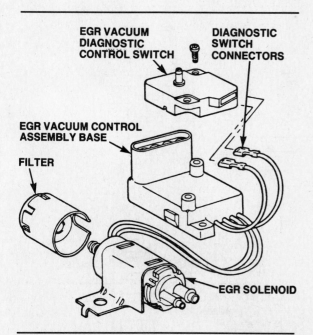

Figure 20-34. GM PWM systems use a diagnostic vacuum switch and serviceable filter on the EGR solenoid. (GM)

Figure 20-35. The integrated electronic EGR valve was introduced on 1987 GM Generation II 2.8L engines.

The EGR solenoid may be a normally open or normally closed version, depending on the system. A vent filter installed on the solenoid, figure 20-34, should be replaced every 30,000 miles (48,000 kilometers).

A diagnostic switch senses exhaust gas temperature as it enters the intake manifold through the EGR valve. If a vacuum circuit failure occurs, the diagnostic switch will set a code in the ECM memory and turn on the instrument panel "CHECK ENGINE" or "SERVICE ENGINE SOON" light. The diagnostic switch can take different forms, as shown in figures 20-33 and 20-34.

There are two basic variations of the PWM system; one was developed by Chevrolet and the other by Buick, but both are used in many different GM models. Both also use throttle position and manifold vacuum as their basic regulating inputs. The Chevrolet system came out first and has a thermal sensor in the base of the EGR valve to delay vacuum application until engine temperature reaches 175°F (79°C). The Chevrolet system does not respond to vacuum changes as rapidly as does the Buick system, and is not fast enough to signal a loss of EGR on turbocharged engines.

The Buick system is more sophisticated and includes a current-regulating module that maintains constant control voltage to the solenoid for more accurate EGR regulation. The Buick system also includes a vacuum switch

that monitors the amount of vacuum applied to the EGR valve; if the vacuum level is outside the programmed limits, the switch will set a trouble code in the ECM memory.

An integrated electronic EGR valve, figure 20-35, was introduced on some 1987 GM engines. The top of the EGR valve contains a vacuum regulator and pintle position sensor sealed inside a nonremovable plastic cover, figure 20-36. This combines all of the control devices in one assembly. The internal solenoid is normally open, causing the vacuum signal to be vented when EGR is not desired. A voltage regulator converts the ECM signal and regulates the current to the solenoid as required to establish the proper pulse width modulation. The pintle position sensor provides a voltage output to the ECM which increases as the duty cycle increases, allowing the ECM to monitor valve operation. A serviceable filter on the side of the assembly (arrow, figure 20-35) provides clean air to the vacuum regulator.

Some GM V-6 engines use an aspirated EGR system, figure 20-37. This delivers EGR flow under low engine vacuum conditions for detonation control. The **aspirator** is a combined regulator and venturi mounted in the air cleaner. The aspirator control valve is installed

Aspirator: A regulator and venturi installed in the air cleaner to provide EGR flow under low engine vacuum conditions to control detonation.

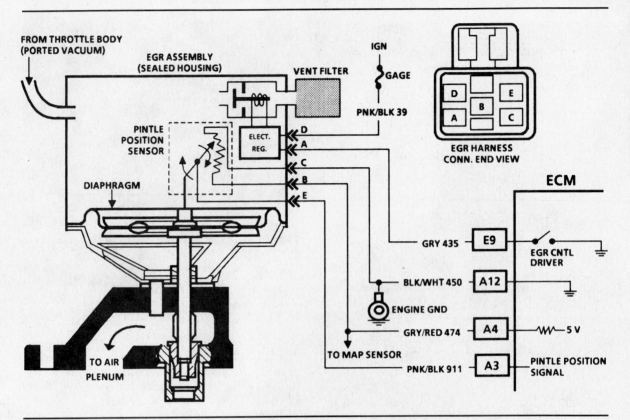

Figure 20-36. The integrated electronic EGR valve contains a built-in vacuum regulator, solenoid, and pintle position sensor. (Oldsmobile)

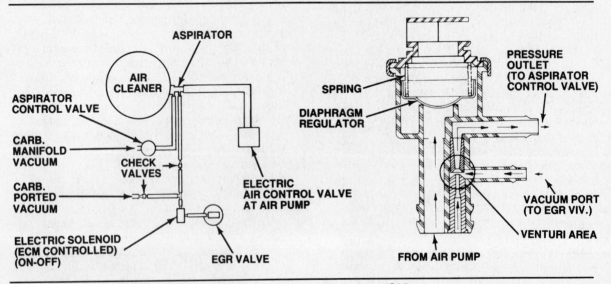

Figure 20-37. The GM aspirated EGR system used on some V-6 engines. (GM)

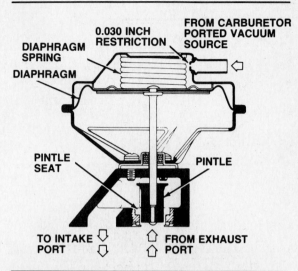

Figure 20-38. This American Motors EGR valve is typical of most single-diaphragm EGR valves. (AMC)

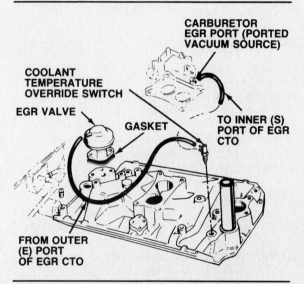

Figure 20-39. Basic AMC V-8 EGR installation. (AMC)

between the aspirator pressure outlet and the carburetor manifold vacuum port. If engine manifold vacuum drops under the aspirator control valve calibration, the valve opens to pass air through the aspirator venturi and create a supplemental vacuum. Once manifold vacuum returns above the aspirator control valve calibration, the valve closes to prevent airflow through the aspirator venturi.

Since the air pump flow goes to the exhaust ports in the open-loop mode (and would not flow through the aspirator), an orifice in the AIR control valve acts as a partial bypass, allowing the aspirator to function in open-loop

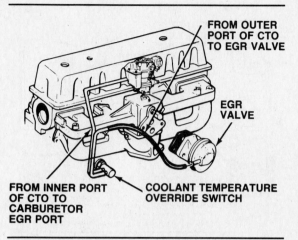

Figure 20-40. Basic AMC 6-cylinder EGR installation. (AMC)

if required. When the engine is in closed-loop mode, the AIR control valve sends pump airflow through the aspirator and into the air cleaner.

AMERICAN MOTORS EGR SYSTEMS

The basic AMC EGR system, as introduced on 1973 models, uses a vacuum-operated EGR valve. When the carburetor throttle is opened beyond the idle position, ported vacuum is applied to the normally closed EGR valve diaphragm, figure 20-38. Moving upward against coil spring pressure, the diaphragm opens the **pintle valve**. This valve permits exhaust gas to be drawn into the engine intake from the manifold crossover exhaust passages on V-8 engines, figure 20-39, or from below the carburetor heat riser on 6-cylinder engines, figure 20-40. The EGR valve is closed during idle and deceleration to prevent a rough idle. California cars use an exhaust backpressure transducer, figure 20-10.

American Motors also uses the following override and modulator devices to control EGR system operation.

Pintle Valve: A valve shaped much like a hinge pin. In an EGR valve, the pintle is attached to a normally closed diaphragm. When ported vacuum is applied, the pintle rises from its seat and allows exhaust gas to be drawn into the engine's intake system.

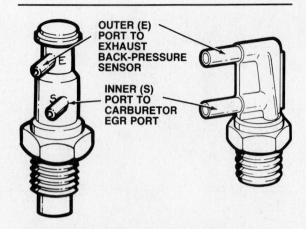

Figure 20-41. American Motors' 2-port EGR coolant temperature override (CTO) switch. (AMC)

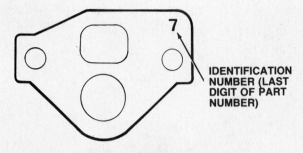

Figure 20-42. American Motors' EGR restrictor plate. (AMC)

Coolant Temperature Override Switch

This EGR coolant temperature override (CTO) switch prevents normal EGR valve operation when engine coolant temperature is below 115°F (46°C). The 3-port switch originally used has been replaced by a 2-port switch, figure 20-41, on 1974 and later models. At coolant temperatures above 115°F or 160°F (46°C or 71°C) depending on the model, vacuum is permitted to reach the EGR valve.

Low- and High-Temperature Vacuum Signal Modulators

Used only on 1973 models, these modulators are connected to the EGR vacuum control line. When air temperature is under 60°F (16°C) the low-temperature modulator weakens the vacuum to the EGR valve. This decreases the amount of exhaust gas flow. At temperatures above 115°F (46°C), the high-temperature modulator restores vacuum to the EGR valve and increases exhaust gas flow.

Exhaust Backpressure Sensor

Used only on California cars during 1973-75, the backpressure sensor, figure 20-10, was extended to all 1976 and later models. The sensor permits EGR flow only when the engine is at normal operating temperature and exhaust backpressure is high. If backpressure is not high enough, and the EGR-CTO switch does not open, the EGR vacuum signal is vented to the atmosphere.

Restrictor Plate

A stainless steel restrictor plate, figure 20-42, is used on some 1974-75 California models, and on all 1976-77 cars. Located between the intake manifold and spacer, the plate is adjusted for each engine and exhaust system. It limits EGR flow rate and improves driveability.

SUMMARY

Combustion chamber temperatures that exceed 2,500°F (1,371°C) cause nitrogen and oxygen to combine rapidly, forming large quantities of NO_x, a prime air pollutant. To reduce NO_x as much as possible, automakers use exhaust gas recirculation (EGR) systems to meter small quantities of exhaust gas into the incoming air-fuel mixture. This dilutes the fuel charge and results in lower combustion chamber temperatures.

Each automaker uses some variation of the basic system to achieve exhaust gas recirculation. Various temperature sensors, flow valves, and other control devices in the EGR system modulate the flow of exhaust gas to maintain driveability while reducing NO_x emissions.

With the advent of more sophisticated engine control systems, EGR system control has become a function of the engine control computer. The computer determines when and how much EGR flow is required and activates a pulse-wide-modulated (PWM) solenoid. The solenoid duty cycle established by the computer determines the flow rate and quantity.

Review Questions

Choose the single most correct answer.
Compare your answers with the correct answers on page 451.

1. Photochemical smog is a result of:
   a. Sunlight + NO_x + HC
   b. Sunlight + NO_x + CO_2
   c. Sunlight + CO + HC
   d. Sunlight + NO_x + CO

2. NO_x forms in an engine under:
   a. High pressure and low temperature
   b. Low pressure and low temperature
   c. High temperature and high pressure
   d. All of the above

3. Which of the following is a relatively inert gas?
   a. NO_x
   b. HC
   c. Exhaust gases
   d. Air

4. EGR is most desirable at:
   a. Speeds of 30-70 mph (48-113 kph)
   b. Idle speeds
   c. High speeds
   d. Low engine temperature

5. Which of the following is *not* part of an exhaust gas recirculation system?
   a. Chrysler's floor jets
   b. Buick's EGR valve
   c. Ported vacuum systems
   d. Slow-idle solenoid

6. Which is *not* true of EGR valves?
   a. They operate on venturi vacuum systems
   b. They operate on ported vacuum
   c. They may be mounted on the intake manifold
   d. They operate at wide-open throttle

7. Which is *not* part of the AMC EGR system?
   a. Low- and high-temperature vacuum signal modulators
   b. Floor jets
   c. Restrictor plate
   d. CTO switch

8. A Chrysler EGR delay timer prevents exhaust gas recirculation:
   a. During wide-open throttle
   b. At idle
   c. For 30 seconds after ignition
   d. At medium speeds

9. The Ford temperature-controlled vacuum valve is called:
   a. CTO
   b. CCEGR
   c. PVS
   d. OSAC

10. The high-speed EGR modulator subsystem shuts off the EGR valve above:
    a. 24 mph (39 kph)
    b. 34 mph (55 kph)
    c. 64 mph (103 kph)
    d. 84 mph (135 kph)

11. The Ford TVS, in addition to controlling EGR vacuum, controls:
    a. The temperature control override
    b. The ported vacuum switch
    c. The diverter valve vacuum
    d. All of the above

12. The combined transducer and EGR valve was introduced in which Buick model year?
    a. 1975
    b. 1976
    c. 1977
    d. 1978

13. Which is *not* one of the basic ways to reduce NO_x formation?
    a. Enrich the air-fuel mixture
    b. Lower the compression ratio
    c. Advance spark timing slightly
    d. Dilute the incoming air-fuel mixture with a small amount of inert gas

14. In a closed-loop electronic control system, a sensor informs the microprocessor of how the system is functioning by sending a:
    a. Position signal
    b. Pressure signal
    c. Either a or b
    d. Neither a nor b

15. Which is *not* a type of EGR valve in use?
    a. Poppet
    b. Modulating
    c. Tapered stem
    d. Pintle

16. General Motors' computer-controlled EGR systems use:
    a. A solenoid vacuum valve
    b. An electronic vacuum regulator
    c. An integrated electronic EGR valve
    d. A ported vacuum valve with a position sensor

17. Which is *not* a temperature control method used to control EGR flow?
    a. A coolant temperature sensor
    b. A temperature-sensitive vacuum switch
    c. A radiant temperature-sensitive valve
    d. A temperature delay valve or restrictor

18. In a GM computer-controlled EGR system, exhaust gas temperature is sensed by:
    a. A diagnostic switch
    b. A radiant temperature-switch
    c. A vane airflow meter
    d. A manifold absolute pressure sensor

19. An aspirated EGR system helps control detonation by delivering EGR flow under:
    a. Low engine vacuum
    b. High engine vacuum
    c. Ported vacuum
    d. Venturi vacuum

Chapter

21
Catalytic
Converters

To meet the strict exhaust emission limits of the late 1970s, automakers turned to the **catalytic converter** to change the harmful hydrocarbons (HC) and carbon monoxide (CO) in the exhaust to harmless byproducts. The device, which looks from the outside like a small muffler or resonator, is installed in the exhaust system between the exhaust manifold and the muffler, and generally is positioned under the passenger compartment. Its location is important, since as much of the exhaust heat as possible must be retained for effective operation.

A simple device, the catalytic converter contains no moving parts; it simply forms a chamber in the exhaust system through which the exhaust gas passes. Inside the converter, the exhaust flows through a honeycomb monolith or pellet-type catalyst material, which turns the exhaust pollutants into harmless byproducts of combustion.

Chances are you will never see the inside of a converter unless you cut one in half, since there is nothing inside that can be repaired. Most converters have a guaranteed life span of 50,000 miles.

The link between converters and a well-tuned engine is important. An engine that misfires or is improperly tuned can destroy a catalytic converter, because the converter cannot withstand exhaust temperatures above about 1,500°F (815°C), and it will not function properly if the air-fuel mixture is too rich. If two spark plugs misfire in succession for a prolonged time, the temperature in the converter will be raised to a point where it could shorten the life of the converter. The more you know about converters, the more you will understand the need for a well-tuned engine.

In this chapter, you will learn:
• Catalytic converter operation
• Differences between oxidation and reduction converters
• Ways to make sure that the converter does its job efficiently.

REDUCING EMISSIONS

One way of lowering hydrocarbons (HC) and carbon monoxide (CO) is to increase the combustion temperature, which causes more complete burning. As combustion temperatures rise, however, so does the formation of the third major pollutant, oxides of nitrogen (NO_x). A second method of turning exhaust gas into nonpolluting materials is the use of the catalytic converter, figure 21-1. By passing the exhaust gas through a **catalyst** in the presence of oxygen, the HC and CO compounds

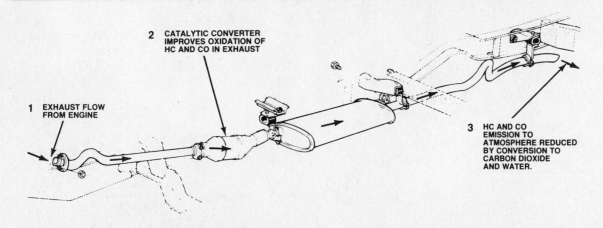

1 EXHAUST FLOW FROM ENGINE

2 CATALYTIC CONVERTER IMPROVES OXIDATION OF HC AND CO IN EXHAUST

3 HC AND CO EMISSION TO ATMOSPHERE REDUCED BY CONVERSION TO CARBON DIOXIDE AND WATER.

Figure 21-1. Typical catalytic converter installation. (Ford)

unite with the oxygen, resulting in two harmless byproducts of the catalytic reaction: water vapor (H_2O) and carbon dioxide (CO_2).

The Oxidation Reaction

A catalyst is a substance that starts or increases a chemical reaction, while remaining unchanged by that reaction. Since it only encourages rather than takes part in the reaction, the catalyst is never used up.

To change HC and CO into harmless materials, the catalytic elements (platinum and palladium) start an **oxidation**, or burning, reaction in the catalytic converter. Oxidation is the addition of oxygen to an element or compound. If there is not already enough oxygen in the exhaust, an air pump or aspirator valve supplies extra air. The oxidation mixes the HC and CO with oxygen to form H_2O and CO_2.

Considerable heat is generated by the oxidation process. The heat of the catalyst will range from 900°F to 1,600°F (482° to 871°C), and the exhaust gas at the outlet end of the converter will be 50° to 200°F (28° to 111°C) higher than at the inlet end. By 1978, automakers were able to reduce the outside, or ''skin'', temperatures of converters by as much as 300°F (167°C). The use of smaller engines and changes in engine timing were responsible for this temperature reduction. In spite of the intense heat, however, oxidation does not generate the flame and radiant heat associated with a simple burning reaction.

The Reduction Reaction

The catalytic oxidation reaction just described has *no* effect on oxides of nitrogen. NO_x control requires a separate reaction, called **reduction**, rather than oxidation. Reduction, which is the chemical removal of oxygen from a material, is the opposite of oxidation. The reduction reaction changes NO_x to harmless nitrogen (N_2) and CO_2 by chemically promoting the transfer of oxygen from the NO_x to the CO compound. The elements rhodium and platinum are used as reduction catalysts.

CATALYTIC CONVERTER CONSTRUCTION

The two main types of catalytic converter design are the conventional oxidation converter (COC), and the oxidation-reduction converter. Both consist of two stamped metal pieces welded together to form a round or oval shell.

Catalytic Converter: A device installed in an exhaust system that converts pollutants to harmless byproducts through a catalytic chemical reaction.

Catalyst: A substance that causes a chemical reaction, without being changed by the reaction.

Oxidation: The combining of an element with oxygen in a chemical process that often produces extreme heat as a byproduct.

Reduction: A chemical process in which oxygen is removed from a compound.

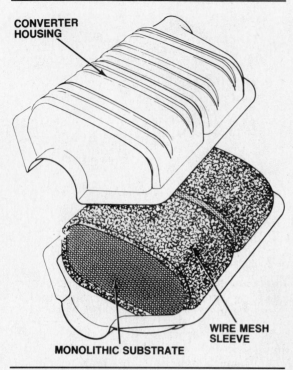

Figure 21-2. Typical catalytic converter with a monolithic substrate.

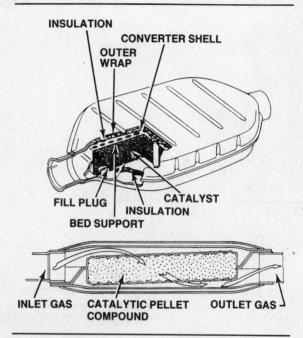

Figure 21-3. Typical catalytic converter with a pellet-type substrate.

The round type contains a ceramic honeycomb **monolith**, figure 21-2; the oval type contains pellets, figure 21-3. The outer housing is made of aluminum or stainless steel because it must be able to withstand the high temperatures associated with oxidation.

The pellet-type, figure 21-3, creates a fair amount of exhaust restriction, but is less expensive to manufacture, and the pellets in some models can be replaced if they become contaminated. Monolithic converters, figure 21-2, have a honeycomb structure that is much less restrictive, but more expensive to manufacture. This type of converter can only be serviced as a unit.

Conventional Oxidation Converter (COC)

The catalytic element generally used in conventional oxidation converters is platinum, or a mixture of platinum and palladium. These two **noble metals** best meet the requirements of an effective catalyst: durability, ability to withstand high operating temperatures, and chemical inactivity. The catalyst is deposited on an aluminum oxide or ceramic **substrate** through which the exhaust gas flows. This substrate must provide a catalyst support which can withstand high temperatures.

Monolithic and pellet substrates

Two forms of ceramic substrate material are used in oxidation converters: tiny pellets or a honeycomb monolith. The substrate can either be a laminated (sandwiched) design or an **extruded** design. The catalyst element is deposited on the surface of the substrate material. Both kinds of substrate material — monolith or pellets — provide several thousand square yards or meters of catalyst surface area over which the exhaust gases flow.

In converters using a monolith substrate material, figure 21-2, a diffuser inside the converter shell allows a uniform flow of exhaust gases over the entire area of the substrate. If a diffuser were not used, the gases would tend to flow only through a central portion of the substrate. In converters using a pellet substrate, figure 21-3, the gas flows over the top and down through the substrate layers.

Monolith substrate is a ceramic material which can break easily when subjected to shock or severe jolts. To prevent damage to the core, it is placed inside a stainless steel mesh which acts as a cushion. This also protects the core from thermal shock caused by temperature extremes, and keeps it properly positioned during final assembly of the converter shell.

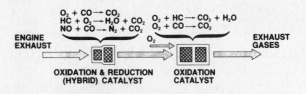

Figure 21-6. Catalytic oxidation and reduction
reactions. (Chrysler)

Two-Stage, Three-Way Converter (TWC)

Because the oxidation and the reduction reactions oppose each other, both cannot occur at the same time and in the same place. An oxidation and a reduction catalyst can be combined in the same converter, but a second oxidation catalyst is then required for complete emission control. An oxidation-reduction catalyst is often called a 2-stage, 3-way converter. It also is called a TWC (because it works on all three major pollutants), or a hybrid catalyst. A hybrid catalyst and a second oxidation catalyst can be installed in opposite ends of the same converter housing, or in two separate converters, figure 21-6.

The 3-way converter works best to reduce NO_x when the CO level in the exhaust is between 0.8 and 1.5 percent. As the CO level increases or decreases from that percentage, the 3-way converter's efficiency decreases, figure 21-7. Exhaust gas first passes through the hybrid catalyst, where the NO_x is changed to N_2 and CO_2. It then goes through the oxidation catalyst, where the HC and CO are changed to H_2O and CO_2.

Monolith: A large block. In a catalytic converter, the monolith is made like a honeycomb to provide several thousand square yards or meters of catalyst surface area.

Noble Metals: Metals, such as platinum and palladium, that resist oxidation.

Substrate: The layer, or honeycomb, of aluminum oxide upon which the catalyst (platinum or palladium) in a catalytic converter is deposited.

Extruded: Shaped by forcing through a die.

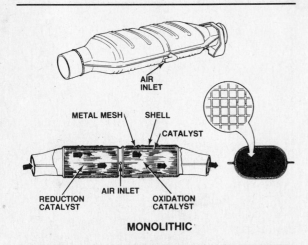

MONOLITHIC

Figure 21-4. Three-way monolithic catalytic converter construction. (GM)

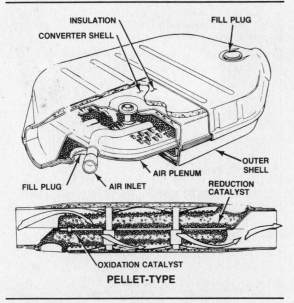

PELLET-TYPE

Figure 21-5. Three-way pellet-type catalytic converter construction. (GM)

Reduction Converter

A typical reduction converter uses two substrates of different sizes coated with platinum or rhodium. In a monolith design, these substrates are surrounded by the protective stainless steel mesh and are encased in a stainless steel shell, figure 21-2. In a 3-way converter (described in the next section), the reduction catalyst is located at the front of the converter housing (monolith design), figure 21-4, or at the top of the housing (pellet design), figure 21-5.

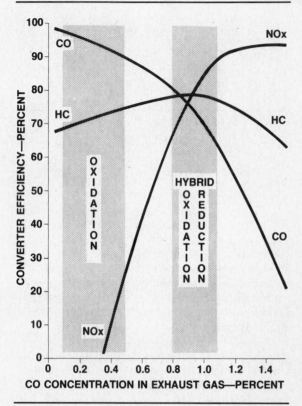

Figure 21-7. Catalyst operating characteristics. (Chrysler)

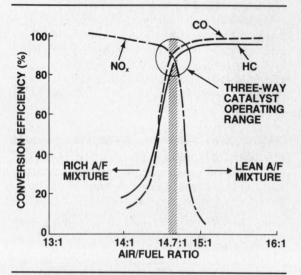

Figure 21-8. A three-way catalyst will only work properly in a narrow air-fuel ratio range. (GM)

Dual-bed monolithic and pellet converters

Catalytic converters using both an oxidation and a reduction catalyst in the same housing are called dual-bed, two-stage or 3-way catalytic converters. Like oxidation converters, the oxidation-reduction converters may use either

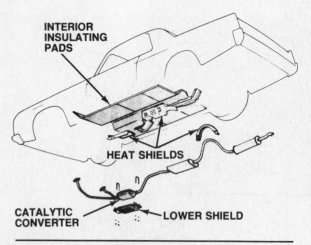

Figure 21-9. Monolithic converters require heat shielding. (Chrysler)

a monolith or pellet substrate. A 3-way converter using a monolith substrate has the reduction catalyst located at the front of the converter housing, figure 21-4. A 3-way converter with a pellet substrate has one placed above the other, with an air plenum separating the two catalysts, figure 21-5. The reduction catalyst is positioned on top of the plenum. In both designs, the oxygen produced during the reduction catalyst's reaction is used in the oxidation process.

Conversion with a 14.7 air-fuel ratio

Oxidation and reduction converters work most efficiently when the air-fuel mixture is maintained at the stoichiometric ratio of 14.7, figure 21-8. The most complete combustion of air and fuel occurs at this ratio, resulting in the least amount of harmful pollutants. HC and CO emissions are high at ratios richer than 14.7; NO_x emissions are greatest with ratios leaner than 14.7.

As we learned in Part Four of this manual, the 3-way converter system is used with an air-fuel management feedback system or electronic engine controls. To help maintain the ideal 14.7 ratio, the 3-way converter system uses an exhaust oxygen (O_2) sensor. This sensor measures the amount of oxygen in the exhaust gas and sends a voltage signal to the engine control microprocessor. The microprocessor then controls the carburetor or fuel injection system to keep the ratio as close as possible to 14.7.

Heat Shields

Monolith converters transmit a considerable amount of heat through their housing. In most installations, heat shields, figure 21-9, are used

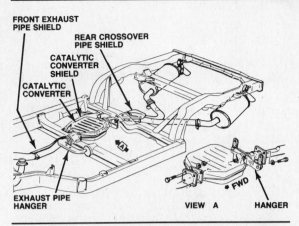

Figure 21-10. Some pellet-type converters may also use heat shields. (Chevrolet)

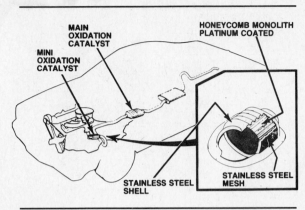

Figure 21-11. Chrysler miniconverter installation. (Chrysler)

to protect the passenger compartment, the automatic transmission and its cooler lines, and other parts of the chassis from excessive heat. Pellet-type converters have an insulated housing that does not transmit as much heat as the monolithic type, but some installations also may use heat shields, figure 21-10.

Size, shape, and placement of these shields vary according to the carmaker and model. The underbody floor pan above the converter is heavily shielded and more heat insulation is placed under the floor mats.

FIRST-GENERATION OXIDATION CONVERTERS

The first catalytic converters used only an oxidation catalyst and worked on HC and CO emissions only. These oxidation converters were used from 1975 through 1978 on domestic cars.

AMC and GM cars first used pellet converters made by the AC Division of General Motors. The pellet catalyst can be removed from the converter housing and replaced with fresh catalyst. Chrysler vehicles used a monolithic converter, as did Ford cars. Some 1977 and later Ford vehicles have converters with two monolithic substrates. The Ford converter requires a secondary air source to keep enough oxygen in the exhaust for complete oxidation of the HC. This is provided by the Thermactor air injection system.

Preconverters or Mini-Converters

Some Ford and Chrysler vehicles have used a small oxidation converter connected directly to the exhaust manifold outlet, figure 21-11. This converter contains a small catalyst surface area

close to the engine which heats up rapidly to start the HC and CO oxidation process more quickly during cold engine warm-up when the main converter has not yet reached its operating temperature. For this reason, they are often called ''light-off'' converters, or LOC. The oxidation reaction started in the preconverter is completed by the larger main converter located under the passenger compartment.

SECOND-GENERATION OXIDATION-REDUCTION CONVERTERS

The first 3-way converters were used by Volvo and Saab on a limited number of cars sold in

■ Catalytic Converter Odors

Although catalytic converters control HC and CO emissions, they also produce other undesirable emissions in small quantities. For example, gasoline contains a little bit of sulfur which reacts with the water vapor inside a converter to produce hydrogen sulfide. This toxic by-product has the distinct odor of rotten eggs. The smell is usually most noticeable while the engine is warming up, or during deceleration.

When the odor is very strong at normal operating temperatures, it may mean that the engine is out-of-tune and is running too rich. In many such cases, the carburetor idle mixture screws are not set right, although the problem also may be caused by a high fuel level or some other carburetor problem. Since the odor does not necessarily mean an incorrect mixture adjustment, the carburetor should not be adjusted simply to get rid of the odor. Changing brands of gasoline may help control the odor in some cases, since the amount of sulfur present in gasoline varies from one brand to another.

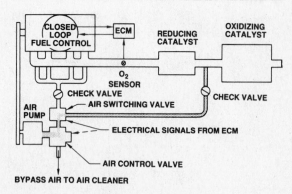

Figure 21-12. Pump air is injected downstream between the reduction and oxidation catalysts when the engine is warm. (AC-Delco)

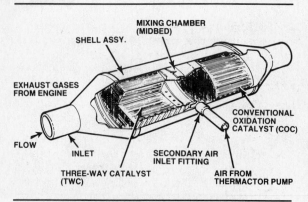

Figure 21-13. Three-way converters contain both catalysts in a single housing with an air inlet between the two catalysts. (Ford)

California during 1977. The 2.3L 4-cylinder engine used in 1978 in California Ford vehicles has a closed-loop feedback emission control system. The feedback is provided by the O_2 sensor. The front half of the hybrid converter has an oxidation-reduction catalyst that controls HC, CO, and NO_x. The rear half has only a platinum catalyst to further oxidize HC and CO.

Some of GM's 1978 California cars also have a closed-loop feedback emission control system. It works about the same as the Ford system. This was the first production use of a closed-loop system on a V-type engine. Since 1980, almost every carmaker has used the 3-way design.

Air Switching

We have already seen that the NO_x reduction catalyst works best with less oxygen and a richer HC and CO content in the exhaust gas, while the HC and CO oxidation catalyst works best with extra oxygen in the exhaust. For this reason, the air switching function in late-model air injection systems (Chapter 19) routes pump air from the exhaust ports during engine warmup to a downstream point in the exhaust once the engine is at operating temperature.

Pump air must enter the exhaust system at a point between the reduction catalyst and the oxidation catalyst, figure 21-12. Some systems use separate reduction and oxidation converters connected by an air inlet pipe. Most late-model installations, however, house both catalysts in a single converter with an air inlet between the two catalysts, figure 21-13.

CONVERTER OPERATING PRECAUTIONS

Since converters have no moving parts, they require no periodic service. Under Federal law, catalyst effectiveness is warranted for 50,000 miles (80,000 kilometers) or 5 years. However, a catalyst will eventually wear out. When it does, the entire converter (monolith) or catalyst (pellet) must be replaced to maintain effective emission control.

However, there are several ways in which a catalytic converter can be damaged or destroyed. Use of the wrong fuel, bad air-fuel mixtures, or excessive combustion heat can all damage a converter.

Fuel Requirements

Cars with catalytic converters must use unleaded fuel. The lead and phosphorous additives in leaded gasoline will coat the catalyst, destroying its efficiency by preventing the exhaust gases from reaching it. Switching to unleaded gasoline will allow the converter to regain some of its efficiency, depending on how long the leaded fuel was used. The only known method of testing a converter's efficiency is with a 4-gas analyzer.

To prevent the use of leaded fuel in cars with catalytic converters, the unleaded gasoline pump nozzles in service stations and the fuel-tank filler neck on cars requiring unleaded gasoline are smaller in diameter than those for use with leaded fuel. In addition, cars which require unleaded fuel have labels reading "Unleaded Gasoline Only" next to the gas tank filler and on the instrument panel in the driver's compartment. A U.S. Federal law makes it illegal to put leaded fuel in converter-equipped cars.

Fuel system cleaning additives should not be used in the fuel tank or inducted into the engine through the carburetor or fuel injection system on converter-equipped cars, because they may harm the catalyst.

Engine Condition

Excessively high temperatures can reduce converter life and destroy the catalyst core. Converters operate best at internal temperatures up to 1,500°F (816°C). At higher temperatures, the catalyst will start to break up or melt. Although temperature-protection systems are used on some vehicles, they work only under certain conditions. Proper engine maintenance is required to prevent the converter from overheating.

When an engine is in poor condition, or needs a tune-up, the exhaust gas fed to the converter contains too much raw fuel. This causes the converter to become a catalytic furnace. If more than two spark plugs misfire at the same time, raw fuel is pumped directly into the catalytic converter. This misfiring over a long time causes internal converter heat to rise rapidly.

Excessive temperatures also may be caused by improper use of an engine in good operating condition. Long idling periods are one of the worst running conditions, since more heat is developed when an engine runs at idle for long periods than when driving at normal highway speeds. Idle periods longer than 10 minutes should be avoided. It is much better to shut off the engine and restart it when required.

Other Precautions

To avoid excessive catalyst temperatures and the possibility of fuel vapors reaching the converter, follow these rules:
1. Do not attempt to start the engine on compression by pushing the vehicle. Use jumper cables instead.
2. Do not crank an engine for more than 40 seconds when it is flooded or firing intermittently.
3. Do not turn off the ignition switch when the car is in motion.
4. Fix immediately problems such as engine dieseling, heavy surging, repeated stalling or backfiring, and other indications of below-normal performance.

5. As a general rule, don't disconnect spark plugs to test the ignition. If an oscilloscope is not available, don't run the engine for more than 30 seconds with the plug wire off or shorted.

SUMMARY

Introduced in 1975, catalytic converters in the exhaust system promote a chemical reaction to change polluting byproducts of combustion into harmless water and carbon dioxide. There are two types of converters: oxidation and reduction. The oxidation type removes HC and CO emissions from the exhaust gases; reduction converters remove NO_x. Late-model engines with feedback fuel systems or electronic engine controls use a 3-way converter which combines the oxidation and reduction functions.

Early emission controls relied upon spark timing and air injection systems to control HC and CO. With the introduction of converters, the role of the air injection system changed from that of a prime oxidation device to an assist device that improved converter efficiency. Cars equipped with an oxidation converter (COC) inject air into the manifold outlet or exhaust pipe where it helps the catalytic reaction and heats the converter. Cars equipped with a reduction converter (TWC) require that the air be switched to a point downstream once the engine is warm.

Converters use a monolithic or pellet-type substrate coated with platinum, palladium, or rhodium to provide a surface on which the oxidation or reduction reactions occur. These catalysts can be damaged by too much heat, the use of leaded fuel, or too much unburned fuel reaching their surface. The only known way to determine the efficiency of a given converter is with a 4-gas analyzer.

Some early converters have a temperature protection system to prevent damage from overheating. These systems were abandoned on most 1976 and later vehicles.

Most monolithic converter installations use a series of heat shields to protect chassis components from damage by excessive heat. Pellet-type converters have insulated housings and do not generally require heat shielding.

Converters do not require periodic service during the 50,000-mile (80,000-kilometer) life span required by U.S. Federal regulations.

Review Questions

Choose the single most correct answer.
Compare your answers with the correct answers on page 451.

1. Catalytic converters:
   a. Increase the HC content in exhaust emissions
   b. Neither add nor remove the oxygen from exhaust emissions
   c. Improve oxidation of HC and NO
   d. Improve oxidation of HC and CO

2. The catalyst material in an oxidation catalytic converter is:
   a. Platinum or palladium
   b. Aluminum oxide
   c. Stainless steel
   d. Ceramic lead oxide

3. A catalyst:
   a. Slows a chemical reaction
   b. Heats a chemical reaction
   c. Increases, but is not consumed by, a chemical action
   d. Combines with the chemicals in the reaction

4. A reduction reaction:
   a. Adds oxygen to a compound
   b. Removes oxygen from a compound
   c. Reduces HC in exhaust gases
   d. Removes H_2O from exhaust gases

5. The outer shell of the oxidation catalyst is made of:
   a. Aluminum oxide pellets
   b. Platinum or palladium
   c. A honeycomb monolith
   d. Aluminum or stainless steel

6. A catalyst is deposited on:
   a. A stainless steel shell
   b. A ceramic substrate
   c. A stainless steel mesh
   d. Any of the above

7. Cars with catalytic converters are required to use:
   a. Premium unleaded fuel
   b. Unleaded fuel
   c. Low-lead fuel
   d. Any of the above

8. Which of the following will damage the converter?
   a. Push starting the engine
   b. Engine misfiring
   c. Long idling periods
   d. All of the above

9. Which of the following is *not* true for cars with catalytic converters?
   a. Engines should not be cranked for more than 60 seconds.
   b. Spark plugs should always be disconnected to test ignition
   c. Engine dieseling, surging, and stalling should be fixed immediately
   d. Ignition should not be turned off while car is moving

10. The reduction converter must be located:
    a. Between the engine and the oxidation converter
    b. Between the oxidation converter and the muffler
    c. After the muffler
    d. Any of the above

11. Hybrid converters were first used on domestic cars in:
    a. 1975
    b. 1976
    c. 1978
    d. 1980

NIASE Mechanic Certification Sample Test

This sample test is similar in format to the series of eight tests given by the National Institute for Automotive Service Excellence (ASE). Each of these exams covers a specific area of automotive repair and service. The tests are given every fall and spring throughout the United States.

For a technician to earn certification in a particular field, he or she must successfully complete one of these tests, and have at least two years of "hands on" experience (or a combination of work experience and formal automobile technician training). Successfully finishing all eight tests earns the person certification as a Master Automobile Technician.

In the following sample test, the questions follow the form of the ASE exams. Learning to take this kind of test will help you if you plan to apply for certification later in your career. You can find the answers to the questions in this sample exam on page 451.

For test registration forms or additional information on the automobile technician certification program, write to:

National Institute for
  AUTOMOTIVE SERVICE EXCELLENCE
1920 Association Drive, Suite 400
Reston VA 22019-1502

1. The three major air pollutants emitted by motor vehicles are:
   a. Sulfates, particulates, carbon monoxide
   b. Sulfates, carbon monoxide, nitrous oxide
   c. Carbon monoxide, oxides of nitrogen, hydrocarbons
   d. Hydrocarbons, carbon dioxide, nitrous oxide

2. Which should be true of a vehicle's stoichiometric air-fuel ratio?
   a. HC is low; CO, O_2, and CO_2 are high
   b. HC and CO are low; O_2 and CO_2 are high
   c. HC, CO, and O_2 are low; CO_2 is high
   d. HC, CO, O_2, and CO_2 are low

3. While the engine is running, a technician pulls the PCV valve out of the valve cover and puts his thumb over the valve opening. There are no changes in engine operation.
   Technician A says the PCV valve could be stuck in the open position.

Technician B says the hose between the intake manifold (carburetor base) and the PCV valve could be plugged.
   Who is right?
   a. A only
   b. B only
   c. Both A and B
   d. Neither A nor B

4. A car with an air pump emission control system backfires when decelerating. Which of these should the technician check?
   a. The operation of the exhaust manifold check valve
   b. The output pressure of the air pump
   c. The operation of the diverter or gulp valve
   d. The air manifolds for leakage

5. Which of the following is true of an EGR system?
   a. Most early-model systems are regulated by a backpressure transducer
   b. Most late-model systems are regulated by a backpressure transducer

c. Even a poorly maintained EGR system has little effect on driveability
   d. EGR systems have numerous parts scheduled for regular service

6. Pressure and volume tests of a mechanical fuel pump are both below specs.
   Technician A says that an air leak in the fuel line between the tank and the pump could be the cause.
   Technician B says a plugged fuel tank pick-up could be the cause.
   Who is right?
   a. A only
   b. B only
   c. Both A and B
   d. Neither A nor B

7. Air injection systems used with electronic engine controls may have:
   a. Air switching valves
   b. Gulp valves
   c. Diverter valves
   d. All of the above

8. A compression test has been made on a 6-cylinder engine. Cylinders 3 and 4 have readings of 10 psi. All other cylinders have readings between 130 and 135 psi.

   Technician A says this could be caused by a blown head gasket.

   Technician B says it could be caused by wrong valve timing.

   Who is right?
   a. A only
   b. B only
   c. Both A and B
   d. Neither A nor B

9. Which of these is least likely to cause a car to hesitate (stumble) when the gas pedal is depressed quickly?

   a. Retarded ignition timing
   b. Low carburetor float level
   c. Leaking carburetor accelerator pump check valve
   d. Leaking carburetor power valve

10. Valve lash is being adjusted on an engine with solid lifters.

    Technician A says too much valve lash can cause poor engine performance.

    Technician B says not enough valve lash can cause valve burning.

    Who is right?
    a. A only
    b. B only
    c. Both A and B
    d. Neither A nor B

11. Which statement is true of a cylinder power balance test?

    a. An engine with electronic idle speed control should be tested at idle
    b. Exhaust emissions should noticeably increase when you cut out one cylinder
    c. Both a and b
    d. Neither a nor b

12. A leaking fuel pump diaphragm may cause:

    a. Backfiring
    b. Crushed fuel tank
    c. Fuel leaks at the filler tube
    d. Diluted oil

13. Which of the following is not a carburetor float adjustment?

    a. Float toe
    b. Float reach
    c. Float drop
    d. Float level

14. A choke adjustment specification that calls for the choke to be set on "index" means:

    a. The choke rod or link must be bent to a specified length
    b. The vacuum break link must be bent until the U-bend is closed
    c. The index mark on the choke cover must be aligned with a similar mark on the housing
    d. The choke link must be placed in the index hole in the choke lever

15. If the rpm gain measured during artificial enrichment tests is less than specified:

    a. The air-fuel ratio is too lean
    b. The engine is overheated
    c. The air-fuel ratio is too rich
    d. The air injection system is not working correctly

16. An engine idles roughly and stalls on light acceleration. When the vacuum line is disconnected from the EGR valve, the problem disappears. This probably means:

    a. The EGR valve is stuck closed
    b. The EGR valve is getting a weak vacuum signal
    c. The EGR valve diaphragm spring is broken
    d. The EGR valve is incorrectly opening at idle

17. High HC exhaust emissions are often due to:

    a. An overheated engine
    b. A restricted air cleaner
    c. Ignition system problems
    d. An inoperative EGR system

18. During inspection of an air injection system, a brittle, burned hose is found on the upstream side of a check valve. This may be due to:

    a. The hose being positioned too close to the engine
    b. The air pump developing excessive air pressure
    c. The injection nozzles being plugged and allowing backpressure to build up in the system
    d. The check valve allowing exhaust gas to leak back into the air injection system

19. A cylinder power balance test is performed while the engine is running by:

    a. Shorting the ignition of each cylinder and noting rpm drop
    b. Shorting the ignition of each cylinder and noting rpm gain
    c. Running the ignition for each cylinder in an open circuit condition and noting available secondary voltage
    d. Opening a vacuum port at the carburetor or intake manifold and noting rpm gain

20. The exhaust manifold heat riser is stuck in the open position.

    Technician A says this can cause poor gas mileage.

    Technician B says this can cause the intake manifold vacuum to be lower than normal.

    Who is right?
    a. A only
    b. B only
    c. Both A and B
    d. Neither A nor B

21. Technician A says the automatic choke is opened by manifold vacuum.

    Technician B says the automatic choke is closed by spring force.

    Who is right?
    a. A only
    b. B only
    c. Both A and B
    d. Neither A nor B

22. While cranking the engine, the reading on the voltmeter shown below is below specs.

Technician A says a low reading can be caused by a bad battery.

Technician B says a low reading can be caused by a bad starter.

Who is right?

a. A only
b. B only
c. Both A and B
d. Neither A nor B

23. In the charging system shown below, the meter reading will show:

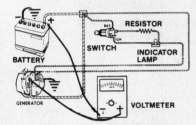

a. Charging output voltage
b. Indicator lamp operating voltage
c. Charging circuit voltage drop
d. Ignition switch voltage drop

24. The oil pressure light stays on whenever the engine is running. The oil pressure has been checked and it meets specs.

Technician A says that a ground in the circuit between the indicator light and the pressure switch could be the cause.

Technician B says that an open in the pressure switch could be the cause.

Who could be right?

a. A only
b. B only
c. Either A or B
d. Neither A nor B

25. A high-rated discharge test (battery capacity test) is being performed on a 12-volt battery.

Technician A says that a good battery should have a voltage reading below 7 volts while under load.

Technician B says that the battery should be discharged (loaded) at 2 times its ampere hour rating.

Who is right?

a. A only
b. B only
c. Both A and B
d. Neither A nor B

26. Which of these is a correct method for testing the instrument voltage regulator (limiter) used in some gauge circuits?

a. Connect an ammeter in series with the voltage regulator; if the reading is above 5 amps, the voltage regulator is O.K.
b. Connect a test light to the voltage regulator output terminal; if the light flashes, the voltage regulator is bad
c. Connect a test light to the temperature sending unit; if the light flashes, the voltage regulator is O.K.
d. Connect a voltmeter between the battery positive post and the temperature sending unit; if the reading is 12 volts, the voltage regulator is O.K.

27. Technician A says a noisy alternator could be caused by a bad diode.

Technician B says a noisy alternator could be caused by a worn bearing.

Who could be right?

a. A only
b. B only
c. Either A or B
d. Neither A nor B

28. All of these could cause high starter current draw *except*:

a. Worn starter bushings
b. Bad starter relay
c. Grounded field coils
d. Grounded armature

29. The starter will not "crank" and the solenoid does not "click" on a car with an automatic transmission. All of these could cause this problem *except*:

a. A misadjusted neutral safety switch
b. An open solenoid hold-in winding
c. An open circuit between the solenoid and the ignition switch
d. An open in the solenoid ground circuit

30. Which of these is true about the scope pattern shown below?

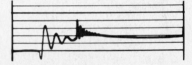

a. The coil primary leads are reversed
b. The condensor is connected wrong
c. The coil tower is badly corroded
d. The spark plugs are badly worn

31. An engine starts but does not keep running when the ignition switch is in the run position. This problem could be caused by an open in the:

a. Ignition resistor bypass circuit
b. Ignition resistor or resistor wire
c. Ignition switch accessory circuit
d. Starter solenoid

32. Alternators are correctly polarized by:

a. Grounding the field terminal
b. Grounding the output terminal
c. Reversing the cable connections at the battery
d. None of the above

33. During cranking, the voltage drop across the battery ground cable (as measured in the diagram below) should not exceed:

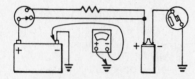

   a. 0.5 volt
   b. 0.2 volt
   c. 1.5 volts
   d. 2.0 volts

34. The normal voltage drop across ignition breaker points with the ignition on, the points closed, and the engine not running, is approximately:
   a. 0.1 volt
   b. 0.5 volt
   c. 1.5 to 3.5 volts
   d. 5.0 to 7.5 volts

35. Which of the following is *not* a recommended method for connecting a timing light to a spark plug cable?
   a. Using an inductive pickup
   b. Making a small hole in the cable with an icepick for use as an adapter
   c. Installing an adapter at the spark plug end of the cable
   d. Installing an adapter at the distributor end of the cable

36. When ignition advance is tested with the distributor in the engine, specifications given in distributor speed and degrees must be:
   a. Multiplied by 2
   b. Divided by 2
   c. Divided by 4
   d. Used without change

37. When adjusting distributor advance mechanisms:
   a. Clean, inspect, and lubricate the distributor before adjusting the advance
   b. Adjust dwell on breaker-point distributors before adjusting the advance
   c. Adjust the centrifugal advance before the vacuum advance
   d. All of the above

38. Transmission switches used with transmission-controlled spark systems may be:
   a. Normally open
   b. Normally closed
   c. Used with a reversing relay
   d. All of the above

39. With a firing order of 1-5-3-6-2-4, number 1 cylinder is at tdc with both valves closed when which cylinder is at tdc with the exhaust valve fully open?
   a. 3
   b. 4
   c. 5
   d. 6

40. Which of the following is *not* a catalyst element used in a catalytic converter?
   a. Palladium
   b. Rhodium
   c. Germanium
   d. Platinum

41. Which of the following exhaust emissions *cannot* be measured with an infrared exhaust analyzer?
   a. CO
   b. CO_2
   c. HC
   d. NO_x

42. A combination of individual transistors, diodes, capacitors, other electronic parts, and an integrated circuit is called a:
   a. Hybrid circuit
   b. Compound circuit
   c. Discrete circuit
   d. Digital circuit

Glossary of Technical Terms

Actuator: An electrical or mechanical device that receives an output signal from a computer and does something in response to that signal.

Adaptive Memory: A feature of computer memory that allows the microprocessor to adjust its memory for computing open-loop operation, based on changes in engine operation.

After Top Dead Center: The position of a piston after it has passed top dead center. Abbreviated: atdc. Usually expressed in degrees, such as 5° atdc.

Air Charge Temperature (ACT) Sensor: A thermistor used to measure intake air temperature or air-fuel mixture temperature.

Air-Fuel Ratio: The ratio of air to gasoline in the air-fuel mixture which enters an engine.

Air Injection: A way of reducing exhaust emissions by injecting air into each of the exhaust ports of an engine. The air mixes with the hot exhaust and oxidizes the HC and CO to form H_2O and CO_2.

Alternating Current: A flow of electricity through a conductor, first in one direction, then in the opposite direction.

Ambient Temperature: The temperature of the air surrounding a particular device or location.

Amperage: The amount of current flow through a conductor.

Ampere: The unit for measuring the rate of electric current flow.

Analog: A voltage signal or processing action that is continuously variable relative to the operation being measured or controlled.

Analog-to-Digital (AD): An electronic conversion process for changing analog voltage signals to digital voltage signals.

Aneroid Bellows: An accordion-shaped bellows that responds to changes in coolant pressure or atmospheric pressure by expanding or contracting.

Antiknock Value: The characteristic of gasoline that helps prevent detonation or ''knocking''.

Antioxidant Inhibitor: A gasoline additive used to prevent oxidation and the formation of gum.

Antioxidants: Chemicals or compounds added to motor oil to reduce oil oxidation, which leaves carbon and varnish in the engine.

API Service Classification: A system of letters signifying an oil's performance; assigned by the American Petroleum Institute.

Aspirator: A regulator and venturi installed in the air cleaner to provide EGR flow under low engine vacuum conditions to control detonation.

Atmospheric Pressure: The pressure caused by the weight of the earth's atmosphere. At sea level, this pressure is 14.7 psi (101 kPa) at 32°F (0°C).

Atomization: Breaking down into small particles or a fine mist.

Available Voltage: The peak voltage that a coil can produce.

Backfire: The accidental combustion of gases in an engine's intake or exhaust system.

Backpresssure: A pressure that tends to slow the exit of exhaust gases from the combustion chamber; usually caused by restrictions in the exhaust system.

Baffle: A plate or obstruction that restricts the flow of air or liquids. The baffle in a fuel tank keeps the fuel from sloshing as the car moves.

Bakelite: A synthetic plastic material that is a good insulator. Distributor caps are often made of Bakelite.

Ballast (Primary) Resistor: A resistor in the primary circuit that stabilizes ignition system voltage and current flow.

Base: The center layer of semiconductor material in a transistor.

Before Top Dead Center: The position of a piston as it nears top dead center. Abbreviated: btdc. Usually expressed in degrees, such as 5° btdc.

Bimetal Temperature Sensor: A sensor or switch that reacts to changes in temperature. It is made of two strips of metal welded together that expand differently when heated or cooled causing the strip to bend.

Binary: A mathematical system consisting of only two digits (0 and 1) which allows a digital computer to read and process input voltage signals.

Block Learn: The long-term effects of integrator corrections. As such, block learn complements adaptive memory. If, for example, the computer continually must overcompensate fuel metering to maintain stoichiometry, it ''learns'' the correction and adapts its memory to make the correction factor part of its basic program.

Blowby: Combustion gases that get past the piston rings into the crankcase; these include water vapor, acids, and unburned fuel.

Blowoff Valve: A spring-loaded valve that opens when boost pressure overcomes the spring tension.

Boost: A measure of the amount of air pressurization, above atmospheric, that a supercharger can deliver.

Bore: The diameter of an engine cylinder.

Bottom Dead Center: The exact bottom of a piston stroke. Abbreviated: bdc.

Breaker Points: The metal contact points that act as an electrical switch in a distributor. They open and close the ignition primary circuit.

Capacitor: A device that can store voltage without affecting the voltage in any way. Formed by bringing two conductive surfaces close together, separated only by an insulator. Also called condenser.

Carbon Monoxide (CO): An odorless, colorless, tasteless poisonous gas. A major pollutant given off by an internal combustion engine.

Carburetor Icing: A condition that is the result of the rapid vaporization of fuel entering a carburetor; the temperature drops enough to freeze the water particles in the airflow.

Catalyst: A substance that causes a chemical reaction, without being changed by the reaction.

Catalytic Converter: A device installed in an exhaust system that converts pollutants to harmless byproducts through a catalytic chemical reaction.

Catalytic Cracking: An oil refining process which uses a catalyst to break down (crack) the larger components of the crude oil. The gasoline produced usually has a lower sulfur content than gasoline produced by thermal cracking.

Cell: A case enclosing one element in an electrolyte. Each cell produces approximately 2.1 to 2.2 volts. Cells are connected in series.

Central Processing Unit (CPU): The processing and calculating portion of a computer.

Centrifugal Force: A force applied to a rotating object, tending to move the object toward the outer edge of the circle in rotation.

Centrifugal (Mechanical) Advance: A method of advancing the ignition spark using weights in the distributor that react to centrifugal force.

Check Valve: A valve that permits flow in only one direction.

Circuit: A circle or unbroken path of conductors through which an electric current can flow.

Clearance Volume: The volume of a combustion chamber when the piston is at top dead center.

Closed-Loop: An operational mode in which the engine control microprocessor reads and responds to feedback signals from the EGO sensor, adjusting system operation accordingly.

Collector: The outside layer of semiconductor material in a transistor that conducts current away from the base.

Compression Ratio: The total volume of an engine cylinder divided by its clearance volume.

Concentric: Having the same center.

Condenser: A capacitor used in breaker-point ignition systems to prevent arcing across the points.

Conductor: A material that allows easy flow of electricity.

Continuous Injection System: A fuel injection system in which fuel is injected constantly whenever the engine is running.

Conventional Theory of Current Flow: The current flow theory which says electricity flows from positive to negative. Also called positive current flow theory.

Cranking Performance Rating: A battery rating based on the amperes of current that a battery can supply for 30 seconds at 0°F, with no battery cell falling below 1.2 volts.

Cross-Firing: Ignition voltage jumping from the distributor rotor to the wrong spark plug electrode inside the distributor cap. Also, ignition voltage jumping from one spark plug cable to another due to worn insulation.

Cycling: Battery electrochemical action and operation. One complete cycle is operation from fully charged to discharged and back to fully charged.

Detented: Positions in a switch that allow the switch to stay in that position. In an ignition switch, the On, Off, Lock, and Accessory positions are detented.

Detergent-Dispersant: A chemical added to motor oil to break down and disperse sludge and other undesirable particles picked up by the oil.

Detonation: Also called knocking or spark knock. An unwanted explosion of an air-fuel mixture caused by high heat and compression.

Diaphragm: A thin flexible wall, separating two cavities, such as the diaphragm in a vacuum advance unit.

Dielectric: The insulating material between the two plates of a condenser, or capacitor.

Dieseling: A condition in which extreme heat in an engine's combustion chamber continues to ignite fuel after the ignition has been turned off.

Digital: A 2-level voltage signal or processing function that is either on/off or high/low.

Digital-to-Analog (DA): An electronic conversion process for changing digital voltage signals to analog voltage signals.

Diodes: Electronic devices made of semiconductor material that allow current flow in one direction but block it in the other.

Direct Current: A flow of electricity in one direction through a conductor.

Diverter Valve: Also called a dump valve. A valve used in an air injection system to prevent backfire. During deceleration it "dumps" the air from the air pump into the atmosphere.

Duty Cycle: The percentage of total time in one complete on-off cycle during which a solenoid is energized.

Dwell Angle: Also called cam angle, or dwell. The measurement in degrees of how far the distributor cam rotates while the breaker points are closed.

Dynamometer: A device used to measure mechanical power, such as the power of an engine.

Eccentric: Off center. A shaft lobe which has a center different from that of the shaft.

Electrolyte: The chemical solution in a battery that conducts electricity and reacts with the plate materials.

Electromagnet: A soft iron core wrapped in a coil of a current-carrying conductor. Current flow in the conductor induces a magnetic force around the core.

Electron Theory of Current Flow: The current flow theory which says electricity flows from negative to positive.

Electronic Fuel Injection (EFI): A computer-controlled fuel injection system which gives precise mixture control and almost instant response to all operating conditions at all speed ranges.

Element: A complete assembly of positive plates, negative plates, and separators making up one cell of a battery.

Emitter: The outside layer of semiconductor material in a transistor that conducts current to the base.

Engine Displacement: A measurement of the volume of air displaced by a piston as it moves from bottom to top of its stroke. Engine displacement is the piston displacement multiplied by the number of pistons in an engine.

Engine Mapping: Vehicle operation simulation procedure used to tailor the onboard computer program to a specific engine/powertrain combination. This program is stored in a PROM or calibration assembly.

Ethanol: Ethyl alcohol distilled from grain or sugar cane.

Evaporative Emission Control (EEC): A way of controlling HC emissions by collecting fuel vapors from the fuel tank and carburetor fuel bowl vents and directing them through an engine's intake system.

Exhaust Gas Recirculation (EGR): A way of reducing NO_x emissions by directing unburned exhaust back through an engine's intake.

Extended-Core Spark Plug: Also called power tip. The insulator core and the electrodes in this type of spark plug extend further into the combustion chamber than they do on other types.

Extruded: Shaped by forcing through a die.

Farad: The unit of measurement of a condenser's ability to store electrical energy.

Fast-Burn Combustion Chamber: A compact combustion chamber with a centrally located spark plug. The chamber is designed to shorten the combustion period by reducing the distance of flame front travel.

Firing Order: The order in which combustion occurs in the cylinders of an engine.

Firing Voltage (Required Voltage): The voltage level that must be reached to ionize and create a spark in the air gap between the spark plug electrodes.

Fixed Dwell: The ignition dwell period begins when the switching transistor turns on and remains relatively constant at all speeds.

Flat Spot: The brief hesitation or stumble of an engine caused by a momentary overly lean air-fuel mixture due to the sudden opening of the throttle.

Float Valve: A valve that is controlled by a hollow ball floating in a liquid, such as in the fuel bowl of a carburetor.

Flooding: A condition caused by heat expanding the fuel in a fuel line. The fuel pushes the carburetor inlet needle valve open and fills up the fuel bowl even when more fuel is not needed. Also, the presence of too much fuel in the intake manifold.

Four-Stroke Engine: The Otto cycle engine. An engine in which a piston must complete four strokes to make up one operating cycle. The strokes are: intake, compression, power, and exhaust.

G-Lader: A type of supercharger pump which compresses air by squeezing it through an internal spiral, then forcing it through ports into the engine.

Galvanic Battery: A direct current voltage source, generated by the chemical action of an electrolyte.

Gasohol: A blend of ethanol and unleaded gasoline, usually at a one to nine ratio.

Ground: The connection of an electrical circuit or unit to the engine or chassis to return electrical current to the battery.

Ground Cable: The battery cable that provides a ground connection from the vehicle chassis to the battery.

Group Number: A battery identification number that indicates battery dimensions, terminal design, holddown location, and other physical features.

Gulp Valve: A valve used in an air injection system to prevent backfire. During deceleration it redirects air from the air pump to the intake manifold where the air leans out the rich air-fuel mixture.

Hall-Effect Switch: A signal-generating switch that develops a transverse voltage across a current-carrying semiconductor when subjected to a magnetic field.

Heat Range: The measure of a spark plug's ability to dissipate heat from its firing end.

High-Speed Surge: A sudden increase in engine speed caused by high manifold vacuum pulling in an excess air-fuel mixture.

High-Swirl Combustion Chamber: A combustion chamber in which the intake valve is shrouded or masked to direct the incoming air-fuel charge and create turbulence that will circulate the mixture more evenly and rapidly.

Hydrocarbon (HC): A chemical compound made up of hydrogen and carbon. A major pollutant given off by an internal combustion engine. Gasoline itself is a hydrocarbon compound.

Ignition Interval (Firing Interval): The number of degrees of crankshaft rotation between ignition sparks.

Impeller: A rotor or rotor blade used to force a gas or liquid in a certain direction under pressure.

Induction: The production of an electrical voltage in a conductor or coil by moving the conductor or coil through a magnetic field, or by moving the magnetic field past the conductor or coil.

Inductive-Discharge Ignition: A method of igniting the air-fuel mixture in an engine cylinder. It is based on the induction of a high voltage in the secondary winding of a coil.

Inert Gas: A gas that will not undergo chemical reaction.

Injection Pump: A pump used on diesel engines to deliver fuel under high pressure at precisely timed intervals to the fuel injectors.

Input Conditioning: The process of amplifying or converting a voltage signal into a form usable by the computer's central processing unit.

Insulated (Hot) Cable: The battery cable that conducts battery current to the automotive electrical system.

Insulator: A material that will not conduct electricity.

Integrator: The ability of the computer to make short-term — minute-by-minute — corrections in fuel metering.

Intercooler: An air-to-air or air-to-liquid heat exchanger used to lower the temperature of the air-fuel mixture by removing heat from the intake air charge.

Ionize: To break up molecules into two or more oppositely charged ions. The air gap between the spark plug electrodes is ionized when the air-fuel mixture is changed from a non-conductor to a conductor.

Keep-Alive Memory (KAM): A form of long-term RAM used mostly with adaptive strategies. Requires a separate power supply circuit to maintain voltage when the ignition is off.

Liquid-Vapor Separator Valve: A valve in some EEC fuel systems that separates liquid fuel from fuel vapors.

Light-Emitting Diode (LED): A gallium-arsenide diode that emits energy as light. Often used in automotive indicators.

Lobes: The rounded protrusions on a camshaft that force, and govern, the opening of the intake and exhaust valves.

Magnetic Pulse Generator: A signal-generating switch that creates a voltage pulse as magnetic flux changes around a pickup coil.

Magnetic Saturation: The condition when a magnetic field reaches full strength and maximum flux density.

Manifold Vacuum: Low pressure in an engine's intake manifold, below the carburetor throttle.

Methanol: Methyl alcohol distilled from wood or made from natural gas.

Micron: A unit of length equal to one millionth of a meter, one one-thousandth of a millimeter.

Minus Rule: Minus metal on the minus side of the distributor breaker points means a minus-capacity condenser.

Misfire: Failure of the air-fuel mixture to ignite during the power stroke.

Module: A self-contained, sealed unit that houses the solid-state circuits which control certain electrical or mechanical functions.

Monolith: A large block. In a catalytic converter, the monolith is made like a honeycomb to provide several thousand square yards or meters of catalyst surface area.

Multigrade: An oil that has been tested at more than one temperature, and so has more than one SAE viscosity number.

Multipoint (Port) Injection: A fuel injection system in which individual injectors are installed in the intake manifold at a point close to the intake valve. Air passing through the manifold mixes with the injector spray just as the intake valve opens.

Mutual Induction: The transfer of energy between two unconnected conductors, caused by the expanding or contracting magnetic flux lines of the current-carrying conductor.

Negative-Ground Electrical System: An automotive electrical system in which the battery negative terminal is connected to ground.

Negative Polarity: Also called ground polarity. A correct polarity of the ignition coil connections. Coil voltage is delivered to the spark plugs so that the center electrode of the plug is negatively charged and the grounded electrode is positively charged.

Negative Temperature Coefficient (NTC) Resistor: A thermistor whose resistance decreases as the temperature increases.

Noble Metals: Metals, such as platinum and palladium, that resist oxidation.

No-Load Oscillation: The rapid, back-and-forth, peak-to-peak oscillation of voltage in the ignition secondary circuit when the circuit is open.

Normally Aspirated: An engine that uses normal vacuum to draw in its air-fuel mixture. Not supercharged.

Octane Rating: The measurement of the antiknock value of a gasoline.

Ohm: The unit for measuring electrical resistance.

Oil Galleries: Passages in the block and head that carry oil under pressure to various parts of the engine.

Open-Loop: An operational mode in which the engine control microprocessor adjusts the system to function according to predetermined instructions and does not respond to feedback signals from the EGO sensor.

Orifice: A small opening in a tube, pipe, or valve.

Oscillating: Moving back and forth with a steady rhythm.

Oxidation: The combining of an element with oxygen in a chemical process that often produces extreme heat as a byproduct.

Oxides of Nitrogen (NO$_x$): Chemical compounds of nitrogen given off by an internal combustion engine which combine with hydrocarbons to produce smog.

Parallel Circuit: A circuit with more than one path for the current to follow.

Particulates: Liquid or solid particles such as lead and carbon that are given off by an internal combustion engine as pollution.

Percolation: The bubbling and expansion of a liquid. Similar to boiling.

Photochemical Smog: A combination of pollutants which, when acted upon by sunlight, forms chemical compounds that are harmful to human, animal, and plant life.

Phototransistor: Also called a photocell. A type of solid-state device that will generate a voltage when exposed to light.

Piezoelectric: Voltage caused by physical pressure applied to the faces of certain crystals.

Piezoresistive: A sensor whose resistance varies in relation to pressure or force applied to it. A piezoresistive sensor receives a constant reference voltage and returns a variable signal in relation to its varying resistance.

Pintle Valve: A valve shaped much like a hinge pin. In an EGR valve, the pintle is attached to a normally closed diaphragm. When ported vacuum is applied, the pintle rises from its seat and allows exhaust gas to be drawn into the engine's intake system.

Plenum: A chamber that stabilizes the air-fuel mixture and allows it to rise to a pressure slightly above atmospheric pressure.

Poppet Valve: A valve that plugs and unplugs its opening by axial motion.

Ported Vacuum: Vacuum immediately above the throttle plate in a carburetor.

Positive Crankcase Ventilation (PCV): Late-model crankcase ventilation systems that return blowby gases to the combustion chambers.

Positive-Ground Electrical System: An automotive electrical system in which the battery positive terminal is connected to ground.

Positive Polarity: Also called reverse polarity. An incorrect polarity of the ignition coil connections. Coil voltage is delivered to the spark plug so that the center electrode of the plug is positively charged and the grounded electrode is negatively charged.

Positive Temperature Coefficient (PTC) Resistor: A thermistor whose resistance decreases as the temperature increases.

Preignition: A premature ignition of the air-fuel mixture before the spark plug fires. It is caused by excessive heat or pressure in the combustion chamber.

Pressure Differential: A difference in pressure between two points.

Pressure Drop: A reduction of pressure between two points.

Programmable Read-Only Memory (PROM): An integrated circuit chip installed in a computer which contains appropriate operating instructions and database information for a particular application.

Purge Valve: A vacuum-operated valve used to draw fuel vapors from a vapor storage canister.

Random-Access Memory (RAM): Temporary short-term or long-term computer memory that can be read and changed, but is lost whenever power is shut off to the computer.

Reach: The length of the spark plug shell from the seat to the bottom of the shell.

Read-Only Memory (ROM): The permanent part of a computer's memory storage function. ROM can be read but not changed, and is retained when power is shut off to the computer.

Reciprocating Engine: Also called piston engine. An engine in which the pistons move up and down or back and forth, as a result of combustion of an air-fuel mixture in the top of the piston cylinder.

Rectified: Electrical current changed from alternating (a.c.) to direct (d.c.).

Recombinant: A nongassing battery design in which the oxygen released by the electrolyte recombines with the negative plates.

Reduction: A chemical process in which oxygen is removed from a compound.

Reference Voltage: A constant voltage signal (below battery voltage) applied to a sensor by the computer. The sensor alters the voltage according to engine operating conditions and returns it as a variable input signal to the computer, which adjusts system operation accordingly.

Relay: An electromagnetic switch. A relay uses a small amount of current flow to control the flow of a larger amount of current through a separate circuit.

Reluctance: An object's resistance to magnetic lines of force. Magnetic lines will concentrate in areas of low reluctance, and avoid areas of high reluctance.

Reserve Capacity Rating: A battery rating based on the number of minutes a battery at 80°F can supply 25 amperes, with no battery cell falling below 1.75 volts.

Resistance: Opposition to electrical current flow.

Resistor-Type Spark Plug: A plug that has a resistor in the center electrode to reduce the inductive portion of the spark discharge.

Road Draft Tube: The earliest type of crankcase ventilation; it vented blowby gases to the atmosphere.

Runners: The passages or branches of an intake manifold that connect the manifold's plenum chamber to the engine's inlet ports.

SAE Viscosity Grade: A system of numbers signifying an oil's viscosity at a specific temperature; assigned by the Society of Automotive Engineers.

Semiconductor: A material that is neither a good conductor nor a good insulator. Semiconductors are the raw material used to make solid-state devices such as diodes and transistors. Silicon and germanium are common semiconductors.

Series Circuit: A circuit with only one path for the current to follow.

Series-Parallel Circuit: A circuit in which some loads are wired in series and some are wired in parallel.

Single Grade: An oil that has been tested at only one temperature, and so has only one SAE viscosity number.

Sintered: Welded together without using heat to form a porous material, such as the metal disc used in some vacuum delay valves.

Siphoning: The flowing of a liquid as a result of a pressure differential, without the aid of a mechanical pump.

Sludge: A thick, black deposit caused by the mixing of blowby gases and oil.

Solenoid: An iron core with a wire coil surrounding it. The core moves when electrical current is applied to the coil. Used to convert electrical energy to mechanical energy.

Solid-State: A method of controlling electrical current flow, in which the parts are primarily made of semiconductor materials.

Spark Voltage: The inductive portion of a spark that maintains the spark in the air gap between a spark plug's electrodes. Usually about one-quarter of the firing voltage level.

Specific Gravity: The weight of a volume of liquid divided by the weight of the same volume of water at a given temperature and pressure. Water has a specific gravity of 1.000.

Starting Bypass: A parallel circuit branch that bypasses the ballast resistor during engine cranking.

Starting Safety Switch: A neutral start switch. It keeps the starting system from operating when a car's transmission is in gear.

Stepper Motor: A direct current motor that moves in incremental steps from deenergized to fully energized.

Stoichiometric Ratio: An ideal air-fuel mixture for combustion in which all oxygen and all fuel will be completely burned.

Stratified Charge Engine: An engine that uses 2-stage combustion: first is combustion of a rich air-fuel mixture in a precombustion chamber, then combustion of a lean air-fuel mixture occurs in the main combustion chamber.

Stroke: One complete top-to-bottom or bottom-to-top movement of an engine piston.

Substrate: The layer, or honeycomb, of aluminum oxide upon which the catalyst (platinum or palladium) in a catalytic converter is deposited.

Sulfation: The crystallization of lead sulfate on the plates of a constantly discharged battery.

Sulfur Oxides: Chemical compounds given off by processing and burning gasoline and other fossil fuels. As they decompose, they combine with water to form sulfuric acid.

Supercharging: Use of an air pump to deliver an air-fuel mixture to the engine cylinders at a pressure greater than atmospheric pressure.

Synthetic Motor Oils: Lubricants formed by artificially combining molecules of petroleum and other materials.

Television-Radio-Suppression (TVRS) Cables: High-resistance, carbon-conductor ignition cables that suppress RFI.

Temperature Inversion: A weather pattern in which a layer or "lid" of warm air keeps the cooler air beneath it from rising.

Tetraethyl Lead: A gasoline additive used to help prevent detonation.

Thermal Cracking: A common oil refining process which uses heat to break down (crack) the larger components of the crude oil. The gasoline which is produced usually has a higher sulfur content than gasoline produced by catalytic cracking.

Thermistor: An electrical conductor that changes its resistance as the surrounding temperature changes.

Thermostatic: Referring to a device that automatically responds to temperature changes in order to activate a switch.

Throttle Body Injection (TBI): A fuel injection system in which one or two injectors are installed in a carburetor-like throttle body mounted on a conventional intake manifold. Fuel is sprayed at a constant pressure above the throttle plate to mix with the incoming air charge.

Thyristor: A silicon-controlled rectifier (SCR) that normally blocks all current flow. A slight voltage applied to one layer of its semiconductor structure will allow current flow in one direction while blocking current flow in the other direction.

Top Dead Center: The exact top of a piston's stroke. Also a specification used when tuning an engine. Abbreviated: tdc.

Total Ignition Advance: The sum of centrifugal advance, vacuum advance, and initial timing; expressed in crankshaft degrees.

Transducer: A device that converts (transduces) one form of energy into another. In an ignition system, it may sense a mechanical movement and change it to an electrical signal.

Transistor: A 3-terminal semiconductor used for current switching, detection, and amplification. Low current flow between one pair of terminals can control high current flow between another pair of terminals, with one common terminal.

Turbo Lag: The time interval required for a turbocharger to overcome inertia and spin up to speed.

Turbocharger: A supercharging device that uses exhaust gases to turn a turbine that forces extra air-fuel mixture into the cylinders.

Vacuum: A pressure less than atmospheric pressure.

Vacuum Advance: The use of engine vacuum to advance ignition spark timing by moving the distributor breaker plate.

Vacuum Lock: A stoppage of fuel flow caused by insufficient air intake to the fuel tank.

Vapor Lock: A condition in which bubbles are formed in a car's fuel system when the fuel gets hot enough to boil. Flow is stopped or restricted as a result.

Vaporization: Changing a liquid, such as gasoline, into a gas (vapor).

Variable Dwell: The ignition dwell period varies in distributor degrees at different engine speeds, but remains relatively constant in duration or actual time.

Varnish: An undesirable deposit, usually on the engine pistons, formed by oxidation of fuel and of motor oil.

Venturi: A restriction in an airflow, such as in a carburetor, that increases the airflow speed and creates a reduction in pressure.

Venturi Vacuum: Low pressure in the venturi of a carburetor, caused by fast airflow through the venturi.

Viscosity: The tendency of a liquid such as oil to resist flowing.

Volatility: The ease with which a liquid changes from a liquid to a gas or vapor.

Volt: The unit for measuring the amount of electrical force.

Voltage: The electromotive force that causes current flow. The potential difference in electrical force between two points when one is negatively charged and the other is positively charged.

Voltage Decay: The rapid oscillation and dissipation of secondary voltage after the spark in a spark plug air gap has stopped.

Voltage Drop: The measurement of the loss of voltage caused by the resistance of a conductor or a circuit device.

Voltage Reserve: The amount of coil voltage available in excess of the voltage required to fire the spark plugs.

Volumetric Efficiency: The comparison of the *actual* volume of air-fuel mixture drawn into an engine to the *theoretical maximum* volume that could be drawn in. Written as a percentage.

Wastegate: A diaphragm-actuated bypass valve used to limit turbocharger boost pressure by limiting the speed of the exhaust turbine.

Water Injection: A method of lowering the air-fuel mixture temperature by injecting a fine spray of water which evaporates as it cools the intake charge.

Water Jackets: Passages in the head and block that allow coolant to circulate throughout the engine.

Index